MW00629312

Systems Analysis

A Computer Approach to Decision Models

CLAUDE McMILLAN, Ph.D.
University of Colorado

RICHARD F. GONZALEZ, Ph.D.
Michigan State University

with a chapter contributed by
THOMAS J. SCHRIBER, Ph.D.
The University of Michigan

 Third Edition · 1973

RICHARD D. IRWIN, INC., Homewood, Illinois 60430

Irwin-Dorsey Limited, Georgetown, Ontario L7G 4B3

Third Edition

First Printing, April 1973
Second Printing, May 1974
Third Printing, December 1975
Fourth Printing, October 1976
Fifth Printing, September 1977

ISBN 0-256-01439-6
Library of Congress Catalog Card No. 72–90537

Printed in the United States of America

Preface

WHEN the first edition of *Systems Analysis* appeared in 1965, it was one of only two or three books about computer simulation. Today there are many books about the subject. Some focus on methodology, while others specialize in one or another of the problem-oriented simulation languages. The literature now reports applications of simulations in every discipline. Recently two major volumes were published in which a wide range of behavioral simulations were described. There is little question that materials such as those included in this edition are necessary for various curricula, and we remain committed to the design and purpose of the earlier editions of *Systems Analysis*.

Computer simulation permits students with modest backgrounds in mathematics to build and process systems models which produce useful information about the behavior of those systems. Simulation is not offered as a substitute for formal analysis, and we are aware of many unanswered questions about its methodology. As a means to understanding complex systems, computer simulation is a legitimate and interesting activity for students of the physical and social sciences.

Simulation requires the use of computer models, and early in the text the student is introduced to a general programming language. From that point on the presentation is dependent upon that language. We have reviewed the question of language dependence through the several revisions of this text and continue to believe that it is essential for students to translate systems concepts into computer processable models using either general or special purpose simulation languages. We have selected FORTRAN as the general language. It continues to be the most widely used and, with the exception of input/output statements, the programs listed in the text can be processed with little modification. If FORTRAN is not available, the programs are documented so that they may be written in another language.

In addition, we have included, in the appendix, BASIC language listings of all programs listed in the text. Solutions for the exercises in both languages are part of the manual which accompanies *Systems Analysis*.

Organization of the Text

This text is characterized by progression from particular to general models. It also moves from consideration of subsystems to the consideration of whole systems. Usually we undertake analysis in order to describe a system generally. Yet we are coming to appreciate the utility, if not the elegance, of focusing attention on specific situations and then, as Forrester has said, "We generalize as far as we dare." Decision makers in real life are interested in solutions for particular problems, and we think that this approach is meaningful to the student as well. Moving from analysis of subsystems to analysis of the whole system reflects the fact that it is still convenient to deal with major subsystems of an organization before attempting to model and analyze the interconnections which exist among subsystems.

Chapters 1 and 2 serve to define generally the notion of system and to apply it to various systems. The subject of model building, particularly the nature and use of computer models, precedes the discussion in Chapter 2 of the methodology of simulation.

Chapters 3, 4, and 5 serve as an introduction to FORTRAN programming, with emphasis on the basic statements which are required to build computer programs. The use of control statements is illustrated in Chapter 5 by reference to the inventory system under conditions of certainty in which the problem is to determine an optimum inventory reorder rule. This problem has an analytical solution which may be obtained directly; however, the manner of computation using the computer employs an enumeration method which qualifies as an elementary search procedure (combing). Using this model, a number of possible reorder rules may be evaluated. At this point the student may challenge the assumptions on which the inventory system is proposed. Information about demand as well as lead time is not perfect, and in fact these two variables are usually treated as random. In Chapter 6 the inventory system is analyzed by constructing a computer model and conducting experiments with that model. Random processes are simulated and the resulting model is more realistic.

Chapter 7 is a new chapter which introduces the modeling of systems by use of flow graphs. Graph theory is used primarily when modeling electrical and communications networks. The notion of network is much more pervasive, however. It applies to transportation systems of all kinds; in fact, any system through which some kind of resource, including information, flows can be modeled as a network. Flow graph methods offer a general scheme for conceptualizing systems, and it is presented in Chapter 7 at an elementary level.

In Chapters 8, 9, and 10 the model of the single channel queue is developed. This model describes many of the physical distribution or service systems which we see in the real world. The queueing system model is first developed analytically, and then computer simulation of the system is presented in Chapter 11. Modeling queueing systems requires that random samples be drawn from various nonuniform distributions. Chapter 10 is devoted to developing generators for obtaining such samples.

A second new and relatively large chapter, Chapter 12 on GPSS, follows. This is the contribution of T. J. Schriber. The first edition of *Systems Analysis* included brief mention of GPSS and a discussion of SIMSCRIPT. Increased use of problem-oriented simulation languages led to the decision in this third edition to include a complete enough discussion of GPSS that students could build models in GPSS. It was chosen as the language for instruction because it is perhaps the most widely used language of its type and is implemented on various IBM systems. The student should conclude that it is a powerful aid in simulation; and true to its claim, it is learned with a minimum of difficulty.

Chapter 13, "Management Planning Models," reflects some special concerns of analysis in simulating business systems. A variety of short-range planning and forecasting routines are discussed. Partial revision of this chapter includes the treatment of some topics in light of the flow graph discussion in Chapter 7.

For the analysis of complex systems, matrix methods are essential; and in this revision we retained those materials in Chapter 14.

This includes development of the simplex algorithm and an efficient FORTRAN routine for processing it.

Chapter 15 has been revised to present some discussion of the work being done in the simulation of human behavior. The body of literature in this field is very large and growing rapidly. Reference to the inventory clerk of Chapter 4 is made, and a behavioral model constructed of his observed decision making. A second situation involving interaction of two human decision makers is presented in the chapter. The work of Bonini is also discussed here. His simulation of the decision and information systems of the firm continues as a significant contribution in the design and conduct of simulation experiments.

Chapter 16 introduces Industrial Dynamics, a particular form of simulation. Conceptually, in Industrial Dynamics continuous change models are used as contrasted to those discussed in the text, which are discrete change models. Industrial dynamics models composed in FORTRAN are presented so the student may distinguish the two model types.

In Chapter 17 a hypothetical firm, made up of various subsystems which were modeled in earlier chapters, is presented. Our purpose is not only to construct the model of a large organization but to use it in order to test and evaluate various decisions and policies.

Finally, in Chapter 18, we call to the student's attention the fact that many methodological questions involving the use of computer simulation have yet to be answered. There are some guides and procedures which the students should follow to avoid grossly inefficient experiments. A proposal by P. Gilmour is included as one way in which an experimenter may choose from among the many statistical measures and procedures available to him.

From the preceding it is perhaps evident that not all materials included in this text can be covered in a single one-term course. At the undergraduate level, assuming that Chapters 3, 4, and 5 required detailed treatment, it has been possible for a three-quarter-hour course to cover the material through about Chapter 11, plus some modified experiments involving the SIMCO model of Chapter 17. At the graduate level, teaching FORTRAN outside the class, and omitting Chapter 14, it is possible to cover most of the text.

As a reminder to both instructor and student, it is strongly recommended that regular assignments of exercises be made. The procedure of conceptualizing a problem and obtaining a computer model is an ill-defined procedure which can only be learned through practice. The same applies to acquisition of even minimum programming skills. No amount of discussion substitutes for the experience and confidence gained from the successful composition of a computer program and its use to obtain information for improving the quality of decision making.

To summarize, systems analysis in the physical and social sciences constitutes a significant and growing discipline. The analysis of complex systems is done economically by the student utilizing simulation. At one point early in our experience, it was our thought that simulation should be the vehicle to carry a course which would essentially be the first introduction of the student to the computer. So many changes have occurred in curriculums as well as hardware and software that an instructor has a variety of alternatives so far as the introduction of the student to the machine. Simulation in its own right is sufficiently important and challenging that it ought to be taught as a form of analysis and frequently in parallel or complement with courses in which formal (mathematical) models are discussed. It is well for the student to understand the potential as well as the limitations of both forms of analysis.

March 1973   C. McMillan
                                               R. F. Gonzalez

Contents

ing. The Decision Rule. The Computer Program as a General Model: *Did We Simulate? When Problems Become Problems. Tools versus Problems. An Alternative Approach. Simulation versus Formal Analysis. A Word about Algorithms.*

chapter 1

Systems and Models

BEFORE describing particular physical or social systems and methods for analyzing them, it is necessary to consider what is meant by the word *system*. The term is used in many ways and has reserved meaning in all disciplines and areas of research. We speak of the education system, information systems, ecological systems, transportation systems, political systems, and so on. Whenever we wish to connote relatedness or interaction with respect to a set of *entities* we use the word system. For our purposes a somewhat ambiguous definition of system will serve.

A system is a set of entities (components) together with relationships between the entities.

The number of system entities may be large and their nature diverse. In physical systems the components are tangible. Biological systems, for example, contain animal populations, water, and food. Abstract objects may be system components—in an economic system we might find profit goals, sales quotas, production standards, and costs.

System components are described by their properties or *attributes*. An individual who is part of a social system would possess a long list of attributes—age, sex, group memberships, memory, beliefs, attitudes, and so on.

Relationships that exist between entities tie the system together. Were it not for relationships the concept of system would be meaningless. Given the set of components and attributes of a system we would be able to identify or postulate a great many relationships. The study of the system focuses on those relationships we think necessary to describe the system and explain the way it undergoes change.

Our definition of system is incomplete without the notion of system *environment*.

The environment is the set of all entities, a change in whose attributes affects the system, and also those entities whose attributes are changed by the behavior of the system.

From the definitions of system and environment it seems that given a set of interacting components we must subdivide it into system and environment. Exactly how this is done is not always clear and sometimes the impression is gained that the division is done quite arbitrarily. The system analyst has discretion and is often guided by what is most convenient for him. Some system models of the business firm have been constructed in which the consumer is made part of the environment. Describing the consumer in terms of taste and income—where a change in either attribute would affect the firm—seems in line with our definition of environment. One might argue, however, for including the consumer within the firm without violating the definition of system.

From the definition of system and environment it follows that a system can be subdivided into subsystems. The complex system we know as the university contains, for example, subsystems for the preparation and delivery of educational "products" to its students. Other subsystems in this complex provide for the creation and maintenance of physical facilities, exchanges of information, and academic and civil governance. These subsystems in turn can be further subdivided. Components belonging to one subsystem may be part of the environment of another subsystem. From the concepts of system and subsystem we can agree with the frequent observation that all systems are subsystems of the next higher system.

In studying a system one may focus on the detailed behavior of subsystems (microscopic behavior), or elect to study the behavior of the system as a whole (macroscopic behavior). Both approaches are necessary to understand the behavior of large systems. An important step is taken when we move from subsystem analysis to analysis of the whole system. Macroscopic analysis forces an investigation of relationships among subsystems. As many systems develop, chance influences the design of subsystems, and rarely is there a practical means to ensure that the designs of the subsystems are compatible. Frequently subsystems are observed whose objectives are not consistent nor mutually reinforcing.

SYSTEMS CLASSIFICATIONS

There are several useful schemes for classifying systems. The first distinguishes between natural and man-made systems. Social, economic, and political systems are man-made, while physical and biological systems are mostly natural. The distinction is blurred these days as our understanding of the concept of system develops. Man's concern about his natural environment has led to the specification of ecosystems in which he uses the natural environment for agricultural or industrial production and recreation.

A second distinction contrasts *open* and *closed* systems.

Most . . . systems are open, meaning they exchange materials, energies, or information with their environments. A system is closed if there is no import or export of energies in any of its forms, such as information, heat, physical materials, etc.[1]

An open system may become closed in two ways. If interaction with the environment is cut off, or if we later choose to include in the system that part of the environment which involved the interchange of energy, materials, or information, the system becomes closed.

A third classification separates systems which are adaptive and those which are not. Adaptive systems react to environmental changes in a way that is desirable considering the purpose the system was designed for. March and Cyert[2] describe the firm as an adaptive system, meaning that environmental change or shock elicits a response (decision) which results in a new system state. Successive shocks and responses, and the observation concerning how successful the response was, become part of the "experience" of the firm. Organizational learning is said to take place through time as those responses that led to preferred system states are recalled and applied.

---

[1] "The Definition of System," *Yearbook for the Advancement of General Systems Theory,* 1956, p. 18. See also A. D. Hall, *A Methodology for Systems Engineering* (Princeton, N.J.: D. Van Nostrand Co., Inc., 1962).

[2] Richard M. Cyert and James G. March, *A Behavioral Theory of the Firm* (Englewood Cliffs, N.J.: Prentice-Hall, Inc., 1963).

The term *system state* was used above. Recall that a system is defined as the set of entities and their interrelated attributes. Attributes through time will take on different values. At any point in time we may describe the state of the system by observing the current value of those attributes.[3]

If the values of a system's attributes remain constant, or within defined limits, the system is stable. In contrast, if the values of the attributes fluctuate widely, the system is unstable. At times the system will be unstable and at other times stable. An example of this behavior will be found in the analysis of subsystems involving waiting lines. A waiting line of variable length develops at a service center (tool crib, customer check-out counter, complaint desk, ticket-selling booth, etc.) because of the relatively fixed capacity of the facility as well as the varying demand for service placed against it.

In analyzing these systems it is common to find that when the service center is opened at the beginning of the day there is an initial interval during which the length of the waiting line increases and decreases erratically. After this initial period the length of the line varies within narrow and predictable limits. The term *transition state* defines the interval during which the erratic behavior occurred. References are also made to an *exploding state*—when the values of the variables (the attributes) indicating the state of the system take on ever-increasing, fluctuating values. The longer the system operates, the greater are the fluctuations.

Equilibrium can be defined in terms of system state. A system is in equilibrium if in the absence of external shock its state remains unchanged. If an external shock to the system is followed by a return to an equilibrium state, then the system is said to be stable.[4]

Finally we may consider systems in which a portion of their output is regularly fed back—that is, introduced as an input to influence future states. The portion of the output fed back for purposes of control consists of information, and we refer to these systems as information-feedback systems. The term *servomechanism* defines man-made systems utilizing feedback. A further definition of the information-feedback system is given by Forrester.

An information-feedback system exists whenever the environment leads to a decision that results in action which affects the environment

[3] See Harry N. Markowitz et al., *SIMSCRIPT: A Simulation Programing Language* (Englewood Cliffs, N.J.: Prentice-Hall, Inc., 1963).

[4] E. F. Beckenbach (ed.), *Modern Mathematics for the Engineer* (New York: McGraw-Hill Book Co., 1956), p. 31.

and thereby influences future decisions. Examples of systems of information-feedback control abound in all parts of our physical world. In the business situation we can point to the following illustrations.

In business, orders and inventory levels lead to manufacturing decisions that fill orders, correct inventories, and yield new manufacturing decisions.

A profitable industry attracts competitors until the profit margin is reduced to equilibrium with other economic forces, and competitors cease to enter the field.

A competitive need for a new product leads to research and development expenditure that produces technological change.[5]

SYSTEMS ANALYSIS

Just as the word system is used in various ways, the term *systems analysis* is given different meanings. Description of systems and explanation of system behavior are the purposes of systems analysis. Given what appears to be an unstructured situation or phenomena our first concern is description. What seems to be involved? How do components appear to interact? Does the system change through time? When a change in component A is observed does a change in B occur?

In many disciplines systems analysis is limited to description. Behavioral scientists hope some day to be able to understand how learning and perception are performed by human beings. Because the systems involved are so complex, analysts of learning and cognitive processes are content to develop descriptions (models) of these processes in specific instances. Description is a necessary first step to the classification of behavior which in turn leads to conjecture about how the observed behavior takes place.

The second purpose of systems analysis is explanation of system behavior. The *how* and perhaps the *why* questions about behavior are answered. This aspect of systems analysis raises a number of philosophical questions. What is meant by the word *explanation?* Explanations of various phenomena and systems behavior have been offered throughout man's history. Most of the explanations have been discarded. If an explanation accounts for system behavior in 8 out of 10 observations is the explanation sufficient? Are there objective measures by which we can evaluate explanations of systems behavior? Is validation of an explanation a separate question

---

[5] Jay W. Forrester, *Industrial Dynamics* (Cambridge, Mass., and New York: The M.I.T. Press and John Wiley & Sons, Inc., 1961), p. 14.

from whether or not the explanation is useful, for example, in the sense that it enables us to predict future system behavior? Questions like these are central to the work of a systems analyst.

As we identify different systems in this book and suggest ways of analyzing them we shall return to the issues of representativeness, sufficiency, validation, and usefulness. Criticisms of systems analysis turns on the understanding or lack of understanding of these concepts.

MODELS

Systems analysis and model building are inseparable notions. To describe a system means that we construct some kind of representation or *model* of it. As we shall note, the media the model builder uses range from the physical to the symbolic. A model is the analyst's description of the system. To be useful for communicating the nature and behavior of the system, the model must be less complicated than the real system. It includes fewer components and relationships than the system, and if the model can be manipulated, it produces behavior which is less variable. Models are often criticized because they exhibit the very properties which make them valuable for purposes of description and communication. They are indeed less than real, often abstract, simple or naïve, and selective in terms of system variables, relationships, and states. To argue that a model is impractical, unreal, or theoretical, should not be taken as criticism but instead acknowledgment of the nature of models.

Models that offer explanations constitute theories of behavior. A theory is a set of conceptual, causal relationships developed to provide a logical chain of reasoning running from well-defined assumptions, proceeding to deductions or conclusions, and conforming to observations of the referent system.[6] Representations of a system which do not explain in this sense but which nevertheless depict observed system structure qualify as models that describe. But some constructs of systems can be built to predict outcomes (behavior) without explaining how the outputs are produced, or describing what the systems look like. These are known as black boxes. A black box is neither a theory nor a model by our definitions. Black box components will be found in several of the models described in later chapters.

---

[6] Harold Guetzkow, Philip Kotler and Randall L. Schultz, *Simulation in Social and Administrative Science* (Englewood Cliffs, N.J.: Prentice-Hall, Inc., 1972), p. 5.

Apart from the general claim that model building is a means for understanding complex systems, more specific advantages result from model building. It aids in the development of theory. We should expect that a model that does a good job of describing the system will lead to suggestions or hypotheses about system behavior. More importantly models help in theory development by raising questions, pointing out gaps in the theory, generating testable hypotheses, and serving as vehicles for experimentation.

"When a model has been tested, and is acceptable, then understanding has been added to the problem. The model which usefully described a given situation is capable of prediction in the sense that changes in the situation can be logically (mathematically) followed through the model."[7] Another writer summarizes model building and formal analysis:

The scientific method is basically the establishment of models (sometimes more abstractly called hypotheses) which must have two properties: First, they must account for all known facts, and secondly, they must enable us to make predictions which may be tested by any unbiased and independent observer. Newton's law of gravity explained all the observations of the positions of celestial bodies. So did many previous models of the universe. Newton's Law has survived because, in addition it could be used, for example, to construct—a thousand years in advance—tide tables whose correctness may be observed by any businessman on a weekend. . . .

Once established by fitting known facts and tested by making predictions for which there are independent observational data, the model is used for experimentation, by which the results of various ways of running the business may be determined. Actual tests on real customers are often expensive, and worse they disturb the situation so that the results are either biased or leave a permanent perturbation.[8]

Classification of Models

Models may initially be distinguished by their correspondence to the system being modeled; i.e., how nearly are they like the real thing? Physical models retain some of the entities of the system they represent. A physical model looks like its referent.[9]

Models that have been constructed from a set of physical objects

---

[7] Edward H. Bowman and Robert B. Fetter, *Analysis for Production and Operations Management* (3rd ed.; Homewood, Ill.: Richard D. Irwin, Inc., 1967), p. 25.

[8] Beckenbach, *Modern Mathematics for the Engineer,* op. cit., pp. 211–12.

[9] The word *referent* means the system or class of systems being modeled.

not found in the real system are called *physical analogues*. For example, electrical components may be used to build a system that behaves like a mechanical system. An electrical system (analogue computer) may be constructed to behave like a hydraulic system, an oil refinery, or perhaps a distribution system for transporting natural gas.

Schematic models are representations in pictorial form and vary in degree of abstraction. Flow diagrams and organizational charts are examples. Their components are lines, symbols, and so on, which are not found in the physical world.

A *mathematical model* of a system consists of a set of equations whose solution explains or predicts changes in the state of the system. The use of mathematical models is a consequence of analytical efforts to abstract and describe the real world. Qualitative descriptions of systems (verbal symbolic models) are of limited help in predicting or precisely specifying the state of a system.

The inadequacy of words becomes apparent when a model is presented quantitatively. It is in the attempt to present relationships with precision, as well as quantitatively, that the use of mathematics is growing in model development. The vagueness, the ambiguity, the lack of clear and specific definitions of the character of a situation described verbally are faults which can be avoided by formalized mathematical presentation of problems. This objective is not always achieved. In the minds of many, formalized models take on an aura of authenticity and accuracy which can lead to misapplication. However, the attempt to develop a formalized, mathematical model in a given situation demands a more thorough analysis of the situation than would otherwise be demanded, and, consequently, problems are often more properly analyzed.

Translating problems stated in verbal terms to precise mathematical problems is not an easy task because most languages do not lend themselves to precise, unambiguous statements.[10]

Mathematical models are highly abstract. Yet it is abstraction that makes mathematical models general, subject to manipulation, and precise in terms of the information gained from their use. A *computer model* (for the present) is simply defined as a mathematical model expressed or written according to a particular set of rules so that the model may be processed by the computer. The set of rules and notations which constitute the algebraic computer programming language, FORTRAN, is the subject of Chapter 3.

---

[10] James E. Howell and Daniel Teichroew, *Mathematical Analysis for Business Decisions* (Homewood, Ill.: Richard D. Irwin, Inc., 1963), pp. 283–84.

Particular and General Models

A particular model describes or explains one system. Examples of particular models are found in the behavioral sciences. Successful models have been developed to imitate the decision making of a human subject. Even though the model imitates the subject's behavior perfectly, no claims are made that the model explains the behavior of any one *except* the person observed. On the other hand, in the physical sciences many different kinds of systems are rather well described and explained by a single, and hence, general model.

The generality of a model is established through experience and experimentation with the model. Model builders are initially content to construct particular models which are useful. Chance plays an important role in establishing the generality of a model. Discovery that a model created in one discipline describes a system in quite a different discipline establishes generality. There are dangers, however, when borrowing models across disciplinary lines. Theorists in the social sciences have used models from physics and mechanics and more recently electrical and hydraulic engineering. Whether these models contain structures that parallel those in the social systems being modeled is a critical question the social scientists must consider.

The systems analyst has an ultimate goal so far as generality is concerned. The search for a so-called general theory of systems is pursued by students of many disciplines. Beginning with the assertion that all systems are subsystems of higher order systems, leads to the conclusion that a general theory of systems must exist. Such a theory would provide definitions, axioms, and a logic such that analysis of all systems, physical, biological, or social, could be conducted in a standard fashion. Models of particular systems would be developed in conformance with the general theory and it follows that all models would be general models. Until that day comes, however, generality is the result of repeated examination of a model and evaluation of how well it explains the behavior of a system not considered at the time the model was created.

Deterministic and Probabilistic Models

Mathematical models may be subdivided into deterministic models and probabilistic models. The use of either type is indicated by the nature of the system being studied.

Systems that deterministic models represent are devoid of uncertainty, and changes of state can be perfectly predicted. The way in which the system behaves can be evaluated according to measures of effectiveness, such as cost, profit, and time. However, we may lack sufficient understanding of the system and so fail to include or properly evaluate some characteristics of the system that have an important bearing on the measure of effectiveness we are trying to maximize (profit) or minimize (cost). If the model is enriched so that it accounts for all important variables and relationships, we may find that we lack the mathematical methods to solve the model for the optimum solution. Until the mathematical techniques are discovered, partial models that we can manipulate mathematically are used, and the solutions gained are recognized to be less than optimum, or to be subject to assumed conditions of complete knowledge—i.e., certainty.

More typically, systems are characterized by attributes that take values which are the result of factors whose interaction is at best poorly understood. These attributes or variables are "produced" by successive trials of stochastic processes. Such processes are described as repetitions of "experiments" whose results are probabilistic—i.e., determined by chance. If in a system periodic values of certain attributes are determined probabilistically, knowledge of the system is less than perfect.

Probabilistic models, by definition, are those that include the representation of stochastic processes or their results. Because uncertainty is more the rule than the exception, most of our models will be probabilistic.

There is a difference between the kind of information a probabilistic model renders and the kind available from a deterministic model. It is not correct to say that the solution, or rather the processing, of a probabilistic model results in an optimum solution. Given that we have adequately modeled a stochastic process with which we can trace probable future system states, there is never complete assurance that the variables will take on the sequence of values which the model outputs simply because the process is stochastic. Models of this type output empirical data. In effect, we manipulate a system model (having probabilistic elements) and synthetically produce future events. We are thus in a position to sit back and ask: "What would the state of the system be with a given system design; or what would be the state if a particular decision were made?" The answers are in the form of inferences based on observations of experiments with the model.

Alternative schemes for the classification of models have been proposed. The two diagrams below summarize the distinctions of Springer, Herlihy, and Beggs.[11] They have in an aggregate fashion divided models into the physical and symbolic as is shown in Figure 1–1.

FIGURE 1–1

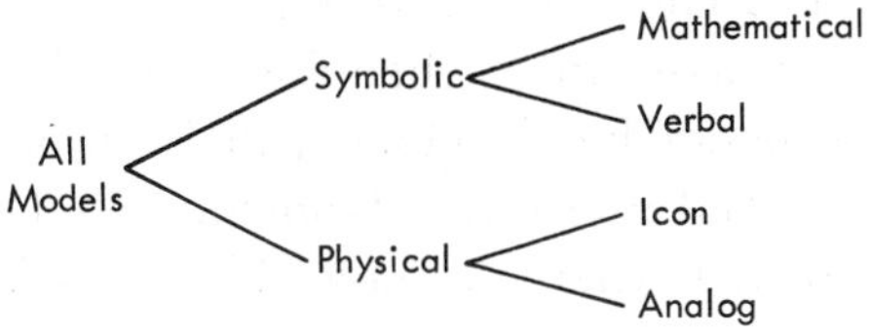

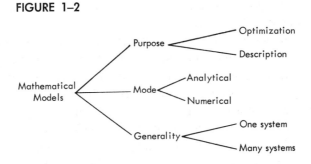

Consider Figure 1–2, a schema of the set of *mathematical* models.

FIGURE 1–2

Most of the terms are self-explanatory. Optimization was discussed earlier, but we referred to such models as deterministic. The concept of mode parallels the distinction made when speaking about the outputs of deterministic versus stochastic models. The attribute of generality was noted by reference to special versus general-purpose models.

Model Building

To the reader whose experience in creating models is limited, the contents of this book may be initially frustrating. It is the authors'

---

[11] Clifford H. Springer, Robert E. Herlihy, and Robert I. Beggs, *Advanced Methods and Models* (Mathematics for Management Series, Vol. 2 [Homewood, Ill.: Richard D. Irwin, Inc., 1965]), pp. 1–14.

design to provide some necessary tools and then by example to involve the reader in building systems models. Repeatedly we will describe a specific system and propose an abstract formulation of it —that is, a model. Keep in mind that that formulation is only one of a number of possible models of that system. Why was that particular model chosen? In most cases the answer is simply that the model provides insight about the system or perhaps is useful in deciding questions about the design and operations of the system. An analyst has no assurance when he proceeds to investigate a system that the model he develops will be useful in any sense. Model building is trial and error. Knowing what to look for is as important as knowing where to look. The question of whether a component or relationship is relevant cannot be determined beforehand. The analyst discovers that he has left something out *after* his model has been constructed and tested. Exactly what the omission is, remains to be discovered. Experience, intuition, insight, and imagination may lead to the discovery of the missing component or the improperly stated relationship.

In this connection, we would distinguish between systems analysis and problem solving. They are not the same. Even though some of the models we later employ enable us to "solve" certain kinds of problems, problem solving is a fringe benefit of the model building. The purpose of analysis, again, is to furnish description and explanation. If this leads to the ability to better specify problems, and to devise solution methods, well and good. A problem exists in a system with respect to an objective criterion which is often established outside the system. The psychologist who models the process used by a child to solve a series of logical problems is not concerned that the child may correctly solve 50, 70, or 90 percent of the problems. He is concerned with satisfying himself that he can understand the process employed by the subject. The intellectual capacity or performance of the child is not at issue; to the analyst such "problems" are not inherent in the system. If external to the system, someone were to specify acceptable behavior as some fraction of correctly solved problems, then we have added a new dimension to our investigation. The same is true for the management scientist analyzing a queuing situation. If adequately modeled, he should be able to learn, among other things, the length of the waiting line throughout the time that a facility is open. Whether a problem exists in terms of the length of that waiting line must be specified by someone outside the system.

SUMMARY

A System as a Collection or Network of Interacting Components

System implies interaction; interdependence. If A, B, and C are entities which bear no relationship one to the other, direct or indirect, then A, B, and C do not constitute a system.

On the other hand if A, B, and C *are* interrelated in some way then they do constitute a system. If we observe that a change in A is accompanied by a change in B and in C, whether or not the change in A *causes* the changes in B and C, we suspect interdependence and we perceive a system.

Let us assume that A, B, and C are attributes or dimensions of three different components (entities). After some observation we perceive that an increase in A induces an increase in B and at the same time a decrease in C. Concomitantly, let's assume that a decrease in A induces a decrease in B and an increase in C. We might represent this interaction by the component identification network in Figure 1–3.

FIGURE 1–3

Component Identification
Network

The directed arrows mean: changes in A produce change in B and in C, but not vice versa. The plus sign indicates that the change is in the same direction; the minus sign indicates a change in the opposite direction.

Consider the urban system model in Figure 1–4. Seven components interact in the urban system shown. The symbols indicate that an increase in the level of modernization produces an increase in the level of sanitation and a decrease in modernization a decrease in sanitation. An increase in sanitation produces a decrease in disease level and a decrease in sanitation an increase in disease level.

Notice the implication of the *loops* in the network. Thus the loop P–M–C–P suggests: "An increase in population tends to increase the level of modernization which stimulates migration into

the city which increases the size of the population." This might be
called a "deviation amplifying loop."

FIGURE 1–4

An Urban System Model

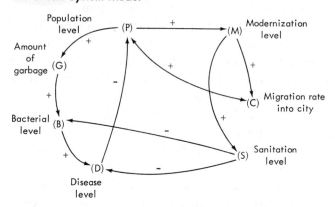

Source: Magoroh Maruyama, "The Second Cybernetics: Deviation Amplifying Mutual Causal Processes," *American Scientist*, Vol. 51, pp. 164–79, 1963.

Now, consider the loop *P–G–B–D–P*. An increase in population
raises the level of garbage flow which increases the bacterial level
which increases the disease level which decreases the population
level. This might be called a "deviation counteracting loop."

Notice that loop *C–P–G–B–D–P–M–C* implies that an increase
in migration into the city indirectly decreases migration. On the
other hand loop *C–P–M–C* suggests that an increase in migration
into the city will induce further migration. Which will dominate?
Is it conceivable that lags in the system, combined with other
parameters which relate the components more precisely, might cause
a pulse of new people migrating into the city to *decrease* the level of
modernization of the city?

The system of interacting components modeled in Figure 1–4 is
clearly a gross simplification of the real world system for which it
is an abstract representation. However, depending on our purpose
it may be a valuable first step in the modeling process. In modeling
systems we begin by identifying the components which are relevant
to our analysis. A next step involves identifying more precisely the
nature of the interaction between components. It is one thing to
say that an increase in *A* induces an increase in *B*, and quite another
to say:

$$B = 2A^2 + 0.4A$$

. . . or, adding a time dimension:

$$B_n = 2A^2_{n-1} + 0.4A_{n-1}$$

. . . where n indicates the nth time period in a discrete dynamic system.

Much of our study of systems in this text will have to do with:

1. Determining the functional relationship between one component in the system and its "neighbors."
2. Studying the behavior which results from the interaction of *many* components in a network of components, each of which perhaps interacts with its neighbors in a different way

In Chapter 6 we will study the interaction of components in an inventory system, as identified in Figure 1–5.

FIGURE 1–5

**Component Identification Graph
for an Inventory System**

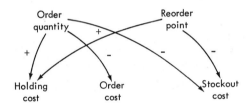

We will approach the inventory system with the intent of not only understanding its behavior but also of controlling it optimally. We will see that when optimum values for components Q, the order quantity, and R, the reorder point, are employed then the demand on the inventory system and the lead time (time required for replenishing the stock) are related to holding cost, order cost, and stockout cost as shown in Figure 1–6.

FIGURE 1–6

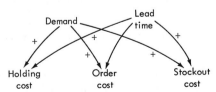

In Chapter 9 we will examine a queuing system, whose components and their interaction are depicted in Figure 1–7.

FIGURE 1–7

A Queue System Model

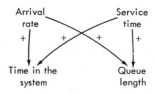

In Chapter 14 we will examine an economic system, consisting of an industrial component, an agricultural component, and a service component (among others) as suggested in Figure 1–8.

FIGURE 1–8

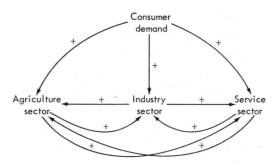

In modeling these and other systems of interacting components we will employ *formal analysis* and also *simulation.* Our purpose will be to explore ways of giving structure to otherwise unstructured situations, to enable us to understand and then to control the behavior of complex systems of interacting components.

SUGGESTIONS FOR FURTHER STUDY

BERRIAN, F. KENNETH. *General and Social Systems.* New Brunswick, N.J.: Rutgers University Press, 1968.

CHURCHMAN, C. WEST. *Systems Approach.* New York: Delacorte Press, 1968.

HARE, VAN COURT, JR. *Systems Analysis: A Diagnostic Approach.* New York: Harcourt, Brace and World, Inc., 1967.

VON BERTALANFFY, LUDWIG. *General System Theory.* New York: George Braziller, Inc., 1969.

chapter 2
Simulation

DEFINITION

IN ITS MOST GENERAL SENSE, simulation means the representation of reality. Hence verbal description and schematic or diagrammatic representation of some part of the real world constitutes simulation. Holstein and Soukup observe, however, that these forms of simulation are not new. On the other hand,

If . . . simulation necessarily involves the use of mathematical expressions and equations which closely approximate random fluctuations in the simulated system, and which are so complex as to be impossible of solution without the aid of massive electronic computers, then simulation is a very recent development.[1]

In this definition we note the references to mathematical models and the computers. Since the system models are processed by the computer, they are *computer models* as the term was defined in the previous chapter.

We use the term "computer model" to denote a special kind of formal mathematical model, namely a model which is not intended to be solved analytically but rather to be simulated on an electronic computer. Simulating a computer model consists in using a digital or analogue computer

---

[1] W. K. Holstein and William R. Soukup, *Monte Carlo Simuation* (Institute Paper No. 23 [Lafayette, Ind.: Institute for Quantitative Research and Economics and Management, Graduate School of Industrial Administration, Purdue University, 1961]), p. 1.

to trace numerically or graphically the time paths of all endogenous variables generated by the model.[2]

Before proposing a definition of computer simulation we think it is useful to note briefly some applications of the technique.

Some of the earliest simulations reported by social scientists involved construction of models to represent large economic and social systems. Working from census data, sociologists modeled human populations of the United States and other countries. Life and death processes, as well as those leading to marriage and family formation, entry and exit from the labor force, and other processes were included in the model.

Processes whereby individuals in a social system are influenced have been studied via simulation. How does information about new farming methods, for example, become diffused throughout a population in an economically underdeveloped nation? Is there a causal system that can be modeled to explain conflict between individuals or nations? Simulation models of historical conflict situations such as World War I have been modeled.

Computer simulation as a tool for analyzing *individual* behavior has a truly remarkable record. We said in Chapter 1 that simulations of this kind tended to be particular models without claims of generality. Even so, the ability to develop a model that imitates the choice or decision-making behavior of an individual in a complex situation is impressive. Equally impressive are the more general models which solve mathematical or logical problems, or engage a human opponent in a game of checkers or chess. These programs are patterned on the observed behavior of individuals and thus qualify as models of human behavior. Business analysts successfully construct computer simulation models to analyze a complex process such as the flow of work through large job shops. They have also modeled consumer behavior such as brand loyalty and brand switching. Simulation models are used to design transportation systems— tanker fleets of oil firms, and the operations of scheduled airlines. Not all simulations in business are so practical as those just mentioned. The simulation of managerial decision making has resulted in several large models of the information-decision system of the firm, one of which is reviewed in another chapter.

Economists have long built and operated models of economic

---

[2] Kalman J. Cohen, "Simulation of the Firm," *The American Economic Review,* May 1960, p. 534.

systems. They use the models to test hypotheses about the outcomes of proposed policies, as well as to anticipate system changes to which economic decision makers should respond.

What we have indicated about the widespread use of systems simulation in the social and behavioral sciences compares modestly with simulation in the physical sciences. The most widely publicized uses of simulation occur in the aerospace activities of NASA, especially those involved in manned space flight. These programs employ a wide range of models and analytic techniques, but foremost has been the use of imaginative simulations in which man and vehicle interact in computer-created environments.

Developments in physics and chemistry are replete with instances in which computer simulation has augmented traditional laboratory facilities. During the infancy of nuclear physics, analysts faced the problem of providing shielding against emissions from radioactive materials. The situations were frequently modeled in the computer and used Monte Carlo methods—techniques discussed in this and in later chapters.

The modeling of large physical and biological systems results from the interests of engineers, urban planners, transportation specialists, and the ever growing number of persons concerned about the quality of the environment. Highway networks are simulated in attempts to move people and materials more rapidly into and out of urban areas. River basins are modeled to investigate a host of questions including those having to do with transportation and navigation, the effects of runoffs, or the dumping of wastes from manufacturing and agricultural activities, the capacity of the system to sustain various forms of wildlife, and the effects of proposals for reclamation and recreation.

Systems models in the biological sciences are similar to the large-scale population models of the sociologists. A major distinction, however, is that biologists try to model the response of an animal population to physical changes in the environment. In some instances processes leading to genetic changes are modeled. Hypotheses are tested about the effects of changes in such factors as climate, disease, food and water supply,. variety and pressure of predators, accidents, as well as changes introduced by forces or events outside the system. If the population were hunted for sport, then changes of public policy involving the length of the hunting season, or the weapons permitted could be evaluated.

From the preceding we conclude that there has been a veritable explosion of simulation in recent years. However, it is not simply the popularity of the technique nor the ease with which it may be employed that recommends it. We need to understand why the technique is applied and what distinguishes it from traditional methods of analysis and problem solving.

WHY SYSTEMS SIMULATION?

Computer simulation has come into increasing widespread use to study the behavior of systems whose state changes over time. . . . Alternatives to the use of simulation are mathematical analysis, experimentation with either the actual system or a prototype of the actual system, or reliance upon experience and intuition. All, including simulation, have limitations. Mathematical analysis of complex systems is very often impossible; experimentation with actual or pilot systems is costly and time consuming, and relevant variables are not always subject to control. Intuition and experience are often the only alternatives to computer simulation available but can be very inadequate.

Simulation problems are characterized by being mathematically intractable and having resisted solution by analytical methods. The problems usually involve many variables, many parameters, functions which are not well behaved mathematically, and random variables. Thus simulation is a technique of last resort. Yet, much effort is now devoted to "computer simulation" because it is a technique that gives answers in spite of its difficulties, costs and time required.[3]

Or, stated somewhat differently:

Mathematical analysis is not powerful enough to yield general analytical solutions to situations as complex as are encountered in business. The alternative is the experimental approach.

The mathematical model of the industrial system is constructed. Such a mathematical model is a detailed description that tells how conditions at one point in time lead to subsequent conditions at later points in time. The behavior of the model is observed and experiments are conducted to answer specific questions about the system that is represented by the model.

"Simulation" is a name often applied to this process of conducting experiments on a model instead of attempting the experiments with their real system. . . .

In business, simulation means setting up in a digital computer the con-

---

[3] Daniel Teichroew and John Francis Lubin, "Computer Simulation—Discussion of the Technique and Comparison of Languages," *Communications of the ACM*, October 1966, p. 724.

ditions that describe company operations. On the basis of the descriptions and assumptions about the company, the computer then generates the resulting time charts [time paths or series] of information concerning finance, manpower, product movement, etc. Different management policies and market assumptions can be tested to determine their effects on company success.

Instead of going from the general analytical solution to the particular special case we have come to appreciate the great utility, if not the mathematical elegance, of the empirical approach. In this we study a number of particular situations, and from these we generalize as far as we dare.[4]

Simulation involves features of both classical experimentation and formal analysis in a way that provides great flexibility in modeling social and physical systems. Starbuck[5] contends that mathematics and simulation are empirical cousins, but whereas the mathematician depends upon his intellect to establish connections between premises and implications, the simulator, having stated his assumptions as a computer program, draws inferences by operating the computer. It is this strategy for making logical inferences that distinguishes simulations from mathematical analysis.

Properties of Simulated Systems

The definitions of simulation described systems (for which simulation methods are appropriate) as being complex, being subject to random fluctuations, and having relationships that are difficult if not impossible to analyze mathematically. By *complexity* we mean that the system is large in terms of the numbers of variables, parameters, relationships, and events to which the system is responsive.

The existence of *random variables* is implied in most definitions which refer to the uncertain nature of inputs of a system. Much of the discussion that follows in this book treats the manner in which random variables, or rather the processes (sequences of events) that assign successive values to the variable, are modeled.

The third property of systems for which simulation is an appropriate method of investigation concerns the relationships among system entities and attributes that are not well behaved or, as the

---

[4] Jay W. Forrester, *Industrial Dynamics* (Cambridge, Mass., and New York: The M.I.T. Press and John Wiley & Sons, Inc., 1961), pp. 17–18.

[5] John M. Dutton and William H. Starbuck, *Computer Simulation of Human Behavior* (New York: John Wiley & Sons, Inc., 1971), p 3.

mathematicians would say, are *not mathematically tractable.* We do not expect that this property, so briefly described, will be immediately meaningful to the student. However, in subsequent expositions of various models the student should become aware that simulation does indeed facilitate the analysis and evaluation of complex, dynamic relationships which, in many instances, cannot be expressed mathematically except with advanced concepts and difficult evaluation procedures.

System Design

The two applications of simulation are the *design* of systems and the *analysis* of system behavior. Design or the design problem simply means that typically the analyst has alternative ways of putting system components together. Given the specification of the desired output of the proposed system, he seeks a design that optimizes some measure of system behavior, such as profit, cost, time, resource utilization, and stability. A model of the system is processed incorporating successive changes that correspond to alternative designs. The influence of design on the measure of effectiveness is traced, and the analyst then has a basis for selecting the design that most effectively achieves the desired result or system output. This application—the comparison of alternative designs—is comparable with those experiments that use physical models of aircraft in wind tunnels or ship models in laboratory basins. When we refer to simulation as a laboratory, we have this application in mind.

To illustrate, consider the problem of designing a retail inventory system (Figure 2–1).

FIGURE 2–1

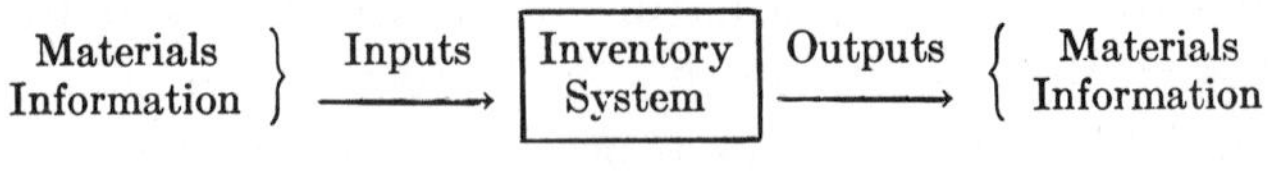

Materials ⎫ Inputs   ⎡Inventory⎤ Outputs ⎰ Materials
Information ⎭ ——————→ ⎣ System ⎦ ——————→ ⎱ Information

The inputs to the system are receipts of new stocks from suppliers and customer orders. The outputs are materials shipped and orders for new stock. Average time to process or fill an order is arbitrarily selected as the measure of system effectiveness. The box labeled Inventory System represents the set of entities, stock items, clerks, and documents which the designer may arrange in any order to minimize the average order processing time.

When he specifies the contents of the box (entities, attributes of entities, and relationships—for example, the way in which attributes take on values) the designer is proposing a design alternative. Assume in this case that the analyst wishes to consider and compare design alternatives A, B, and C (design A is the standard configuration, B and C represent changes or alterations from design A). When design A is modified we have indeed specified a different system, but it is convenient to simply speak of changes in a model rather than different models.

Alternative designs may differ in the number of clerks, amount of documentation, order in which customers are serviced, rules for reordering stock, and so forth. Now suppose that a model of design A is provided with information about a sequence of customer orders

FIGURE 2–2

Simulation for System Design

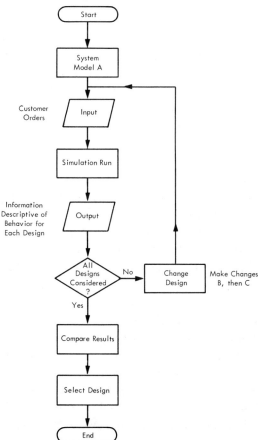

and that the model is processed or "run" so that it traces the activity of filling orders and replenishing stocks of the inventory items. Assume also that the model can be made to report periodic values of various attributes—inventory level, stock on order, back orders, and others. From this information the analyst can obtain the measure of effectiveness dependent on design A.

Next, design A is modified so that the alterations or changes we summarized as design B are introduced. The procedure is repeated. Then changes corresponding to design alternative C are made and the model is processed. Using the three values of the measure of effectiveness, the analyst has a comparative basis for settling on one of the designs for implementation—i.e., construction in the real world. This procedure is shown schematically in Figure 2–2. It should also be noted that our principal use of simulation in this textbook will be for deciding the design of particular systems.

Systems Analysis

The second general application of simulation is to analyze the behavior of systems. The analyst observes systems inputs and outputs and seeks to explain how the transformation is achieved. He postulates a configuration of the system in terms of entities and their relationships, composes a computer model of his theoretical system, provides the model with inputs like those in the real system, and attempts to produce outputs from the model that correspond to those of the real world. The degree to which he succeeds is taken as a measure of the validity of the model—i.e., verification that the analyst can explain what took place in the real system.

The two applications appear to be similar, but in fact they are not. In the first case simulation is used to obtain information about a system(s) that the analyst has created and about which he knows a great deal. In the second case the analyst uses simulation to test hypotheses about a system that he does not know well, and whose behavior he can explain only by presuming the existence of particular entities and relationships. The procedure for systems analysis via simulation is diagrammatically shown in Figure 2–3.

The analyst frequently views the real world system as a "black box," the contents of which he wishes to describe by inferring from the observations of system inputs and outputs. As stated before, the theory of system behavior represented by the model is validated by comparing differences between outputs of the real world system,

FIGURE 2–3

Simulation–Systems Analysis

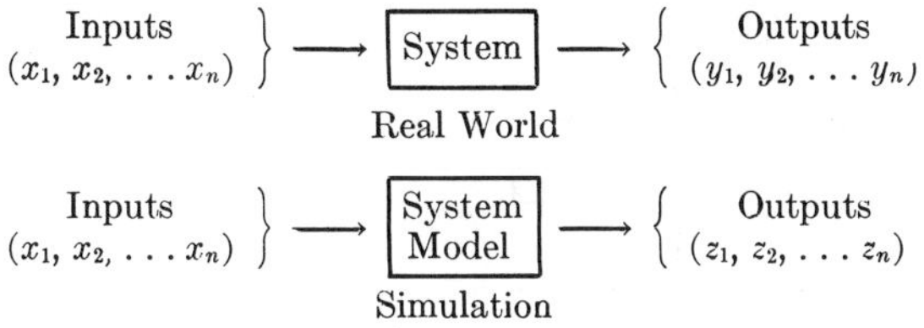

$$\text{Inputs}\atop(x_1, x_2, \ldots x_n)\Big\} \longrightarrow \boxed{\text{System}} \longrightarrow \Big\{ {\text{Outputs}\atop(y_1, y_2, \ldots y_n)}$$

Real World

$$\text{Inputs}\atop(x_1, x_2, \ldots x_n)\Big\} \longrightarrow \boxed{\text{System} \atop \text{Model}} \longrightarrow \Big\{ {\text{Outputs}\atop(z_1, z_2, \ldots z_n)}$$

Simulation

$y_1, y_2, \ldots y_n$, and outputs of the system model, $z_1, z_2, \ldots z_n$. Modifications are made and the model is rerun until the outputs are arbitrarily similar—or until the analyst discards his particular theory in favor of another.

METHODOLOGY

In the following we present the general methodology of computer simulation (regardless of the application), but it is, of course, the purpose of the text to illustrate in detail how the methodology is implemented. The flowchart, Figure 2–4, outlines the procedure.

Computational Concepts in Simulation

Reference has been made to a number of concepts which should now be defined. Attributes of system entities may change through time; then we call them *system variables* or, alternatively, *state variables*. The second term is often used since the set of attribute values at any point in time defines the "state of the system." The state of our inventory system at any time would be obtained by noting the values of such attributes as inventory on hand, and inventory on order, which are attributes of the entity, stock item. Attributes of other system entities would also be noted.

Parameters are considered to be those attribute values that do not change during the simulation. For example, a stock item might have the attribute cost per unit. For certain cases this attribute would be fixed during a simulated time, and it is necessary to state only initially what the parameter value is. System or state variables, on the other hand, must be given an initial value, but relationships in the system are periodically evaluated so that the system model is said to generate values for these variables. And (not to add to the

FIGURE 2–4

Simulation Procedure*

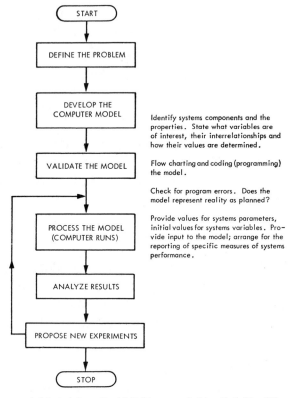

START

DEFINE THE PROBLEM

DEVELOP THE
COMPUTER MODEL

Identify systems components and the
properties. State what variables are
of interest, their interrelationships and
how their values are determined.

VALIDATE THE MODEL

Flow charting and coding (programming)
the model.

Check for program errors. Does the
model represent reality as planned?

PROCESS THE MODEL
(COMPUTER RUNS)

Provide values for systems parameters,
initial values for systems variables. Provide input to the model; arrange for the
reporting of specific measures of systems
performance.

ANALYZE RESULTS

PROPOSE NEW EXPERIMENTS

STOP

* Adapted from Daniel Teichroew and John F. Lubin, "Com-
puter Simulation: Discussion of the Technique and Comparison of
Languages" (Working Paper No. 20 [Stanford, Calif.: Graduate
School of Business, Stanford University, 1964]), pp. 27–29.

confusion) we might point out that because these values are generated within the model, and depend on what happened earlier in the
simulation, these values—or rather the variables to which the
values are assigned—are called *endogenous variables.* Thus we will
use the three terms interchangeably—*system, state,* and *endogenous*
variables.

To process a model it is not only necessary to state parameter
values and initial values for system variables, but also some provision must be made for "moving the model through time." We are
interested in the dynamic behavior of the system. Typically, the
simulation begins at time zero, when the parameters and system
variables have the initial values provided by the analyst.

Next, various events are generated or input to the model which cause changes to take place and which result in new values for the system or state variables. For example, in the inventory system the receipt of the first customer order (an event) results in changes in inventory and in the value of customer billings (or accounts receivable). The reduction in inventory might occasion an order to the supplier for new stock. In the computer all this activity takes place in a fraction of a minute, but it corresponds, let us say, to the firm's activity during a full day.

Now provision for advancing the clock or the calendar is required; that is, we move to the next day or we input the next exogenous event, and the model processes the information describing the event, and, according to the relationships contained in the model, a second set of values of the state variables is computed. The process continues until all events have been input or until the simulation has run for the desired length of time.

Finally, two additional computational requirements are necessary in order to conduct simulations. They are the provision for generating values of random variables and the recording of the results of the simulation. These are briefly discussed in the example below.

SIMULATION AND DECISION MAKING

Relationships among entities and attributes take several forms. One kind of relationship may be illustrated by considering some attributes (variables) of a stock item. Arbitrarily name the variables:

B_n beginning inventory.
E_n ending inventory.
D_n quantity demanded.
S_n quantity sold.
O_n quantity ordered.
R_n quantity received.

The subscripting of the variables denotes that the variables will take values sequentially through n time periods. The use of this notation and difference equations are discussed in Chapter 4. It is often convenient in simulation to write equations explicitly as functions of time. The variables listed are measured in *units* of the stock item; the values of n are the integers 1, 2, 3, ...

For any period n, assume that observations of the variables B,

D, and S occur at the beginning of the period; that E, O, and R are recorded at the end of the period. The relationships listed below are representative of some that might be interesting to the decision maker. The first two are simple equations, the third and fourth are identities explained by the manner in which we have treated time, the fifth and sixth are conditional relationships.

1. $E_n = B_n - S_n + R_n$
2. $B_n = B_{n-1} - S_{n-1} + R_{n-1}$

3. $R_n = O_{n-1}$ or $O_n = R_{n+1}$
4. $B_n = E_{n-1}$ or $E_n = B_{n+1}$

$\left\{\begin{array}{l}\text{when a delay of one period be-}\\ \text{tween placement and receipt of}\\ \text{an order is assumed.}\end{array}\right.$

5. If $D_n \leq B_n$, then $S_n = D_n$
6. If $D_n > B_n$, then $S_n = B_n$

$\left\{\begin{array}{l}\text{these relationships simply state}\\ \text{that the amount sold cannot ex-}\\ \text{ceed the quantity on hand dur-}\\ \text{ing the period.}\end{array}\right.$

The conditional relationships 5 and 6 are especially interesting to the decision maker. Another is the one used to determine when and how much new stock to periodically order. Suppose the manager used the following:

If $B_n \leq 50$ units, then $O_n = 200$ units.

This is a *decision rule*, sometimes called a trigger rule, because if the premise is satisfied ($B_n \leqq 50$ units) the reorder decision follows automatically. Whether an order is placed is conditional on the quantity of inventory on hand, B. At the same time, O is given the value 0 or 200 recalling the assumption that it takes but a single period to translate an order into received merchandise. The value of B is noted only once each period, which rules out the issuance of more than a single order in a period. At the start of the simulation, O might be given an initial value of 0 and would remain so until the reorder rule that assigns $O = 200$ was activated. The following period, O would be decreased on delivery of the order. We can anticipate that the relationships tying together several present and future values of the stock item will need to be specified. The values would probably take on the more familiar and descriptive names like inventory on hand, inventory on order, and inventory received.

Simulation is especially powerful for testing and comparing the way decision rules affect system behavior. Many design changes are changes of the parameters of decision rules (50 and 200 in our example) as well as changes of the form of the rule. For example, we might wish to substitute as a reorder rule the following:

Order 100 units every day.

Not all decision making is so unambiguous. Neither are certain decisions made regularly. Yet, as we have implied, decision making can be interpreted literally as modifying the state of a system.

Decision Making

The decision maker is assumed to act periodically to influence the design of the system in order to transform a set of inputs into a set of outputs which have economic value. We assume further that the system has been designed to achieve transformation or conversion of inputs in a reasonably effective fashion. However, we may observe that in the best designed systems conversion does not always measure up to the designer's plans. Things go wrong—availability of inputs of required quantity or quality are not completely controllable. Faulty production occurs, orders are delayed in processing, machines break down, the market places changing values on the product or service output of the systems, and so on.

The effects of such events change the system state in a way that prompts the decision maker to modify something about the system. Perhaps he rearranges the set of inputs, or changes its composition. These changes, modifications, or redesign of the system constitute decision making of a particular kind. The decision maker elects to modify the system in order to better achieve the purpose(s) or ideal set of outputs for which the system was created, given information that outputs are not being achieved according to the measure of effectiveness. Decisions of this type may also be made on the basis of anticipated environmental changes which could lead to unsatisfactory system behavior.

There is a second type of decision, unlike that described above, which is irregularly imposed on the decision maker. Some decisions are routinely required simply because the system is not automatic. Here we might imagine that activity takes place within the system and that the conversion of inputs proceeds to a particular state, the description of which is available to the decision maker. He then initiates one of several regular courses of action. He is constrained by existing policy or he uses the information in conjunction with a decision rule of the form described above.

Courses of action usually involve commitments either to purchase or to hire resources: for example, the decision rule that when the inventory of stock item $Z \le x$ units, order A number of units from the supplier; or, if the number of jobs scheduled today $> H$ number of machine hours, start up the standby machine; or, if plant utilization $< P$ percent this week, lay off workers.

Decision making is a response by the manager who tries to control the behavior of the system. Conditions, or rather events exogenous to the system, can compel the manager to make decisions; or decisions may in part be planned and periodic responses required to sustain activity in the system. Simulation is used to improve the quality of both kinds of decision making.

AN ILLUSTRATIVE EXAMPLE

To summarize many of the concepts and the simulation methodology, let us consider a small exercise in simulation which is intended merely to demonstrate certain features of the procedure. The student should not hazard an evaluation of simulation on the basis of the example in which simplifying assumptions are made and methodological shortcuts used.

We fall back on the classical problem of the newsboy who seeks to fashion an inventory ordering rule so that the amount of his profit is maximized. Uncertainty exists in this situation because the number of papers purchased daily by his customers cannot be predicted. In such an inventory system we have the entities newspapers, customers, newsboy, and profit. The entity newspapers has the variables:

O_n quantity ordered each day.
S_n quantity sold each day.
D_n quantity demanded each day.

These variables are recorded in units of the stock item, which also have parameters *cost* and *price* which we may call C and P with *per unit* values respectively of 5 and 15 cents.

Profit has one variable of interest, its *magnitude* each day, which we'll designate P. The subscript n serves as our calendar. Each day n takes on the next value from the set of integers. With the variables, parameters, and calendar specified we can write the equation to calculate P:

$$P_n = (S_n \cdot P) - (O_n \cdot C).$$

The state variables O and S must be generated. O daily takes values produced by using an arbitrary decision rule devised by the newsboy. The rule is to *order* each day a quantity of papers equal to the quantity *demanded* the *preceding* day.

$$O_n = D_{n-1}$$

remembering that n is today's date.

S is determined partly by the exogenous event D. S also is a function of O. Two conditional relationships are evaluated, one of which produces S.

1. If $D_n \leq O_n$, then $S_n = D_n$.
2. If $D_n > O_n$, then $S_n = O_n$.

S values are conditional, and 1 and 2 simply operate to ensure that $S \leqq O$. The opportunity loss when $D > O$ is ignored to simplify the illustration.

To generate values for demand D we now resort to a shortcut, the implications of which are fully developed in Chapter 6. Suppose that the newsboy knows from past experience that customer demand (daily) may be 15, 16, 17, 18, 19, or 20 newspapers. He also knows from his experience the relative frequency with which each value occurred and can thus construct the following table.

Demand	Relative Frequency
15	1/12
16	2/12
17	4/12
18	3/12
19	1/12
20	1/12
	12/12

He considers that the value of demand D is determined by chance, but that in the long run the values occur with the frequencies noted. Therefore our newsboy constructs a type of roulette wheel in which the area is divided into six segments, each marked with a value of the variable, and each segment proportional in size to its relative frequency. (See page 32.)

Each day the wheel is spun and the number of the segment taken to be the value of the variable D. He is now ready to simulate the system and test his reorder rule. Table 2–1, which shows an average daily profit of $1.62, summarizes his activity for 10 days.

To begin the simulation, our newsboy spins his demand-generating wheel and lets the first value represent D_{n-1}, (D_0). This is

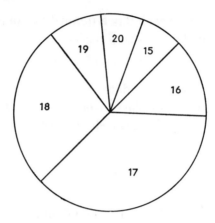

necessary since his reorder rule requires a prior value (in our trial this value was 18). Therefore $O_1 = 18$ units. Next the wheel is used to generate D_1, demand for the first day. As we performed the simulation this value turned out to be 17. Comparing quantity demanded and quantity ordered for day 1, customer demand was less than quantity ordered. Employing his rule, the newsboy determines that S_1 is 17 and $P_1 = (17)(0.15) - (18)(0.05) = \$1.65$.

The variable n next takes the value $n + 1$ or 2, which has the effect of moving us to the second simulated day. The activity through 10 days is repeated.

The newsboy could now propose changes in the system, specifically in the reorder rule. He might wish to test a rule in which, for example, he orders an amount equal to average sales over perhaps the last three or five days. Other changes might be proposed. If he

TABLE 2–1

Newsboy Simulation

n	D_n	O_n	$D_n \leq O_n$	$D_n > O_n$	S_n	P_n	P_n Cumulative
0	18	—	—	—	—	—	—
1	17	18	yes		17	1.65	1.65
2	17	17	yes		17	1.70	3.35
3	16	17	yes		16	1.55	4.90
4	17	16		yes	16	1.60	6.50
5	15	17	yes		15	1.40	7.90
6	17	15		yes	15	1.50	9.40
7	18	17		yes	17	1.70	11.10
8	20	18		yes	18	1.80	12.90
9	17	20	yes		17	1.55	14.45
10	18	17		yes	17	1.70	16.15

had reason to believe that the variable, customer demand, might change, he could model the anticipated change. We are not suggesting that a 10-day simulation run produces reliable information, nor that we have considered all properties of the system, but the illustration serves to point out how the methodology is implemented. The meanings of such concepts as entities, attributes, state variables, parameters, decision rule, and calendar are, hopefully, a little more meaningful.

The illustration points up another aspect of simulation. If we were to expand our model and propose a simulation run of several hundred or several thousand days for each of a series of system designs, we could readily appreciate the amount of effort involved. It is precisely for this reason that we call in the digital computer, and turn to the subject of computer programming in the next chapter.

SUGGESTIONS FOR FURTHER STUDY

DUTTON, JOHN M., and STARBUCK, WILLIAM H. *Computer Simulation of Human Behavior.* New York: John Wiley & Sons, Inc., 1971.

EMSHOFF, JAMES R., and SISSON, ROGER L. *Design and Use of Computer Simulation Models.* New York: The Macmillan Company, 1970.

NAYLOR, T. H.; BALINTFY, J. L.; BURDICK, D. S.; and CHU, K. *Computer Simulation Techniques.* New York: John Wiley & Sons, Inc., 1966.

TOCHER, K. D. *The Art of Simulation.* Princeton, N.J.: D. Van Nostrand Co., Inc., 1963.

EXERCISES

1. Substitute the following reorder rule in the newsboy problem: $O_n = 17$ units. Set up a table like Table 2–1 and conduct the experiment for 10 days. Compute average daily profit for the simulated period.

You will have to devise a mechanism for generating D_n. Use 12 chits; 1 marked 15, 2 marked 16, 4 marked 17, 3 marked 18, 1 marked 19, and 1 marked 20. Draw a chit to generate D_n, but remember to replace it in the container before generating the next demand value.

2. Repeat exercise 1 for the rule: $O_n = (D_n + D_{n-1})/2$. Round off your answer and use an integer value for O_n.

3. Two players, A and B, repeatedly flip a coin. If heads, B pays A $1; if tails, A pays B $1. Each player starts the game with $10. Assume a fair coin and that the integrity of the players is not at issue. Use a coin and set up a table to record the outcome (head/tail) and the cash balance of each player through 10 trials of the game.

chapter 3

Introduction to Programming

PROGRAMMING is the composition of programs. A computer program, as we shall see, is a model. It is a unique model in two ways: (1) it is constructed in conformity with a number of rather rigorous conventions, peculiar to computer logic, and thereby (2) the model itself is intelligible to a computer in the sense that if the model is introduced or fed into the computer, the computer will respond by performing certain operations which the model calls for.

Programs may be written in any of a number of "languages," but the computer itself understands only one language—so-called machine language. Developing fluency in machine language requires a great deal of study, and constructing programs in machine language is tedious and slow. Fortunately, there are several other languages that require minimal effort to understand and to use in building powerful computer models. When programming is done in any language other than machine language, it must first be "translated" into machine language by means of a special intermediary program called a *compiler*. A computer equipped with the proper compiler can do the translating.

FORTRAN (an abbreviation for FORmula TRANslation) is a language for which compilers are rather universally available. There are many variations in FORTRAN compilers, but most versions are sufficiently similar that minor modifications in any FORTRAN program will make it susceptible to translation by most FORTRAN compilers, and hence usable on most computers.

Thus FORTRAN becomes a somewhat universal language, ideally suited to analytical model building, and a good "basic language" from which to learn other computer languages when the need arises.

BASIC Language Equivalents in Appendix B

While we will explore the programming of computers in the context of FORTRAN, a number of other scientific languages are equally appropriate, especially BASIC, ALGOL and PL/1. In view of the increasing availability of BASIC compilers, especially in a time-share mode, for each complete FORTRAN program presented in this text a BASIC equivalent is presented in Appendix B.

A FORTRAN program consists of a number of statements, or instructions, to the computer. To develop some fluency in FOR–TRAN we will first examine some of the basic conventions governing FORTRAN programming, and then we will explore the mechanical process by which a FORTRAN program is prepared for submission to the computer for compilation and subsequent execution.

ALGEBRAIC EXPRESSIONS, MEMORY, AND THE SEQUENCE OF OPERATIONS

Several different kinds of statements make up the list of possible FORTRAN instructions. The basic algebraic statement is one of these. It consists of a variable, an equal sign, and some expression to the right of the equal sign. When such a statement is encountered the computer gives to the variable on the left side of the equal sign the value of the expression on the right side of the equal sign. Thus, on encountering the statement AHC = 40.00 the computer stores in its memory the value 40.00 for AHC. Later, if we call for the value of the variable AHC to be printed out for us, the value 40.00 will be printed out (assuming that the value of AHC has not been changed through subsequent operation).

The expression to the right of the equal sign can be a more involved mathematical expression—for example, AHC = 70.00 + 20.00 − 50.00. The computer will perform whatever computation is called for by the expression to the right of the equal sign, and then will give to the variable on the left of the equal sign the value resulting from the computation. It should be emphasized that a variable—and only one variable—can appear to the left of the equal sign in an algebraic statement in FORTRAN. The following has no meaning in FORTRAN: AHC + 10.00 = 50.00.

The computer reads statements (instructions) in a program from the top down unless specifically instructed to do otherwise. Furthermore, a succeeding algebraic statement can supersede a prior one. For example, the variable AHC is given two different values in the following three statements: AHC = 40.00, AOC = 25.00, and AHC = 60.00. The computer, on encountering the first of the above statements, stores 40.00 for the variable AHC, but by the time the last statement has been executed AHC has the value 60.00, the 40.00 having been replaced by 60.00.

Thus far we have used only constants to the right of the equal sign in our algebraic statements. In most programs variables also appear on the right side of the equal sign. An appropriate FOR–TRAN algebraic statement might also be: TAC = AHC + AOC.

On encountering the above algebraic statement the computer would add together the values currently stored for the variables AHC and AOC, and would store the value of the sum for the variable TAC. (By the time a statement such as that above is encountered, the variables AHC and AOC should, of course, have been given the desired values.)

A great deal of flexibility is permissible in writing variable names; however, there *are* a few rules.

1. Variables can consist of no more than six letters or six letters and numbers.
2. Every variable must begin with a letter.
3. All letters must be capitals (there are no lowercase letters in FORTRAN).

OPERATIONAL SYMBOLS

Some FORTRAN operational symbols are like ordinary mathematical symbols, but some are not. The customary mathematical symbols, their meanings, and the corresponding FORTRAN symbols that will concern us most appear below.

Mathematical Symbol	Meaning	Corresponding FORTRAN symbol
+	add	+
−	subtract	−
÷	divide	/
×	multiply	*
$(\ )^2$	raise to a power (square)	** 2
$\sqrt{\ }$	take the square root of	SQRT( )

A few examples will illustrate the use of these symbols and will increase our understanding of FORTRAN programming.

The compound interest formula, which gives the amount (S) to which an initial deposit (P) will grow in n years when compounded at r percent annually, is $S = P(1 + r)^n$.

We might instruct the computer to determine the amount to which \$1,000[1] invested at 4 percent compounded annually would grow in 6 years by the following program segment:[2]

$$P = 1000.0$$
$$R = .04$$
$$N = 6$$
$$S = P * (1.0 + R) ** N$$

A question might be raised at this point: How, in the final statement above, does the computer know whether to multiply P times the quantity $(1 + R)$ *before* or *after* raising the quantity $(1 + R)$ to the sixth power? There is a *hierarchy of operations* in FORTRAN, and it should be *memorized*.

THE HIERARCHY OF MATHEMATICAL OPERATIONS IN AN ALGEBRAIC EXPRESSION

The computer first scans everything that appears to the right of the equal sign in an algebraic expression, then

Everything that appears inside a set of parentheses is done first.
Exponentiation is done next.
Then *multiplication and division* are done.
Finally, *addition and subtraction* are done.

Whenever one of the above rules does not answer the query, What should be done next? the computer moves from left to right, executing operations called for in that order.

As we will see, parentheses can be used extensively to group portions of a complex algebraic expression in order to minimize the likelihood of error. Also, parentheses can be nested, with one set inside another.

At the end of the above program the computer would have stored for the variable S the value of our deposit at the end of the sixth year.

---

[1] In FORTRAN, commas cannot be used to group digits in an algebraic expression.

[2] This job could also, of course, have been done by the statement:
$$S = 1000.0 * (1.0 + .04) ** 6.$$

THE *WRITE* STATEMENT

There are several FORTRAN statements whose purposes are to input and output data. The WRITE statement causes to be printed out for one or more specified variables the current values stored for those variables. Thus if the statement WRITE (6,—)N,S is inserted at the end of the compound interest program above, it will cause the value of N and the value of S to be printed out at the end of the program.

The blank in the parentheses above indicates that we have left out something. Specifically, we have left out reference to what is termed a FORMAT statement. A FORMAT statement is used to specify the format in which we want the printout to appear; i.e., whether the values of N and S should appear side by side, one above the other, with some identifying terminology, or otherwise. More will soon be said about FORMAT statements.

NUMBERED STATEMENTS AND THE *GO TO* STATEMENT

FORTRAN statements can be numbered. For a variety of reasons (which will soon become apparent) it is useful to number many FORTRAN statements. These numbers always appear to the left of the statement.

It was pointed out earlier that, unless otherwise specified, statements in a FORTRAN program will be executed in top-to-bottom order. The GO TO statement is one of a variety of statements which can be used to change this order of execution. Every GO TO statement must have a number after the words GO TO. On encountering a GO TO statement, the computer will proceed to the statement whose number appears after the words GO TO, whether the statement whose number is given appears before or after the GO TO statement. To understand the use of the GO TO statement, examine the program segment in Figure 3–1.

With this program the computer is instructed to calculate the amount to which a $1,000 deposit, earning 4 percent compounded, would grow in 1 year. The value of the deposit at the end of the year, S, is printed out. This value is then viewed as the initial deposit (P is set equal to S in the next to last statement), and the computer is sent back to calculate the amount to which the new deposit will grow at the end of the next year by the statement GO TO 2.

FIGURE 3–1

Program Segment Containing
Go *To* Statement

$$P = 1000.00$$
$$R = .04$$
$$N = 1$$
$$2 \quad S = P * (1.0 + R) ** N$$
$$WRITE(6,—)S$$
$$P = S$$
$$GO\ TO\ 2$$

COUNTERS

In many programs one finds need of a counter to count the number of times a repetitive program has been repeated. We might use a counter in the above program to keep track of the number of years our $1,000 has been on deposit, and to print this information out, along with the value of the balance on deposit at the end of each year. In the following program segment the variable YEAR serves as our counter, and every time statements number 2 through the GO TO statement are repeated the value of the variable YEAR is increased by 1.

$$YEAR = 0.0$$
$$P = 1000.00$$
$$R = .04$$
$$N = 1$$
$$2 \quad S = P * (1.0 + R) ** N$$
$$YEAR = YEAR + 1.0$$
$$WRITE(6,—)\ YEAR,S$$
$$P = S$$
$$GO\ TO\ 2$$

(NOTE: The choice of numbers to employ in numbering statements is limited only by the fact that statement numbers must be non-zero, positive integers of five digits or less. Where many numbers are employed in a program they *need not* appear in consecutive order.)

THE *IF* STATEMENT

The IF statement is a "conditional" GO TO statement, and is best illustrated by an example: IF (YEAR − 10.0)2,4,7.

When the above statement is encountered, the computer will evaluate the expression that appears inside the parentheses after the word IF in precisely the same fashion that it evaluates the expression to the right of an equal sign in an algebraic statement. If the value of the result is negative, the computer will proceed immediately to statement number 2; if the value of the result is equal to 0, the computer will proceed immediately to statement number 4; if the value of the result is positive, the computer will proceed immediately to statement number 7. It does not matter whether statements number 2, 4, and 7 appear before or after the IF statement.

In our compound interest problem we might use an IF statement —in place of the GO TO statement—to stop the repetitive process of calculating the balance on hand at the end of, say, 10 years:

```
    YEAR = 0.0
    P = 1000.00
    R = .04
    N = 1
  2 S = P * (1.0 + R) ** N
    YEAR = YEAR + 1.0
    WRITE(6,—) YEAR,S
    P = S
    IF (YEAR − 10.0)2,4,4
  4 CONTINUE
```

On the 10th iteration the value of the expression in parentheses becomes zero, and the flow of control is sent to statement number 4. In our program the expression in parentheses would never become greater than zero (positive), so we really need only statements number 2 and 4. However, the IF statement must mention three statement numbers after the parentheses, and each of the numbers must refer to a statement in the program. To conform to this FOR-TRAN convention we simply write: IF (YEAR − 10.0)2,4,4.

The CONTINUE statement serves only to provide a statement for the number 4. When the CONTINUE statement is encountered, in this program, the computer passes on to the statement that follows the CONTINUE statement.

THE *STOP* AND *END* STATEMENT

The preceding program segment is a complete FORTRAN program except for the specification of the FORMAT for printing out the answer (left blank in the WRITE statement) and except for a terminal statement—that is, a STOP and an END statement. (STOP statements can be used at times without an END statement, but an END statement, which must terminate all programs, must be preceded by a STOP statement.)

Our complete FORTRAN program for determining the amount to which $1,000 would grow if compounded annually at 4 percent for 10 years (complete except for the FORMAT requirement referred to above) would be as follows:

```
      YEAR = 0.0
      P = 1000.00
      R = .04
      N = 1
   2  S = P * (1.0 + R) ** N
      YEAR = YEAR + 1.0
      WRITE(6,—) YEAR,S
      P = S
      IF (YEAR − 10.0)2,4,4
   4  CONTINUE
      STOP
      END
```

THE DO STATEMENT

We could achieve the same results as those we have achieved in the above program by a simpler scheme using a powerful FORTRAN statement called the DO statement or the DO loop. Like the GO TO and the IF statements, the DO statement influences the order of execution of statements in a program. The DO statement is also best explained by an example: DO 4 J = 5,35,3.

The 4 following the word DO refers to a statement (statement number 4) which must *follow* the DO statement. On encountering the above DO statement the computer will give the variable J the value 5. It will then proceed down *through* statement number 4 as in any other program. On reaching statement 4 the computer will execute statement number 4 and then will return to the DO statement, whereupon it will increase the value stored for the variable J by 3 (making it 8), then it will proceed as before through statement number 4, returning again to the DO statement, increasing the value stored for the variable J by an additional 3 units (making it now 11), and so on. This looping process will continue until J has grown to the point where to repeat the loop again would cause J to be greater than 35, whereupon the looping process is discontinued, and the computer proceeds to the statement that follows statement number 4 (the end of the DO loop) and continues through the remainder of the program.

Much more remains to be said about DO loops if their full potential is to be utilized, but we will allow ourselves only three comments at this point.

1. If only two numbers follow the equal sign in the DO statement, the third number (the amount by which the value of the variable is to be increased each time the loop is repeated) is presumed to be 1.
2. Variables, rather than numbers, *can* be used to the right of the equal sign in the DO statement, making it possible to cause the number of times the loop is to be repeated dependent on prior calculations in the program.
3. The variable to the left of the equal sign in the DO statement can, *but need not necessarily,* be employed in the program anywhere else except in the DO statement itself.

Now that we have introduced the DO statement, we can write a more economical program (Figure 3–2) to cause the computer to calculate for us the balance of our $1,000 deposit after 10 years compounding at 4 percent per year.[3]

FIGURE 3–2

"Economic" Version of Sample Compounding Program

```
      P = 1000.00
      R = .04
      N = 1
      DO 3 J = 1,10
      S = P * (1.0 + R) ** N
      P = S
    3 WRITE(6,—)J,S
      STOP
      END
```

---

[3] Admittedly, we could determine the answer to our compound interest problem more simply (as suggested in footnote 2). However, we have deliberately used the compound interest formula in this way so as to introduce the basic kinds of statements of which most FORTRAN programs are composed.

WRITING AND PUNCHING A PROGRAM

We now know enough about FORTRAN to write some rather powerful programs. However, before proceeding to use our knowledge of programming to deal with problems of this character, we would do well to explore the fashion in which a FORTRAN program is prepared to be fed into the computer for compiling and subsequent execution.

Communicating with the computer will be described in the context of *batch processing* via punched cards. For those readers equipped with time-shared computing facilities, and with interactive FORTRAN, the bulk of what follows will be fully applicable and will need only to be supplemented by some reference to local convention.

We have seen that a FORTRAN program essentially consists of a series of statements. To introduce a program into the computer we need to transpose our written statements to a set of punched cards. Transposition is achieved by simply typing, on the typewriter-like keyboard of a special card-punch machine, the FOR-TRAN statements in our program. Our FORTRAN statements become a deck of cards, with holes punched in them. In general, each statement appears on a separate card, although, as will be shown, if a statement is too long to be punched on one card as many as 10 cards can be employed to accommodate one statement.

When a letter, number, or other symbol is typed on the keyboard of the card-punch machine, one or more holes are punched in one or more of 12 possible positions in a vertical column on the card. The pattern of holes tells the computer which symbol is intended, and it is in this way that our FORTRAN instructions are communicated to the computer.

Figure 3–3 shows how the FORTRAN statement we have used in our compound interest program (to calculate the growth of our deposit in one year) might appear on a punched card.

Several rather strict FORTRAN conventions govern the preparation of punched cards, and they must be learned. Most of these conventions have to do with the placement of symbols on the card. As shown in Figure 3–3, each card has 80 columns. Columns 1 through 5 are reserved for statement numbers, and FORTRAN statement numbers must be punched in any one or more of these columns. (Column 1 has an additional function which will be described shortly.)

FIGURE 3–3

FORTRAN Punched Card Version for the Statement of the Compound Interest Program

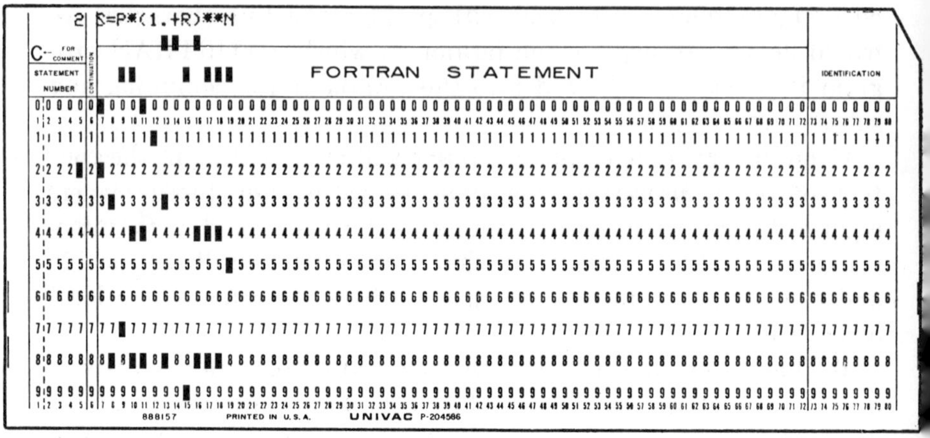

Columns 7 through 72 are reserved for the FORTRAN statement proper. Except in FORMAT statements (discussed below), spaces may be employed rather freely in punching a FORTRAN statement. Thus the preceding statement could be punched as shown in Figure 3–3, or it could be spread out to consume all the columns from 7 to 72.

Columns 73 to 80, inclusive, are ignored by the computer; they may be used by the programmer to number his cards or identify them in some other way for his own convenience.

Column 6 is used to indicate a continuation where a statement is too long to be punched on one card. If one card is sufficient for a statement, column 6 can be left blank or punched with a zero. If additional cards are required for one statement, a nonzero integer must be punched in column 6 of each of the cards on which the continued statement is continued. A good practice is to leave column 6 blank if one card is sufficient for a statement. If more than one card is required, punch a zero in column 6 of the first card of the statement, punch a 1 in column 6 of the first continuation card, a 2 in column 6 of the second continuation card, and so on.

A FORTRAN program is ready for submission to the computer when the statements have been punched in conformance with the rules described above and when the card deck is arranged in consecutive order, with the card corresponding to the first statement on top.

THE FORMAT STATEMENT

We have deliberately postponed introducing the FORMAT statement until card punching was described. Of all FORTRAN conventions, those having to do with the FORMAT statement require the most rigorous attention to form, and rigorous attention to form means, chiefly, rigorous conformance to space specification requirements.

One use of the FORMAT statement has been mentioned: by use of a FORMAT statement we specify for the computer precisely the format in which we want data to be printed out for us following computations called for in the program. A second use of the FOR-MAT statement, in which data is read into the computer, will be described later.

In our previous use of the WRITE statement we employed a blank to indicate that something—a statement number—had been left out. Our complete WRITE statement for the program, shown in Figure 3–1, might be written: WRITE (6,8)S.

The number 8 refers to a FORMAT statement whose number is 8. (All FORMAT statements are numbered statements.) A set of parentheses must follow the word FORMAT in a FORMAT statement. Inside the parentheses the arrangement of the data to be printed out is specified. The FORMAT statement referred to in our WRITE statement above might be written: 8 FORMAT (1H0,10X,F8.2).

The first expression in the parentheses, 1H0, specifies that prior to each printout (i.e., prior to the printing out of each new value of our deposit S at the end of each succeeding year) we want the printing mechanism associated with the computer to double-space. Each succeeding value for S, therefore, will be printed on a separate line, with a blank line between. With the expression 1H1 in the first position in the parentheses we could cause each value for S to be printed out on a new page (hardly appropriate here but frequently desirable). Finally, if we were content with single spacing we would employ the expression, 1H (i.e., we would leave a blank space after the H).

In the third expression, F8.2, the F specifies that the value we expect to be printed out for S will have a fractional part; i.e., it will contain a decimal. Had we made provision throughout our program to deal only with integers, we would have used an I rather than an F specification. More will be said later about the need to distinguish between integers and decimal quantities.

The 8 in the 8.2 specifies that 8 columns or spaces should be reserved for printing out the various values of S. The .2 specifies that 2 spaces should be reserved for digits to the right of the decimal point. The space to be reserved for the printing out of data must be clearly specified in the FORMAT statement. One space must be reserved for each digit, one for the decimal point, and one for the *sign* of the number to be printed out (indicating whether it is a positive or negative quantity). If we expect the values of S to be 9999.00 or less, then 8 spaces would be adequate.

It is permissible to reserve more spaces than will be required, but care should be taken to reserve enough spaces so that no part of our answer gets truncated except that part we want truncated. In the process of computing the values of S each time through our program, the computer will carry its calculations well beyond the two decimal places we are interested in as an answer. (How far beyond two decimal places the computation will be carried depends on the word length of the computer.) Each time the WRITE statement is encountered the computer will round off the value of S to two significant digits (since we specified two digits to the right of the decimal point in the FORMAT statement to which our WRITE statement refers), and will print out only the *rounded* answer, dropping the decimal digits that were carried during the computation.

The second expression in the parentheses, 10X, specifies that the 8 spaces reserved for printing out the value of S should begin 10 spaces to the right of the left margin of the sheet on which the values of S are to be printed out. Thus we specify *blank* spaces with the use of Xs.

When a great deal of data is to be printed out—data of a number of different types—it is frequently useful to provide identifying remarks for the printed out data. This can be done with an H specification. To understand how the H specification might be used, recall the WRITE statement of our final compound interest program (Figure 3–2): 3 WRITE(6,9)J,S.

We will let 9 refer to a FORMAT statement, which we will write as follows:

9   FORMAT (1H ,22HAT END OF YEAR NUMBER ,I4,
            5X,11HBALANCE = $,F8.2)

When our WRITE statement is executed, the computer will first cause to be printed out, beginning at the left margin, the following:

AT END OF YEAR NUMBER. Twenty-two spaces were reserved for this group of words and spaces, as shown by the number 22 preceding the H, which precedes the first word of the group. The H indicates that the 22 characters and spaces that follow it should be printed out precisely as they appear inside the parentheses of the FORMAT statement.

In the next four spaces will be printed out the current value of the variable J, since four spaces are reserved for the value of J by the next expression in the FORMAT statement, I4. The next expression, 5X, will cause five spaces to be skipped. Next, the group for which 11 spaces were provided in the FORMAT statement will be printed out: BALANCE = $.

Finally, in the next eight spaces the current value of the variable S will be printed, since eight spaces were reserved for the value of S by the expression F8.2 in the FORMAT statement.

Our printout for the first three times through the DO loop would therefore appear as follows:

```
AT END OF YEAR NUMBER    1    BALANCE = $ 1040.00
AT END OF YEAR NUMBER    2    BALANCE = $ 1081.60
AT END OF YEAR NUMBER    3    BALANCE = $ 1124.86
```

Notice that a plus sign would not be printed out for the values of S. Negative values are indicated by a minus sign on printout, but positive values simply are given no sign at all, in conformance with algebraic custom. However, if a value is expected to be positive, space still must be reserved for the sign, whether or not it will be printed out.

In our WRITE and FORMAT statements above we have provided for printing out only two values, one for the current value of the variable J and one for the current value of the variable S. Note that the computer automatically associates the first variable mentioned in the WRITE statement with the space reserved by the first specification (the I specification) in the FORMAT statement, the second variable mentioned in the WRITE statement with the space reserved by the second specification (the F specification) in the FORMAT statement, and so on.

It is possible to have a WRITE statement and a corresponding FORMAT statement where no numerical values of program variables at all are to be printed. Instead of the scheme used above for identifying output data we might have used two sets of WRITE and FORMAT statements to create a two-column matrix for output data, with a heading above each column. Thus, before the DO statement in the program shown in Figure 3–2, we might have written:

WRITE (6,10)
10   FORMAT   (1H0,2X,4HYEAR,2X,10HBALANCE($))

Then, at the end of the DO loop, we might place the following two statements, with the first statement (the WRITE statement) *inside* the DO loop:

WRITE (6,11)J,S
11   FORMAT (1H ,2X,I4,3X,F8.2)

With this arrangement the printout, by the third time through the DO loop, would appear as follows:

```
YEAR   BALANCE( $ )
  1       1 0 4 0 . 0 0
  2       1 0 8 1 . 6 0
  3       1 1 2 4 . 8 6
```

One has a rather high degree of freedom in arranging data printouts since most computers are equipped to print up to 120 characters on one line. But note that there must be no unaccounted-for spaces inside the parentheses of a FORMAT statement, and that each specification group inside the FORMAT parentheses is separated from the others by commas.

More will be said about FORMAT statements as the need arises, but in many future discussions of FORTRAN programs the FORMAT statement will not be added. Reference to a FORMAT statement will be made, as before, by a WRITE statement with a blank. Constructing FORMAT statements is a somewhat mechanical process and we are more interested in model building concepts than in processing details.

FLOATING–POINT AND FIXED–POINT VARIABLES AND CONSTANTS

There are two classes of variables and constants in FORTRAN.

1. Integer variables and integer constants.
2. Floating point variables and floating point constants.

Integer constants are constants that do not have a fractional part; i.e., constants that require no decimal point. *Floating point* constants have a decimal point (fractions can be expressed in FOR-TRAN only in decimal form).

An important rule in FORTRAN is that a floating-point value (constant) should not be given to an integer variable unless it is desired that the fractional part of the value be dropped. If a floating-point constant is given as a value to an integer variable, only the integer part of the constant is stored; the fractional part will be lost. Unless truncation is desired—and sometimes it is—one should be careful not to intermix floating-point and integer quantities in this fashion.

An integer variable is any variable whose first letter is an I, J, K, L, M, or N. If in a given program we do not expect to give a variable a value with a decimal part, we can use integer variables through-out. But we must be prepared for what are sometimes surprising results when division is involved. Thus, if the variable IST has a value of 3, the variable LDM has a value of 2, and the statement KS = IST/LDM is encountered, KS will have the value 1 stored for it. The fractional part of the quotient is truncated.

If we expect that we may load a variable with a quantity that has a decimal part, we should use a floating-point variable. Also, if we expect to add, subtract, multiply, and divide variables on the right side of the equal sign in an algebraic expression, and if one of those variables is a floating-point variable, then *all* should be floating-point variables. This last rule does not apply, however, when exponentiation is involved. A floating-point quantity may be raised to an integer power.

One of the rules of the DO statement is that any variables that appear in the DO statement must be integer variables.

MISCELLANEOUS FORTRAN CONVENTIONS

In our discussion of operational symbols it was shown that we can raise a value to the ½ power, that is, take its square root as follows:

$$SQRT(\ )$$

On encountering this expression to the right of an equal sign in an algebraic statement the computer will take the square root of the quantity (constant or variable) in the parentheses and will replace the expression with the square root.

Other FORTRAN functions we may call for and for which we have frequent use are:

ALOG() . . . which is replaced by the natural logarithm of the quantity that appears in the parentheses.

EXP()   . . . which is replaced by the base of the natural logarith, *e*, raised to the power that appears in the parentheses.

The Logical IF Statement

Another useful form of the IF statement is the *logical* IF statement. In the logical IF statement the computer looks inside the parentheses that follow the word IF and assesses whether what is "stated" inside the parentheses is true. If it is true the computer will obey the instruction that follows the parentheses; if it is not true the computer will pass on to the succeeding instruction. For example, on encountering the statement

IF (A .GE. 10.0) K = 4

if A is "greater than or equal to" 10.0 the computer will give K a value of 4 and proceed to the next instruction. If A is not greater than or equal to 10.0 the computer will *not* give K a value of 4 but instead will proceed immediately to the succeeding instruction.

On encountering the statement

IF (14.7 .EQ. B) GO TO 7

if B is equal to 14.7 the computer will go to statement number 7; otherwise the computer will proceed immediately to the succeeding instruction.

Other symbols that may appear inside the parentheses of a logical IF statement and their meanings appear below.

.GT.   . . . greater than.
.LT.   . . . less than.
.LE.   . . . less than or equal to.
.NE.   . . . not equal.

Carriage Control

It was pointed out that we can control the carriage and hence call for single spacing, double spacing, or others on printout by use of the symbols 1H—, 1H0, and so on as the first expression inside the parentheses of a FORMAT statement. Spacing can also be achieved by use of the diagonal inside the parentheses of the FOR–MAT statement. For example, with the FORMAT statement

$$5 \quad \text{FORMAT} \quad (\text{F6.2}/\,/)$$

we cause the computer to print out, in accordance with specification F6.2, the value of some variable named in the WRITE statement which refers to FORMAT statement number 5, and then to *double space*. Use of three diagonals would have yielded triple spacing.

SUGGESTIONS FOR FURTHER STUDY

ALLUISI, EARL A. *Basic FORTRAN for Statistical Analysis*. Homewood, Ill.: The Dorsey Press, 1967.

COUGER, J. DANIEL, and SHANNON, LOREN E. *FORTRAN IV: Programmed Instruction Approach*. Homewood, Ill.: Richard D. Irwin, Inc., 1968.

EMERICK, PAUL L., JR., and WILKINSON, JOSEPH W. *Computer Programming for Business and Social Science*. Homewood, Ill.: Richard D. Irwin, Inc., 1970.

GONZALEZ, RICHARD F., and MCMILLAN, CLAUDE, JR. *Machine Computation: An Algorithmic Approach*. Homewood, Ill.: Richard D. Irwin, Inc., 1971.

MCCRACKEN, DANIEL D. *A Guide to FORTRAN IV Programming*. New York: John Wiley & Sons, Inc., 1965.

ORGANICK, ELLIOTT I. *A FORTRAN IV Primer*. Reading, Mass.: Addison-Wesley Publishing Co., Inc., 1966.

EXERCISES

1. Write FORTRAN statements that will cause the computer to store in the variable RESULT the value of each of the following expressions (assuming that the computer already has values stored for w, x, y, and z).

a) $x + y^2$

b) $(x - y)^3$

c) x^4

d) $x + y/z$

e) $\dfrac{x - y}{z}$

f) $w + \dfrac{x}{y - z}$

g) $\dfrac{x + y}{y - z} + w^2$

h) $(x/y)^{z-1}$

2. In each of the following FORTRAN expressions remove parentheses, where parentheses *can* be removed, without changing the meaning.

a) $(A * B)/C$

b) $(A + X) * (B/Y)$

c) $(A/B) * C$

d) $(A ** (I - 2) + B ** (I + 3))$

3. Write each of the following as a FORTRAN statement.

a) $r = \dfrac{a + bx}{c - dx}$

b) $b = -\dfrac{1}{2x} + \dfrac{a^2}{4x^2}$

c) $fy = x \cdot \dfrac{x^2 - y^2}{x^2 + y^2}$

d) $j = 4k - 6k_1k_2$

4. Smith deposits $42,967.14 in the bank at the beginning of the year. Interest on Smith's deposit will be compounded annually at 5.75 percent per year. Write a FORTRAN program that will cause the computer to calculate and print out: (*a*) SMITH BALANCE AT END OF YEAR _____IS $_____; (*b*) Smith's balance at the end of each of 10 successive years, with the number of the year in each case in the first blank space in the statement above, and the amount of the deposit at the end of that year in the second blank space in the statement above.

5. Write a FORTRAN program that will cause the computer to determine how many years Smith's money (Exercise 4) will have to remain on deposit at 5:75 percent, compounded annually, before it will grow to at least $1,000,000.

6. Write a FORTRAN program that will cause the computer to determine the interest rate Smith will have to earn, compounded annually, for his initial deposit of $42,967.14 to grow to at least $1,000,000 in 10 years.

7. Peter Minuit, governor of the Dutch West India Company, is reputed to have purchased Manhattan Island from the Indians for $24 in 1626. Assume that the Indians invested their receipts at 6 percent, compounded annually, and write a FORTRAN program that would determine and print out the value of their investment at the end of each of the following years: 1676, 1726, 1776, 1826, 1876, 1926, and 1976. In your printout identify the year associated with each investment value.

chapter 4

Value Analysis
and Iterative Processes

In MANY KINDS of system studies the facility of the computer in dealing with difference equations is extremely useful. We would do well to review some of the algebra of difference equations. In this chapter we will apply this knowledge to problems of value analysis, and will use it further in later chapters as we address ourselves to forecasting, industrial dynamics, Markov processes, and more advanced systems study.

DIFFERENCE EQUATIONS

We could have treated our compounding process in the previous chapter in the context of linear, first-order difference equations. The program in Figure 3–2 could have been written:

```
        R = 0.04
        DO 3 J = 1,10
        S = S * (1.0 + R)
    3   WRITE (6,4)S
    4   FORMAT ( )
        STOP
        END
```

The third statement in the program above, $S = S * (1.0 + R)$, is a FORTRAN representation of a difference equation. In general, any time we compose a FORTRAN instruction in which the variable on the left of the equal sign also appears on the right of the equal sign we have a difference equation. In the third statement in the program above, the S on the right of the equal sign represents the "state" of a dynamic system at one period in time, and the S on the left of the equal sign represents the state of the system at a succeeding period in time. *Before* execution of the statement S = S * (1.0 + R) the state of the system is the value stored for S (the value that the S on the right side of the equal sign *will be replaced by* when the statement is executed by the computer). *After* execution of the statement the state of the system is the new value stored for S.

Expressed in customary algebraic form the statement S = S * (1.0 + R) becomes:

$$S_{n+1} = S_n(1.0 + R). \tag{4-1}$$

Expression (4–1) is a linear, first-order difference equation. It tells us how the state of a dynamic system in one period (i.e., period $n + 1$) is related to the state of that system in the previous period (i.e., period n).

The general form of a linear, first-order difference equation is:

$$Y_{n+1} = f_1(n)/f_2(n) \times Y_n + g(n)/f_2(n)$$

where f_1 and $f_2 \neq 0$.

If f_1, f_2 and g are constants, our general form becomes:

$$Y_{n+1} = AY_n + B \tag{4-2}$$

where A and B are constants, and $A \neq 0$. If $B = 0$, then (4–2) becomes a linear, first-order, *homogeneous* difference equation.

Note that $Y_{n+2} = aY_{n+1} - 7Y_n + 3n$ is linear but it is a *second-order* equation, involving three periods. Note that $Y_{n+1} = Y_n^2 + 9n$ is first-order but not linear.

State Variables and the "State Vector"

Our interest-compounding system is quite a simple system. Its *state* in time period n is the value of *state variable S* in period n; i.e., S_n. Systems of any complexity generally have many state variables. For example, variables of concern in the model of a municipal utility might include cash on hand (COH), accounts receivable (AR) and inventories (INV). If these three variables had values of 1,000, 3,000, and 4,000 respectively, in period n, we might represent the state of the system in period n as follows:

$$COH_n = 1,000$$
$$AR_n = 3,000$$
$$INV_n = 4,000$$

. . . or, in vector notation:

$$\begin{bmatrix} COH \\ AR \\ INV \end{bmatrix}_n = \begin{bmatrix} 1,000 \\ 3,000 \\ 4,000 \end{bmatrix}$$

. . . where the column vector of variables to the left of the equal sign is called the *state vector*.

Assume that the management of the utility deliberately employs policies which, as the population of the municipality grows, cause *COH, AR,* and *INV* to increase at rates of 10 percent, 12 percent and 7 percent per year. The state of the system in period $n + 1$ is related to its state in period n as follows:

$$\begin{bmatrix} COH \\ AR \\ INV \end{bmatrix}_{n+1} = \underbrace{\begin{bmatrix} 1.10 & 0 & 0 \\ 0 & 1.12 & 0 \\ 0 & 0 & 1.07 \end{bmatrix}}_{\substack{\text{transition} \\ \text{matrix}}} \begin{bmatrix} COH \\ AR \\ INV \end{bmatrix}_n . \qquad (4\text{--}3)$$

Matrix equation (4–3) is the *state model* of the system and the matrix to the right of the equal sign is the transition matrix.

No interdependence among the state variables is indicated by the transition matrix in (4–3). A *system* is a collection of interacting entities or components. In (4–4), *COH* and *AR* are seen to be dependent on each other and on *INV,* from period to period. The interaction between these components is fully specified in the transition matrix of (4–4).

$$\begin{bmatrix} COH \\ AR \\ INV \end{bmatrix}_{n+1} = \begin{bmatrix} 1.10 & .20 & -.6 \\ -.08 & 1.0 & 0 \\ -.09 & 0 & 1.20 \end{bmatrix} \begin{bmatrix} COH \\ AR \\ INV \end{bmatrix}_n \qquad (4\text{--}4)$$

Note that the state model in (4–3) is analogous to the state model of our compound interest system in (4–5):

$$[S]_{n+1} = [1 + r][S]_n. \qquad (4\text{--}5)$$

We will return to the modeling of systems of interacting components via systems of difference equations in later chapters.

Difference Equations versus Differential Equations

The rate of change in the value of our deposit from period n to period $n + 1$ would be: $(S_{n+1} - S_n)$ per period. From (4–1) this rate of change is:

$$S_{n+1} - S_n = rS_n, \tag{4-6}$$

which says that the rate of change of our deposit is a function of the interest rate and a function of the size of the deposit, S_n.

The counterpart in calculus of our rate of change equation (4–6) is:

$$\frac{dS}{dt} = rS \tag{4-7}$$

which says that the *instantaneous* rate of change of our deposit, S, with respect to time, t, is a function of the interest rate and a function of the size of the deposit, S. Rearranging the terms of (4–7) we obtain:

$$\frac{dS}{S} = rdt, \quad \text{or} \quad \frac{1}{S} dS = rdt. \tag{4-8}$$

In the calculus "solution" has a special meaning. The solution of the differential equation of expression (4–8) means an algebraic equation, which when differentiated yields the differential equation of (4–8). To obtain the solution we take the integral of (4–8):

$$\int_{S_o}^{S_n} \frac{1}{S} dS = \int_0^n rdt$$

from which we obtain:

$$LnS_n - LnS_o = rn, \quad \text{or} \quad Ln(S_n/S_o) = rn$$

from which we obtain:

$$e^{rn} = S_n/S_o \quad \text{or} \quad S_n = S_o e^{rn}. \tag{4-9}$$

Expression (4–9) is the continuous compounding model which tells us how our deposit S in period n is related to our original deposit S_o if our interest is compounded, not annually, or semiannually, or quarterly, or daily, but *continuously*.

The expression e^{rn} in (4–9) is, of course, the limit

$$[(1 + r/k)^k]^n, \quad k \to \infty$$

in which k is the frequency of compounding.

SOLUTION OF A DIFFERENCE EQUATION

Solving a differential equation in the calculus means determining the algebraic equation from which the differential equation was obtained, as we observed above.

Solving a difference equation has a special meaning also. Recall that a difference equation shows how the state of a system in a period is related to the state of that system in the previous period. The solution of a difference equation tells us how the state of a system in any period is related to the initial state of the system. The solution of the difference equation $S_{n+1} = S_n(1 + r)$ would be a new equation that tells us how the state of this system in any period n is related to the initial state of the system. We obtain this solution by recursive analysis:

from $S_{n+1} = S_n(1 + r)$,

$$\text{when } n = 0 \text{ we have: } S_1 = S_0(1 + r)$$
$$\text{when } n = 1 \text{ we have: } S_2 = S_1(1 + r) = S_0(1 + r)^2$$
$$\text{when } n = 2 \text{ we have: } S_3 = S_2(1 + r) = S_0(1 + r)^3$$

and by inference: $S_n = S_0(1 + r)^n$, the *solution* of our difference equation. Our solution is, of course, the compound interest model.

PRESENT VALUE

Using the compound interest model, for which we just solved, we would find that if we invest $5,584 at 6 percent compounded annually in 10 years we would have $10,000. If we are willing to part today with $5,584 with the expectation of receiving in 10 years $10,000 but unwilling to part with this sum for any less than $10,000 in 10 years, then we can say that to us $5,584 is the present value of the right to receive $10,000 in 10 years. This is tantamount to saying we regard $5,584 today as being the *equivalent* of $10,000, 10 years from now.

To determine the present value equivalent of a sum of money to be delivered at some future date we discount the sum to be delivered by the factor $(1 + r)^{-n}$. Our discount factor is the amount we would have to invest today at rate r in order to have $1 in n years, and we find that factor by giving S_n a value of $1 and solving for S_0 from the expression $S_n = S_0(1 + r)^n$.

We might equip ourselves with a table of discount factors that provides four different interest rates ranging from 4 percent through

7 percent, and discount periods from 1 through 10 years with the following FORTRAN program:

```
      DO 1  N = 1,10
      PV4 = 1.04 ** (−N)
      PV5 = 1.05 ** (−N)
      PV6 = 1.06 ** (−N)
      PV7 = 1.07 ** (−N)
    1 WRITE(6,2)N,PV4,PV5,PV6,PV7
    2 FORMAT( )
      STOP
      END
```

Table 4–1 at the end of this chapter was generated from a program of this type. We can employ the discount factors in Table 4–1 to assess the present value equivalent of future outlays (and receipts), and thus equip ourselves to choose among alternative asset investments whose costs (and receipts) are not symmetrical in magnitude and timing.

For example, suppose that we are confronted with a choice between two machines, machine A and machine B, each of which will do a particular job equally well and each of which has a useful life of three years. The expected costs and salvage value associated with each of the two machines are shown below.

	Machine A	Machine B
Cost installed	$7,000	$6,000
Annual maintenance cost	1,000	700
Salvage value	2,000	1,800

Assuming that we value money at 5 percent compounded annually, the present value equivalents of the expected costs associated with machine A would be:

$$\begin{array}{rl}
\$7,000 \times (1.000) = & \$7,000 \\
1,000 \times (0.952) = & 952 \\
1,000 \times (0.907) = & 907 \\
1,000 \times (0.864) = & 864 \\
\hline
 & \$9,723
\end{array}$$

For simplicity, assume that maintenance cost occurs at the end of the year.

$$\begin{array}{rl}
-2,000 \times (0.864) = & -1,728 \\
\hline
\text{Present value of machine A:} & \$7,995
\end{array}$$

The present value equivalents of the expected costs associated with machine B are:

$6,000 × (1.000) =	$6,000
700 × (0.952) =	666
700 × (0.907) =	635
700 × (0.864) =	605
	$7,906
−1,800 × (0.864) =	−1,555
Present value of machine B:	$6,351

Clearly machine B is more attractive than machine A by a factor whose present value is $7,995 − $6,351 = $1,644.

It makes sense for us to employ "time zero," the present, as the point in time by reference to which we assess values of varying magnitudes that occur at different moments in time. However, the choice is somewhat arbitrary. For example, we might assess the *future* value of the expected costs associated with each machine. We might project ourselves forward in time three years from now and compare the future values of the expected costs associated with machine A and machine B. An investment today will grow in three years by the factor $(1 + r)^3$, which is, of course, the reciprocal of $(1 + r)^{-3}$. We might therefore use the reciprocals of the elements of Table 4–1, at the end of this chapter, to assess future values. The future value equivalents of the expected costs associated with machine A are:

$7,000 × 1/(0.864) =	$ 8,106
1,000 × 1/(0.907) =	1.103
1,000 × 1/(0.952) =	1,050
1,000 × 1/(1.000) =	1,000
	$11,259
−2,000 × 1/(1.000) =	−2,000
Future value of machine A:	$ 9,259

The future value equivalents of the expected costs associated with machine B are:

$6,000 \times 1/(0.864)$ =	$6,948
$700 \times 1/(0.907)$ =	772
$700 \times 1/(0.952)$ =	735
$700 \times 1/(1.000)$ =	700
	$9,155
$-1,800 \times 1/(1.000)$ =	$-1,800$
Future value of machine B:	$7,355

Machine B is again more attractive than machine A by a factor whose future value, three years from now, is $9,259 - 7,355 = $1,904. The present value of a $1,904 payment three years from now is $1,904 \times (0.864) = $1,644, the present value superiority of machine B disclosed in our comparison of the two assets based on the present value criterion.

ANNUITIES

For many purposes a useful table is one whose elements tell us the present value of a stream of future periodic payments, all of equal magnitude. In the analysis above an annuity table of this sort might have enabled us to assess the present value of our three years of maintenance costs with only one instead of three calculations. What we need is a table that will tell us the present value of a payment of $1 at the end of each year for the next n years, money being compounded at rate r annually.

Each element in our table will be the sum of a series of the form:

$$(1 + r)^{-1} + (1 + r)^{-2} + (1 + r)^{-3} + \cdots (1 + r)^{-n}.$$

The sum of the series proves to be:

$$\frac{1 - (1 + r)^{-n}}{r}.$$

Employing this relationship in a FORTRAN program similar to that suggested previously for generating the elements of Table 4–1, we would obtain Table 4–2, at the end of this chapter.

In our assessment of the relative attractiveness of machine A and machine B above we employed the *present value criterion*. When we use the present value criterion we express costs (and receipts) as an equivalent single cost at time zero, the present.

A second criterion for comparing the attractiveness of alternative assets is the *uniform equivalent annual cost criterion*. It is the equivalent of the present value criterion, except that the present value of the asset is expressed as an annuity over the useful life of the asset. To convert the present value of the expected costs associated with machine A in our example to a uniform equivalent annual cost over its useful life, we would simply ask ourselves what annuity for a period of three years is the equivalent of $7,995 today. Referring to Table 4–2, we find that at 5 percent an annuity of $1 per year for three years is the equivalent of a single payment today of $2.72. The three-year annuity equivalent of $7,995 at 5 percent would therefore be $7,995/$2.72 = $2,571 per year. The three-year annuity equivalent of the expected costs associated with machine B is $6,351/$2.72 = $2,335.

The uniform equivalent annual cost criterion is frequently preferred to the present value criterion because it tells us what we might expect the *annual* cost associated with an investment to be, and we commonly think of costs in this fashion.

Another advantage in the uniform equivalent annual cost criterion is that it enables us to compare assets with unequal useful lives. Let us imagine we wanted to compare machine B, above, with a third one, machine C, which has a useful life of six years. Let's assume that an analysis of the expected costs associated with machine C shows their present value to be $11,080. A sequence of two machines of type B would give us comparable productive capacity over the six-year period. To assess the relative attractiveness of a sequence of two machines of type B alongside one machine C we reason that the present value of the first machine B would be an amount equal to the present value of the first machine B discounted by the factor $(1 + r)^{-3}$. The present value of our sequence of two machines of type B then becomes:

Present value of first machine .... $6,351 × (1.000) =	$ 6,351
Present value of second machine ..... 6,351 × (0.864) =	5,487
Present value of sequence of 2 machines	$11,838

One type C machine, with a useful life of six years, would be more attractive than a sequence of two type B machines, each with a useful life of three years.

Notice that if we ask ourselves what would be the uniform equivalent annual cost associated with a sequence of two type B machines, each lasting three years, we obtain: $11,838/$5.076 = $2,335

($5.076 being the cost of an annuity of $1 per year for six years at 5 percent compounded annually).

This is the same as the uniform equivalent annual cost associated with one machine of type B lasting three years. Thus the uniform equivalent annual cost criterion enables us to compare two or more machines whose useful lives are not whole number multiples of one another.

THE CHAIN OF MACHINES PROBLEM AND OPTIMUM USEFUL LIFE

In our comparisons of machines A, B, and C we assumed that we knew the useful lives of the machines. With periodic maintenance and repair the life of an asset can frequently be prolonged indefinitely. In our analysis above we assumed that maintenance costs were constant over the lives of our machines. While maintenance prolongs the life of an asset, as the machine ages maintenance costs tend to become larger. Our assessment of the costs associated with a machine would be more realistic if we assumed that maintenance costs increase.

As maintenance and operating costs increase through time, salvage value tends to decrease. This suggests that rather than employing the same machine indefinitely it would pay to retire a machine after some period of usage and replace it with another of the same type. The least cost over time would be that cost associated with replacing the machine at the end of some optimum period, its optimum useful life. Thinking in these terms we might best compare alternative machines by asking ourselves what present value is associated with operating each machine for its optimum useful life, replacing it with another of the same sort, and repeating this cycle indefinitely. The best choice would be that machine with which is associated the minimum present value for the infinite sequence.

For example, assume that we contemplate acquiring an asset which costs new $3,000. Assume that the maintenance cost is expected to behave as follows:

Maintenance Cost

End of first year $190
End of second year 280
End of third year 370
And so on—

that is, maintenance is expected to cost $190 the first year, increasing by $90 each year thereafter. We might express maintenance cost, MC, by the following difference equation:

$$MC_{n+1} = MC_n + 90. \tag{4-10}$$

Let's solve this difference equation by recursive analysis.

When $n = 0$ (4–10) becomes $MC_1 = MC_o + 90$
When $n = 1$ (4–10) becomes $MC_2 = MC_1 + 90 = MC_o + 90 \times 2$
When $n = 2$ (4–10) becomes $MC_3 = MC_2 + 90 = MC_o + 90 \times 3$

and by inference:

$$MC_n = MC_o + 90n.$$

From our maintenance schedule above, $MC_1 = 190$. But since $MC_1 = MC_o + 90$, $MC_o = 100$, and the *solution* of our difference equation is:

$$MC_n = 100 + 90n. \tag{4-11}$$

Let's assume that the salvage value of this asset is expected to decrease about 14 percent each year. We can therefore express the salvage value, SV, by the following difference equation:

$$SV_{n+1} = .86SV_n. \tag{4-12}$$

As before:

When $n = 0$, from (4–12) $SV_1 = .86SV_o$
When $n = 1$, from (4–12) $SV_2 = .86SV_1 = .86^2SV_o$
When $n = 2$, from (4–12) $SV_3 = .86SV_2 = .86^3SV_o$

and by inference:

$$SV_n = .86^nSV_o.$$

SV_o is our salvage value when the asset is new. Therefore we can write:

$$SV_n = .86^n(3,000). \tag{4-13}$$

The two relevant costs in owning and operating this asset each year are: (1) the maintenance cost, and (2) the loss in salvage value.

If we acquire one of the assets and keep it three years, the present value of our expected experience with the asset will be:

$$PV_3 = 3,000 + 190(1+r)^{-1}$$
$$+ 280(1+r)^{-2}$$
$$+ 370(1+r)^{-3} - .86^3(3,000)(1+r)^{-3}. \quad (4\text{--}14)$$

The subscript 3, in PV_3, suggests we contemplate owning and utilizing one of these assets (a "sequence of 1") for three years. Notice that we have discounted the year-end maintenance costs by the factor $(1+r)^{-n}$ to get their present value, and we have discounted the salvage value credit [i.e., $.86^3(3,000)$] by the factor $(1+r)^{-3}$ to get its present value.

The present value of a second asset which we would acquire in three years and utilize for three years would be, *on the day we acquire it*, PV_3. To determine the present value *today* of the second one of these assets we would discount PV_3 by the factor $(1+r)^{-3}$. The present value of the sequence of two of these assets would therefore be:

$$PV_3 + PV_3(1+r)^{-3}.$$

The present value of a sequence of three of these assets would be:

$$PV_3 + PV_3(1+r)^{-3} + PV_3(1+r)^{-2(3)}.$$

The present value of an infinite sequence of these assets would be:

$$PV_3 + PV_3(1+r)^{-3} + PV_3(1+r)^{-2(3)} + PV_3(1+r)^{-3(3)} + \cdots$$

Factoring out PV_3 in the expression above we have:

$$PV_3[1 + (1+r)^{-3} + (1+r)^{-2(3)} + (1+r)^{-3(3)} + \cdots] \quad (4\text{--}15)$$

If we keep the asset not three years but n years before trading for another of the same type, expression (4–15) becomes:

$$PV_n[1 + (1+r)^{-n} + (1+r)^{-2n} + (1+r)^{-3n} + \cdots] \quad (4\text{--}16)$$

The expression in brackets is a series with an infinite number of terms, in which n is the number of years we plan to keep each asset in this infinite sequence of like assets. Each term in the series is smaller than its predecessor term. Therefore as terms are added the sum increases but by decreasing amounts. If we observe the behavior of this series as it increases, perhaps with the following FORTRAN program segment in which we have arbitrarily given n a value of two years and r, the rate of compounding, a value of 10 percent,

```
      S = 1.0
      N = 2
      DO 1 J = 1,10
      S = S + (1.10) ** (-J * N)
    1 WRITE(6,4)S
    4 FORMAT (  )
```

we find that the sum of the series seems to approach a finite limit:

$$S$$

1.826
2.509
3.074
3.540
3.926
4.245
4.508
4.726
4.905
5.054

In fact it does approach a limit, and the value of that limit as the number of assets in our sequence approaches infinity is:

$$\frac{1}{1 - (1 + r)^{-2}}$$

or, more generally, when the rate of compounding is r and the number of years each asset will be kept is n:

$$\frac{1}{1 - (1 + r)^{-n}}. \qquad (4\text{–}17)$$

The present value of the expected costs associated with an infinite sequence or chain of assets, each of which is employed for n years, is therefore:

$$PV_n \left[\frac{1}{1 - (1 + r)^{-n}} \right]. \qquad (4\text{–}18)$$

The present value of the first of our sequence of assets can be expressed more economically as follows:

$$\$3,000 + \left[\sum_{j=1}^{n} (\$100 + \$90 \times j)(1 + r)^{-j} \right] - (.86^n(\$3,000)(1 + r)^{-n}.$$

The FORTRAN counterpart of the summation sign is the DO statement, and we might cause the computer to determine PV_n, given an interest rate of 10 percent, and to store that value at address E with the following instructions:

```
        N = _____
        E1 = 0.0
        DO 1 J = 1,N
        T1 = J
  1     E1 = E1 + (100.0 + 90.0 * T1) * (1.10) ** (−J)
        SV = .86 ** N * 3000.0 * (1.10) ** (−N)
        PVN = 3000.0 + E1 − SV
```

To determine the present value of the expected cost associated with an infinite sequence of these assets, each employed for n years, we form the product of *PVN* and (4–17), requiring the addition of the following instruction:

$$E = PVN * 1.0/ (1.0 − (1.10) ** (−N))$$

The optimum useful life of the asset would be that value for n which causes E to be a minimum. A FORTRAN program that would determine the present value of the expected costs associated with a chain of these assets, each kept for n years as n varies from 1 through 4 (at 10 percent interest) might be as follows:

```
        DO 2 N = 1,4
        E1 = 0.0
        DO 1 J = 1,N
        T1 = J
  1     E1 = E1 + (100.0 + 90.0 * T1) * (1.10) ** (−J)
        SV = .86 ** N * 3000.0 * (1.10) ** (−N)
        PVN = 3000.0 + E1 − SV
        E = PVN * 1.0/(1.0 − (1.10) ** (−N) )
  2     WRITE(6,3)N,E
  6     FORMAT (   )
        STOP
        END
```

The output of the program appears as follows:

N	E
1	$9100.00
2	9048.57
3	9041.49
4	9071.25

The optimum useful life of our asset proves to be $n = 3$ years, and the present value of the expected costs associated with an infinite sequence of these assets, each utilized for three years, is $9,041.49.

The appropriate strategy for comparing one asset with an alternative asset would be to determine the optimum useful life for each and then to choose that asset for which the present value of the costs associated with an infinite sequence, with each asset being kept for its optimum useful life, is a minimum.

It may seem unrealistic to compare assets on the assumption that we will replace each with another of precisely the same sort, ad infinitum, in an age of rapid technological change. The analysis is not really invalidated, however, by admission that we will not, in fact, replace the asset with another of precisely the same sort. We are asking ourselves: "Given uncertainties about each of these assets and considerable uncertainty about future technological improvements which may make them all obsolete, can we not decide optimally between them by assessing which among them would be the best choice if we *did* expect to stay indefinitely with the one we choose?"

The analysis seems less implausible also if we reflect that when we express the costs associated with an asset by use of the uniform equivalent annual cost criterion, the annual cost is the same whether we operate one of them for its useful life of n years and stop, or whether we replace it with another of the same sort for a second interval of n years, and so on ad infinitum. Thus we might have based the analysis above on the uniform equivalent annual cost associated with keeping the machine $n = 1$ year versus $n = 2$ years versus $n = 3$ years, and so on. The optimum useful life would have been the same by either approach.

In subsequent chapters we will deal further with iterative processes that enable us to identify optimum policies.

TABLE 4-1

Present Value of an Amount

YEAR	.040	.045	.050	.055	.060	.065	.070	.075
1	0.9615	0.9569	0.9524	0.9479	0.9434	0.9390	0.9346	0.9302
2	0.9246	0.9157	0.9070	0.8985	0.8900	0.8817	0.8734	0.8653
3	0.8890	0.8763	0.8638	0.8516	0.8396	0.8278	0.8163	0.8050
4	0.8548	0.8386	0.8227	0.8072	0.7921	0.7773	0.7629	0.7488
5	0.8219	0.8025	0.7835	0.7651	0.7473	0.7299	0.7130	0.6966
6	0.7903	0.7679	0.7462	0.7252	0.7050	0.6853	0.6663	0.6480
7	0.7599	0.7348	0.7107	0.6874	0.6651	0.6435	0.6227	0.6028
8	0.7307	0.7032	0.6768	0.6516	0.6274	0.6042	0.5820	0.5607
9	0.7026	0.6729	0.6446	0.6176	0.5919	0.5674	0.5439	0.5216
10	0.6756	0.6439	0.6139	0.5854	0.5584	0.5327	0.5083	0.4852
11	0.6496	0.6162	0.5847	0.5549	0.5268	0.5002	0.4751	0.4513
12	0.6246	0.5897	0.5568	0.5260	0.4970	0.4697	0.4440	0.4199
13	0.6006	0.5643	0.5303	0.4986	0.4688	0.4410	0.4150	0.3906
14	0.5775	0.5400	0.5051	0.4726	0.4423	0.4141	0.3878	0.3633
15	0.5553	0.5167	0.4810	0.4479	0.4173	0.3888	0.3624	0.3380
16	0.5339	0.4945	0.4581	0.4246	0.3936	0.3651	0.3387	0.3144
17	0.5134	0.4732	0.4363	0.4024	0.3714	0.3428	0.3166	0.2925
18	0.4936	0.4528	0.4155	0.3815	0.3503	0.3219	0.2959	0.2720
19	0.4746	0.4333	0.3957	0.3616	0.3305	0.3022	0.2765	0.2531
20	0.4564	0.4146	0.3769	0.3427	0.3118	0.2838	0.2584	0.2354

TABLE 4-2

Present Value of an Annuity

YEAR	.040	.045	.050	.055	.060	.065	.070	.075
1	0.9615	0.9569	0.9524	0.9479	0.9434	0.9390	0.9346	0.9302
2	1.8861	1.8727	1.8594	1.8463	1.8334	1.8206	1.8080	1.7956
3	2.7751	2.7490	2.7232	2.6979	2.6730	2.6485	2.6243	2.6005
4	3.6299	3.5875	3.5460	3.5051	3.4651	3.4258	3.3872	3.3493
5	4.4518	4.3900	4.3295	4.2703	4.2124	4.1557	4.1002	4.0459
6	5.2421	5.1579	5.0757	4.9955	4.9173	4.8410	4.7665	4.6938
7	6.0021	5.8927	5.7864	5.6830	5.5824	5.4845	5.3893	5.2966
8	6.7327	6.5959	6.4632	6.3346	6.2098	6.0888	5.9713	5.8573
9	7.4353	7.2688	7.1078	6.9522	6.8017	6.6561	6.5152	6.3789
10	8.1109	7.9127	7.7217	7.5376	7.3601	7.1888	7.0236	6.8641
11	8.7605	8.5289	8.3064	8.0925	7.8869	7.6890	7.4987	7.3154
12	9.3851	9.1186	8.8633	8.6185	8.3838	8.1587	7.9427	7.7353
13	9.9856	9.6828	9.3936	9.1171	8.8527	8.5997	8.3576	8.1258
14	10.5631	10.2228	9.8986	9.5896	9.2950	9.0138	8.7455	8.4892
15	11.1184	10.7395	10.3797	10.0376	9.7122	9.4027	9.1079	8.8271
16	11.6523	11.2340	10.8378	10.4622	11.1059	9.7678	9.4466	9.1415
17	12.1657	11.7072	11.2741	10.8646	10.4773	10.1106	9.7632	9.4340
18	12.6593	12.1600	11.6896	11.2461	10.8276	10.4325	10.0591	9.7060
19	13.1339	12.5933	12.0853	11.6077	11.1581	10.7347	10.3356	9.9591
20	13.5903	13.0079	12.4622	11.9504	11.4699	11.0185	10.5940	10.1945

EXERCISES

1. Expression (4–11) in this chapter tells us the maintenance cost in year n for our hypothetical machine. Compose an algebraic expression that will tell us the loss in salvage value in year n.

2–1. Compose a *general* FORTRAN model which will determine the optimum useful life of an asset with the following costs (base the analysis on the chain of assets concept):

Cost new, installed: OC.
Cost of maintenance at end of year n: $MC_n = MC_o + An$.
Salvage value at the end of year n: $SV_n = X^n(OC)$.
Value of money: R, compounded annually.

2–2. Repeat what is called for in part 1, above, but this time base the analysis on the uniform equivalent annual cost criterion for a "sequence of 1" asset rather than an infinite "chain of assets."

3. In expression (4–18) of this chapter we have a convenient means for determining the present value of the expected costs associated with an infinite chain or sequence of assets when the present value of the costs associated with the first one is PV_n. How might we alter expression (4–18) to equip ourselves to determine the present value of the costs associated with a sequence of J of these assets, each of which we keep n years, assuming that J is a finite but large number?

4. Compose a FORTRAN program to determine the optimum useful life of an asset with the following cost data:

Cost new, installed: $38,000.
Maintenance cost at end of year n: $MC_n = \$2,000 + \$1,000(1.02)^n$.
Salvage value at the end of year n: $SV_n = \$6,000 + .72^n(38,000)$.

5. In the chain of assets example presented in this chapter the interest rate employed was 10 percent compounded annually. Alter the program (presented in this chapter) designed to determine the optimum useful life in such a way as to show us how the optimum useful life is influenced by changes in the interest rate from 7 percent through 12 percent by increments of 1 percent.

6. Three machines, machine 1, machine 2, and machine 3, are equally capable of performing a particular function. Installed costs and maintenance and salvage values for these machines through time are portrayed in the table below. Using the chain of assets analysis developed in this chapter, determine which machine would be the best choice among the three.

	Machine 1	Machine 2	Machine 3
Cost new, installed ..	$8,000	$12,000	$19,000
Maintenance cost in year n	$MC_n = \$600 + \$50n$	$MC_n = \$200 + \$100n$	$MC_n = \$30n$
Salvage value in year n	$SV_n = .75^n SV_o$	$SV_n = .8^n SV_o$	$SV_n = .9^n SV_o$

7. In London, periodically, there is an auction in which persons with an interest in an estate they are destined to take possession of on the death of another person (a "remainder") sell their rights to the estate to the highest bidder. The bidder's maximum bid would be based on the forecast value of the estate on the death of the present owner, the life expectancy of the present owner, and so on.

What would be a maximum reasonable bid on a remainder with the following attributes:

The estate today is valued at $1,462,928. All of it is invested in government bonds yielding $4\frac{1}{2}$ percent. All bond interest goes toward purchase of additional bonds under the same terms.

On the death of Abigail Fluston-Pearce, who is 82 years old, the estate will pass to the seller of the remainder. When Abigail dies the British government will take 28 percent of the face value of the bonds.

Money is expected to depreciate (due to inflation) at a rate of about $2\frac{1}{2}$ percent per year in real purchasing power.

Assume that money in risks of this character is worth 8 percent compounded annually and that the life expectancy of a woman aged 82 is as follows:

Systems Analysis

Probability of survival to age 83 is .19
"   84   .17
"   85   .15
"   86   .13
"   87   .11
"   88   .09
"   89   .07
"   90   .05
"   91   .03
"   92   .01
"   93   .00
                                1.00 (approximate sum)

8. When a new product is produced the cost of producing the second unit of that new product is generally less than the cost of producing the first unit. Thus the cost to Boeing to produce the second 727 was less than the cost to produce the first, the cost to produce the third was less than the cost to produce the second, and so on. The decreasing cost is, of course, attributable to improved processing methods, increased employee skills, reduced scrap, and so on.

The curve of per unit cost versus number produced is commonly referred to as the "learning curve" in industry. Assume that the learning curve of a particular product can be approximated by the expression:

$$C_n = .8^n(\$200{,}000) + \$100{,}000 \tag{1}$$

where C_n is the cost of producing the nth unit.

Expression (1) is the *solution* of a difference equation.

a)   Find the difference equation for which (1) is the solution.

b)   Assume that we plan to produce 12 units of this product. Write a FORTRAN program that will cause the computer to determine what we should charge, per unit of the product, if we are to recover our costs of production plus 20 percent.

c)   Some learning processes are better approximated by the relationship:

$$C_n = n^{-b}(\$A) + \$B$$

Assume that a particular learning process is closely approximated by the relationship:

$$C_n = n^{-.152}(\$200{,}000) + \$100{,}000 \tag{2}$$

Repeat what is called for in parts (a) and (b) of this exercise, this time using expression (2) as the learning curve relationship.

d)   A particular learning process is believed to be closely approximated by the relationship:

$$C_n = n^b C_1 \tag{3}$$

where C_1 is the cost of producing the first unit. Production of the first units shows that doubling the number of units produced reduces the per unit cost by 10 percent, thus:

$$C_2 = .90C_1$$
$$C_4 = .90C_2$$
$$C_8 = .90C_4$$

Use the computer to determine the approximate value for the exponent b such that this learning process will be well represented by expression (3).

9. Part (a)

Monthly sales of Keynes Co., Inc., are increasing at a rate of 20 percent per month. The cost of sales is 90 percent of sales. Forty percent of sales are cash sales and the remainder are charge sales which are collected during the succeeding month. At the end of each month Keynes Co. management adjusts its stock level so that inventory is one half of the month's sales. On January 1, Keynes Co. accounts appear as follows:

Sales during previous month (SDM) = $300,000
Accounts receivable (AR) = 180,000
Inventory level (VEN) = 150,000
Cash on hand (COH) = 228,000

Assume that Keynes Co. sales continue to increase 20 percent per month, and write a FORTRAN program that will determine and print out end-of-month statements for:

SDM
AR
VEN
COH
COS (cost of sales)
GP (gross profit: SDM − COS)

Arrange to have these month-end statements printed out with each statement identified as to the month of the year it applies to, and print out statements *through* the first month in which Keynes Co. runs out of cash.

Part (b)

Consider the following to be "state variables" for the Keynes Co. system:

SDM, AR, VEN, COH, COS, and GP.

Construct a state model for the Keynes Co. system such that a transition matrix portrays the interdependence among the state variables.

chapter 5

The Inventory System under Certainty

INVENTORY SYSTEMS exhibit behavior important in systems analysis. They lend themselves to "solution" both via simulation and via formal analysis, and they provide a basis for identifying varying levels of automaticity. (Around inventory systems sophisticated computer data processing systems are built.)

In this chapter and in Chapter 6 we will explore the inventory system both to acquaint ourselves with additional systems concepts and to see how FORTRAN programming can be applied to more complex systems.

A retailer stocks units of item A for sale to his retail customers. Each item A unit costs the retailer $500 delivered, and the retailer figures that the cost of holding a unit of item A in inventory for one year is 20 percent of the delivered cost of the item.

The cost of processing an order for a new shipment of units of item A is $20 per order.

Our retailer expects the demand for item A to be 365 units during the year, and he expects the demand rate to be constant; that is, exactly 1 unit will be demanded by his customers per day, every day of the year.

Finally, our retailer knows that lead time (the time that elapses between placement of an order for a new shipment of units of item A and receipt of the new shipment) is exactly two days.

Since the retailer knows that daily demand will be one unit and that lead time is two days—that is, since there are no uncertainties —stock-outs are easy to avoid. Our retailer can be assured that a stock-out need never occur, and yet he can contribute toward a low average inventory level simply by reordering whenever the stock level of item A drops to two units: in two days the new order will arrive, and the two units on hand when the order was placed will have just been consumed. Thus the level of stock in item A will drop to zero at the moment a new shipment arrives, and with the arrival of the new shipment a stock-out is just avoided.

We have determined, therefore, that the optimum reorder point, $\hat{R}$, is two units.[1] To determine the retailer's best inventory management policy we need now to determine the optimum order quantity, $\hat{Q}$.

We might adopt a policy of ordering a new shipment of item A every two days, ordering two units with each order. Our inventory "curve" with this policy would look something like that shown in Figure 5–1.

FIGURE 5–1

"Item A" Inventory Curve

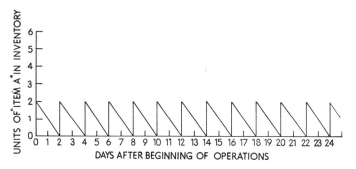

DAYS AFTER BEGINNING OF OPERATIONS

Under this policy the inventory level varies from a low of zero units to a high of two units. With this policy our retailer's average inventory level is one unit, and therefore annual inventory holding cost will be $100 (i.e., 1 unit $\times$ 0.20 $\times$ $500).

An alternative policy might be to order a new shipment of item A every 20 days, ordering 20 units with each order. Under this policy the inventory level would look something like that of Figure 5–2. With this policy our retailer's average inventory level is 10 units, and annual inventory holding cost will be $1,000 (i.e., 10 units $\times$ 0.20 $\times$ $500).

---

[1] $\hat{Q}$ and $\hat{R}$ signify the optimum order quantity and the optimum reorder point, respectively.

FIGURE 5–2

Alternative "Item A" Inventory Policy

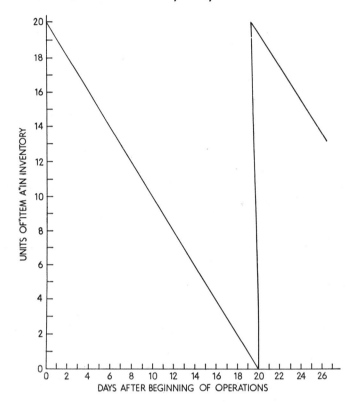

We are also concerned with ordering costs. Under the first policy our retailer is obliged to place 182.5 orders per year (at 2 units per order 182.5 orders will be required to meet the annual demand of 365 units). Annual ordering cost, therefore, would be $3,650 (i.e., 182.5 orders × $20 per order).

Under the second policy our retailer is obliged to order only 18.25 times per year, and annual ordering cost is $365.

It is apparent that low inventory holding cost is achieved at the expense of high ordering cost, and that low ordering cost is achieved at the expense of high inventory holding cost. The nature of the inventory problem is demonstrated by the three cost curves shown in Figure 5–3.

Either extreme is bad, and the total cost curve—which is simply the sum of the holding cost curve and the ordering cost curve—has

FIGURE 5–3

Three Inventory Cost Curves

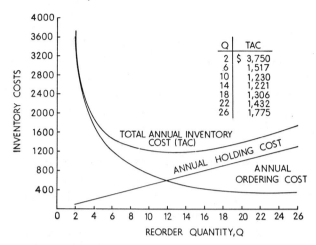

REORDER QUANTITY,Q

Q	TAC
2	$ 3,750
6	1,517
10	1,230
14	1,221
18	1,306
22	1,432
26	1,775

a minimum somewhere between the two extremes. Our objective is to find the optimum order quantity, $\hat{Q}$, which corresponds to this minimum point on the total annual cost curve.

We could do this in several ways, but we will do it by developing a mathematical model for our retailer's total annual inventory cost, TAC. Our model will consist of two parts:

1. *Annual holding cost:* $0.20(\$500) \times Q/2 = \$50Q$.
2. *Annual ordering cost:* $365/Q \times \$20 = \$7,300/Q$.

Total annual cost, TAC, would be the sum of these two costs, and our inventory model becomes

$$\text{TAC} = \$7,300/Q + \$50Q. \tag{5-1}$$

SOLVING FOR THE OPTIMUM ORDER QUANTITY: $\hat{Q}$

Referring to our graph of the total cost curve (Figure 5–3) and observing its somewhat U-shaped character, it becomes apparent that we could deduce $\hat{Q}$ from (5–1) by a simple iterative process. We could:

a) Select some small value for Q.
b) Calculate TAC from (5–1).

c)   Increase Q by a small increment.

d)   Recalculate TAC from (5–1).

e)   Compare the second TAC with the first TAC. If the second is smaller, then go back to (*c*) above and repeat the process, comparing each time the new value of TAC with the value previously calculated until the new value is equal to or greater than the value previously calculated, at which point we reason that we have reached the bottom of our U-shaped curve, whereupon we stop and adopt as our optimum Q the one employed to get our lowest value for TAC.

If it has not already occurred to the reader, a moment's reflection should convince him that the simple iterative process we have described above is almost a computer program. All we need to do to make it a computer program, and thereby to cause the computer to solve our retailer's inventory problem, is to adopt FORTRAN statements. The following program (Figure 5–4) will do this. Note that in this program the variable TAC1 gets the value of the first calculation of TAC, and the variable TAC2 gets the value of the second calculation of TAC, in which Q has been increased by 1. In the IF statement, TAC2 is then compared with TAC1 to see if we are still "moving down the U-shaped curve" toward the bottommost point.

FIGURE 5–4[2]

Conversion of Iterative Statements into FORTRAN Statements

```
      Q = 2.0
   1  TAC1 = 7300.0/Q + 50.0 * Q
      Q = Q + 1.0
      TAC2 = 7300.0/Q + 50.0 * Q
      IF  (TAC2 − TAC1)1,2,2
   2  Q = Q − 1.0
      WRITE  (6,3)Q,TAC1
   3  FORMAT  (1H0,12HOPTIMUM Q = ,F8.2,2X,
         14HMINIMUM  TAC = ,F5.1)
      STOP
      END
```

---

[2] Our page width will not accommodate on one line the full 72 characters available on a punched card. Henceforth in this textbook where indentation is encountered the indented part should be viewed as a continuation of the line above it, as in FORMAT statement Number 3, Figure 5–4.

Notice in the program above that when it has been determined in the IF statement that TAC2 is smaller than TAC1, TAC1 is then given the value of TAC2 by returning the computer to statement 1, whereupon TAC1 is recalculated, using the Q previously employed to calculate TAC2. A new value for TAC2 is then calculated with an increased Q. This scheme is synonymous with giving P the value stored for S in our compound interest program (Figure 3–1, Chapter 3) in preparation for a new iteration.

Notice also that when the iteration is discontinued (i.e., when the computer goes to statement number 2) TAC1 is either equal to or less than TAC2. This suggests that TAC1 is likely to give us a better approximation of the minimum total annual cost than TAC2. We would therefore prefer to have printed out for us TAC1 and the value for Q which yielded it. Since the Q last employed was that employed to calculate TAC2, we subtract 1.0 from Q before arranging for a printout.

Documentation: Flowcharting

Before further development of our inventory model we would do well to pause and discuss documentation, an important computer programming practice. Sometime during the preparation of a computer program, and preferably before the program itself is written, all but the most elementary programs should be documented. When one documents a program he supplements it with auxiliary information to facilitate interpreting the program. Documentation may amount to no more than inserting COMMENT statements at appropriate places throughout the program so that the purpose of the statements immediately following the COMMENT statement can be more readily understood. Our inventory model above might be documented by this technique as shown in Figure 5–5.

The letter C, entered in column 1 on the punched card, identifies a COMMENT statement. The computer ignores COMMENT statements entirely, so that as far as the computer is concerned the documented program above is precisely the same as its predecessor in Figure 5–4.

Another way in which programs may be documented is by flow diagramming or flowcharting. A flowchart is a pictorial representation of the flow of control and of the processing required for execu-

FIGURE 5–5

Documentation of Inventory Model by COMMENT Insertions

```
C      INITIALIZE Q AT SOME SMALL VALUE
       Q = 2.0
C      CALCULATE TAC1
     1 TAC1 = 7300.0/Q + 50.0 * Q
C      INCREASE Q BY 1
       Q = Q + 1.0
C      CALCULATE TAC2
       TAC2 = 7300.0/Q + 50.0 * Q
C      COMPARE TAC1 WITH TAC2 AND DECIDE
          WHETHER TO CONTINUE ITURATION
       IF (TAC2 - TAC1)1,2,2
     2 Q = Q - 1.0
       WRITE (6,3)Q,TAC1
     3 FORMAT (1H0,12HOPTIMUM Q = ,F8.2,
          2X,14HMINIMUM TAC = ,F5.1)
       STOP
       END
```

tion of a computer program. The choice of symbols to use in a flow-chart, and the arrangement of the symbols, is arbitrary, but a somewhat prevalent convention for their use has come into being, and we will confine ourselves to a few more or less standard forms. Figure 5–6 is a sample flowchart which might be employed to document our inventory model. Processes (or procedures) are represented by boxes, decisions are represented by diamonds, and the direction of flow is indicated by arrows.

It should be readily apparent that the undocumented program (Figure 5–4), the computer program documented with COMMENT statements (Figure 5–5), and the flowchart (Figure 5–6) say very much the same thing.

An experienced programmer probably would not bother to document a program so short and simple as that of our inventory model. As he becomes involved in composing more complex programs, however, even the experienced programmer finds some form of documentation useful. Long, complex programs can be written more easily if they are written from a flowchart that was composed in advance; and a flowchart also facilitates an individual's interpretation of another's program. If one adopts the practice of documenting his programs he will find that learning programming is easier,

FIGURE 5–6

Optimum Order Quantity: Flowchart for
Determining Economic Order Quantity*

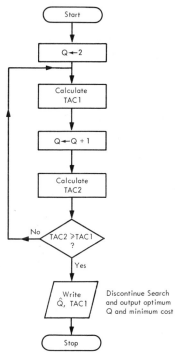

* In computing it is more common to use the
arrow "←" than the equal sign, in flowcharting.
Where the equal sign implies the indicative mood,
the arrow implies the imperative mood, as if to
say *"assign* to the variable named the value specified." We will observe this convention.

and that recalling the nature of programs he has written some time
in the past is much easier.

We will exploit our retailer's inventory problem to introduce
several further comments about FORTRAN. Our retailer's inventory program might have been written in the form shown in
Figure 5–7.

In this program the variable MINTAC serves as the standard to
which succeeding calculations of TAC are compared, as TAC1 did
in the previous program. We load MINTAC with a very large number to make certain that the first TAC we calculate will be smaller
than MINTAC.

Notice that in our inventory program above we have employed an

FIGURE 5–7

MINTAC Variable in Retailer's Inventory Program

```
      MINTAC = 999999.9
      DO 2 IQ = 2,1000
      Q = IQ
      TAC = 7300.0/Q + 50.0 * Q
      IF (TAC − MINTAC)2,3,3
   2  MINTAC = TAC
   3  IQ = IQ − 1
      WRITE (6,4)IQ,MINTAC
   4  FORMAT (1H0,12HOPTIMUM Q = ,I3,2X,
         14HMINIMUM TAC = ,F8.2)
```

IF statement to "get out of" the DO loop *before* the variable IQ has been given all the values called for in the DO statement. By specifying that IQ should take successive values up through 1,000, we have assured ourselves of this. The important thing to observe here is that one can transfer OUT OF the middle of a DO loop before the looping called for is finished, but one cannot get back into the middle of a DO loop. Entry into a DO loop must always be at the beginning of the loop, with the DO statement itself.

THE DECISION RULE

If we allow the computer to solve our retailer's inventory problem we find that his total annual cost, TAC, will be a minimum $1,208 per year if he orders 12 units with each new order. We have already determined that the best reorder point is two units. Therefore our retailer's *decision rule* for minimizing total annual inventory cost is: "When the stock level in Item A drops to two units, order a new shipment of 12 units."

THE COMPUTER PROGRAM AS A GENERAL MODEL

Anyone familiar with calculus will almost certainly be inspired to observe that calculus offers a simpler way to determine optimum $\hat{Q}$. Furthermore, such an observer might propose that by using calculus we could even develop a *general model*. Thus, given the certainty conditions of our retailer's inventory system, we could reason:

1. *Annual holding costs are* UHC × CPU × Q/2 *where:*

   UHC = annual unit holding cost as a percent
         of the cost price/unit;
   CPU = the cost price per unit;
   Q = the order quantity in units.

2. *Annual ordering costs are* CPO × DPY/Q *where:*

   CPO = the ordering cost/order processed;
   DPY = the demand per year in units.

Our total annual inventory cost model, then, would be : TAC = UHC × CPU × Q/2 + CPO × DPY/Q.

By use of calculus we could develop a general model for determining optimum $\hat{Q}$ in terms of all the other unknowns. Thus, differentiating TAC with respect, to Q, we have:

$$\frac{dTAC}{dQ} = \frac{UHC \times CPU}{2} - \frac{CPO \times DPY}{Q^2}.$$

Equating the expression on the right side of the equal sign to zero, and solving for Q, we have:

$$\hat{Q} = \sqrt{\frac{2(CPO \times DPY)}{UHC \times CPU}}. \qquad (5\text{--}2)$$

Finding EOQ using Calculus

Indeed (**5–2**) would be a general model for our retailer to use in determining optimum ordering quantity $\hat{Q}$, given

1. The cost price of one unit of Item A.
2. The cost of holding a unit of Item A in inventory for one year as fraction of the delivered price of one unit.
3. The cost of processing one order.
4. The annual demand for units of Item A.

Herein, it may be argued, lies the power of the calculus.

However, in precisely this same sense, a computer program can itself be a *general model*. A computer program that is a general model for our retailer's inventory system, in precisely the same sense as (**5–2**), is shown in Figure 5–8.

Like (**5–2**), our program in Figure 5–8 requires that values for UHC, CPU, CPO, and DPY be input into the model to determine optimum $\hat{Q}$.

We could modify our program and approach the "perfect" $\hat{Q}$ with any degree of accuracy we desire, doing with our computer program

FIGURE 5–8

Computer Program as General Model for Determining
Optimum Order Quantity

```
      MINTAC = 999999.9
      DO 2 IQ = 1,10000
      Q = IQ
      TAC = UHC * CPU * Q/2 + CPO * DPY/Q
      IF (TAC − MINTAC)2,3,3
   2  MINTAC = TAC
   3  IQ = IQ − 1
      WRITE (6,4)IQ,MINTAC
   4  FORMAT (1H0,12HOPTIMUM Q = ,I4,2X,
         14HMINIMUM TAC = ,F8.2)
      STOP
      END
```

anything that can be done with the general model developed by
calculus.

Did We Simulate?

In this chapter, thus far, we *modeled* an inventory system, then
operated on the model to determine the optimum policy, i.e., the
optimum value of the one control variable, order quantity Q. Did
we simulate the retailer's inventory system?

FIGURE 5–9

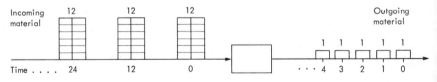

In the schematic diagram of Figure 5–9 the flow of materials in
the retailer's inventory system is modeled when the decision rule we
found to be optimal is employed, Q = 12 units. Shipments are received in lots of 12 units at 12-day intervals. Withdrawals at a rate
of 1 per day emerge from the system.

FIGURE 5–10

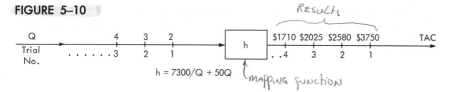

However accurate the model of Figure 5–9 may be it is not a pictorial representation of the model we built and analyzed.

Figure 5–10, on the other hand, is an accurate pictorial representation of the model we built. Order quantites of increasing magnitude are input at the left, are operated on by *mapping function* h, and TAC is output at the right.

At box h, in Figure 5–10, we have installed an operator (mapping function) which characterizes action performed by the real world system which we are modeling—on whatever input we introduce into it; i.e., order size, Q. In the system that we've modeled the *cost function*—which we've approximated with operator h—is not subject to our control. However, the input, Q, *is* subject to our control. In many systems analyses the input will be an exogenous variable, frequently random, and our purpose will be to design an operator— an operator over which we do have control—so as to achieve the desired system behavior.

Note that Figure 5–9 seems to be a schematic of a model of *things*. Figure 5–10, on the other hand, suggests *information*. It is information that we process in making decisions, not things. Since our concern is decision making we will build *information* models, and since the models themselves become systems (abstract systems, representing some real world system) we will find ourselves throughout this book dealing with information system models.

Again, did we simulate the retailer's information system? Insofar as a model simulates that which it represents, we did simulate the retailer's information system. That is, with our mathematical model —programmed in Figure 5–4, flowcharted in Figure 5–6 and represented schematically in Figure 5–10,—we simulated the annual cost experience he would have had had the retailer tried order quantities of 2,3,4 . . . and so on.

Are all functions in applied mathematics simulations? Mathematical functions are clearly abstract representations, models of some real world system, portraying the relations between components (variables) in some real system.

Does their *use* therefore constitute simulation?

If we employ the function πr^2 to map radii of magnitudes 1,3,5, and 6 into circle areas 3.14, 28.3, 78.6, and 116:

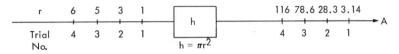

. . . are we simulating?

Consider a rope 12 feet long, to be shaped in the form of a rectangle. If the width of the rectangle is W its length will be $6-W$, since $2W + 2L = 12$. Its area will therefore be $W(6-W)$. If we try widths varying from 1 through 5, in an effort to find the dimensions of that rectangle with perimeter 12 which has the largest area, we map these widths into corresponding areas as follows:

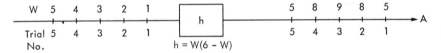

Are we simulating?

If in using the model in Figure 5–6 we were simulating, then it appears that finding the rectangle width which produced the maximum area was simulation, even if mapping radii into areas was not.

When Problems Become Problems

There are always many ways to model a system. The model we build incorporates those entities in the system which are relevant to our purpose and ignores the others.

When we address ourselves to solving a problem we begin with an *image* of a solution procedure, based on procedures employed successfully on similar problems. Indeed, problems don't come to be regarded as problems until some solution procedure is at least imaginable. Prior to the 1940s how to put a man on the moon was not a problem for the United States. In the 1940s it became a problem worthy of enormous resources, as a means for solving it became imaginable.

Tools versus Problems

The system analyst, confronted with a situation, identifies the problem in the context of solution procedures suitable to the problem. This means that he is partially tool (procedure or technique) oriented rather than problem oriented. We approached the inventory problem in this vein, calling upon well-known theory regarding inventory systems; that theory reflected in the simple cost function, $TAC = \$7300/Q + \$50Q$.

There are other ways to model the retailer's inventory system in such a way as to produce the optimum solution. We will look at another way now, and then we will make further comments on models, simulation, and systems analysis in the context of the inventory system.

An Alternative Approach

Let us assume that our retailer employs the order quantity we found to be optimal, $Q = 12$. It should be apparent that the behavior of his stock level can be represented by the following difference equation:

$$INV_{n+1} = INV_n + Q_n - 1 \qquad (5\text{-}3)$$

. . . where:

$$INV_n = \text{inventory on hand in period } n$$
$$Q_n = 12, \text{ when } n \text{ is a multiple of 12,}$$
$$\text{and } = 0 \text{ otherwise.}$$

If $Q = 12$ a new shipment will be delivered every 12 days. If the beginning inventory were 12 units ($INV_0 = 12$) INV would decrease by 1 unit each day (as n increases) until $n =$ some multiple of 12, whereupon $Q_n = 12$ rather than 0, a new shipment would arrive, and a stock-out would just be avoided.

The dynamic character of the system is apparent in model 5–3. However, the placing of an order and the charge therefore, plus the charge for holding stock are not reflected in 5–3. Since these are features we are interested in, let us take the next step and introduce these into the model. We will do so in flowchart form so that the *decision points* and the *cost measurement points* will be fully apparent.

Consider Figure 5–11. We assume that 4 units are on hand and

FIGURE 5–11

Periodic Review System Simulation

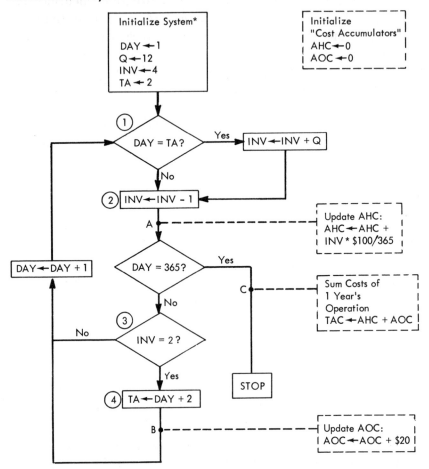

* New shipments from the supplier, if any, arrive first thing in the morning, and a new shipment of Q is ordered at end of day if stock level is at reorder point.

that an order for 12 units, destined to be received in two days (*TA*, time of arrival, equals 2), is outstanding when the simulation portrayed in Figure 5–11 begins. Each new shipment is assumed to arrive first thing in the morning. At box 1, in Figure 5–11, variable DAY is compared to TA to determine if a new shipment of Q units is to arrive. If so, the inventory level is increased by 12 units and we move to box 2. If not we move directly to box 2 and a unit of inventory is withdrawn, reflecting the day's business. At the end of the day, box 3, the inventory level is compared to two units and an order is placed if the reorder point has been reached. At box 4 the date of arrival of the next shipment is stored, for future comparison, at TA.

Figure 5–11 portrays a periodic review system. Each day the inventory level is compared to the reorder point, two units, and a decision is made whether to reorder.

"Instrumentation" (measurement) is applied to the information system model at point A to increment the accumulating holding cost, at point B to increment the accumulating order cost, and at point C to summarize the total cost after 365 days of simulated operations.

Imagine now, that we withdraw instruction "$Q \leftarrow 12$" from the "Initialization" box, and imbed the model of Figure 5–11 at box 1 in the larger model displayed in Figure 5–12.

FIGURE 5–12

Optimum Policy Search Simulation

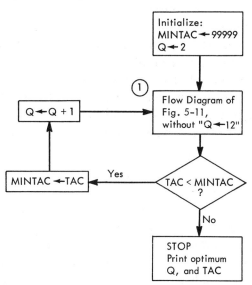

In the model of Figure 5–12 the order quantity, Q, is systematically increased from two units and TAC is checked, after one year's simulated operation, until to increase Q further would cause TAC to grow larger rather than smaller.

The similarity and the difference between the models in Figures

5–11 and 5–12 is apparent. That the two models are *simulation* models is rather persuasive, by our description of simulation in Chapter 2. Consider now how they contrast with the model of the same inventory system in Figure 5–6. The changing *state* of the system—fluctuating stock level—is not apparent in the model of Figure 5–6 but is in the models of Figures 5–11 and 5–12.

On the other hand the model of Figure 5–11 does not *solve* our system problem, whereas that in Figure 5–12 does, as does that in Figure 5–6.

Simulation versus Formal Analysis

Simulation is the avenue of last resort. Wherever possible the systems analyst employs *formal analysis* in his search for solutions. In expression 5–2 formal analysis in a "pure" form is employed to find the optimum order quantity by calculus. In the models of Figures 5–6 and 5–10 we might say that formal analysis and simulation are combined: the attributes of the system are portrayed formally in the total annual cost function, but the optimum policy is searched for through experimentation (simulation). In the model of Figure 5–12 "pure" simulation is employed.

Clearly, for our retailer's simple system, formal analysis is the more efficient solution procedure. For very complex systems we shall see, the tools of formal analysis fail and we resort to simulation to understand and control system behavior.

A Word about Algorithms

An algorithm is an iteractive procedure for arriving, in a finite number of steps, at a solution to a problem. We employ algorithms both in formal analysis and in simulation. In the algorithmic approach to the analysis of systems we begin with the system in some *state*. Thus we initialized the inventory system at the beginning of our simulation in Figure 5–12. We then modify its state iteratively stopping only when we know, by some rule we can trust, that the solution is at hand. The validity of stopping rules and the proof of the algorithm's convergence to the solution, as well as other attributes of the algorithmic approach will demand our attention in future chapters.

EXERCISES

1. Write a FORTRAN program that will cause the computer to calculate and print out the total annual inventory cost to Smith Company for 10 successive order quantities ranging from 10 units per order through 100 units per order (by increments of 10), given that:

Cost price per unit   = $200.
Demand during year   = 1,825 units.
Cost of holding inventory   = 20 percent of cost per
                               unit per year.
Cost of processing one order = $25.

(Begin, before writing your program, by composing a flow diagram.)

2. Write a FORTRAN program that will cause the computer to calculate and print out the economic order quantity and the corresponding total annual inventory cost for Smith Company (Exercise 1). *Note:* Cause the economic order quantity to be determined within five units of the exact EOQ.

3. Write a FORTRAN program that will cause the computer to do what is called for in Exercise 2 for each of the following five values of annual demand: 1,825, 3,650, 5,475, 7,300, and 9,125 units.

Plot a curve showing the relationship between the economic order quantity and the annual demand for Smith Company. (Begin by composing a flow diagram.)

4. Write a FORTRAN program for the model in Figure 5–11. Now imbed it in the larger model of Figure 5–12. Modify and then run the program so that Q and TAC will both be printed out for values of Q ranging from 2 through that value which produces the minimum TAC. How does the optimum policy, and its associated TAC, compare with that produced in our analysis via the model of Figure 5–6; i.e., $Q = 12$, $TAC = \$1,208$? How might any differences be explained?

chapter 6

The Inventory System under Uncertainty

Two ASSUMPTIONS in our retailer's inventory model, Chapter 5, made it somewhat unrealistic: the constant demand rate from one day to the next, and the constant lead time from one order to the next. By assuming these factors to be constant, uncertainties were eliminated, shortages were easily and economically avoided, and the problem became extremely simple—and correspondingly unrealistic.

We will now introduce some uncertainties, which complicate the inventory management problem but which make it more realistic. As before, we will develop the model by an example; then we will concern ourselves with a *general model*. Our example will be the invntory system of Brown Eloctronics Company.

BROWN ELECTRONICS COMPANY

Brown Company stocks purchased units of item A, a component used in subsequent assembly. Brown knows that:

1. Each unit of item A costs $500.
2. The cost of holding item A in inventory is 20 percent of its cost price per year.
3. The cost of processing an order for any number of units of item A is $20 per order processed.
4. Brown Company can expect a demand for 365 units during the year.

5. All units of item A demanded but not available are back ordered, and are filled immediately when a new shipment arrives.

But two uncertainties stand out in Brown Electronics Company's operations:

1. Brown is uncertain about the day-to-day demand for item A.
2. Brown is uncertain about lead time.

However, Brown has the records of last year's experience and believes that this year's experience will be the same. Specifically, Brown's records show that the demand rate and lead time last year were as shown in Tables 6–1 and 6–2:

TABLE 6–1

Demand for Item A during Past Year*

Units Demanded per Day	Frequency of Demand
0	40% of the days
1	30%
2	20%
3	10%
	100%

* It is assumed that there is no seasonal pattern in demand and lead time; and that both are random, with the frequency distributions shown.

TABLE 6–2

Lead Time for Item A during Past Year

Lead Time (Days)	Frequency of Lead Time
1	25% of the lead time periods
2	50%
3	25%
	100%

Brown's problem is, in order to minimize total inventory cost: (1) *How many units of item A should we order at one time?* [reorder quantity Q], and (2) *At what point as the stock level drops should we place an order?* [reorder point R̂].

In our retailer's inventory problem (Chapter 5) we were not willing to permit a stock-out to occur. Also, in our retailer's problem we were able to determine the optimum reorder point R̂ independently of the optimum order quantity Q̂. In the Brown Electronics Company case, involving an inventory system under uncertainty, we will discover that R cannot be determined independently of $\widehat{Q}$, but that we must find an optimum combination of $\widehat{Q}$ and $\widehat{R}$; we will also find that setting R at a level where an occasional stock-out is expected is a good policy. We will, however, postpone consideration of *why* this is true until we've advanced a bit further in our study of the nature of Brown's expected demand and lead time experience.

Since permitting an occasional stock-out may be desirable for Brown Electronics Company, we need, for planning purposes, to

FIGURE 6–1

A Sample of Brown Company's Inventory Experience*

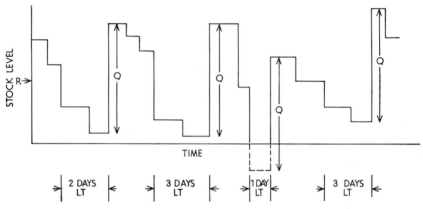

* ←LT→ represents a lead time period; R is reorder point; Q represents reorder quantity.

have some notion of the seriousness of the consequences of a stock-out. Brown estimates that the monetary measure of the cost of a stock-out is \$40 per unit of item A demanded but unavailable at the moment it is needed.

Placing a cost figure on a unit stock-out is frequently resisted by inventory managers. Admittedly, it may be difficult to assess the monetary measure of the consequence of running short. However, when a cost datum is worth having, skillful decision makers can generally get it.

In many inventory systems inventory is not exhausted when a "stock-out" occurs. When it becomes apparent that a stock-out is imminent emergency replenishment procedures are invoked. Thus air freight, rather than truck freight, may be employed to acquire quickly a small supply adequate to last until a shipment is received through routine procedures. The unit stock-out cost, then, would be added cost associated with the emergency replenishment procedure.

Our understanding of the inventory system under uncertainty will be improved if we consider a graphic representation of the expected inventory experience of Brown Electronics Co.

Particular attention should be focused on the period during lead time (see Figure 6–1), since it is only during the lead time period that a stock-out can occur.

The magnitude of the shortages that can be expected during the average lead time is dependent on the reorder point, the various lead times that might be experienced, the various demands that might be experienced during lead times, and the probabilities that these lead times and demands will occur *simultaneously*.

In order to determine the optimum values of $\hat{Q}$ and $\hat{R}$ we must know what is the *expected shortage* during a lead time period. And in order to determine the expected shortage during a lead time period we must determine the expected demand during a lead time period.

In Table 6–1 are data that tell us the various quantities which might be demanded on any one day and the relative frequency with which these various demands are expected. If we view relative frequency as a measure of probability, Table 6–1 would appear in the form shown in Table 6–3.

TABLE 6–3

Possible Demand in a Day in Units	Probability of This Demand
0	.40
1	.30
2	.20
3	.10
	1.00

In a similar way, Table 6–2 would become Table 6–4.

TABLE 6–4

Possible Lead Time in Days	Probability of This Lead Time
1	.25
2	.50
3	.25
	1.00

What we need now is a similar table of data to tell us the various amounts of item A that might be demanded during the various lead time periods throughout the year, and also the probability of these various demands. From such a table we could calculate the expected value of stock-out per lead time period corresponding to various reorder points; and with this knowledge we could build a mathematical model of the inventory system under uncertainty. To construct a table of this sort we might reason as follows.

Demand during lead time could be as high as nine units. This is apparent because lead time could be as long as three days and the demand rate could be as high as three per day on each of the three days. Now, the probability that nine units will be demanded during lead time is the *joint probability* that lead time will be three days and that a demand rate of three per day will occur on three successive days. The joint probability that the demand will be for three units on each of three successive days is (.10) × (.10) × (.10). The joint probability of "lead time of three days" *and* "demand for three units on each of three successive days" is (.25) × (.10) × (.10) × (.10), or .00025, which we will round to .0003.

Demand during lead time could also be eight units. This is apparent because lead time could be three days, and on two of these days three units could be demanded each day, followed by a demand for two on the third day. The sequence of these events could, of course, occur three different ways (as shown in Table 6–5, along with their various probabilities of occurrence).

The combined probability of these events is the *sum* of their individual probabilities of occurrence, or .0015.

Proceeding in this fashion we could develop a table that would give all the possible demands during lead time and the probability

TABLE 6–5

Probability That 8 Units Will Be Demanded during Lead Time

Ways in Which Demand for 8 Might Occur	*Probability That This "Event" Might Occur*
(1) First day, 3 demanded .... Second day, 3 demanded .... Third day, 2 demanded	(.25) (.10) (.10) (.20) = .0005
(2) First day, 3 demanded .... Second day, 2 demanded .... Third day, 3 demanded	(.25) (.10) (.20) (.10) = .0005
(3) First day, 2 demanded .... Second day, 3 demanded .... Third day, 3 demanded	(.25) (.20) (.10) (.10) = .0005

of their occurrences. Another way to develop a combined probability distribution—and a more practicable way to deal with complex systems of this sort—is by Monte Carlo simulation.

MONTE CARLO SIMULATION

The possible events described in Table 6–3 could be simulated by a sampling process involving different colored balls. We could place together in a jar four white balls, three blue balls, two yellow balls, and one green ball. Then, if we drew a ball at random, recorded its color, replaced it, drew another, recorded its color, replaced it, and so on, stirring the balls each time, we would expect that if we continued this sampling process long enough 40 percent of the time we would find ourselves drawing white balls, 30 percent of the time blue balls, 20 percent of the time yellow balls, and 10 percent of the time green balls. To simulate Brown Electronics Company's expected daily demand pattern, we simply consider the drawing of a ball to be the simulation of a day's operation, equating:

White balls as demand for *0 units*.
Blue balls as demand for *1 unit*.
Yellow balls as demand for *2 units*.
Green balls as demand for *3 units*.

If a white ball is drawn, we reason that on that simulated day of operations 0 units of item A were demanded; if a blue ball is drawn 1 unit was demanded; if a yellow ball is drawn 2 units were demanded; and if a green ball is drawn 3 units were demanded. Since we have loaded the jar with 4 white balls, 3 blue balls, 2 yellow balls, and 1 green ball, over the long run 0 units will be demanded 40 percent of the days; 1 unit will be demanded 30 percent of the days; 2 units will be demanded 20 percent of the days, and 3 units will be demanded 10 percent of the days. Thus our sampling process will perfectly simulate Brown Electronics' expected daily demand pattern.

In the same way we could simulate Brown's expected lead time pattern. In a *separate* jar 1 white ball might be deposited to represent a lead time of 1 day; 2 blue balls for a lead time of 2 days; and 1 yellow ball for a lead time of 3 days.

Simulating Brown Electronics Company's Demand during Lead Time

Now, to simulate demand during lead time, we would proceed as follows.

1. Draw a ball from jar two (representing Table 6–4).
   a) If a white ball was drawn, we reason that in our first simulated experience lead time was one day. Therefore we draw one ball from jar one (representing Table 6–3). If we draw a white ball from jar one we record "demand zero." If we draw a blue ball we record "demand 1"; if a yellow ball, "demand 2," and so on.
   b) If a blue ball was drawn, we reason that in our first "simulated experience" lead time was two days, so we draw one ball from jar one, record our experience, replace the ball, draw *another* ball, record our experience, and add up the resulting "demands" for the two days in order to determine *total* demand during the *two* days of lead time.
   c) If a yellow ball was drawn, we proceed as above, but we draw from jar one *three* times.
2. Draw a second ball from jar two to simulate a second lead time experience, and proceed as in (a), (b), and (c) above.
3. Draw a third ball from jar two to simulate a third lead time experience, and proceed as in (a), (b), and (c) above, and so on.

If we continued this simulation process over a large number of trials we would expect to find that a demand during lead time (DDLT) of nine units would occur 0.03 percent of the time—and that a DDLT of eight units would occur 0.15 percent of the time—since we have already developed these probabilities analytically.

Where a great number of combinations of demands per day and lead time durations are possible, an analytical solution becomes impracticable, and Monte Carlo simulation is very useful.

In actual practice, however, we do not use colored balls but rather a random number list. From the preceding chapter recall that we expect in a list of two-digit random numbers that each number is as likely to occur next (reading the list from the top down, for example) as any other two-digit number; and we can cause the reading of a number to be the equivalent of drawing a ball by the following scheme:

Let number 00 through number 39	represent a demand for	0 units
" 40	69	1 unit
" 70	89	2 units
" 90	99	3 units

And

Let number 00 through number 24	represent a lead time of	1 day
" 25	74	2 days
" 75	99	3 days

We now read a number from our two-digit random number list to determine the number of days in our simulated lead time; and, depending on the outcome, read one, two, or three numbers to determine total demand during lead time for that simulated lead time experience.

Monte Carlo Simulation on the Computer

This process of reading a number and recording its interpretation in terms of the system being simulated would be cumbersome if we were obliged to do it in the fashion described above. By a variety of schemes we can cause the computer to do this for us. We will develop one possible FORTRAN program for doing this, but first we will introduce the READ statement, another important FORTRAN device.

The READ Statement

The READ statement bears some similarity to the WRITE statement, except that where the WRITE statement causes the computer to print out (or output) data, the READ statement causes the computer to read in (to input) data. Recall that in our compound interest program the statement WRITE (6,——) YEAR,S could be used to cause the values currently stored for the variables YEAR and S to be printed out.

The statement READ (5,——) IRN, DA could be used to cause the computer to *give to* (store in memory for) the variable IRN some value, and to give the variable DA another value. In a fashion similar to the WRITE statement, the READ statement must refer to a FORMAT statement which will tell the computer the format in which the values to be given to IRN and DA will be found. To make this clear, we must say a word about inputting data into the computer.

Inputting Data

As we have seen thus far, the computer performs various operations on data given to it. We have also seen how data can be given to the computer from within the FORTRAN program. Thus in the program:

```
        YEAR = 0.0
        P = 10000.00
        R = .04
        N = 1
        DO 3 I = 1,5
        S = P * (1.0 + R) ** N
        YEAR = YEAR + 2.0
   3    WRITE (6,—) YEAR,S
        STOP
        END
```

the first four statements supply the computer with data to be operated on in the remainder of the program.

Data can also be introduced at the end of the program, *after* the END statement. Data supplied at the end of the program are supplied as purely numerical data. A random number list is data of this type. We can cause the computer to "read" a list of random numbers, from top down, and to conduct our Monte Carlo simulation for us. To cause the computer to read or input data into the computer in this fashion we must prepare a data deck of punched cards. On each card we punch one two-digit random number, arranging our deck in the order in which the numbers are encountered in our random number table. Each two-digit number will be punched in the same two columns on its card as all the other numbers.

A FORMAT statement is then added to the main program (all that precedes the END statement) in which the computer is advised *where,* on each data card, the random numbers are to be found. Suppose, for example, that we wanted to leave the first four columns blank and to punch our two-digit numbers in columns 5 and 6. Our FORMAT statement might appear thus: 15 FORMAT (4X,I2). (Since our random numbers are integers, we use an I rather than an F specification in the FORMAT statement.)

Although we need only one kind of data for our Monte Carlo simulation (i.e., our random numbers list) it should be observed that many data can be read into the computer with one execution of one READ statement. Thus we might provide for reading into the computer two lists of numbers by punching two numbers on each data card. Our data deck, for example, might represent these two lists of numbers:

06	3000.00
71	4000.00
18	5000.00
49	6000.00

Let us assume that the first digit of the numbers in the column on the left is punched in column 5 and the first digit of the numbers in the column on the right is punched in column 15. These lists might be read into the computer by the two statements:

READ (5,15) IRN, DA
15   FORMAT (4X,I2,8X,F8.2)

The FORMAT statement tells the computer the precise arrangement of the data to be found on each punched card in the data deck. When the READ statement above is encountered, the first pair of numbers will be read in; that is, the variable IRN will have stored for it the value 06, and the variable DA will have stored for it the value 3000.00. The next time the READ statement is encountered the values previously stored for IRN and DA will be erased, and 71 and 4000.00 will be stored for IRN and DA, respectively.

In punching data cards it should be observed that all 80 columns in a data deck can be used, and that data may be arranged in any fashion to suit the programmer. Thus our two lists could occupy only the first nine columns of the card. This is possible because in inputting data (if no sign is indicated) the computer will assume that the sign is positive, and therefore no space need be left for a sign in inputting data *except* where the data are negative. Our data might therefore be punched in this fashion:

063000.00
714000.00
185000.00
496000.00

And they might be read in by these statements:

READ (5,16) IRN, DA
16   FORMAT (I2,F7.2)

FIGURE 6–2

Monte Carlo Simulation Flowchart for Simulating Demand during Lead Time for One Lead Time Period

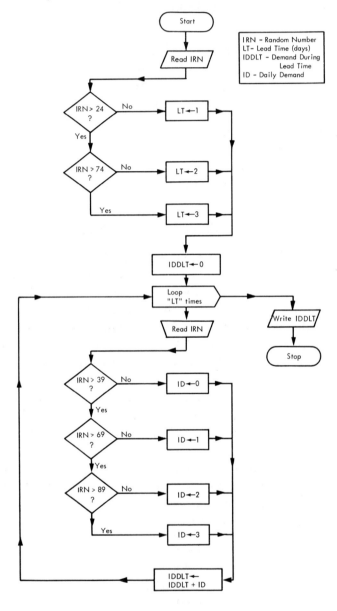

It is possible to have many different lists compose a complete data deck, with data in each list arranged differently from data in the other lists. In these circumstances all the individual decks (each corresponding to one list) are simply stacked together in the order in which they are to be read in, and the complete data deck is added to the main program deck following the final END statement. The main program must contain a pair of READ and FORMAT statements for the data deck segment corresponding to each list, and provision must be made in the main program for reading in *all* the data in one list *prior* to reading in any data from the data deck segment which follows it.

(*Note:* by use of input data *tapes,* rather than input data *cards,* this limitation can be avoided and data from a number of different lists can be read in selectively. Since the limitation associated with inputting data via a data deck is no problem to us at this stage, we will concern ourselves only with the data deck as a scheme for reading data into the computer's memory.)

We are now equipped to write a FORTRAN program to cause the computer to READ a two-digit random number list and to conduct a Monte Carlo simulation of Brown Electronics Company's demand during lead time experience. We will compose a list of FORTRAN statements to cause the computer to:

1. Read the first random number (from our input data deck) and interpret the number of days of lead time it represents; then
2. Read as many more random numbers as there are days in the lead time period (in step 1); and
3. Add up the daily demands to get DDLT (demand during lead time).

In Figure 6–2 the steps called for above are diagrammed in flowchart form, while Figure 6–3 shows a FORTRAN program segment that should simulate one lead time period.

Each time through the program (Figure 6–3), one lead time experience is simulated. The statements preceding the DO statement cause the computer to determine the number of days lead time. The DO statement then causes the statements through 14 to be executed the number of times there are days in the lead time period currently simulated. Each time the computer passes from statements 7 through 13, one day's demand is simulated. In statement 14, the demands for each of the days in the lead time period are summed, so that by the time the DO loop has been completed the variable

FIGURE 6–3*

FORTRAN Program Segment Simulating One Lead Time Period

```
2  READ (5,—) IRN
   IF (IRN − 24)3,3,4
3  LT = 1
   GO TO 7
4  IF (IRN − 74)5,5,6
5  LT = 2
   GO TO 7
6  LT = 3
7  IDDLT = 0
   DO 14 I = 1, LT
   READ (5,—) IRN
   IF (IRN − 39)8,8,9
8  ID = 0
   GO TO 14
9  IF (IRN − 69) 10,10,11
10 ID = 1
   GO TO 14
11 IF (IRN − 89) 12,12,13
12 ID = 2
   GO TO 14
13 ID = 3
14 IDDLT = IDDLT + ID
```

* LT = lead time, in number of days; IRN is the variable that holds the most recently read-in two-digit random number; ID represents the demand in one *day*, in units; IDDLT represents the demand during lead time. (We add the Is to make these integer variables.)

Note: We have seen that statement numbers in a FORTRAN program do *not* have to be in consecutive order. From this point on, however, we will number statements consecutively, wherever practicable, to facilitate interpretation.

IDDLT holds the number of units demanded during the simulated lead time period. This value could be printed out, and the computer could be returned to statement 2 to simulate another lead time experience.

We would, of course, want to go further and let the computer keep score (count up the frequency) of the various demands during lead time that were simulated over an adequate sample, and then calculate and print out for us a probability distribution for demand during lead time. (To do this efficiently we will need to employ an additional FORTRAN device, the subscripted variable, but it would be best to return to consideration of our inventory model under

TABLE 6–6

Brown Electronics Company's (Monte Carlo) Demand during Lead Time Probability Distributions

Possible Demand during Lead Time (Units) DDLT	Probability of This Demand	Cumulative Probability (Probability Demand Will Be Greater)
0	.1960	.8040
1	.2310	.5730
2	.2260	.3470
3	.1797	.1673
4	.0935	.0738
5	.0477	.0261
6	.0190	.0071
7	.0053	.0018
8	.0015	.0003
9	.0003	.0000

uncertainty before introducing this added programming convention.) To facilitate interpretation of what is yet to come in the development of our inventory model under uncertainty, Table 6–6 provides the probability distributions that a complete Monte Carlo simulation would yield.

In the last column we have added the probability that demand during a lead time period will be *greater* than DDLT, and the usefulness of this probability will become apparent shortly. The determination of the values in the last column is quite simple: the probability that DDLT > 9 is 0, since (as we saw earlier) 9 is the maximum possible demand during lead time. The only way DDLT can be greater than 8 is for it to be 9. Since the probability of a DDLT of 9 is .0003, clearly the probability that DDLT > 8 is .0003. The only way in which DDLT can be greater than 7 is for it to be 8 *or* 9. Since these probabilities are additive, the probability of a DDLT > 7 is the sum of the probability of a DDLT of 8 plus the probability of a DDLT of 9, or 0.0018. The other values in the last column of Table 6–6 are calculated in this same way.

The Expected Value of Stock-out

We are now equipped to determine the expected (or average) stock-out per lead time period, given any particular reorder point, R. In what follows it will be useful to focus attention on the lead time period and to think of R as the beginning inventory during a span of time which is the lead time period.The ending inventory will either be zero or some positive value, depending on R and DDLT.

Table 6–6 makes it apparent that if we place R at 9 units (that is, if we reorder the moment the stock level drops to 9 units) we will never be caught short, since the probability of a DDLT > 9 is 0. But if we place R at 8 units, what is the expectation? Clearly a stock-out can occur, and it is expected to occur 0.03 percent of the lead time periods since the probability of a DDLT > 8 is .0003. The "expected value of stock-out" *per lead time period,* assuming Brown Electronics Company reorders at R = 8 units, is (9 − 8) × .0003 = .0003 units.

To make this more persuasive, consider what would happen in the long run—given a policy of reordering at R = 8 units. Assume that Brown operates its inventory system, with a policy of reordering at R = 8, over 10,000 lead time periods. We would expect that Brown would experience a shortage of 1 unit (9 − 8) in 3 of these 10,000 lead time periods (0.03 percent of 10,000). A stock-out of 3 units in 10,000 lead time periods is an "average" of .0003 units *per* lead time period.

What if Brown follows a policy of reordering at R = 7 units? Over the long run Brown would expect to run short 0.18 percent of the time, since the probability of DDLT > 7 is 0.0018. But what is Brown's expected or average stock-out *per lead time period* under this policy? Over 10,000 lead time periods Brown would expect:

1. A shortage of 2 units (9 − 7) during 3 lead time periods, since the probabiltiy of nine being demanded is .0003.
2. A shortage of 1 unit (8− 7) during 15 lead time periods, since the probability of 8 being demanded is .0015.

Thus Brown's expected total number of units demanded, but unavailable, would be 2 × 3 + 1 × 15 = 21 units in 10,000 lead time periods, or an average of .0021 *per* lead time period.

In a similar way, we could determine the expected value of stock-out (expected number of units short) per lead time period if Brown reorders at R = 6 units:

$$
\begin{aligned}
(9 - 6) &\times .0003 = .0009 \\
+ (8 - 6) &\times .0015 = .0030 \\
+ (7 - 6) &\times .0053 = .0053 \\
\hline
\text{Total} &= .0092
\end{aligned}
$$

Under this policy Brown's expected stock-out per lead time period is .0092 units. We will label this quantity $E(DDLT > R)$, meaning the expected amount by which DDLT is greater than R (the reorder point), or the expected stock-out per lead time period, in units short.

Clearly, Brown will never be caught short .0092 units—or any other fractional part of a unit—but for purposes of policy determination the concept of an expected fractional stock-out is necessary. The reason for this will become more apparent if we return now to consider why a policy in which an occasional stock-out is expected may be a desirable policy under conditions of uncertainty, and why optimum order quantity, $\hat{Q}$, and optimum reorder point, $\hat{R}$, cannot be determined independently of each other. Since the reason for this interdependence of $\hat{Q}$ and $\hat{R}$ under conditions of uncertainty is not readily apparent, a few words about the inventory problem under uncertainty might be appropriate.

The Nature of Conditions of Uncertainty

In our retailer's inventory problem we did not bother to defend our policy of reordering when the stock level dropped to two units, rather than reordering at some point *less* than R = 2. Since one unit was certain to be demanded each day (in our retailer's hypothetical system), and since lead time was two days, we simply assumed that while our retailer would want R to be as low as possible (to keep the average inventory level low) he would not be willing to tolerate a stock-out. This policy clearly needs no defense: to lower the reorder point to one, for example, would yield a *certain* stock-out of one unit each lead time period. If buying, storing, and reselling units of item A is profitable to our retailer, then the savings in inventory holding cost by reordering at one unit would be *less* than the lost profits from unsatisfied demand. Therefore our retailer would want to set R at the lowest level, but not so low as to permit a stock-out of even one unit.

Under conditions of *uncertainty*, however, setting R at a level that makes a stock-out a possibility may be very desirable. In our retailer's problem we found that lowering R by one unit *below* two units yielded an "increased stock-out," per lead time period, of one unit. In the Brown Electronics case, lowering the reorder point by one unit, from nine to eight units, would yield an "increased stock-out" per lead time period of .0003 units. And by lowering the reorder point from nine to eight units we can make a very significant contribution to decreased holding costs at practically no increase in stock-out costs.

In short, under conditions of uncertainty an inventory policy that makes a stock-out impossible is almost certain to cost more than it is worth. Our problem, then, is to balance stock-out costs against (1) holding costs and (2) ordering costs, in order to find the policy that minimizes total costs.

The cost of expected stock-out *per lead time period* is the expected number of units demanded but not available during a lead time period *times* the cost per stock-out. We assumed that the monetary measure of the seriousness of a stock-out of one unit is $40.[1] The cost of expected stock-out per lead time period, then, would be $E(DDLT > R) \times \$40$.

The cost of expected *annual* stock-out is the expected stock-out cost per lead time multiplied by the expected number of lead time periods in a year. The expected number of lead time periods is the expected number of units demanded in one year divided by the order quantity, Q, or $365/Q$. Therefore the expected annual stock-out cost for Brown Electronics would be $E(DDLT > R) \times \$40 \times 365/Q$.

We have just seen how the expected annual stock-out cost is dependent both on Q and on R, and *also* we have seen that the size of R influences average inventory and hence annual holding cost. But inventory holding cost is also dependent on Q. Therefore $\hat{Q}$ and $\hat{R}$ are interdependent, and we cannot, as in our retailer's problem, solve for one independently of the other. Rather we must seek an optimum combination of Q and R.

THE INVENTORY MODEL UNDER UNCERTAINTY

We are now equipped to construct our total annual inventory cost model for Brown Electronics Company under conditions of uncertainty. Our total annual cost model for Brown Electronics consists of three parts: (1) annual inventory holding cost, (2) annual ordering cost, and (3) annual stock-out cost. We will now develop each of these.

---

[1] We will assume further that the stock-out cost is linear; i.e., the cost of a stock-out of two units is twice the cost of a stock-out out of one unit; the cost of a stock-out of three units is three times the cost of a stock-out of one unit; and so on.

Annual Holding Cost

As we have seen, Brown's average inventory level is dependent on R as well as Q. To get at Brown's average inventory level let us examine a *simplified* curve of Brown's expected inventory experience *if no stock-outs ever occurred* (Figure 6–4). If no stock-outs ever occurred Brown's *average* inventory pattern would be as depicted in Figure 6–4. If our assumption that no stock-out would ever occur were a valid assumption, then clearly Brown's *average* inventory level would be Q/2 + ΔQ.

FIGURE 6–4

Brown Electronics Company's Average Inventory Pattern
(assuming no stockouts occur)

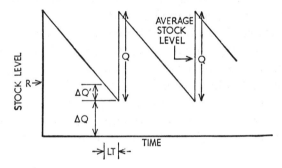

It should be apparent from Figure 6–4 that ΔQ is R − ΔQ′, and that ΔQ′ is the expected or average demand during lead time, assuming no stock-outs. We can calculate the expected demand during lead time from our demand and lead time distributions (Tables 6–3 and 6–4).

$$
\begin{array}{rcl}
0 \times .40 & = & 0.00 \\
+\ 1 \times .30 & = & 0.30 \\
+\ 2 \times .20 & = & 0.40 \\
+\ 3 \times .10 & = & 0.30 \\
\hline
\text{Total} & = & 1.00
\end{array}
$$

Accordingly, average daily demand is for one unit. Furthermore:

$$
\begin{array}{rcl}
1 \times .25 & = & 0.25 \\
+\ 2 \times .50 & = & 1.00 \\
+\ 3 \times .25 & = & 0.75 \\
\hline
\text{Total} & = & 2.00
\end{array}
$$

and thus average lead time is two days.

If expected or average lead time is two days, and average daily demand is for one unit, then expected or average demand during lead time is for two units.

Referring again to Figure 6–4, $\Delta Q'$ is seen to be two units, and hence $\Delta Q = R - 2$. It therefore follows that average inventory, assuming no stock-outs occur, would be $Q/2 + R - 2$.

But we expect an occasional stock-out, and hence our analysis (above) would seem to be invalid. If we assume that a stock-out *can* occur, then, during those lead time periods when a stock-out does occur the actual withdrawal from inventory, and hence the reduction of the inventory level, will be less than $\Delta Q'$ by an amount equal to the amount demanded but not available. The average ΔQ, therefore, would be greater by the stock demanded but not available, and hence our average inventory level throughout the year would seem to be larger than $Q/2 + R - 2$.

Recall, however, that back ordering is permitted in the Brown Electronics Company inventory system, and that unsatisfied demand is satisfied immediately on receipt of a new shipment. This would mean that following a lead time period when a stock-out occurs, the inventory level falls short of rising to a level equal to the reorder quantity, Q, by an amount equal to the back ordered demand. (A second look at Figure 6–1 should substantiate this expectation.)

It develops therefore that the errors in our calculation of average inventory level (above) tend to cancel each other, and Brown's average inventory level can be considered to be:[2]

$$Q/2 + R - 2. \qquad (6\text{-}1)$$

Since the cost of holding inventory for one year amounts to 20 percent of its value, Brown's expected annual inventory holding cost will be:

$$0.20(\$500)(Q/2 + R - 2). \qquad (6\text{-}2)$$

Annual Ordering Cost

Annual ordering cost is—as before with our retailer—the cost per order times the number of orders processed per year:

$$\$20 \times (365/Q). \qquad (6\text{-}3)$$

---

[2] *Note:* If back ordering is not permitted, i.e., if unsatisfied demand is lost demand, then $Q/2 + R - 2$ does *not* precisely represent the average inventory level. In a great many cases, however, it is a very close approximation, and therefore the general validity of our model is not seriously limited.

Annual Stock-out Cost

Annual stock-out cost, as was shown, is:

$$\$40 \times E(DDLT > R) \times 365/Q. \tag{6-4}$$

Brown's total annual inventory cost is the sum of (**6–2**), (**6–3**), and (**6–4**), or:

$$\begin{aligned}
TAC = {} & 0.20(\$500)(Q/2 + R - 2) \\
& + \$20(365/Q) \\
& + \$40 \times E(DDLT > R) \times 365/Q. \tag{6-5}
\end{aligned}$$

To deal with (**6–5**) we might reason—somewhat as we did with our retailer's model—that if we set our reorder point at 1 (let R = 1) and then vary Q from a small to a very large value, we would get a **U**-shaped total annual cost curve. As before, we might search this curve for the minimum TAC.

This would give us the minimum TAC for a reorder point of 1, and we have reason to believe that the minimum TAC associated with a reorder point of 2 is lower than the minimum TAC associated with a reorder point of 1 (a look at Table 6–7 will make this apparent). With R = 1 we must expect a stock-out of more than one unit each lead time period. If it is profitable to purchase, hold, and then utilize or resell units of item A, then quite probably the savings in holding cost resulting from ordering at R = 1 rather than at R > 1 cannot be sufficient to compensate for the loss due to a stock-out per lead time period of this magnitude.

We have already seen that the savings in holding cost by reducing R from 9 (where stock-outs are eliminated altogether) to 8 is almost certain to be more than enough to compensate for the negligible loss due to expected stock-out where R = 8.

Our objective, then, is to search among a *family* of **U**-shaped TAC curves (much like the three curves shown in Figure 6–5) to find the lowest point among them. In fact, there will be nine of these **U**-shaped curves, corresponding to each of our nine reorder policies. The Q and R combination that yields the lowest TAC among this family of curves is the optimum Q, R combination.

In our retailer's inventory problem, Chapter 5, TAC was a function of Q only, and we were able to portray the relationship between TAC and Q in a two-dimensional graph (Figure 5–3). In Brown Electronics Company's inventory system TAC is a function of *two* variables, Q and R. We might portray the relationships between Q, R, and TAC via a three-dimensional graph, as in Figure 6–5.

FIGURE 6–5

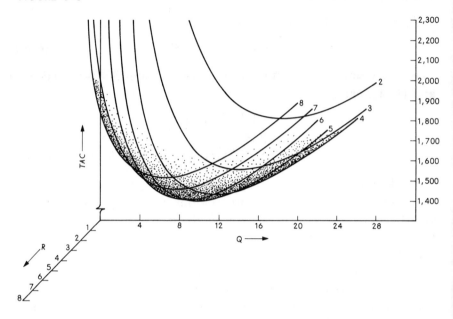

Each curve in Figure 6–5 is in a different plane. For each plane the coordinates are TAC (the vertical axis) and Q (the horizontal axis). The family of curves represented in Figure 6–5 constitutes a bowl with a somewhat U-shaped cross section. Our objective is to find that combination of values for Q and R which corresponds to the bottommost point in the bowl.

The only difficulty in conducting this search is encountered in dealing with the expression E(DDLT > R) in our TAC model, **(6–5)**.

If we could determine all the possible values for E(DDLT > R), and then if we could call forth the value for E(DDLT > R) corresponding to the reorder point currently under consideration, as we go through an iterative process searching for the best R, we could write a FORTRAN program that would cause the computer to conduct the search for us. To do this most easily, we must introduce a powerful FORTRAN device called the *subscripted variable*.

The Subscripted Variable

A subscripted variable differs in appearances from a nonsubscripted variable in that it has a set of parentheses associated with it. The following are subscripted variables:

$$AHC(1), \ TAC(3), \ CPU(47)$$

Many constant values can be stored simultaneously for one subscripted variable, in contrast to a nonsubscripted variable which can have only one value stored at a time. A subscripted variable might be thought of as a row of pigeonholes or positions into each of which a different numerical value can be stored. The number in the parentheses associated with the subscripted variable indicates which position is intended when one of the values stored for the subscripted variable is referred to.

If AHC(1) were encountered on the right side of the equal sign in a FORTRAN algebraic expression, the computer would substitute for AHC(1) the value currently stored for the subscripted variable AHC in position 1. If TAC(3) were encountered on the right side of the equal sign in an algebraic expression, the computer would substitute the value currently stored for the subscripted variable TAC in position 3.

In a fashion similar to that of the nonsubscripted (sometimes called a zero-dimension subscripted) variable, the computer stores (in the position indicated by the number in parentheses) the value of the expression to the *right* of the equal sign when a subscripted variable is encountered to the *left* of an equal sign in an algebraic statement. Thus, if CPU(47) were encountered to the left of an equal sign, the computer would store in position number 47 (for the subscripted variable CPU) the value of the expression to the right of the equal sign.

The subscripted variable's usefulness is enhanced enormously because it is possible to place a *variable* (but only an integer variable) rather than a constant in the parentheses. Thus, P(N), COH(MN),AR(KIT) may also be legitimate subscripted variables.

The variable in the parentheses can take any value (within the limits of the computer's memory) as long as it is a positive integer and greater than zero. If the subscripted variable P(N) were encountered to the right of an equal sign in an algebraic statement, P(N) would be replaced by the value currently stored in position N (whatever N happens to be at that moment in the computer's memory) for the subscripted variable P.

The same rules that govern both nonsubscripted integer and floating point variables apply to subscripted variables. Thus, if the integer subscripted variable J(8) is given the value 16.23, the two digits to the right of the decimal will be truncated and only the value 16 will be stored in position 8 of the variable J.

In addition to one-dimension subscripted variables, we can also have two- and three-dimension subscripted variables.

$$\text{P(N,M)} \quad (two\ dimension)$$
$$\text{COH(MN,L3T,KD)} \quad (three\ dimension)$$

The DIMENSION Statement

Every FORTRAN program that contains a subscripted variable must contain a DIMENSION statement. At the beginning of the program the DIMENSION statement causes the computer to reserve in memory for the subscripted variable (or variables: one DIMENSION statement can be used for a number of different subscripted variables) the number of storage locations required to accommodate the subscripted variable.

Thus, the statement DIMENSION ES(9) could be used to cause the computer to reserve nine storage locations to accommodate the nine values for expected stock-out in our program for Brown Electronics Company. (*Note:* The DIMENSION statement must precede all statements in which a variable appears.) Let us, then, return to Brown Electronics Company's inventory problem and see how a subscripted variable might be employed.

We should begin by completing our list of expected stock-outs, per lead time period, as R varies from 1 through 9. Proceeding as before, we would find that

TABLE 6–7

Reorder Policies and Associated Expected Stock-outs

With a Reorder Point, R, of:	Expected Stock-out per Lead Time Period, $E(DDLT > R)$, Would Be:
1	1.1964
2	0.6234
3	0.2764
4	0.1091
5	0.0353
6	0.0092
7	0.0021
8	0.0003
9	0.0000

We can store this array of values for $E(DDLT > R)$ in computer memory by using a subscripted variable. While recalling that when a *variable* is employed in the parentheses of a subscripted variable it must be an integer variable, let us designate the subscripted variable, into which our values for $E(DDLT > R)$ will be stored, as ES(IR).

Now if we think of IR as not only the position indicator for our subscripted variable, ES(IR), but also as our reorder point, then we would want to store in position IR =1, the expected value of stock-out per lead time period when the reorder point is 1. We would want to store in position IR = 2, the expected value of stock-out per lead time period when the reorder point is 2, and so on, until all our expected values of stock-out are stored in the array, ES(IR).

If we now list, after the END statement at the end of a FOR-TRAN program, all the nine values for E(DDLT > R), and if we compose a suitable READ statement to successively read in these values for E(DDLT > R), we can load our subscripted variable, ES(IR). The following statements should do this:

$$\text{DO 1 IR} = 1,9$$
$$\text{READ (5,—) E}$$
$$1 \quad \text{ES(IR)} = \text{E}$$

The first time through the DO loop the variable E will be given the value of the first E(DDLT > R) in our data list, and then in statement 1 this value will be stored in position 1 of our subscripted variable since, the first time through the DO loop, IR = 1. The second time through the DO loop, the variable E will be given the value of the second E(DDLT > R) in our data list, and this value will be stored in position 2 since, the second time through the DO loop, IR = 2.[3] After completion of the nine loops called for in the DO statement all values for E(DDLT > R) will have been stored. All we must do now to call forth the expected value of stock-out per lead time period when R equals any particular value, say 6, is to give the variable IR the value 6, and then employ the subscripted variable ES(IR) itself.

We can now write a FORTRAN program that will cause the computer to search for the best Q, R combination. We want our computer model to begin with a reorder point of 1, vary Q, search the TAC curve corresponding to R = 1, and store the minimum TAC on this curve in some variable; then increase R to 2, vary Q, search the TAC curve corresponding to R = 2, and compare the minimum TAC on this curve to the lowest TAC corresponding to R = 1 (previously stored); then continue increasing R until this comparison shows us we have reached the absolute minimum TAC.

---

[3] We could also have input these data in the main program by the following statements:

| ES(1) = 1.1964 | ES(3) = 0.2764 | ES(5) = 0.0353 | ES(7) = 0.0021 |
| ES(2) = 0.6234 | ES(4) = 0.1091 | ES(6) = 0.0092 | ES(8) = 0.0003 |

FIGURE 6–6

Optimum Inventory Policy—Flow Diagram for Determining Optimum Order Quantity (Q̂), Optimum Reorder Point (R̂), and Corresponding Least Total Annual Inventory Cost (TAC)

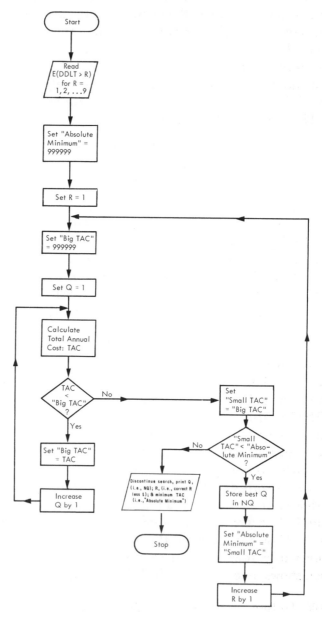

The Q, R combination that yielded this absolute minimum will be the optimum Q, R combination.

We want our computer model to do what appears diagrammatically in the flowchart shown in Figure 6–6. In the flowchart the variable "Big TAC" is used to store (as a standard for comparison) the values of TAC as Q is increased; the variable "Small TAC" is used to store values of TAC as R is increased; and the variable "Absolute Minimum" is used to store the minimum TAC from a previous search. A FORTRAN program that should do this for us is shown in Figure 6–7.

In the final DO statement, DO 2 IQ = 1,10000, we provide for many loopings so as to guarantee that we reach the lowest point on the curve prior to completion of the looping process. The IF statement (which precedes statement 2) provides for getting us out of the DO loop as soon as the low point has been found, thereby discontinuing the looping and avoiding waste of computer time.

FIGURE 6–7

FORTRAN Program for Brown's Optimum Inventory Policy

```
    DIMENSION ES(9)
    DO 1 IR = 1,9
    READ (5,—) E
1   ES(IR) = E
    ABSMIN = 999999.9
    DO 5 IR = 1,9
    R = IR
    BIGTAC = 999999.9
    DO 2 IQ = 1,10000
    Q = IQ
    TAC = 0.2 * 500.0 * (Q/2.0 + R − 2.0) + 20.0 * 365.0/Q + 40.0 * ES
      (IR) * 365.0/Q
    IF (TAC − BIGTAC)2,3,3
2   BIGTAC = TAC
3   SMTAC = BIGTAC
    IF (SMTAC − ABSMIN)4,6,6
4   NQ = IQ − 1
5   ABSMIN = SMTAC
6   IR = IR − 1
    WRITE (6,—),NQ,IR,ABSMIN
    STOP
    END
```

The Optimum Inventory Policy

It develops that Brown Electronics Company will experience a minimum total annual inventory cost of $1,534, with a $\hat{Q}$ of 13 units and an $\hat{R}$ of 4 units. Brown's *decision rule* for minimizing total annual inventory cost is: "When stock level in item A drops to 4 units, order a new shipment of 13 units."

Post Optimality Analysis

We know the optimum policy which should be employed to minimize TAC. However, by further analysis, using the model in Figure 6–7, we can learn much more of importance about the behavior of and the means for controlling Brown's inventory system.

Frequency of Stock-outs. Referring to Table 6–6, we see that with a reorder point of four units the probability of Brown's being caught short in a lead time period is 0.0738. That is, 7.38 percent of the lead time periods Brown Electronics Company can expect to experience a shortage of some magnitude. If the reorder quantity is 13 units, Brown can expect 28 lead time periods per year (365/13). Clearly, then, Brown can expect stock-outs of some magnitude about two times a year (7.38 percent of 28).

Sensitivity of Total Annual Cost to Policy Change. Our computer model for determining optimum inventory policy for Brown Electronics Company's inventory system was designed to search each of a family of U-shaped TAC curves for the Q,R combination corresponding to the lowest possible TAC. If we had made provision in our computer program for printing out all values of Q, R and TAC, we would have obtained data that would enable us to plot only the left half of the U in each of our family curves. From these curves we could get some notion of the consequences in increased total annual cost from adopting a policy of reordering *less* than 14 units, but we would also like to know about the consequences of ordering 14 or more units.

We can get the required data with a few alterations in our computer model. In the two-dimensional graph of Figure 6–8 Brown's total annual inventory cost curves are shown for reorder policies in which R varies from 3 units through 6 units, and Q varies from 10 through 18 units. From these curves it is apparent that within the range $11 \leq Q \leq 16$ and $3 \leq R \leq 6$ total annual inventory cost varies about 10 percent from the minimum possible cost.

FIGURE 6–8

Brown Electronics Company's Inventory Cost Curves

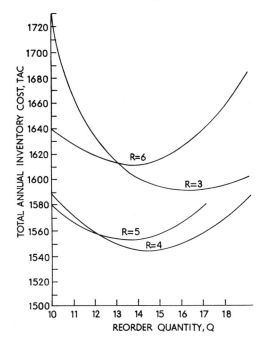

In these circumstances Brown might be tempted to increase R from the optimum of four and thereby reduce expected stock-out frequency to less than two per year. By reordering at R = 6 rather than at R = 4, stock-outs could be reduced to about one every five years. This is deduced from Table 6–6 where, with a reorder point of 6, the probability of a stock-out in one lead time period is 0.0071; and 0.0071 × 28 = 0.199.

By adopting a policy of ordering 12 units when the stock level drops to 6 units, Brown's expected stock-out rate goes from two stock-outs per year to one every five years, and total annual inventory cost goes from $1,534 to $1,619, an increase of only about 5 percent.

In spite of the apparent attractiveness of this policy change, the change would, in fact, be undesirable unless Brown has inaccurately estimated the monetary value of the consequence of being caught short. This brings us to the question: "How sensitive is Brown's inventory system to variations, and hence to inaccuracies in estimating stock-out (and other) costs?"

Sensitivity of Optimum Policy to Changes in System Parameters.
Additional alterations in our computer model would enable us to
obtain data on which to evaluate the effect on the optimum inventory policy when the per unit stock-out cost is varied.

In Table 6–8 the optimum inventory policies associated with

TABLE 6–8

Optimum Inventory Policies and Varying per Unit Stock-out Costs

Stock-out Cost (per Unit)	Corresponding Optimum Inventory Policy $\hat{Q}$	$\hat{R}$	Minimum Total Annual Cost (Based on Optimum Policy)	Total Annual Cost (If Policy Is Based on Estimated Stock-out Cost of $40 Unit)	Added Inventory Cost (Attributable to Ignorance of Actual Stock-out Cost)
$10	14	2	$1,384	$1,442	5.6%
20	14	3	1,466	1,473	0.5
30	13	4	1,503	1,503	0.0
40	13	4	1,534	1,534	0.0
50	13	5	1,561	1,564	0.2
60	13	5	1,571	1,595	1.5
70	13	5	1,581	1,625	2.8
80	13	5	1,591	1,657	4.2

varying per unit stock-out costs are tabulated. Also shown are the
minimum total annual inventory costs corresponding to the optimum policy in each case. In column 5 are shown total annual inventory costs Brown Electronics would actually incur if it based
its inventory policy on a belief that stock-out cost was $40 per unit
of stock-out (leading to a policy of Q = 13 and R = 4) when, *in fact,*
stock-out cost was as shown in column 1.

Clearly the Brown Electronics inventory model is not highly
sensitive to miscalculations in stock-out cost. If Brown bases its inventory policy on a belief that stock-out cost is $40 per unit stock-
out, when *actual* stock-out cost is anywhere from $10 to $80, the
consequences in increased annual costs attributable to imperfect information are not serious.

A similar analysis might be made of other parameters: holding
cost and its components, and ordering costs. We could also enrich
our model to account for nonlinearity in parameters—that is, that
the cost of being caught short two units is not exactly *twice* the cost
of being caught short one unit. Similarly, we could deal with the

case in which the cost of holding 20 units in inventory is not exactly twice the cost of holding 10 units. Furthermore, with a few additional statements we could read into the computer's memory an array representing a delivered cost schedule, and could cause the computer to search this schedule—once what is believed to be an optimum Q has been determined—to discover if unit cost discounts arising out of larger orders might justify altering the reorder policy.

Additional Constraints on the Control Variables

Let us suppose that Brown's supplier specifies a minimum order quantity of 25 units. This is clearly in excess of the quantity Brown would prefer to order. The question occurs to us: "If 25 units are to be ordered, each time an order is placed, is R = 4 still the appropriate reorder point?" Knowing the interdependence of $\hat{Q}$ and $\hat{R}$ we suspect that it is not.

Again referring to the model of Figure 6–7 we find that a reorder point of 3 units is more appropriate if Q is to be 25 units rather than 13. However, the advantage is small: only $2.30 per year in reduced total annual cost.

We should not be surprised with this result. If Q is increased from 13 to 25 the number of lead time periods per year, and hence the number of stock-out opportunities, decreases by about one half. With fewer stock-out opportunities it pays to incur a higher stock-out risk per lead time period by decreasing R; i.e., to trade off increased stock-out cost for decreased holding cost.

"Base" or "Safety" stock is generally defined to be the quantity on hand, on the average, when a new shipment is received: R − EDDLT. Suppose that Brown's treasurer, concerned about a short cash position, insists that safety stocks be temporarily reduced and it is decided that R will be reduced to two units, for item A. Is Q = 13 still the appropriate order quantity?

Further use of the model of Figure 6–7 reveals that with R = 2 TAC is $100 lower with Q = 18 rather than 13. With a higher risk of stock-out during lead time it pays to reduce the number of stock-out opportunities per year by increasing Q; i.e., to trade off increased holding cost for decreased stock-out cost (and decreased order cost since, with Q increased, we will order less frequently). The interdependence of $\hat{Q}$ and $\hat{R}$ is again apparent. That is, when TAC is minimal, $\hat{Q}$ is a function of $\hat{R}$ and $\hat{R}$ is a function of $\hat{Q}$.

On Turnover as a Decision Rule

Turnover is commonly employed as a criterion in evaluating whether inventories are too high, and hence is a sort of inventory management decision rule. As a gross measure by means of which the reasonableness of a multiproduct inventory level might be evaluated turnover has some value. Let us test turnover as a criterion for evaluating performance in the management of item A.

Turnover usually means the number of times per year that the inventory is "replaced" or turned over, and is defined as annual sales divided by average inventory. In Brown's inventory system annual sales would be annual demand, since backordering is permitted. Turnover, therefore, would be:

$$DPY/\text{Average Inventory} = 365/(Q/2 + R - 2)$$

When the optimal policy is employed this becomes:

$$365/(13/2 + 4 - 2) = 43 \text{ times per year}$$

Is turnover of this magnitude possible via any other policy? That is, are there other combinations of Q and R which produce the same turnover?

$$\text{Solving for Q in } 365/(Q/2 + R - 2) = 43$$

. . . we have: $Q = 21 - 2R$. Returning to the model of Figure 6–7 and letting R take on the values 2 through 6 we have the following policies which all produce a turnover of 43 times per year:

Q	R	TAC
17	2	$1,814
15	3	1,605
13	4	1,534
11	5	1,560
9	6	1,676

Only one policy gives both a turnover of 43 and the minimum total annual inventory cost. We cannot specify the optimum policy in terms of turnover alone and we cannot evaluate the skill with which an item in inventory is being managed solely by reference to its turnover.

A General Inventory Model under Uncertainty

The model that we developed in Figure 6–7 may have general validity in a wide variety of cases, where some sort of discrete demand and lead time distributions can be estimated with some confidence.

By substituting *variables* in the Brown Electronics Company model (where we have employed *constants*) we have the following *general model* (Figure 6–9), which Brown might use during *periodic reviews* and also, as various costs associated with its inventory system change, to determine when a change in policy is appropriate (Figure 6–9).

Values for the system parameters—i.e., N, UHC, CPU, EDDLT, CPO, DPY, STKCOS and the array ES(IR)—as defined in the comment statements (Figure 6–9) should be initialized at the beginning of the program, and a data deck containing the expected values of stock-out schedule (expected number of units short per lead time period, corresponding to various reorder points) should be read in as provided for in the first DO loop of the program. The program provides for printing out the optimum reorder quantity, $\hat{Q}$, the optimum reorder point, $\hat{R}$, and the minimum total annual inventory cost associated with these values, TAC.

Completing Our Monte Carlo Simulation Model

In building our inventory model under uncertainty we became acquainted with the subscripted variable. We are now equipped to explore how the subscripted variable could be used to keep score in our Monte Carlo simulation and to print out a probability distribution for our demand during lead time pattern.

Referring to Figure 6–3, we developed a program that would simulate Brown Company's lead time periods and would give the variable IDDLT, following one pass through the program, a value corresponding to the number of units of item A demanded during the lead time period just simulated.

Let us let SCORE(I) be a subscripted variable in which we store the number of times various demands during lead time are experienced. We will need 10 positions in our array, SCORE(I), 1 for each of the 10 possible demands during lead time.

We should empty the SCORE(I) array by equating all 10 positions to 0 prior to statement 2 in Figure 6–3. We might do this with the statements:

```
        DO 1 I = 1,10
    1   SCORE(I) = 0.0
```

FIGURE 6–9

Computer Program for a General Inventory Model under Uncertainty

```
C   GENERAL INVENTORY MODEL UNDER UNCERTAINTY
C   PARAMETERS
C   N = NUMBER OF POSITIONS IN THE ARRAY REPRESENT-
        ING THE EXPECTED VALUES OF STOCKOUT
        'SCHEDULE'
C   UHC = ANNUAL UNIT HOLDING COST AS A PERCENT OF
        THE COST PER UNIT
C   CPU = COST PER UNIT
C   EDDLT = EXPECTED DEMAND DURING LEAD TIME
C   CPO = ORDERING COST PER ORDER PROCESSED
C   DPY = DEMAND PER YEAR
C   STKCOS = STOCKOUT COST PER UNIT STOCKOUT
C   ES(IR) HOLDS THE EXPECTED STOCKOUT SCHEDULE
        DIMENSION ES( ) 9
        N = 9
        UHC =
        CPU =
        EDDLT =
        CPO =
        DPY = 365
        STKCOS =
        DO 1 IR = 1,N 9
        READ (5,—) E
    1   ES(IR) = E
        ABSMIN = 999999.9
        DO 5 IR = 1,N
        R = IR
        BIGTAC = 999999.9
        DO 2 IQ = 1,10000
        Q = IQ
        TAC = UHC * CPU * (Q/2.0 + R − EDDLT) + CPO *
        (DPY/Q) + STKCOS * ES(IR) * DPY/Q
        IF (TAC − BIGTAC)2,3,3
    2   BIGTAC = TAC
    3   SMTAC = BIGTAC
        IF (SMTAC − ABSMIN)4,6,6
    4   NQ = IQ − 1
    5   ABSMIN = SMTAC
    6   IR = IR − 1
        WRITE (6,—)NQ,IR,ABSMIN
        STOP
        END
```

Now, immediately following statement 14—in which a new IDDLT is determined in our program (Figure 6–3)—we should place the following statement:[4]

15 SCORE(IDDLT + 1) = SCORE(IDDLT + 1) + 1.0.

As a result of statement 15, the score of the appropriate demand— of our 10 possible demands during lead time—is increased by 1 following the simulation of each new lead time period.

Demand during lead time in our model can be zero, and hence IDDLT will sometimes be zero. It will be recalled, however, that in FORTRAN the subscript in a subscripted variable must be a positive, nonzero integer. Therefore we are obliged to let the position IDDLT + 1 in our array, SCORE(I), hold the score for the demand during lead time, represented by the current value of the variable IDDLT. Thus when IDDLT = 0, position 1 in our array will have 1 added to its current score.

```
     DIMENSION SCORE(10)
     DO 15 K = 1,1000
 2   READ (5,—) IRN
     IF (IRN — 24)3,3,4
 3   LT = 1
     GO TO 7
 4   IF (IRN — 74)5,5,6
 5   LT = 2
     GO TO 7
 6   LT = 3
 7   IDDLT = 0
     DO 14 I = 1, LT
     READ (5,—) IRN
     IF (IRN — 39)8,8,9
 8   ID = 0
     GO TO 14
 9   IF (IRN — 69) 10,10,11
10   ID = 1
     GO TO 14
11   IF (IRN — 89) 12,12,13
12   ID = 2
     GO TO 14
13   ID = 3
14   IDDLT = IDDLT + ID
15   SCORE(IDDLT + 1) = SCORE(IDDLT + 1) + 1.0
```

---

[4] Note: Simple algebraic expressions *can* be employed inside the subscript; thus SCORE(IDDLT + 1). The complexity of the algebra permitted inside the parentheses varies with FORTRAN compilers.

By the time this loop is completed our score for 1,000 simulated lead time experiences has been stored in the 10 positions of the SCORE(I) array. To convert these scores to probabilities and print them out, we might add the statements:

```
      DO 16 J = 1,10
      PROB = SCORE (J)/1000.0
      K = J - 1
  16  WRITE (6,17) K, PROB
  17  FORMAT (1H0,28HPROBABILITY OF A DEMAND
         FOR ,I2,2X,20HDURING LEAD TIME IS ,F12.10)
```

The complete Monte Carlo program for generating and printing out the data required for the first two columns in Table 6–6 becomes Model 6–1 (but without the FORMAT statement referred to in the 2 READ statements, and without the input random number list).

The Random Number Generating Function

Most user-oriented, special-purpose computer languages, like FORTRAN, have a number of commonly used functions built into them. Thus, SQRT( ), when encountered to the right of the equal sign in an algebraic statement, is replaced with the square root of the quantity in the parentheses.

Since random numbers are needed frequently in systems work a "random fraction generator" is common in FORTRAN language compilers. Each time the appropriate function name is encountered to the right of the equal sign it is replaced with a *new* random fraction. In the program segment below RANF(0) is such a function name, in which the 0 in the parentheses is a dummy variable. The program below would cause to be generated and stored successively at address RN 50 random fractions:

```
      DO  2 I = 1,50
  2   RN = RANF(0)
```

If we wanted a list of 50 two-digit integers, we might modify our program segment to read:

```
      DO 2  I = 1,50
  2   IRN = 100.0 * RANF(0)
```

By forming the product $100 \times \text{RANF}(0)$ we move the decimal point in the fraction two places to the right. Then by storing the product at integer address IRN we truncate the remaining fractional part.

MODEL 6–1

Monte Carlo Program

```
      DIMENSION SCORE(10)
      DO 1 I = 1,10
 1    SCORE(I) = 0.0
      DO 15 K = 1,1000
 2    READ (5,—)IRN
      IF (IRN − 24)3,3,4
 3    LT = 1
      GO TO 7
 4    IF (IRN − 74)5,5,6
 5    LT = 2
      GO TO 7
 6    LT = 3
 7    IDDLT = 0
      DO 14 I = 1, LT
      READ (5,—)IRN
      IF (IRN − 39)8,8,9
 8    ID = 0
      GO TO 14
 9    IF (IRN − 69)10,10,11
10    ID = 1
      GO TO 14
11    IF (IRN − 89)12,12,13
12    ID = 2
      GO TO 14
13    ID = 3
14    IDDLT = DDLT + ID
15    SCORE(IDDLT + 1) = SCORE(IDDLT + 1) + 1.0
      DO 16 J = 1,10
      PROB = SCORE(J)/1000.0
      K = J − 1
16    WRITE(6,17)K,PROB
17    FORMAT (1H0,28HPROBABILITY OF A DEMAND
         FOR ,I2,2X,20HDURING LEAD TIME IS ,F12.10)
      STOP
      END
```

Clearly the interaction of daily demand and lead time to produce demand-during-lead-time could be done more easily by generating two-digit random integers, as above, than by reading such a list into the computer as was done in Model 6–1.

In Chapter 11 we will explore ways for generating random fractions algebraically.

Analysis versus Simulation of the Brown Inventory System

In Chapter 5 we constructed a mathematical model of the retailer's inventory system under certainty. The mathematical model
we constructed was a *mapping function* (expression 5–1) which
modeled the way the retailer's system would respond to various
inventory policies—values for Q—to produce annual inventory
cost. We then employed a simulation experiment, an iterative search
process, to identify the optimum inventory policy. Input variable
Q interacted with the mapping function to produce TAC. The mapping function (*h*, in Figure 5–10), which we designed to represent
our understanding of the cost behavior of the real inventory system,
was not subject to our control; control variable Q was.

Most systems of any complexity consist of subsystems. Just as
each subsystem consists of interacting components, the larger system consists of the subsystems, which interact to produce the behavior of the larger system—its response to inputs.

The Interacting Components in the Brown Inventory System

We can improve our insights into the behavior of systems and
the means for modeling and controlling them by closer examination
of the contrasts between the Brown Electronics inventory system
and the retailer's system of Chapter 5.

Consider the three-phase procedure we employed in building the
model of Figure 6–7. We began by modeling the subsystem whose
two inputs are demand and lead time and whose output is demand
during lead time (phase 1):

Demand ⟶ h_1 ⟶ Demand during
Lead Time ⟶   Lead Time

Two discrete input functions interact with each other to produce
one discrete output function. All three are functions of random
variables. We modeled their interaction (operator h_1) analytically,
Table 6–5, and again via simulation, Figure 6–2 and Model 6–1.

The discrete function demand-during-lead-time and control variable R then became an input for a second subsystem, in phase 2, the
output of which was the discrete function expected-stock-out-
during-lead-time, $E(DDLT > R)$:

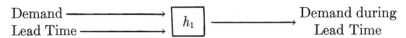

Reorder Point, R ⟶ h_2 ⟶ Expected Stock-out
Demand during Lead Time ⟶   during Lead Time

We modeled the transformation of DDLT into $E(DDLT > R)$, i.e., operator h_2, *analytically*.

Finally, in phase 3 we modeled the interaction of $E(DDLT > R)$ and the remaining cost components to produce mapping function h_3 in the following subsystem:

$$Q \longrightarrow$$
$$\text{Expected Stock-out during Lead Time} \longrightarrow \boxed{h_3} \longrightarrow TAC$$
$$R \longrightarrow$$

. . . where h_3 is the function on the right of the equal sign in expression 6–5:

$$h_3 = .20(\$50)(Q/2 + R - 2)$$
$$+ \$20(365/Q)$$
$$+ \$40 \times E(DDLT > R) \times 365/Q$$

It is important to observe that these three phases were also invoked in modeling the retailer's system under certainty. The difference is that in that system modeling the interaction of daily demand and lead time to produce demand during lead time was trivial. Furthermore, since no stock-outs were to be tolerated in the retailer's system, $E(DDLT > R)$ was of no concern and the appropriate value for control variable R was established with little effort, independently of Q.

A "Pure" Simulation Approach

The three-phase procedure we employed in modeling Brown's inventory system was a mix of formal analysis and simulation. We will now see how the interaction of random variables daily demand and lead time and of control variables Q and R to produce output TAC might be determined through "pure" simulation.

Consider the flowchart of Figure 6–10. The model of Figure 6–10 is similar to that of Figure 5–9, for the retailer's system. Notable differences, however, are:

1. The presence of R as a control variable in Figure 6–10.
2. Provision at box 6 for generating the random variable "demand" and at box 9 for generating the random variable "lead time."
3. Provision (at measurement point D) for accumulating stock-out cost.

FIGURE 6–10

Periodic Review System Simulation (Brown Electronics Company)

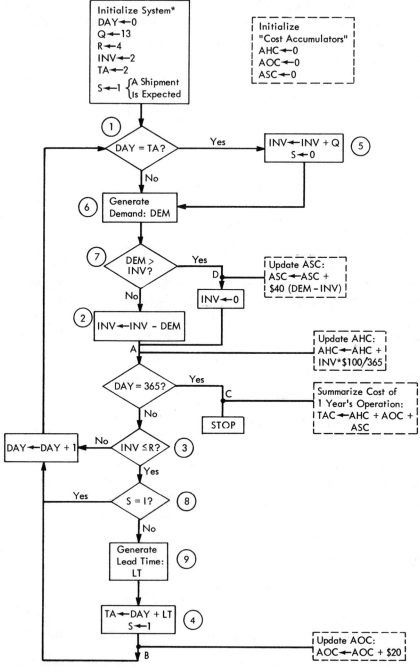

* New shipments from the supplier, if any, arrive first thing in the morning, and a new shipment of Q is ordered at end of day if: (1) stock level is at or below reorder point, and (2) an order is NOT already outstanding.

Note that we have arbitrarily initialized the system, at the beginning of the simulation, in the *state* shown at the top of the flowchart. A new variable, S, has been added to indicate whether an order for a replenishment supply is outstanding. "S = 1" means a shipment is expected; "S = O" means no order is outstanding.

In the initialization box "TA ← 2" indicates an order is destined to be received two days after the beginning of the simulation.

If, at box 1, a shipment is due on the day being simulated then at box 5 the inventory level is adjusted to reflect its arrival and S is set to 0 to indicate that no order is outstanding.

At box 6 the day's demand is generated. This might be done in a manner similar to that achieved in statements 7 through 13, Model 6–1. At box 7 the day's demand is compared to stock on hand and a stock-out charge is made at point *D* if a shortage is experienced.

At box 2 the stock level is updated to reflect the day's withdrawals. At the end of the day, box 3, the stock level is compared to the reorder point. If the stock on hand is less than or equal to R and if a shipment is not expected (box 8) we move to box 9 and generate the lead time we are destined to experience with the order about to be placed. This might be done in a manner similar to that achieved in statements 2 through 6 in Model 6–1.

The date the new order is destined to be received is then calculated and stored at TA (box 4), and at point *B* an additional ordering charge is made.

When 365 days of operations have been simulated the year's total cost is calculated at point *C* and the simulation is ended.

The model of Figure 6–10 simulates the behavior of the system when the optimum policy is employed.

We can, of course, use the model iteratively to search for the optimum policy and hence to solve Brown Electronic's inventory problem via "pure" simulation rather than analytically. To do so we simply withdraw the statements "Q ← 13" and "R ← 4" from the initialization box, then imbed the model of Figure 6–10 in a larger model as we did in Figure 5–10 for the retailer's model. We will leave this for the exercises.

We concluded in Chapter 5 that formal analysis was superior to simulation in finding the retailer's optimum inventory policy under certainty. For the inventory system under uncertainty it appears that formal analysis with some reliance on simulation may be most appropriate.

Whether this is generally true depends on the size and character of the demand and lead time distributions and whether they can be approximated by well-behaved density functions. The problem may be further complicated by discontinuities and nonlinearities in cost and price functions; as, for example, when the delivered cost of the item being stocked is a function of the quantity ordered.

Response Surface Methodology

A careful study of the total annual cost function in Chapter 5 and in this chapter demonstrates that for positive, real values of Q and R (the only ones we're interested in) the TAC curve is "well behaved." It is continuous and differentiable; and it also lends itself easily to the search procedure employed in the models of Figures 6–7 and 6–9. Suppose, however, that the TAC function had not been so well behaved. Suppose, for example, that for some values of R the relation between Q and TAC had been like that portrayed in Figure 6–11.

Beginning with a small value for Q and incrementing Q, unit at a time, we would have stopped at point "*A*," a "local optimum" rather than at point "*B*," the "global optimum."

In the search procedure employed in Figure 6–7 the domain within which Q and R fall is small and could have been predicted easily. This made "exhaustive search" among all reasonable integer values for $\hat{Q}$ and $\hat{R}$ a sensible search procedure.

In simulation modeling where many variables are involved and where discontinuous and nonlinear functional relationships are present the *design* of the search procedure itself is an important problem for the systems analyst. The analyst must begin by asking how the "response surface" is to be searched. That is, how the n-dimensional surface, which is the set of points (values) of the cost function corresponding to the sets of relevant values for the control

FIGURE 6–11

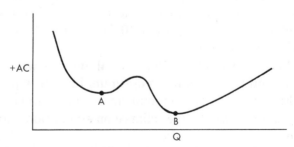

variables, is to be surveyed. The bowl in Figure 6–5 is such a response surface, an exceedingly well-behaved one.

Much attention has been given to this question by analysts in an effort to reduce the cost of the search and to avoid local optima. The field is sometimes referred to as Response Surface Methodology. The interested reader is referred to the bibliography at the end of the chapter for more on RSM.

Sample size is also a question of considerable importance. In our inventory simulations we've based our estimate of the total annual cost on one year's simulated experience. Is this adequate? More than enough? While the cost of simulations of this sort on most computers is small it is by no means negligible. Each additional day's simulation costs the same as its predecessor, but yields progressively less information. Questions of experimental design will be treated in the final chapter.

Discontinuous Cost Functions and the FORTRAN "Function Subprogram"

Notice that although the demand during lead time probability distribution on which the total annual cost model of expression (6–5) was based is a *discrete* probability distribution, the total annual cost function of model (6–5) is a *continuous* cost function. That is, the cost function of (6–5) properly portrays the way our total annual cost, TAC, is related to the order quantity and the reorder point for the Brown Electronics Company system, regardless of what positive values we choose for Q and R.

Many costs in economic systems are not continuous in this sense, but change as certain specifications of the system change. Let us see how we might deal with a discontinuous cost function in a computer optimization study. In doing so we will acquaint ourselves with an added FORTRAN convention, the "function subprogram," whose usefulness will be readily apparent.

Continental Rent-A-Car's demand for cars in a particular market area is found to be distributed as follows.

Demand per Day (Cars)	Probability
0	.4
1	.3
2	.2
3	.1

Continental's home office levies a charge of $3 per day for each car not rented, a charge of $1 per day for each car demanded but not available, and gives the local agent a credit of $10 per day for each car rented.

If s = number of cars stocked and x = number of cars demanded in a day, then:

$$\text{when } 0 \le x \le s \text{ net daily credit is: } \$10x - \$3(s - x)$$
$$x > s \qquad\qquad\qquad 10s - 1(x - s)$$

The possible events, their probabilities, their consequences, and the products of their probabilities and consequences when the agent follows a policy of stocking $s = 2$ cars are shown below.

	Possible Events	Probability	Consequence	Probability × Consequence
$0 \le x \le s$	$x = 0$	.4	$\$10(0) - \$3(2-0)$	$.4(-6) = -\$2.40$
	$x = 1$	.3	$10(1) - 3(2-1)$	$.3 \ (7) = 2.10$
	$x = 2$	.2	$10(2) - 3(2-1)$	$.2 \ (20) = 4.00$
$x > s$	$x = 3$	.1	$10(2) - 1(3-2)$	$.1 \ (19) = 1.90$
				Expected daily credit: $5.60

Continental's daily credit function changes as the relationship between x and s changes. Two functions are required, as shown in the example. Let us name the credit function appropriate when $0 \le x \le s$ "CRE1F," credit function 1, and name the credit function appropriate when $x > s$ "CRE2F," credit function 2. Both these functions are functions of the two variables x and s, and in conformance with algebraic custom we might identify them as follows:

$$\text{CRE1F}(x,s) = \$10x - \$3 \ (s-x)$$
$$\text{CRE2F}(x,s) = \ 10s - \$1 \ (x-s)$$

in which the arguments x and s are shown, separated by commas, in parentheses.

If we will now express these functions as FORTRAN expressions, as shown below, and if we will then precede any executable statements in a program with these expressions, we can use them in a most convenient way:

```
CRE1F(X,S) = 10.0 * X − 3.0 * (S − X)
CRE2F(X,S) = 10.0 * S − (X − S)
```

Later in the program if we have values for X and S and we want to cause the computer to calculate credit function 1, given these values for X and S, and to store the value of the function at address CREDIT, for example, we simply write:

$$\text{CREDIT} = \text{CRE1F(X,S)}$$

or if we want the value of function 2 to be calculated for these same values of X and S and stored at CREDIT we write:

$$\text{CREDIT} = \text{CRE2F(X,S)}$$

The computer interprets the function name appearing on the right of the equal sign—complete with identification of the values currently stored for X and S—to mean: calculate the value of the function named at the beginning of the program on the basis of the values currently stored for X and S.

A complete FORTRAN program that would search for the optimum stock size for Continental Rent-A-Car in which the use of our FORTRAN function subprograms is shown more explicitly, appears below.

```
      CRE1F(X,S) = ((10.0 * X) − (3.0 * (S − X)))
      CRE2F(X,S) = ((10.0 * S) − (1.0 * (X − S)))
      C = 0.0
      DO 1 I = 1,4
      EMV = 0.0
      S = I − 1
      DO 2 J = 1,4,1
      X = J − 1
      PX = 0.4 − X/10.0
      IF (X.GE.0.0.AND.X.LE.S) GO TO 3
      CREDIT = CRE2F(X,S)
      GO TO 4
    3 CREDIT = CRE1F(X,S)
    4 C = CREDIT * PX
      EMV = EMV + C
    2 CONTINUE
    5 FORMAT ( )
      WRITE(6,5) S,EMV
    1 CONTINUE
      STOP
      END
```

Our printout shows:

Cars Stocked (S)	Expected Credit
0	−$1.00
1	4.40
2	5.60
3	4.00

Continental Rent-A-Car's daily credit will be maximized if S = 2 cars are stocked.

Any legitimate FORTRAN variable name may be employed to "name" a function, but the last character in that name in many FORTRAN compilers must be an F. It should be observed that the variables mentioned in the naming or defining of the function at the beginning of the program, mentioned as arguments, are really dummy variables. The variables employed in the *use* of the function later in the program are completely unrelated to those employed as dummies in the naming of the function. The purpose of the dummy variables is simply to establish how the expression values in the use of the function should be substituted into the program set up from the definition.

In the Continental Rent-A-Car example the function subprogram is not greatly useful. It should be apparent, however, that if we were obliged to call on the computer to evaluate a function many times in a program, it would be easier to define the function only once (particularly if the function is quite involved) and then simply call on it as future need requires.

SUGGESTIONS FOR FURTHER STUDY

BUFFA, ELWOOD S. *Production-Inventory Systems: Planning and Control.* Homewood, Ill.: Richard D. Irwin, Inc., 1968.

HUNTER, J. S., and NAYLOR, T. H. "Experimental Designs for Computer Simulation Experiments," *Management Science,* Vol. 16, No. 7 (March 1970), pp. 422–34.

(For a good bibliography on Response Surface Methodology.)

SCHLAIFER, ROBERT. *Probability and Statistics for Business Decisions,* chaps. 4 and 15. New York: McGraw-Hill Book Co., 1959.

EXERCISES

(Begin each of the following problems by composing a flow diagram.)

1. A retailer forecasts demand per day for an item (which he buys and resells) according to the following distribution:

Possible Demand	Probability
0	0.05
1	0.10
2	0.25
3	0.30
4	0.20
5	0.10
	1.00

Compose a FORTRAN program that will read these data into memory from a data deck, and will calculate the retailer's average or expected daily demand.

2. Assume that the retailer in Exercise 1 must pay \$1 for the item, that he resells them at \$5 each, and that items stocked one day but unsold that day are a total loss due to perishability.

Compose a FORTRAN program that will interpret the retailer's payoff matrix and will determine and print out the number of units of this item which the retailer should stock each day in order to maximize his expected profit.

3. During the coming year ABC, Inc., anticipates a demand pattern with the following distribution:

Weekly Demand	Probability
11	0.10
12	0.40
13	0.25
14	0.15
15	0.07
16	0.03
	1.00

Past experience suggests that lead time for replenishing stock will be distributed as follows:

Weeks of Lead Time	Probability
2	0.15
3	0.45
4	0.20
5	0.15
6	0.05
	1.00

If the demand and lead time patterns anticipated by ABC, Inc., materialize, what sort of distribution should ABC expect for demand during lead time?

Write a FORTRAN program that will determine the expected demand during lead time distribution through Monte Carlo simulation.

4. *a*) Construct a FORTRAN program for the model of Figure 6–10. Simulate 365 days of operating experience by running the program. Compare the cost of the year's operation, based on your simulation experiment, with that produced analytically for Brown's inventory system (i.e., \$1,534).

b) Now modify your program so that it can be employed to search for the optimum inventory policy. Initialize the simulation at $R = 3$ and $Q = 11$. Increment Q, unit at a time, until $Q = 16$. Then increment R by 1 and again increment Q from 11 to 16. Continue through $R = 6$.

On the basis of your results would you say this inventory system is highly sensitive to deviations from the optimum policy? That is, are modest deviations from the optimum policy accompanied by significant changes in total annual cost?

5. In regression analysis

$$Y - \bar{Y} = b(X - \bar{X})$$

is a straight line which crosses the Y axis at $\bar{Y} - b\bar{X}$, and crosses the X axis at

$$\frac{b\bar{X} - \bar{Y}}{b}$$

where:

$$\bar{X} = \frac{1}{n}\sum_{i=1}^{n} X_i$$

$$\bar{Y} = \frac{1}{n}\sum_{i=1}^{n} Y_i$$

$$b = \frac{\sum_{i=1}^{n}(X_i - \bar{X})(Y_i - \bar{Y})}{\sum_{i=1}^{n}(X_i - \bar{X})^2}$$

X and Y being the coordinates of a set of points. (X_1, Y_1), (X_2, Y_2), . . . (X_n, Y_n).

From a data deck of not over 1,000 cards, each containing three data fields in the form FORMAT (F8.4,F8.4,I1), we want to determine a regression line. The first two fields on each data card contain values for X and Y, respectively. The third data field contains a zero in every card in the data deck except the last card. The last card is a "dummy" card with zeros in the first two data fields and a 1 in the third data field.

Compose a FORTRAN program which will:

a) Read a data deck consisting of up to 1,000 cards and then calculate and print out the statement: REGRESSION LINE IS Y — BARY = B(X — BARX), substituting in this statement for BARY, BARX and B the values calculated for these quantities in the program.

b) Ignore the last card *except* as an indication that the deck has been completed, whereupon it will terminate the program.

6. In the Brown Electronics Company problem (Chapter 6) annual inventory holding cost was assumed to be 20 percent of the delivered cost of the items in inventory. If inventory holding cost is assumed to be related to the size of the average inventory in a nonlinear fashion, specifically,

$$\text{AHC} = \$400 + \$120 \text{ (average inventory)}^{1.2},$$

per unit holding cost clearly varies with the size of the order quantity, Q.

Assume that annual inventory holding cost is represented by the function expressed above, and write a FORTRAN program that will determine and print out Brown Electronics Company's optimum order quantity, reorder point, and corresponding total annual inventory cost, all other parameters of the model remaining as described in Chapter 6.

7. Aikens Company expects a demand during lead time pattern precisely like that of Brown Electronics Company (Chapter 6) for each of its three principal inventory items—item X, item Y, and item Z. Costs and other data associated with each of these three items are shown below.

	Item X	Item Y	Item Z
Unit holding cost (UHC)	0.12	0.20	0.32
Cost per unit (CPU)	$120	$380	$813
Cost per order processed (CPO)	$ 20	$ 20	$ 30
Demand per year (DPY)	365	365	365
Stock-out cost (STKCOS)	$ 14	$125	$ 56

Employ a modified version of the general inventory model of Figure 7–9 to determine and print out $\widehat{Q}$, $\widehat{R}$, and the corresponding TAC for each of these three items in Aikens' inventory.

8. Blackstone Manufacturing Company wants to determine $\widehat{Q}$, $\widehat{R}$, and minimum TAC for each of four products used in the manufacture of its electronic control gear—product 1, product 2, product 3, and product 4. Costs and other data associated with these products are shown in the two tables below.

	Product 1	Product 2	Product 3	Product 4
UHC	0.20	0.20	0.20	0.20
CPU	$500	$ 35	$210	$ 16
CPO	$ 25	$ 25	$ 25	$ 25
DPY	400	350	285	300
STKCOS	$ 48	$ 72	$ 14	$110

Assume that expected demand during lead time (EDDLT) for each of the four products is 2.0 (a bit unrealistic for products 2 and 4, but acceptable for our purposes).

Use a modified version of the general model of Figure 6–9 to determine and print out $\widehat{Q}$, $\widehat{R}$, and minimum TAC for each of these four products, whose inventory management is of current concern to Blackstone Manufacturing Company.

With a Reorder Point, R, of:	Product 1	Product 2	Product 3	Product 4
		Expected stock-out (Units Short) per Reorder Period E(DDLT > R)		

With a Reorder Point, R, of:	Product 1	Product 2	Product 3	Product 4
1	1.172	2.416	1.911	3.912
2	0.612	2.121	0.701	3.701
3	0.256	1.800	0.301	3.201
4	0.100	0.702	0.191	2.719
5	0.090	0.500	0.070	2.408
6	0.070	0.312	0.050	2.176
7	0.040	0.191	0.020	1.615
8	0.012	0.050	0.004	1.298
9	0.005	0.010	0.000	0.898
10	0.000	0.000	0.000	0.000

9. Employing the Brown Electronics Company model that was described in Chapter 6, determine whether total annual inventory cost is more sensitive to EQUAL PERCENTAGE changes in (1) delivered price per unit, or (2) stock-out cost per unit.

10. It was found that with a cost price per unit of $500 Brown Electronics Company's optimum inventory policy was $\hat{Q} = 13$ units and $\hat{R} = 4$ units. Assume that the Brown Company is given the following delivered price schedule by its supplier.

Size of Order (Units)	Cost Price Per Unit
1 through 20	$500
21 through 40	490
41 and over	489

Modify the general model of Figure 6–9 to cause the computer to consider quantity discounts in determining optimum inventory policy, and cause the computer to calculate and print out $\hat{Q}$, $\hat{R}$, and associated TAC, assuming that the above delivered price schedule is quoted by Brown's supplier.

11–1. Assume that 20 integers, each consisting of four digits or less (which occupy 20 fields of four columns each on one data card), represent the 20 possible demands during lead time.

Assume that 20 fractions, each consisting of three digits plus the decimal point (which occupy 20 fields of four columns each on another data card), represent the 20 probabilities associated with the various possible demands mentioned in the preceding paragraph.

Compose a FORTRAN program segment that will:

a) Read into the one-dimension subscripted variable, DEMAND (M), the data representing the 20 possible demands during lead time from the first data card.

b) Read into the one-dimension subscripted variable, PROB(M), the data representing the 20 probabilities associated with these various possible demands.

c) Calculate, from the data in the array DEMAND(M) and the array PROB(M) (1) average or expected demand during lead time, EDDLT, and (2) a schedule of 20 expected stock-outs per lead time period, E(DDLT > R), corresponding to each of the demands in DE- MAND(M) viewed as reorder points. Cause the computer to store the schedule of the 20 expected stock-out quantities in the one-dimension subscripted variable, STKOUT(M).

Assume that five floating-point numbers, each occupying one field of 15 columns on one data card, constitute (respectively) the following data associated with an inventory system, reading the data card from left to right.

> Unit holding cost (UHC)
> Cost per unit (CPU)
> Cost per order processed (CPO)
> Demand per year (DPY)
> Stock-out cost per unit stock-out (STKCOS)

Compose a FORTRAN segment that will read these data and store them in the variable names shown above.

11–2. Tempo, Ltd., purchases, stocks, and uses—or resells—320,000 different items. A clerk keeps records concerning each of these items. These records contain the information required for punching the three data cards described in (*a*), Exercise 11–1.

A master inventory file consists of four cards on each of the 320,000 items. The first of the four cards contains only two data—one to identify the stock number of the item, the other to indicate whether any of the data in the remaining three cards (those described in [*a*], above) have changed, and hence whether the reorder policy bears review. The first data field on this card consists of the first column on this card. If the inventory policy applicable to the item demands review, the first field of the first card contains a 1. If the inventory policy applicable to the item does not require review, the first field of the first card contains a 0.

The second field of the first card consists of columns 11 through 30, and contains the stock number of the item to which the four cards apply, punched as an integer of 20 or fewer digits.

When the inventory clerk is provided with new data for updating the master file, she punches new cards where necessary, and thus prepares the master file for periodic review.

Write a FORTRAN program that will incorporate the essential ele- ments of the general inventory model of Figure 6–9, plus the three pro- gram segments called for in (*a*); that will serve to read, as input data, the complete master file of Tempo's inventory; and that will (on encountering a four-card group pertaining to an item that bears review) recalculate the optimum order quantity and optimum reorder point, and print out these data in association with the stock number of the item to which they pertain.

12. If one is to periodically review inventory policy, and if review involves reexamination of several thousand records, each requiring a search for the optimum Q, R combination, then computer time becomes a rather significant cost item.

If expected demand during lead time is in the range of several hundred units for a particular item carried in inventory, then our general model depicted in Figure 6–9 would not be efficient. It would almost certainly be better, under this condition, to initialize R and Q at some value greater than 1 and to increase them, as the search for Q and R is conducted, by an increment larger than 1.

Add to the general model of Figure 6–9 to cause the computer to inquire about the size of the expected demand during lead time, and to conduct a search involving *unit* increases in Q and R only after approximating optimum Q and optimum R through a *gross* search.

Suggestion:

a) If $1 \leqq$ EDDLT $<$ 100, initialize Q and R at 1 and increase by increments of 1.

b) If $100 \leqq$ EDDLT $<$ 1000, initialize Q and R at 10 and increase by increments of 10, then proceed as in (*a*) after $\hat{Q}$ and $\hat{R}$ have been grossly approximated.

c) If $1,000 \leqq$ EDDLT $<$ 10,000, initialize Q and R at 50 and increase by increments of 50, then proceed as in (*b*) after $\hat{Q}$ and $\hat{R}$ have been grossly approximated.

13. On the morning of November 1, Raintree County found that 116,472 hunters had applied for grouse licenses. As each application was received a number (starting with 1) was placed opposite the name of the applicant in a log book. The final applicant was given the number 116,472.

To protect the grouse population it has been decided to issue only 36,000 licenses. Compose a FORTRAN program that will select at random 36,000 applicants to whom licenses should be issued and will also print out the numbers (i.e., from 1 to 116,472 inclusive) assigned to those applicants.

14. Assume that Brown Electronics Company (Chapter 6) insists on a service level of 99.726 percent. That is, Brown Company does not want to lose more than 0.274 percent of its expected annual demand of 365 units because of stock-outs. What order quantity and reorder point combination will yield the lowest total annual inventory cost while maintaining a service level of 99.726 percent? How much added total annual inventory cost would Brown Company incur per year by insisting on maintaining a service level of **99.726** percent?

15. The commercial loan officer of the Mercantile Trust Bank follows the following procedure (in a somewhat deliberate fashion) in deciding whether to lend money to the bank's industrial customers, how much to lend, and at what interest rate.

If the client's ratio of current assets to current liabilities is **1.5** or higher, if his cash on hand is at least **9** percent of his total assets, and if his average profit during the past three years has been **12** percent or higher, then the loan officer will approve the loan (up to an amount equal to three times the client's current cash position) at a rate of interest equal to **3** percentage points higher than the current U.S. Treasury bond rate.

Use the following *input* data:

$$
\begin{aligned}
\text{CA} &= \text{client's current assets} \\
\text{CL} &= \text{client's current liabilities} \\
\text{TA} &= \text{client's total assets} \\
\text{CSH} &= \text{client's cash on hand (cash position)} \\
\text{P3} &= \text{client's profit three years ago} \\
\text{P2} &= \text{client's profit two years ago} \\
\text{P1} &= \text{client's profit last year} \\
\text{TR} &= \text{current U.S. Treasury bond rate}
\end{aligned}
$$

and write a FORTRAN program that will cause the computer to make the loan officer's future decisions for him and that will print out the amount of money any client may obtain and the interest rate he will have to pay.

16. On the X-Bar-X hog ranch the production of pork is stimulated by adding hormone-treated water to the hog swill. Each day 1 gallon of hormone-treated water is withdrawn from a 1,000-gallon tank and is added to the swill. Immediately after the 1 gallon of hormone-treated water is withdrawn, a faucet is turned on and a gallon of fresh water is added to fill the tank again.

On January 1 the hormone concentrate in the 1,000-gallon tank stands at 250 pounds per 1,000 gallons (i.e., there are 250 pounds of hormone concentrate dissolved in the 1,000 gallons of water).

When the level of hormone concentrate drops to 162 pounds per 1,000 gallons of water it becomes necessary to add more concentrate to increase the strength of the solution.

Write a FORTRAN program that will simulate this daily hormone diluting process and will print out the number of days that will elapse before additional hormone concentrate will have to be added.

17. We can compose computer programs that can cause the computer to study a collection of data and to pose and test a variety of hypotheses

about that data, thus doing much of the hackwork associated with quantitative data in research. A simple example will show how this is possible.

A data deck contains 100 cards, each of which has three integers
punched on it. The third integer bears some relationship to the first and
second intergers. Specifically, the third integer is either:

1. The product of the first and the second integers.
2. The sum of the first and the second integers.
3. The largest common denominator of the first and second integers
   (i.e., the largest integer that can be divided into *both* the first and
   the second integers a whole number of times).

One and only one of these three possible relationships is "operative" in
the full 100-card deck. However, at least two of the three relationships
could apply to some of the cards. Thus to the set:

First:	Second:	Third:
2	2	4

relationships (1) and (2) could apply. And to the set:

First:	Second:	Third:
−16	20	4

relationships (2) and (3) could apply.

A FORTRAN program is desired that will pose and test each of the
above relationships as a hypothesis, and will print out an answer to the
question: "Which of the three possible relationships is operative in the
full 100-card deck?"

Compose such a hypothesis-testing program. Assume that the statement READ (5,1) I,J,K will cause the first number on a data card to
be stored in the variable I, the second in the variable J, and the third in
the variable K.

18. In the Brown Electronics Company inventory problem, Model
6–5 gives the total annual cost associated with the inventory system described. We found in Chapter 6 that the optimum policy is:

$$R = 4 \text{ units}$$
$$Q = 13 \text{ units}$$

and that associated with this optimum policy is a total annual cost of
$1,534.

Assume that Brown's supplier refuses to ship less than 25 units in an
order. Assume that Brown orders the minimum order quantity. Should
Brown still employ a reorder point of $R = 4$? Compose a FORTRAN program that will cause the computer to provide the answer. Why might we
expect that an increase in the order quantity might make a lower reorder
point more appropriate? If Brown uses the reorder point that best com-

plements its minimum allowable order quantity of $Q = 25$, how much more added annual inventory cost can Brown expect as a consequence of the fact that orders less than $Q = 25$ will not be accepted?

19.   Suppose that the last order Brown fills reduces the stock level to two units (two units below the desired reorder point of $R = 4$). Clearly during the current lead time period $R = 2$ rather than 4. Should Brown order $Q = 13$ units or some other amount assuming now that the supplier will fill an order of any size? Compose a FORTRAN program that will determine the answer. Why might we have expected that an order quantity other than $Q = 13$ would best complement a reorder point of $R = 2$?

chapter 7

Systems Modeling
via Flow Graph

A SYSTEM is a group of interacting components. Components interact in a number of different ways. Random variables demand and lead time interact in an inventory system to produce demand during lead time. In a multiple warehouse inventory system random demands on the various warehouses interact in a different way to produce the random demand on the total system. In a queue system random time between arrivals interacts with random service time—in still a different way—to produce a fluctuating queue.

The interaction of time related functions, such as those mentioned above, can be thought of and usefully modeled in an "input-output" fashion. This seems quite natural to us in the queue system: arriving customers enter a facility, are operated on in some way, and are then output. It seems less natural to think of demand or lead time as an input, with their interaction "demand during lead time" being the output.

In this chapter we will discover the value of modeling the interaction of system components in this way. The flavor of this modeling method is easily seen in the example which follows.

Smith deposits $1 at the end of year 0 (beginning of year 1) at 10 percent compounded annually, and deposits nothing thereafter. In *flow graph theory* Smith perturbed a system with a *unit impulse* —an input of 1, at time 0, and nothing thereafter.

The bank's "compounding system" then operates on Smith's unit impulse input to produce the following output stream: $1,1.10,1.21, 1.33, . . . The question might occur to us: How would a system which gave this response to a unit impulse input respond if Smith deposited \$1 the first year, \$2 the second, \$4 the third, etc.?

In this chapter we will see that another way to pose this question is: How does the time function: 1,1.10,1.21,1.33, . . . *convolve* with the time function: 1,2,4,8,16, . . . ? And still another way we will pose this question is: How does the *system* 1,1.10,1,21,1.33, . . . interact with the *system* 1,2,4,8,16, . . . ?

We will see that such systems can be modeled via a system of difference equations, and that for each such system of difference equations there can be constructed an equivalent flow graph. Thus output g_n is produced by summing inputs f_n and h_n: $g_n = f_n + h_n$, which in flow graph form is:

$$\text{input} \rightarrow \quad \begin{matrix} f_n \searrow \\ \\ h_n \nearrow \end{matrix} \quad \circ \rightarrow\!\!-\ g_n \rightarrow \text{output}$$

In a different system output g_n is produced by summing g_{n-1} and f_n:

$$\underbrace{g_n = g_{n-1} + f_n,}_{(A)}$$

which in flow graph form is:

$$f_n \rightarrow\!\!-\!\circ \underset{Z}{\overset{1}{\frown}} \circ\!\!-\!\!\rightarrow g_n$$

We will see further that if f_n, in equation A above, is:

$$f_n = k_n + j_n \qquad\qquad (B)$$

. . . in which input f_n in equation A is output f_n in equation B, that is:

$$\underbrace{\begin{matrix} k_n \searrow \\ \\ j_n \nearrow \end{matrix} \circ\!\!-\!\!\rightarrow f_n}_{(B)} \quad\longrightarrow\quad \underbrace{\circ \underset{Z}{\overset{1}{\frown}} \circ\!\!-\!\!\rightarrow g_n}_{(A)} \qquad (C)$$

. . . then system A and system B *convolve* with each other to produce system C, in the same sense that Smith's investment stream convolves with the bank's interesting compounding system.

Thus whereas each equation in a system of difference equations portrays relationships between a subset of the components in the total system, the flow graph ties the components together to create a unified model of the total system. Finally, by the application of rules germane to flow graph theory the behavior of the total system can be studied and predicted by analysis of the flow graph model.

Some conversancy with these topics will give us a new perspective toward the systems we have examined thus far. It will also acquaint us with some rather sophisticated concepts in systems analysis which are relevant to topics we will examine in subsequent chapters, including queueing systems, PERT network analysis, exponential smoothing in forecasting and matrix methods in systems modeling.

Steps in the Modeling of Systems

The modeling of complex systems commonly proceeds in the following fashion:

1. The components of the system are identified.
2. Each component is then further divided into subcomponents until a level of simplicity is reached such that tools at our disposal can be employed to model the subcomponents with a high degree of specificity.
3. The subcomponents are then related to each other or *interfaced* in a *network* of subsystems which is representative of their interaction as perceived in the real world.
4. The network of components (subsystems) is then reduced, by combining components, to one equivalent system which lends itself more readily to behavioral analysis and control.

In the third step the analyst endeavors to adopt the *total system viewpoint,* momentarily losing sight of the inner workings of the subsystems. His attention is focused on the input each subsystem accepts and the output it produces. In a schematic context the subsystems are "black boxes" whose contents are of no immediate concern. Depending on the stage of analysis a black box might house operations of a very complex sort. On the other hand its operation may be extremely simple—representative of the most elemental system.

The steps in systems analysis, above, and the black box orientation are apparent in the function of the systems engineer or perhaps the project director who's purpose is to relate physical components in a hardware system or projects in a complex of activities.

Black boxes are thus the building blocks of systems.

Systems as Operators

A *model* of a real world system, we argue, is itself a *system*, a collection of interacting components. Each component is also a system. We will want to address ourselves shortly to the *most elemental system* . . . a concept of considerable importance. First, however, let us consider what we mean by a system being an operator.

It is useful to think of a system as an operator, operating on a string of input elements to produce a string of output elements. Consider, for example, that resource-consuming, health-producing system we call a hospital. From the viewpoint of its administrator inputs include patients with a variety of needs, medicinal materials, man-hours of skills (medical, surgical, custodial, and so on), and its outputs include serviced patients, bills to individuals and health insurors, purchase orders for replenishment supplies, additions to medical history records, and so forth.

In the four-step procedure for studying systems, set forth above, in step 2 we subdivide components in search of more elemental components, each sufficiently simple that we can design "primitive operators" to represent them.

Consider our approach to the retailer's inventory system in Chapter 5. We began by modeling the holding cost operator (system).

FIGURE 7–1

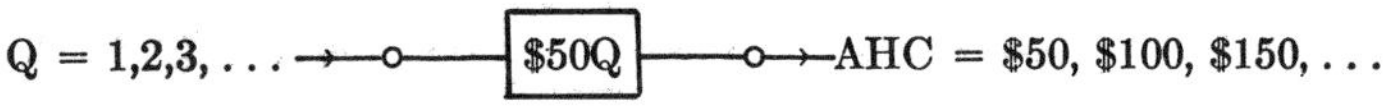

Q = 1,2,3, . . . →—o——| $50Q |——o→AHC = $50, $100, $150, . . .

The operator "$50Q" operates on the input string Q (order quantity) to produce the output string AHC (annual holding cost).

We then modeled the annual ordering cost operator.

FIGURE 7–2

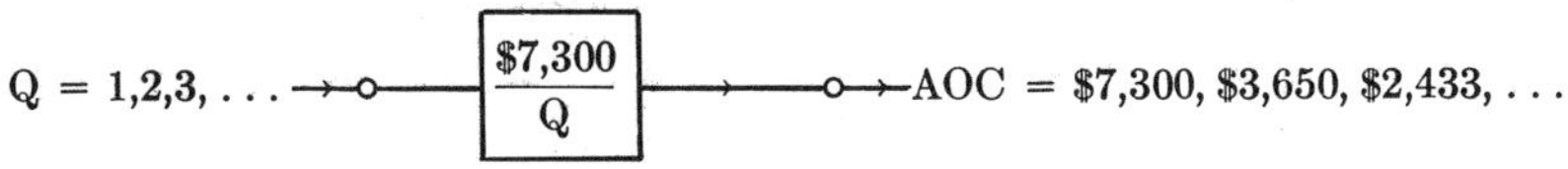

$$Q = 1,2,3, \ldots \to o \quad \frac{\$7,300}{Q} \quad \to o \to AOC = \$7,300, \$3,650, \$2,433, \ldots$$

We then connected (interfaced) these component systems to produce the larger system whose output is total annual cost.

FIGURE 7–3

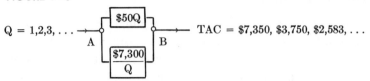

The schematic above has the following meaning: At point A send the input to each of the two systems and at point B combine their outputs (form their sum) to produce TAC.

Having interfaced the components we then combined them (step 4) to form the equivalent system shown in Figure 7–4.

FIGURE 7–4

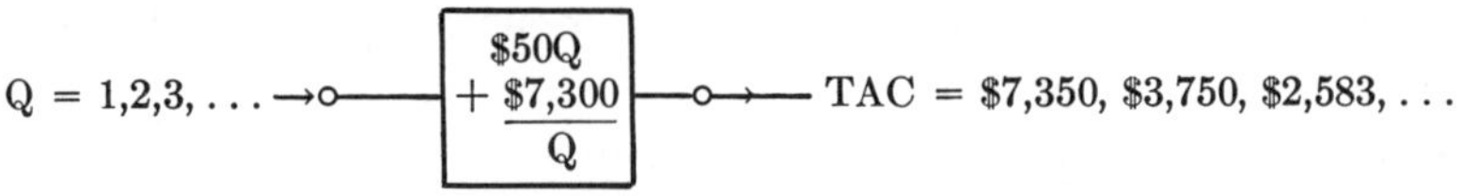

$$Q = 1,2,3, \ldots \rightarrow\!\!\!\circ\!\!-\!\!\boxed{\frac{\$50Q}{Q} + \$7,300}\!\!-\!\!\circ\!\!\rightarrow\!\!- \text{TAC} = \$7,350, \$3,750, \$2,583, \ldots$$

Combining components was easy in this case because:

1. The input signal was deterministic.
2. The operators, being simple algebraic expressions, were easily combined by addition.
3. Neither of the component systems which we combined exhibited delay or feedback—the complexity of which will become apparent shortly.

Note that we followed the same *four-step procedure* in the inventory system of Chapter 6, but there are important differences. (See Figure 7–5.)

FIGURE 7–5

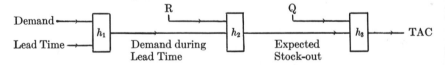

It should be apparent that the operators in the schematic of Figure 7–5 are not simple algebraic functions. In system h_1 random variable "daily demand" and random variable "lead time" are operated on to produce "demand during lead time." The operation is not a simple algebraic function. Also the nature of the *interface* between the components is more involved than with the retailer's model. The consequence is that combining components h_1, h_2, and h_3 to produce the system shown in Figure 7–6 is rather involved.

FIGURE 7–6

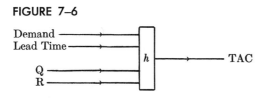

In fact we *did* combine components h_1, h_2, and h_3 in Chapter 6 (see Figure 6–9), but in Figure 7–6 we did not succeed in expressing operator h as a simple algebraic expression.

Time-Related Functions

We commonly speak of functions as "mapping functions." Thus the function πr^2 "maps" radii (the arguments) into areas. In the diagram below a set of five radii are mapped into a set of five areas.

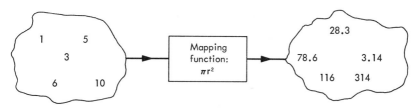

Time-related functions may be thought of as mapping functions also. However in employing time-related functions we generally increment the argument, unit at a time, from time 0, and lay the output string out correspondingly. We do this because we are interested in the behavior *through time* of the system being modeled. In the system which follows we have made the time dimension of input function f and output function g more fully apparent.

$$f(n) = 2,3,1,7, \ldots \quad n = 0,1,2,3, \ldots$$

$$\boxed{\begin{array}{c} h: \\ x \quad 3 \end{array}}$$

$$g(n) = 6,9,3,21, \ldots \quad n = 0,1,2,3,4, \ldots$$

We frequently find it profitable to increment, unit at a time, the arguments of functions which are *not* time related, as we did in the system of Figure 7–4, searching for the optimum argument. It should be observed, however, that the input function in that case was not time related.

The *real world systems* of which Figures 7–1 through 7–5 are models *are* time-related systems. Shipments are received through time, units are withdrawn, and inventory levels fluctuate. However, we did not model the time dimension explicitly in the models of Figures 7–1 through 7–5. The inputs and the outputs in these *models* were not functions of time. By avoiding the time dimension we were able to model the components in the system to achieve our purpose with reliance on simple algebraic operations.

Avoiding explicit deference to the time dimension is not always so easy. When components in a system exhibit *delay* or *feedback* more sophisticated means are required if the components are to be combined by simple algebraic operations.

Delay and feedback in a very *simple* system are easily modeled, however, and we would do well to explore them in some detail in a schematic context.

The Delay Operator

Consider the system shown in Figure 7–7.

FIGURE 7–7

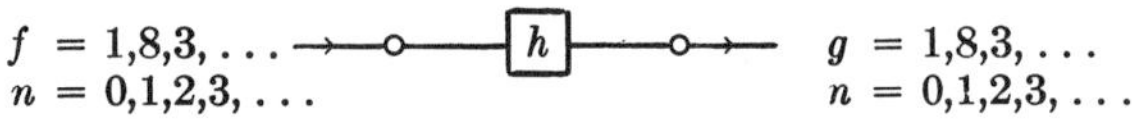

$$f = 1,8,3,\ldots \rightarrow\!-\!o\!-\!\boxed{h}\!-\!o\!\rightarrow\!- \quad g = 1,8,3,\ldots$$
$$n = 0,1,2,3,\ldots \qquad\qquad\qquad\qquad n = 0,1,2,3,\ldots$$

Notice that operator h in 7–7 does not change the input but merely transmits it to the output. Such an operator is sometimes called an identity operator and correspondents to the unit matrix in matrix algebra.

Now consider the system portrayed in Figure 7–8.

FIGURE 7–8

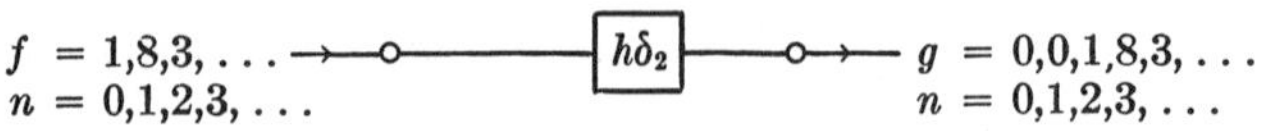

$$f = 1,8,3,\ldots \rightarrow\!-\!o\!-\!\boxed{h\delta_2}\!-\!o\!\rightarrow\!- \quad g = 0,0,1,8,3,\ldots$$
$$n = 0,1,2,3,\ldots \qquad\qquad\qquad\qquad n = 0,1,2,3,\ldots$$

In the system of Figure 7–8 operator h is a delay operator, delaying input function f by two periods. Delay in a system can be represented in a number of ways. In a difference equation a delay (a time shift) is indicated by subscripts. Thus $S_{n+1} = S_n(1 + .10)$ indicates that to produce output S_{n+1} we multiply input S_n by 1.10 and delay it one period.

In flow graph modeling it is common to indicate a delay of k periods by the symbol δ_k, called "del sub k." Thus $h\delta_2$ means that h delays f by two periods, as shown in Figure 7–8. We might also represent the relation between f, h, and g—as it is implied by the schematic of Figure 7–8—as follows:

$$g = F(h,f) \qquad \ldots \text{"g is a function of h and f"}$$

specifically:

$$g = f\delta_2 \qquad \ldots \text{"g is f delayed two periods"}$$

or:

$$g(n) = f(n - 2) \qquad \text{``}$$

Most time-related systems contain one or more delay operators. In the system portrayed in Figure 7–9, $f(n)$ is the demand on an inventory system.

FIGURE 7–9

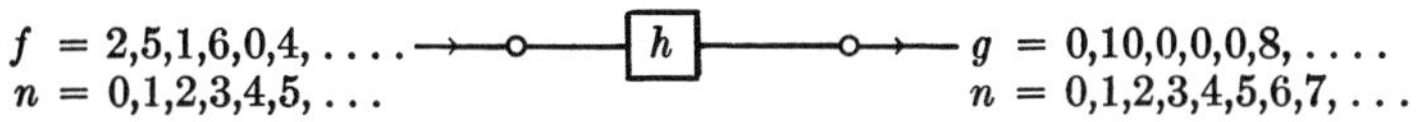

$f = 2,5,1,6,0,4, \ldots$
$n = 0,1,2,3,4,5, \ldots$

$g = 0,10,0,0,0,8, \ldots$
$n = 0,1,2,3,4,5,6,7, \ldots$

System h operates on f to produce replenishment orders. In the second and the sixth time periods orders are placed for 10 and 8 units, respectively. Operator h, in addition to other things, is a delay operator.

The Unit Impulse

The *unit impulse* is a special *input* string which consists of a 1 at time 0 followed by zeroes thereafter:

$$\text{Unit impulse} = 1,0,0,0, \ldots$$
$$n = 0,1,2,3, \ldots$$

With a bit of ingenuity we can design an operator which will transform the unit impulse into *any* (nonrandom) output string. Thus while the unit impulse specifies the behavior of perhaps the

simplest system, among dynamic systems, in a sense it is the ultimate *driver* of all systems.[1]

Feedback Operator

Consider the system portrayed in Figure 7–10.

FIGURE 7–10

A Simple Feedback System

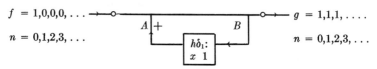

$f = 1,0,0,0, \ldots$

$n = 0,1,2,3, \ldots$

$g = 1,1,1, \ldots$

$n = 0,1,2,3, \ldots$

System 7–10 has a *feedback loop*. In period 0 a unit is input from
f and transmitted without change to the output at g. However, at B,
through suitable "instrumentation," the output is measured, tapped
off and sent to the box in the feedback loop. There, it is: (*a*) multiplied by 1, and (*b*) delayed one time period. In the next period
the quantity fed back (and delayed) is added to the next input at
A to produce output g in period one.

Note that the feedback loop is itself a simple system—accepting
input at B and producing output at A. Note also that output g is a
"unit step function," rising from 0—for all time periods prior to
time 0—and persisting at 1 from period 0 to infinity.

Elemental Systems

We will call a system such as that in Figure 7–11 an *elemental system*. The elemental system is the basic component in flow graph

---

[1] Cybernetics—the science of communication and control—has generally been
identified as the science of *self-regulating* systems. In their models, theoreticians
have emphasized deviation-*countering* feedback, which promotes stability and equilibrium.

In recent years, however, more attention has been given to deviation-*amplifying*
feedback in systems. Some theories of economic development, for example, assume
that with a suitable "kick" in the right direction an underdeveloped economy can
break out of a vicious cycle of poverty; that an injection of capital, properly directed, will be amplified through positive feedback.

We see many examples in which a kick is amplified. An investment of $1 at time
zero produces an amplifying effect which continues. A tractor crossing the tundra
in the Arctic is such a kick. The slight scar it leaves exposes the permafrost which
was previously insulated from the warming rays of the sun. Within a few years
a modest scar becomes a small canyon. The invention of television was a kick whose
repercussions continue.

modeling. In theory any system, however complex, can be subdivided into elemental systems. In many elemental systems h_1 or h_2 may perform no function: either (but not both) may be a product operator with value 0. Thus the systems in Figures 7–10 and 7–8 may be considered elemental systems.

FIGURE 7–11

An Elemental System

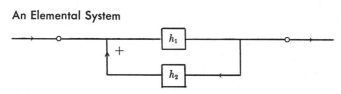

In our effort to deal with complex problems we commonly endeavor to find fundamental elements in the larger problem which we *can* deal with and then to relate "solutions" for the fundamental elements to the solution of the larger problem. We look for fundamental building blocks whose behavior in isolation can be understood; and then we look for ways to synthesize the building blocks.

In systems theory the elemental system is such a building block.

The Impulse Response

Next consider the system in Figure 7–12.

FIGURE 7–12

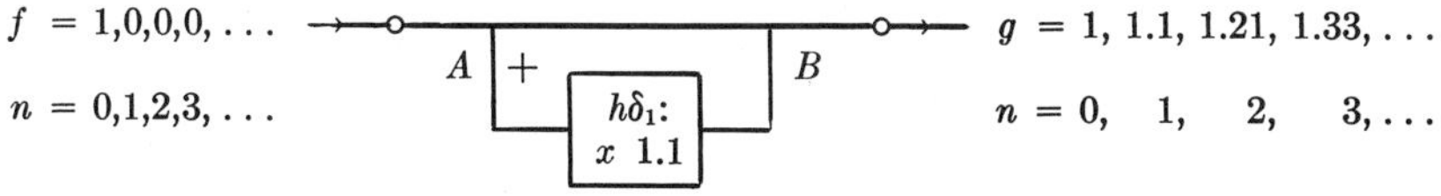

$$f = 1,0,0,0, \ldots$$
$$n = 0,1,2,3, \ldots$$

A + $\quad$ $h\delta_1:$ $\quad$ x 1.1 $\quad$ B

$$g = 1, 1.1, 1.21, 1.33, \ldots$$
$$n = 0, \quad 1, \quad 2, \quad 3, \ldots$$

The feedback loop in Figure 7–12 adds 10 percent to the output g, delays the result one period, then adds the result to the next element input from f.

A system's impulse response is the output function which that system produces when it is subjected to a unit impulse input. The output string g, in Figure 7–12, is that system's impulse response. Unit step function g is the impulse response for the system in Figure 7–10.

Frequently we can express a system's impulse response in *closed form,* as a function of time. For example, in the system of Figure 7–12 we have:

$$\text{Impulse response} = (1 + .10)^n$$

It is apparent that the system in Figure 7–12 is an interest compounding system with an interest rate of 10 percent.

When we refer to a string (vector) of elements in a time function we will use a letter unsubscripted; thus: $f = 1,0,0, \ldots$; $g = 1,1.1,1.21,1.33, \ldots$. When we represent that same function in closed form we will subscript the function's name; thus $g(n) = (1 + .10)^n$. Strictly speaking g refers to the string and $g(n)$ refers to the nth element in that string.

(*Note:* In the past, when we've spoken of the compound interest model we always represented the time dimension, n, as a subscript: S_n; S_{n+1}; and so on. It is frequently convenient to represent the time element as we have in this chapter, with n appearing as an argument: $f(n)$, rather than f_n; and $g(n)$ rather than g_n. We will have occasion to use the same letter to represent several operators, in an elemental system, and we want to avoid double subscripts. It should be recognized that in the time context the two systems of notation are interchangeable.)

"Specifying" a System

There are many ways we might *specify* a system; i.e.: to differentiate it from other systems; to describe its unique behavior. One way is by specifying its impulse response. It can be shown that for that special class of systems called *linear systems* any system can be uniquely specified by its impulse response—its response to the unit impulse input.

It can also be shown that once we know a system's impulse response we can predict its response to any input function by *convolving:* (1) the input function in question, with (2) the system's impulse response function.

Thus Smith deposits $1 at 10 percent compounded annually in year 0 (at the beginning of year 1), $2 in year 1, $4 in year 2, $8 in year 3, and so forth. Smith's input function in closed form is: $f(n) = \$2^n$. Figure 7–13 portrays the nature of Smith's investment system:

FIGURE 7–13

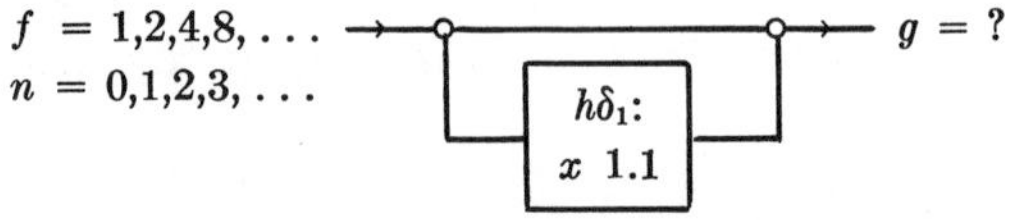

$f = 1,2,4,8, \ldots$

$n = 0,1,2,3, \ldots$

$h\delta_1:$

$x\ 1.1$

$g = ?$

The output string which is the value of Smith's investment in successive years is a function of two things: (1) The impulse response function for the system of 7–13; and (2) The input function which is Smith's successive annual deposits: $\$2^n$.

These two functions interact or *convolve* with one another to produce the output. Convolution is not a simple algebraic operation like division or exponentiation. We want to understand it in order that we might learn how to reduce complex systems, through combining their components, to simple systems, even when delay and feedback are attributes of their components. The methods we will employ are restricted to linear systems and we should begin by identifying a linear system.

Linear Systems

We will continue to concern ourselves only with discrete, time-related systems, although what we say has some applicability to continuous systems.

We have spoken of system inputs and outputs as "strings." We will sometimes use the terms "signal" and "vector" to mean the same thing. Thus "input signal or vector f" and "input string f" mean the same.

A system is linear if the output of the system, when subjected to the sum of any two input signals, is the sum of the outputs when each is input separately. Imagine f_1 and f_2 to be input vectors whose corresponding output vectors are g_1 and g_2 respectively. The system is a linear system if inputting $af_1 + bf_2$ yields output vector $ag_1 + bg_2$, where a and b are constant weights.

Figure 7–14 illustrates linear system operator h.

FIGURE 7–14

Linearity in a System

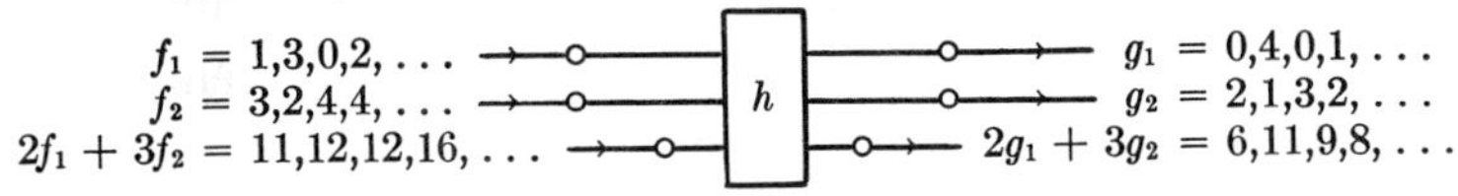

$$f_1 = 1,3,0,2,\ldots \quad \xrightarrow{\quad} \quad \boxed{h} \quad \xrightarrow{\quad} \quad g_1 = 0,4,0,1,\ldots$$
$$f_2 = 3,2,4,4,\ldots$$
$$g_2 = 2,1,3,2,\ldots$$
$$2f_1 + 3f_2 = 11,12,12,16,\ldots \qquad 2g_1 + 3g_2 = 6,11,9,8,\ldots$$

Most real world systems are not linear, but many can be approximated by linear system models. The physical scientist assumes "frictionless pulleys" and "weightless rope" to simplify the modeling process. The system theorist assumes linearity for the same reason.

We will simplify further by concerning ourselves only with *time invariant* systems. A system is time invariant if delaying the introduction of input vector f by, say, k time periods, serves only to delay each and every element of the output vector g by k periods, as in Figure 7–15

FIGURE 7–15

Time Invariance in a System

$f_1 = 2,4,7, \ldots$ ——◦———   ◦—— $g_1 = 3,10,7, \ldots$
$f_2 = 0,0,0,2,4,7, \ldots$ ——◦——| h |—◦—— $g_2 = 0,0,0,3,10,7, \ldots$

In a particular inventory system replenishment orders are placed when the stock level drops to $R = 1{,}400$ units. However, orders are never placed during the last 10 days of the month. This system is NOT time invariant. We are concerned with linear, time invariant discrete systems only. Our field of discourse, however, is not of purely theoretical interest. Many real world systems can be assumed to be linear and time invariant except where capacities are exceeded. As a consequence the model structure we are developing, based on the elemental system, has applied value.

System Operator h as the System's Impulse Response

In past examples of systems we have specified a system operator, h, as a product function, operating on each element of the input (and perhaps delaying it) to produce the output. However, we have argued that any system can be uniquely specified by its impulse response. We have also argued that any system's response to a particular input can be determined by convolving the input function with the system's impulse response function. *The operator, therefore, is the system's impulse response function!* Since the impulse response function is a discrete function of time, h will be such a function. Therefore we might better portray the system of Figure 7–12 as it is shown in Figure 7–16(a).

FIGURE 7–16

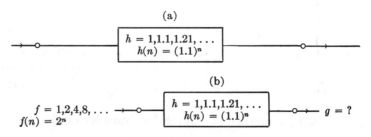

(a)

——◦————————| $h = 1,1.1,1.21, \ldots$ |————————◦——
                | $h(n) = (1.1)^n$ |

(b)

$f = 1,2,4,8, \ldots$ ——◦——| $h = 1,1.1,1.21, \ldots$ |—◦—— $g = ?$
$f(n) = 2^n$ | $h(n) = (1.1)^n$ |

Note that operator h, in system 7–16, incorporates the effect of the feedback loop, although that loop is not shown in the figure.

The Convolution Sum

The term *convolution* suggests *interaction*. At the beginning of the chapter we suggested that two time functions may interact in a number of ways. Daily demand and lead time interact in an inventory system to produce demand during lead time. Random time between arrivals in a queue system interacts with random service time to produce a fluctuating queue.

Figure 7–16(b) illustrates a third kind of interaction between time functions. We will reserve the term *convolution* for this type of interaction. In Figure 7–16(b) impulse response function h convolves with input function f to produce output g. In closed form, $(1.1)^n$ convolves with 2^n to produce $g(n)$.

To make the nature of the interaction more apparent, let's assume that Smith opens a *new* account each year. At the end of year 0 (the beginning of year 1) he deposits $1 in the first account. At the end of year 1 he deposits $2 in the second account. At the end of year 2 he deposits $4 in the third account; and so on. Smith's investment system is properly portrayed by the system in Figure 7–16(b), where output vector $g(n)$ is the value of Smith's various accounts collectively, at the end of year n, $n = 0,1,2,3, \ldots$.

Each row in Table 7–1 shows the value in succeeding years of *one* of Smith's accounts.

TABLE 7–1

End of year number →	0	1	2	3
Account number 1	$(1.1)^0$	$(1.1)^1$	$(1.1)^2$	$(1.1)^3 \ldots$
" " 2	0	$2(1.1)^0$	$2(1.1)^1$	$2(1.1)^2 \ldots$
" " 3	0	0	$4(1.1)^0$	$4(1.1)^1 \ldots$
" " 4	0	0	0	$8(1.1)^0 \ldots$
.	.	.	.	.
.	.	.	.	.
.	.	.	.	.

To determine Smith's total holdings in a particular year, say at the end of year 3, we sum the balances in the various accounts, rather arbitrarily starting with the newest account:

$$8(1.1)^0 + 4(1.1)^1 + 2(1.1)^2 + (1.1)^3 = 16.15$$

. . . which is the vector product (the "inner product"):

$$[(1.1)^0 \quad (1.1)^1 \quad (1.1)^2 \quad (1.1)^3] \begin{bmatrix} 8 \\ 4 \\ 2 \\ 1 \end{bmatrix} = 16.15.$$

To determine $g(n)$, the value of Smith's total in any year, n, we form the vector product:

$$g(n) = [(1.1)^0 \quad (1.1)^1 \quad (1.1)^2 \ldots (1.1)^n] \begin{bmatrix} 2^n \\ 2^{n-1} \\ 2^{n-2} \\ \cdot \\ \cdot \\ \cdot \\ 2^0 \end{bmatrix} \qquad \text{(7-1)}$$

Vector product (**7–1**) is an example of the convolution sum. By giving n the appropriate value we can determine the nth element of $g(n)$ from (**7–1**). Applying (**7–1**) sequentially from $n = 0$ we produce:

$$g = \$1, \quad 3.1, \quad 7.41, \quad 16.15, \ldots$$
$$n = 0, \quad 1, \quad 2, \quad 3, \quad \ldots$$

We will examine another example of the convolution sum operation. Consider the system in Figure 7–17.

FIGURE 7–17

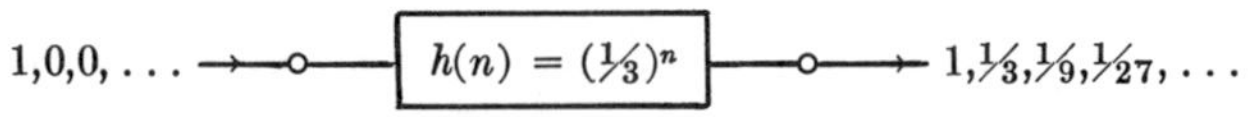

$1,0,0,\ldots \longrightarrow \!\!-\!\!\circ\!\!-\!\!\boxed{h(n) = (\tfrac{1}{3})^n}\!\!-\!\!\circ\!\!-\!\!\longrightarrow 1,\tfrac{1}{3},\tfrac{1}{9},\tfrac{1}{27},\ldots$

The impulse response function for this system is shown both as an infinite string (the output) and is shown in the box in closed form. Suppose that we want to determine the response of this system to the following input: $1,1/2,1/4,1/8, \ldots = (1/2)^n$. We want to determine the output function g, in the system of Figure 7–18.

FIGURE 7–18

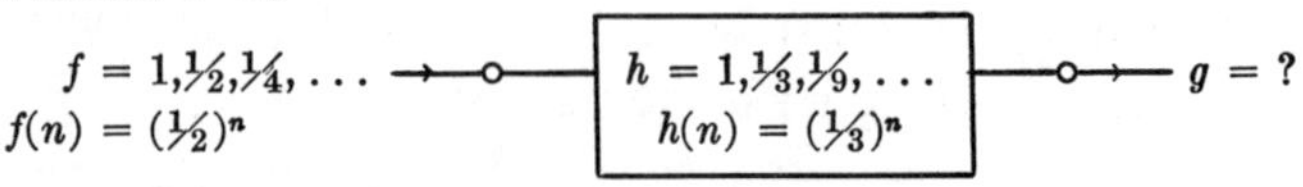

$f = 1,\tfrac{1}{2},\tfrac{1}{4},\ldots \longrightarrow \!\!-\!\!\circ\!\!-\!\!\boxed{\begin{array}{c} h = 1,\tfrac{1}{3},\tfrac{1}{9},\ldots \\ h(n) = (\tfrac{1}{3})^n \end{array}}\!\!-\!\!\circ\!\!-\!\!\longrightarrow g = ?$
$f(n) = (\tfrac{1}{2})^n$

To determine output g, the convolution of f and h, we give n the values $0,1,2,3, \ldots$ and evaluate for each value of n the following convolution sum:

$$g(n) = \left[(\tfrac{1}{2})^0 \quad (\tfrac{1}{2})^1 \quad (\tfrac{1}{2})^2 \ldots (\tfrac{1}{2})^n\right] \begin{bmatrix} (\tfrac{1}{3})^n \\ (\tfrac{1}{3})^{n-1} \\ (\tfrac{1}{3})^{n-2} \\ \cdot \\ \cdot \\ \cdot \\ (\tfrac{1}{3})^0 \end{bmatrix}$$

Doing so produces the output below (shown also in closed form):

$$g = 1, \quad {}^5\!/_6, \quad {}^{19}\!/_{36}, \quad {}^{65}\!/_{216}, \ldots; \quad g(n) = 3(\tfrac{1}{2})^n - 2(\tfrac{1}{3})^n$$
$$n = 0, \quad 1, \quad 2, \quad 3, \quad \ldots$$

Another format in which to calculate the output vector is shown below. The elements in the two vectors being convolved are arrayed

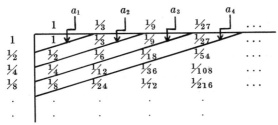

along the top and the side of the table. To produce the elements in the first column of the table we form the product of: (1) the first element of the vector along the top; and (2) each element of the vector along the left side. To produce the elements in the second column we form the product of: (1) the second element of the vector along the top, and (2) each element of the vector along the left side; and so on. The first element of the vector which is their convolution is the element in the diagonal labeled a_1. The second element of the convolution vector in the *sum* of the elements in the diagonal labeled a_2; and so forth.

For conciseness we might represent the convolution sum operation as follows:

$$g(n) = f(n) \mathbin{\#} h(n) \tag{7-3}$$

. . . where $g(n)$ is the nth element of output g, and is produced by performing the convolution sum operation on input f and impulse response function h. (*Note:* In most discussions of the convolution sum operation the asterisk is employed rather than the symbol "#." However, since the asterisk means multiply in FORTRAN we will use "#" to avoid confusion.)

The Input as an Impulse Response Function

Thus far we have considered h to be the impulse response function which specifies a system. And we have considered f to be an input to that system. To determine the nth element of the output we form the convolution sum $f(n) \# h(n)$. But it should be apparent that f must be the output of *some* system. And with a bit of effort we could surely design that system so that f is in fact its impulse response. Viewed in this fashion the convolution sum is a way of determining the interaction of two systems; that is, to determine the nature (the output) of the interaction of two systems *we convolve their impulse response functions.*

Convolution as System Reduction

Clearly in convolving two systems we reduce them to an equivalent single system. Thus we convolved f and h to produce g. The system reduction which resulted from their convolution is made apparent in Figure 7–19: systems (a) and (b) are equivalent.

FIGURE 7–19

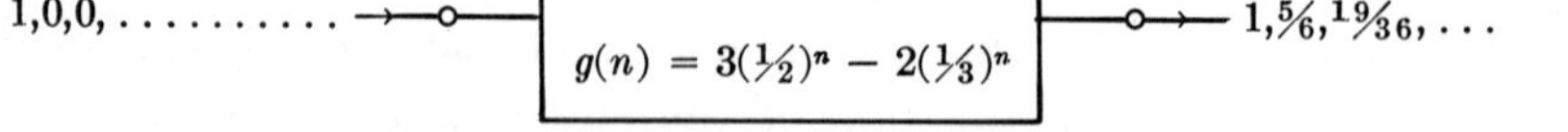

(a)

$1,0,0,\ldots \rightarrow\!\!-\!\!o\!-\!$ | $f = 1,\frac{1}{2},\frac{1}{4},\ldots$
 $f(n) = (\frac{1}{2})^n$ | $-\!o\!-\!$ | $h = 1,\frac{1}{3},\frac{1}{9},\ldots$
 $h(n) = (\frac{1}{3})^n$ | $-\!o\!\rightarrow$ $g = 1,\frac{5}{6},\frac{19}{36}$
 $g(n) = 3(\frac{1}{2})^n$
 $- 2(\frac{1}{3})^n$

(b)

$1,0,0,\ldots\ldots\ldots \rightarrow\!\!-\!\!o\!-\!$ | $g = 1,\frac{5}{6},\frac{19}{36},\ldots$
 $g(n) = 3(\frac{1}{2})^n - 2(\frac{1}{3})^n$ | $-\!o\!-\!$ $1,\frac{5}{6},\frac{19}{36},\ldots$

It should also be evident that we would have achieved the same output in Figure 7–19 if h had been considered the input and f the system's impulse response function (as suggested in Figure 7–20).

FIGURE 7–20

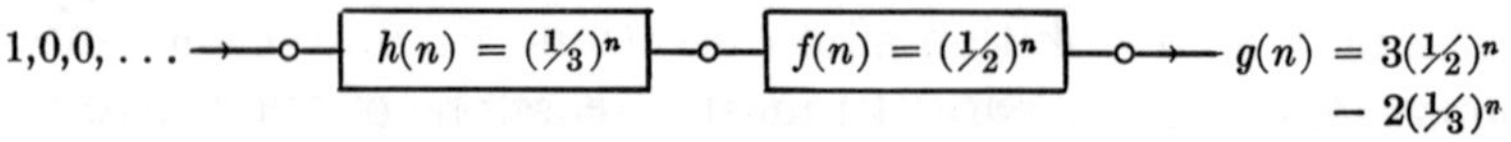

$1,0,0,\ldots \rightarrow\!\!-\!\!o\!-\!$ | $h(n) = (\frac{1}{3})^n$ | $-\!o\!-\!$ | $f(n) = (\frac{1}{2})^n$ | $-\!o\!\rightarrow$ $g(n) = 3(\frac{1}{2})^n$
 $- 2(\frac{1}{3})^n$

By portraying two systems schematically *in series* as in Figure 7–19(a) we really mean to specify that the two convolve with one another. Thus Figure 7–12 portrays the convolution between a unit impulse function and the function $(1.1)^n$. The nth element of their interaction (output) is determined by the convolution sum operation.

By employing the convolution sum operation we can reduce a system of many components into an equivalent system with one impulse response function. By this means the larger system can be modeled in a more tractable fashion.

In many systems analyses performing the convolution sum operation to determine the interaction of components is quite appropriate. A computer program can easily be written to do it. However, there are times when performing the convolution sum is awkward. Another approach to system synthesis (and to analysis) involves the Z transform.

The Z Transform

Imagine that we were confronted with the problem: evaluate the function $3.29^{2.6} \times 62.9 \times .08^{-.4}$, and while we dislike exponentiating we do not object to multiplication and addition. If we had a table of logarithms we could achieve our purpose by shifting into the "logarithm domain" to evaluate the function. We would write: $2.6\mathrm{Ln}3.29 + \mathrm{Ln}62.9 - .4\mathrm{Ln}\,.08$. Performing the operations called for (no exponentiation) we could then use our log table again to find the anti-log of the result and thus obtain our answer.

The Z transform is a transformation also. To shift into the logarithm domain we replaced a function by its logarithm. To shift into the transform domain we replace a discrete, time function by its Z transform.

In order to determine the interaction of two discrete time functions in the TIME DOMAIN we are obliged to perform the convolution sum operation which, as we stated, is sometimes awkward. If we shift into the TRANSFORM DOMAIN we can employ ordinary multiplication to determine the interaction of two discrete time functions. To do this we replace input function f by its transform, which we will label f^T, and we replace the system's impulse response function by its transform, h^T. The transform of the output, function, g^T, is then the simple product of f^T and h^T. (See Figure 7–21.)[2]

---

[2] We must remember, of course, that T, in f^T, is *not* an exponent.

FIGURE 7–21

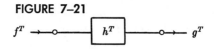

. . . and:

$$g^T = f^T \cdot h^T \tag{7-4}$$

Operator h^T is a product operator rather than a convolution sum operator. To obtain $g(n)$, the output, we find the "inverse transform" of g^T—that is, we return from the transform domain to the time domain.

Producing the Z Transform of a Function

Given a vector whose elements are the values of a discrete, time function for time periods 0 through infinity, to form the function's transform we multiply the elements in the vector by increasing powers of Z, and then form the sum of the products. Thus, given the unit step function:

. . . that is, the function:

$$f_1 = 1,1,1,\ldots$$
$$n = 0,1,2,3,\ldots$$

. . . to form its transform we multiply successive terms in vector f_1^T by increasing powers of Z and form their sum:

$$f_1^T = 1 \cdot Z^0 + 1 \cdot Z^1 + 1 \cdot Z^2 + 1 \cdot Z^3 + \ldots$$
$$= 1 + Z + Z^2 + Z^3 + \ldots$$

Note again that we have designated the transform of f as f^T. In fact, since f^T is a function of Z we might express the transform of $f(n)$ as follows:

$$\text{Transform of } f(n) = f^T(Z). \tag{7-5}$$

We might express this product-summation operation as the following vector product:

$$
\begin{bmatrix} 1 & 1 & 1 \dots \end{bmatrix}
\begin{bmatrix} Z^0 \\ Z^1 \\ Z^2 \\ \cdot \\ \cdot \\ \cdot \end{bmatrix}. \qquad (7\text{–}6)
$$

To form the transform of a *unit ramp function:*

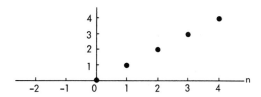

. . . that is, the function:

$$
f_2(n) = 0,1,2,3, \dots
$$
$$
n = 0,1,2,3, \dots
$$

. . . we form the product:

$$
\begin{bmatrix} 0 & 1 & 2 & 3 \dots \end{bmatrix}
\begin{bmatrix} Z^0 \\ Z^1 \\ Z^2 \\ \cdot \\ \cdot \\ \cdot \end{bmatrix}. \qquad (7\text{–}7)
$$

We use "transform variable Z" as an unknown multiplier and we don't really care what its value is. However, let us assume that the series we are producing, as in (7–6) and (7–7), converge: as the number of terms increases and approaches infinity the sum approaches a finite quantity. This being the case expression (7–6) proves to be:

$$
f_1^T = 1/(1 - Z) \qquad (7\text{–}8)
$$

. . . and (7–7) proves to be:

$$
f_2^T = Z/(1 - Z)^2. \qquad (7\text{–}9)
$$

Notice that (**7–8**) is the transform of the system in Figure 7–10. We specify a system by its impulse response and the response of Figure 7–10 to the unit impulse is the unit step function. Now, just as a linear system can be specified by its impulse response function it can be uniquely specified by the transform of its impulse response function. We might specify the system of Figure 7–10 as it is shown in Figure 7–22.

FIGURE 7–22

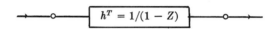

$$h^T = 1/(1 - Z)$$

The schematics of Figures 7–10 and 7–22 are different. But so far as we are concerned they portray precisely the same system: each processes the unit impulse input to produce the same output.

Now, suppose that we would like to know how the system in Figure 7–22 would respond to the following input: $f(n) = 0,1,2,3, \ldots$. Recall that we have agreed to represent a system's operator, in the future, by that system's impulse response function, or its transform. We are therefore posing the convolution problem: "How does a system, whose response to a unit impulse is a step function, respond to a ramp function input?" (See Figure 7–23.)

FIGURE 7–23

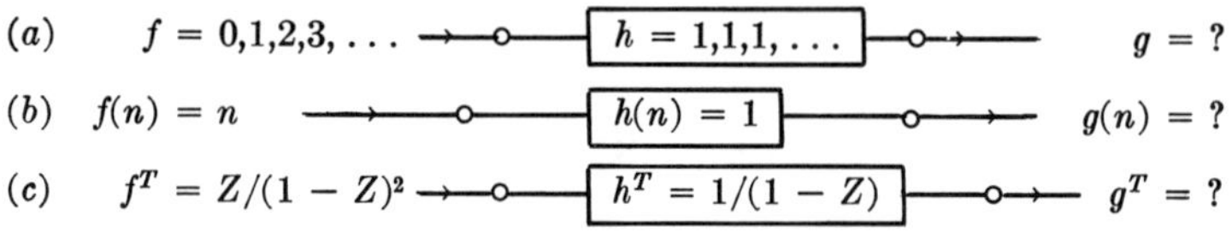

(a) $f = 0,1,2,3, \ldots \longrightarrow \boxed{h = 1,1,1, \ldots} \longrightarrow \qquad g = ?$

(b) $f(n) = n \longrightarrow \boxed{h(n) = 1} \longrightarrow \qquad g(n) = ?$

(c) $f^T = Z/(1 - Z)^2 \longrightarrow \boxed{h^T = 1/(1 - Z)} \longrightarrow \qquad g^T = ?$

The question marks associated with the outputs in (*a*), (*b*) and (*c*), Figure 7–23, all pose the same question:

a)   Asks: "How will a system whose response to a unit impulse is the step function respond to the input: 0,1,2,3, . . . ?"

b)   States the same thing, expressed in closed form.

c)   Asks: "How will a system, the transform of whose impulse response function is $1/(1-Z)$, respond to an input whose transform is $Z/(1-Z)^2$?"

From expression (**7–8**) the transform of $g(n)$, i.e., g^T, is the product of the transforms of: (1) the input; and (2) the system's impulse response function, as shown in expression (**7–10a**).

In the transform domain:

$$g^T = f^T \cdot h^T = [Z/(1 - Z)^2][1/(1 - Z)] \qquad \textbf{(7–10a)}$$

$$\uparrow$$

$$\text{equivalent}$$

In the time domain:

$$\downarrow$$

$$g = f \,\#\, h \qquad\qquad \textbf{(7–10b)}$$

Forming the product called for in **(7–10a)** we have:

$$g^T = Z/(1 - Z)^3. \qquad\qquad \textbf{(7–11)}$$

Clearly the product of f^T and h^T in the transform domain is the equivalent of the convolution operation in the time domain: $f \,\#\, h$.

In going from a discrete time function to its transform we are shifting from the time domain to the transform domain. While $f(n)$ is a function of time, its transform is not time related, but rather is a function of transform variable Z. In fact, it may be considered a continuous function of Z. (Perhaps transforms should be *shown* as functions of Z. So that it will look less forbidding, however, we will show f's transform as f^T rather than $f^T(Z)$.)

To determine the output of the system in Figure 7–23 we need now to return from the transform to the time domain. We need to determine $g(n)$ from g^T in expression **(7–11)**. To achieve this we need to find the "inverse transform" of g^T.

Transferring from the Time to the Transform Domain and Back

It should be apparent that the Z transform operates on a *function* to produce another *function*. When we form the logarithm of a function we produce another function. Similarly, when we form the derivative of a function we produce another function.

In calculus (infinite mathematics) it is common to employ a table of derivatives. By referring to the table of derivatives we can make the transfer from the "finite" to the "infinite" domain and vice versa. The derivative table specifies the operations which must be observed in transferring domains.

The rules for transferring from the time to the transform domain and back again are specified by elements in a transform table. Consider the "transform pairs" in transform Table 7–2.

TABLE 7–2

Transform Table

Pair No.	Time Function	Its Transform
1 .... $f(n)$		$f^T = \sum\limits_{0}^{a} f(n)Z^n$
2 .... $af(n)$, a = constant		af^T
3 .... $af_1(n) + bf_2(n)$		$af_1^T + bf_2^T$
4 .... $f(n)\delta_1$		Zf^T
...$f(n)\delta_k$		$Z^k f^T$
5 .... $f(n)\delta_{-k}$		$Z^{-k}[f^T - f(0) - f(1)$ $-f(2)Z^2 \ldots - f(k-1)Z^{k-1}]$
6 .... 1 (for $n = 0$) \} unit		
0 otherwise $\}$ impulse		1
7 .... 1 (for $n \geq 0$) unit step		$1/(1 - Z)$
8 .... n (for $n \geq 0$) unit ramp		$Z/(1 - Z)^2$
9 .... $\dfrac{(n+1)(n+2)}{2}\beta^n$		$1/(1 - \beta Z)^3$
10 .... a^n		$1/(1 - aZ)$
11 .... na^n		$aZ/(1 - aZ)^2$
12 .... $a^n f(n)$		$f^T(aZ)$
13 .... $(-1)^n$		$1/(1 + Z)$

Pair 1, in Table 7–2, relates a time function to its transform, specifying the symbols to be employed in the rest of the table.

Pair 2 states that multiplying a function by a constant is equivalent to multiplying its transform by the same constant.

Pair 3 expresses the additive property.

Pair 4 states: "If f^T is the transform of $f(n)$, then the transform of $f(n)\delta$,—i.e., function $f(n)$ delayed on period—is simply Zf^T," and also that delaying a function by k periods is the same as multiplying its transform by Z^k.

Pair 5 suggests advancing a function k time periods.

Pair 6 through the remainder of the table expresses a number of special relationships.

To see how we might use the table, return to the convolution problem posed in (a) of Figure 7–23. To avoid the convolution sum operation we elect to shift into the transform domain. We refer to pair 7 and to pair 8 in the table. The transforms of the impulse response and the unit ramp function are $1/(1-Z)$ and $Z/(1-Z)^2$, respectively. Forming their product we obtain the transform of the output:

$$g^T = Z/(1 - Z)^3.$$

There is no function in the table for which this is the transform, but note that the transform can be written:

$$g^T = Z[1/(1 - Z)^3].$$

The term in brackets is the transform of $\dfrac{(n + 1)(n + 2)}{2} \beta^n$, pair 9 in the table, where $\beta = 1$. Since multiplying a transform by Z is the equivalent of delaying the function by one period, the output is:

$$g\delta_1 = \frac{(n + 1)(n + 2)}{2}. \tag{7–12}$$

Incrementing n from 0 we produce output vector g:

$$g = 0,1,3,6,10, \ldots$$
$$n = 0,1,2,3,4, \ldots.$$

Approximating Transforms

In producing g, expression (**7–12**), we operated on two transforms both of which were expressed in closed form. Suppose that we found it impossible to conceive of a way to express an impulse response function in closed form. We might simply operate on the strings which are the power series in Z. Consider, for example, the convolution called for in Figure 7–20, reproduced below:

$f(n) = (\frac{1}{2})^n = 1,\frac{1}{2},\frac{1}{4}, \ldots \longrightarrow \!\circ\!\!-\!\!\boxed{h(n) = (\frac{1}{3})^n = 1,\frac{1}{3},\frac{1}{9}, \ldots}\!-\!\!\circ\!\!\longrightarrow\! g(n)$

From Table 7–2:

$$f^T = 1/(1 - \tfrac{1}{2}Z) = 1 + (\tfrac{1}{2})Z + (\tfrac{1}{4})Z^2 + \cdots$$

and

$$h^T = 1/(1 - \tfrac{1}{3}Z) = 1 + (\tfrac{1}{3})Z + (\tfrac{1}{9})Z^2 + \cdots$$

If the series, which are f^T and h^T, converge rapidly we should be able to approximate g^T as follows:

$$g^T \approx [1 + (\tfrac{1}{2})Z + (\tfrac{1}{4})Z^2][1 + (\tfrac{1}{3})Z + (\tfrac{1}{9})Z^2]$$
$$= 1 + (\tfrac{5}{6})Z + (\tfrac{19}{36})Z^2 + (\tfrac{10}{72})Z^3 + (\tfrac{1}{36})Z^4.$$

Replacing the plus signs with commas, and eliminating the Zs we have the time function:

$$g \approx 1,\tfrac{5}{6},\tfrac{19}{36},\tfrac{10}{72},\tfrac{1}{36},0,0,0, \ldots.$$

The actual convolution is:

$$g = 1,\tfrac{5}{6},\tfrac{19}{36},\tfrac{10}{72},\tfrac{65}{216}, \ldots.$$

The use of more terms, in forming the product of the two power series in Z, would improve the approximation.

Transform Variable Z as a "Place Marker"

When we first introduced transform variable Z we referred to it as an "unknown multiplier." It can also be usefully thought of as a "place marker." The exponents of Z in the transform domain specify the positions which Zs coefficients will occupy in the time domain. This is apparent from the approximation above.

The inspiration for inventing Z can now be elaborated. It is evident that time function $f = a_1, a_2, a_3, \ldots$ is indeed a *function*—a discrete function. However, its *terms* are not connected by arithmetic operators as are those in the polynomial $f(x) = 2X + 3X^2 - X^4 + 7X^5$. We have familiar and effective ways of dealing with functions whose terms are connected by such operators.

We might replace the commas in a time series by plus signs. But if we did so the "transformed" function would be indistinguishable from all other time functions whose terms have the same sum. It's not just the elements in a time function which differentiate that function from others, but their *position* in the series.

Therefore we conjured up place marker Z and let its exponents "freeze" each element in its proper place in the time series when the commas were replaced with plus signs, and the continuous function of Z was produced.

A Further Word about Systems as Inputs and as Operators

We observed in connection with the convolution sum that that operation is a way of determining the nature of the interaction of two time functions. We should not forget that modeling the interaction between f and h and modeling the way h transforms f (or vice versa) are equivalent. Consider again the system in Figure 7–23, reproduced in Figure 7–24 below.

FIGURE 7–24

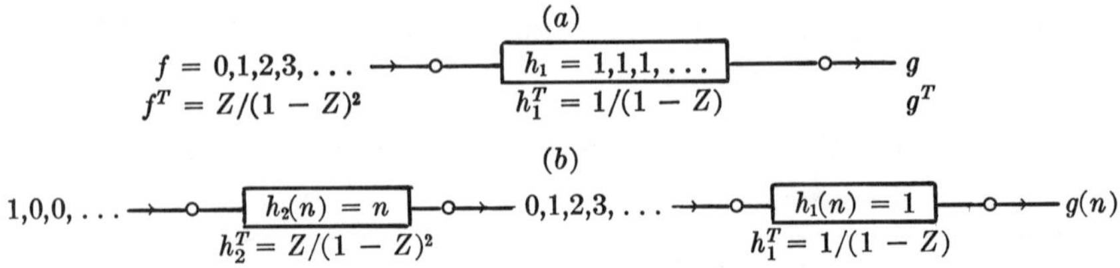

(a)

$$f = 0,1,2,3,\ldots \;\rightarrow\!\!-\!\!\circ\!\!-\!\boxed{\; h_1 = 1,1,1,\ldots \;}\!-\!\!\circ\!\!-\!\!\rightarrow\; g$$
$$f^T = Z/(1 - Z)^2 \qquad\qquad h_1^T = 1/(1 - Z) \qquad\qquad g^T$$

(b)

$$1,0,0,\ldots \;\rightarrow\!\!-\!\!\circ\!\!-\!\boxed{\; h_2(n) = n \;}\!-\!\!\circ\!\!-\!\!\rightarrow\; 0,1,2,3,\ldots \;\rightarrow\!\!-\!\!\circ\!\!-\!\boxed{\; h_1(n) = 1 \;}\!-\!\!\circ\!\!-\!\!\rightarrow g(n)$$
$$h_2^T = Z/(1 - Z)^2 \qquad\qquad\qquad\qquad\qquad h_1^T = 1/(1 - Z)$$

Systems (a) and (b), Figure 7–24, are equivalent. Input f, in system (a), is nothing more than operator h_2 in system (b). In systems (a) and (b) we are modeling the interaction of two time functions, connected in a series.

In the future, for convenience, we will discontinue showing black box operators in our flow diagram schematics. Instead we will employ a network branch (a directed arrow) to represent a component system. Associated with each branch will be the impulse response of the system it represents, *or* its transform. Thus the schematic in Figure 7–25 will represent precisely the same system network as that in Figure 7–24(b).

FIGURE 7–25

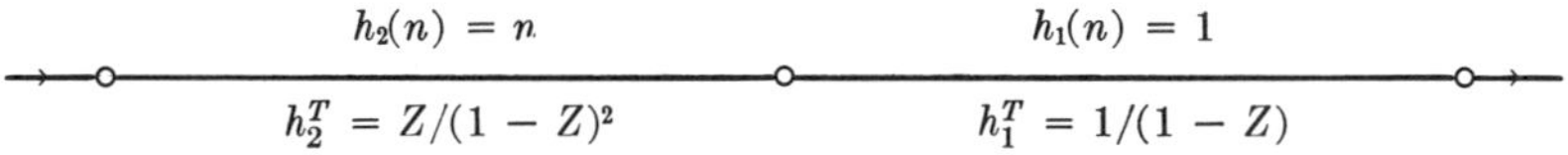

$$h_2(n) = n \qquad\qquad h_1(n) = 1$$

$$h_2^T = Z/(1 - Z)^2 \qquad\qquad h_1^T = 1/(1 - Z)$$

We have already begun *economizing* in our schematics. System h_2, Figure 7–24(b), can also be modeled as follows:

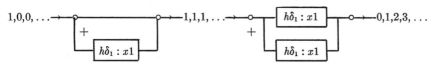

. . . but obviously less concisely.

Sometimes it is difficult to conceive of a schematic such as that above which will operate on a unit impulse input to produce a desired output string. We really needn't bother trying. So long as we know the desired output we can declare that output to be some system's response to a unit impulse and hence designate the desired output as that system's impulse response function.

Consider again the implications of the commutative property in "transform algebra":

$$\begin{aligned} g^T &= h_2^T(Z) \cdot h_1^T(Z) \\ &= h_1^T(Z) \cdot h_2^T(Z) \end{aligned}.$$

The system in Figure 7–25 is therefore the same as that in Figure 7–26.

FIGURE 7–26

$$h_1(n) = 1 \qquad\qquad h_2(n) = n$$

A System's Transfer Function

The transform of a system's impulse response function is called its *transfer function*. The transfer function is the ratio of the transform of the system's output to the transform of its input. Therefore to obtain the transform of the output we simply form the product of the system's transfer function and the transform of its input, as suggested below:

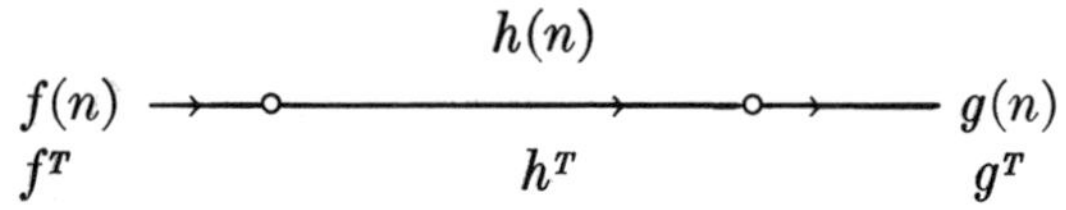

$$h(n)$$

$$f(n) \longrightarrow \!\!\!\!\text{o} \!\!\!\!\longrightarrow\!\!\!\! \text{o} \!\!\!\!\longrightarrow g(n)$$
$$f^T \qquad\qquad h^T \qquad\qquad g^T$$

Transfer function

$$h^T = g^T/f^T$$

. . . and

$$g^T = h^T \cdot f^T$$

Reduction of Systems in Series

Output $g(n)$, in Figure 7–24(b), is the response to the unit impulse of two systems connected in series: $h_1(n)$ and $h_2(n)$. It is therefore apparent that in arriving at expression (**7–12**) we have produced the impulse response function for a single-component equivalent of the two components in series in Figure 7–24(b). We have reduced a two-component network, by combining components, into an equivalent single-component system, as suggested in **Figure 7–27.**

FIGURE 7–27

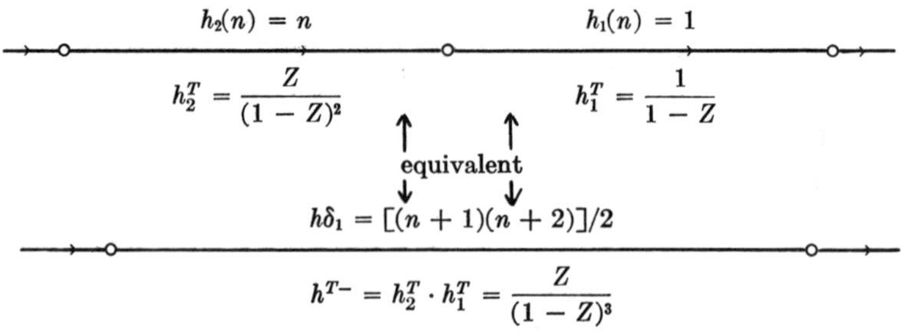

$$h_2(n) = n \qquad\qquad h_1(n) = 1$$

$$h_2^T = \frac{Z}{(1-Z)^2} \qquad\qquad h_1^T = \frac{1}{1-Z}$$

equivalent

$$h\delta_1 = [(n+1)(n+2)]/2$$

$$h^{T-} = h_2^T \cdot h_1^T = \frac{Z}{(1-Z)^3}$$

To reduce a network of systems in series to a single-equivalent system we form the product of their transforms.

Reduction of Systems in Parallel

Consider the system network portrayed in Figure 7–28.

FIGURE 7–28

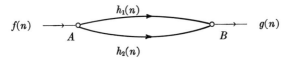

$f(n)$ $h_1(n)$ $g(n)$
  A $h_2(n)$ B

The juncture at A means: "send along each path the input signal $f(n)$." The juncture at B means: "sum the outputs from h_1 and h_2 to produce $g(n)$." In the time domain output g may be produced by forming the sum, at each time period, of the elements output by system h_1 and those output by system h_2. In the transform domain to produce g^T we form the sum of the transforms of h_1 and h_2:

$$g^T = h_1^T + h_2^T. \qquad (7\text{–}13)$$

Reduction of the Feedback System

Refer again to the system in Figure 7–22, reproduced in Figure 7–29 below, without the black box.

FIGURE 7–29

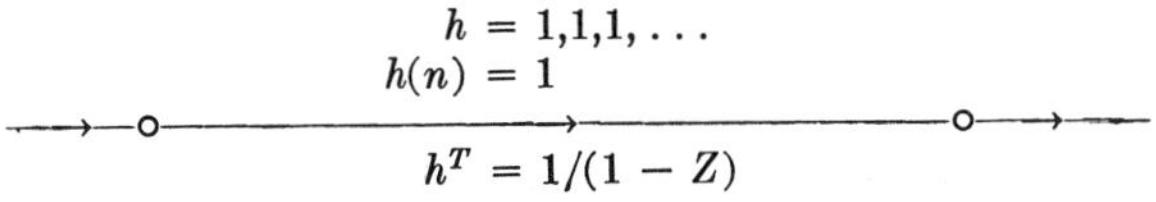

$$h = 1,1,1, \ldots$$
$$h(n) = 1$$
$$h^T = 1/(1 - Z)$$

Figure 7–29 is really the simple feedback system portrayed in Figure 7–10.

In flow graph representation the elemental feedback system is portrayed as shown in Figure 7–30a.

FIGURE 7–30

(a)

h^T

←equivalent→

(b)

$$\frac{1}{1 - h^T}$$

It can be shown that the system of Figure 7–30a is equivalent to the system of 7–30(b). If h^T is the transform of the system which is the loop, and if the loop system does nothing more than add the output back in to the input, after a delay of one period, then the transfer function of the feedback system is simply $1/(1-Z)$ since h^T, in Figure 7–30(b), is the transform of the unit step function.

Figure 7–30 therefore shows how to reduce a feedback system in the transform domain.

A somewhat different system and its equivalent are shown in Figure 7–31.

FIGURE 7–31

The means for reducing such a system is shown in Figure 7–31.[3]

Difference Equations and Their Flow Graph Counterparts

The systems reduction techniques described above are made more intelligible and their usefulness more apparent when we examine their difference equation counterparts. Several of these are shown in Figure 7–32.

Some Illustrative System Problems

An Investment System.   Their father agrees to divide equally between his twin sons such funds as he can spare each year in anticipation of their college education. The first son elects to invest his in a savings and loan account at 10 percent compounded annually. The second son decides to invest his in a savings account at 6 percent compounded annually.

The second son's employer volunteers to accept the second son's balance, at the end of each year, and to invest it in his business, paying a guaranteed 8 percent on it, compounded annually. A wealthy uncle agrees that the year the two sons withdraw their funds and depart for college he will double their collective holdings.

---

[3] There is a substantial literature on system graph reduction techniques. See the bibliography at the end of the chapter for further information on system reduction.

FIGURE 7-32

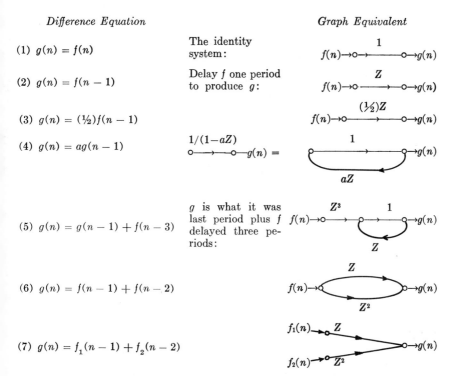

Difference Equation		Graph Equivalent

(1) $g(n) = f(n)$ — The identity system:

(2) $g(n) = f(n-1)$ — Delay f one period to produce g:

(3) $g(n) = (\frac{1}{2})f(n-1)$

(4) $g(n) = ag(n-1)$

(5) $g(n) = g(n-1) + f(n-3)$ — g is what it was last period plus f delayed three periods:

(6) $g(n) = f(n-1) + f(n-2)$

(7) $g(n) = f_1(n-1) + f_2(n-2)$

We would like to model this investment system so as to determine output $g(n)$: the value of their joint holdings the year the two sons withdraw them.

A gross flow graph of this investment system is shown below. At A, one half of their father's input goes to each son. In year n, when the holdings are withdrawn, they are combined at B, doubled by the uncle and output at C.

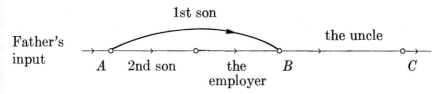

We would like to determine the output for a variety of inputs from the father and it would be good if we could reduce the network of four components to an equivalent single system.

The first son's component would be:

$$\frac{1}{1-1.1Z}$$

The second son's component, including the employer:

$$\frac{1.06Z}{1} \quad \frac{1/(1-1.08Z)}{}$$

Assembling the two components and adding the component for the uncle:

or: F^T ———o ——————— $\dfrac{2/(1-1.1Z)+2.12Z/(1-1.08Z)}{}$ ————————o→ g^T

By long division $2/(1 - 1.1Z)$ becomes:

$$2 + 2(1.1)Z + 2(1.1)^2Z^2 + \ldots ;$$

. . . and $2.12Z/(1 - 1.08Z)$ becomes:

$$2(1.06)Z + 2(1.06)(1.08)Z^2 + 2(1.06)(1.08)^2Z^3 + \ldots .$$

Forming the sum of the two series we have, in closed form:

$$g^T = 2 + 2\sum_{n=1}^{m}\left[(1.1)^n + (1.06)(1.08)^{n-1}\right]Z^n,$$

. . . where m is the year in which the holdings are withdrawn.

Returning to the time domain it is easy to produce the system's response to the unit impulse (a \$1 deposit by the father at time 0). Assume that the father deposits the following stream: \$1,000, \$3,000, \$500, \$1,500. Convolving this with the system's response to the unit impulse we have, as an output:

$$\$2,000, \$16,320, \$18,669, \$26,763.$$

A Watershed System

Refer to the figure below. The weather in the Spring is predominantly from the West. Warm moist air from the West cools as it rises over the mountains causing rain over the plains, P. As Spring arrives, warming weather also melts snow in the mountains. Both these sources supply reservoir R with water.

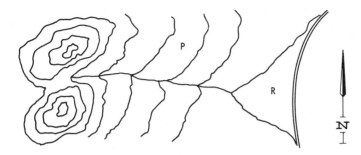

Water is withdrawn from the reservoir daily but sometimes unusually heavy inflows threaten an overflow condition in the reservoir, whose average fill in the Spring is only $\frac{3}{10}$ capacity.

It has been observed that even with normal drainage from the reservoir one day of hard Spring rain, on day 0, yields the following water level pattern in the reservoir:

$$L_1 = .30, \quad .45, \quad .55, \quad .40, \quad .35, \quad .30$$
$$n = 0, \quad 1, \quad 2, \quad 3, \quad 4, \quad 5$$

. . . where the elements in vector L_1 indicate fraction filled.

Other observations show that an abnormally high temperature (above 60°F.) in the mountains on day 0 produces the following water level pattern in the reservoir:

$$L_2 = .30, \quad .35, \quad .40, \quad .40, \quad .35, \quad .30$$
$$n = 0, \quad 1, \quad 2, \quad 3, \quad 4, \quad 5$$

The reservoir at the end of February is at .30 capacity. Heavy rains and unseasonably high temperatures are expected beginning March 1. Specifically, heavy rains are forecast for March 1, 3, 7, and 8 and temperatures above 60°F. are expected in the mountains on March 2, 6, 9, and 10.

We would like to determine the expected level of the water in the reservoir during March.

The response to a unit impulse is the *change* in the level of water in the reservoir. The response to hard rain on February 28 (time 0) is:

Change: .15, .25, .10, .05, 0, 0, 0, . . .
March: 1,   2,   3,   4,   5, 6, 7, . . .

We want to know how a system which responds in this way to a unit impulse will respond to the input string:

Days of heavy rain: 1, 0, 1, 0, 0, 0, 1, 1, 0, 0, 0 . . .
March: 1, 2, 3, 4, 5, 6, 7, 8, 9, 10, 11, . . .

To form the convolution sum we form the matrix:

		.15	.25	.10	.05
March 1	1	.15	.25	.10	.05
2	0	0	0	0	0
3	1	.15	.25	.10	.05
4	0	0	0	0	0
5	0	0	0	0	0
6	0	0	0	0	0
7	1	.15	.25	.10	.05
8	1	.15	.25	.10	.05

The addition to the reservoir in early March resulting from heavy rains which are forecast is therefore (summing the diagonals):

.15, .25, .25, .40, .10, .15, .15, .40, .30, .25, .15
March: 1,   2,   3,   4,   5,   6,   7,   8,   9,   10,   11

Proceeding in this fashion we produce a convolution table for unseasonably warm days in early March:

		.05	.10	.10	.05
March 1	0	0	0	0	0
2	1	.05	.10	.10	.05
3	0	0	0	0	0
4	0	0	0	0	0
5	0	0	0	0	0
6	1	.05	.10	.10	.05
7	0	0	0	0	0
8	0	0	0	0	0
9	1	.05	.10	.10	.05
10	1	.05	.10	.10	.05

The addition to the reservoir in early March resulting from unseasonably warm days is therefore:

.0, .05, .10, .10, .05, .05, .10, .10, .10, .15, .20, .15, .05
March: 1,   2,   3,   4,   5,   6,   7,   8,   9,   10, 11, 12, 13

In flow graph form our system is represented by three inputs in parallel:

1.   The normal inflow which keeps the level of water in the reservoir at .30 under normal conditions.

2. The inflow added as a result of heavy rains.
3. The inflow added as a result of warm weather.

. . . as suggested by the following diagram:

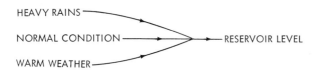

Summing the three inputs we have:

.15,	.25,	.25,	.40,	.10,	.15,	.15,	.40,	.30,	.25,	.15,	0,	0
+ .30,	.30,	.30,	.30,	.30,	.30,	.30,	.30,	.30,	.30,	.30,	.30,	.30
+ 0,	.05,	.10,	.10,	.05,	.05,	.10,	.10,	.10,	.15,	.20,	.15,	.05
.45,	.60,	.65,	.80,	.45,	.50,	.55,	.80,	.70,	.70,	.65,	.45,	.35

Clearly if the forecast is accurate the reservoir will not overflow.

A Sales-Inventory System

Sales fluctuate in a particular sales-inventory system, but the mean value of daily sales appears to be constant. A desired inventory level has been established and inventories are managed by reference to the *deviation* from that level, where $i(n)$ is the deviation in period n. (We might think of the deviation as a quantity of inventory which is, at times, positive, zero, and negative.)

In an effort to keep the deviation as close as possible to zero an addition or withdrawal $p(n)$ is made each morning, out of special reserves. The adjustment is determined by averaging i the previous two periods:

$$p(n) = -\tfrac{1}{2}[i(n - 1) + i(n - 2)]. \tag{7-14}$$

At the end of the day i is simply:

$$i(n) = i(n - 1) + p(n) - s(n). \tag{7-15}$$

Clearly i is a function of p and s, and p is a function of i. We therefore have a system of three components, interacting through time.

To produce a flow graph of the system—now modeled by the two difference equations (**7–14**) and (**7–15**)—consider first the character of the three components. Component i differs from the other two in that it is an *accumulator*. A unit fed into inventory remains there until withdrawn. Its response to a unit impulse—a unit of inventory introduced at time 0, followed by nothing thereafter—is the step function: the unit remains unless withdrawn. To model the inventory component we therefore need a component like that in Figure 7–31 (1), namely:

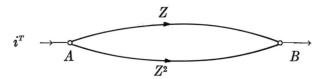

$$i^T \qquad = 1/(1 - Z)$$

To form the sum called for in the brackets in expression (**7–14**), we produce the parallel system:

Vector $i(n)$, whose transfer function is i^T, is input to both systems at point A. It is delayed one period by the top branch to produce $i(n-1)$ and two periods by the lower branch to produce $i(n-2)$. To produce $p(n)$ we now connect in series the product operator $-\frac{1}{2}$, whose transform (from Table 7–2) *is* $-\frac{1}{2}$. See Figure 7–33.

FIGURE 7–33

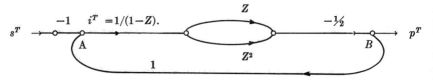

Figure 7–33 is the precise flow graph counterpart of difference equation (**7–14**). We need now to incorporate difference equation (**7–15**). Expression (**7–15**) says, "To produce $i(n)$ add to $i(n-1)$ the difference between $p(n)$ and $s(n)$." Since $s(n)$ is the driver of the system—the exogenous variable—we will introduce it at the left as shown in Figure 7–34.

FIGURE 7–34

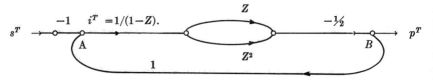

Note that $s(n)$ is converted to its negative by the operator in the next to leftmost branch, then added to $p(n)$ at point A to form the desired difference. Figure 7–34 now corresponds perfectly to the system of two difference equations (7–14) and (7–15), *IF* we can be sure that $i(n-1)$ gets added to the difference between $p(n)$ and $s(n)$ to produce $i(n)$, as called for in expression (7–15). But that is precisely what we achieve by assigning to i^T the transfer function $1/(1-Z)$, as shown in Figure 7–34.

Now, to *reduce* the system of Figure 7–34 we might first reduce the two components which are in parallel; producing:

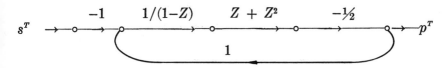

Next we reduce the three components which are in series by forming the products of their transfer functions:

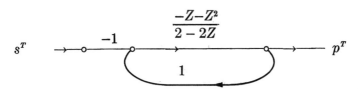

To achieve the next reduction we refer to Figure 7–31 and produce:

$$s^T \longrightarrow \circ \underset{-1}{\longrightarrow} \circ \xrightarrow{\quad \dfrac{\dfrac{-Z-Z^2}{2-2Z}}{1-\dfrac{-Z-Z^2}{2-2Z}} \quad} \circ \longrightarrow p^T$$

. . . or, finally:

FIGURE 7–35

$$s^T \longrightarrow \circ \xrightarrow{\quad \dfrac{Z+Z^2}{2-Z+Z^2} \quad} \circ \longrightarrow p^T$$

Transfer function $= p^T/s^T = \dfrac{Z+Z^2}{2-Z+Z^2}$

. . . and

$$p^T = s^T \left[\frac{Z + Z^2}{2 - Z + Z^2} \right]$$

The system of Figure 7–35 is the equivalent of the system of Figure 7–34. It is also the flow graph equivalent of the system of difference equations (7–14) and (7–15). The transfer function of Figure 7–35 tells how $s(n)$ will be transformed into $p(n)$.

It would also be useful to know how the inventory component, $i(n)$, will behave. In the transfer function of Figure 7–35 we have the ratio of p^T to s^T. We would like the ratio of i^T to s^T. That is, we would like the transfer function of a system whose input is $s(n)$ and whose output is $i(n)$ rather than $p(n)$. This involves the formation of a slightly different flow graph and we will leave it for the exercises.

To transform the transfer function of the sales-inventory system into a more tractable form we first divide both numerator and denominator by 2, then put all the Zs in the numerator by long division as shown below.

$$
\begin{array}{r}
(\tfrac{1}{2})Z + (\tfrac{3}{4})Z^2 + (\tfrac{1}{8})Z^3 - (\tfrac{5}{16})Z^4 + \cdots \\
1 - (\tfrac{1}{2})Z + (\tfrac{1}{2})Z^2 \overline{\smash{\big)}\ (\tfrac{1}{2})Z + (\tfrac{1}{2})Z^2 } \\
\underline{(\tfrac{1}{2})Z - (\tfrac{1}{4})Z^2 + (\tfrac{1}{4})Z^3} \\
\underline{(\tfrac{3}{4})Z^2 - (\tfrac{1}{4})Z^3} \\
\underline{(\tfrac{3}{4})Z^2 - (\tfrac{3}{8})Z^3 + (\tfrac{3}{8})Z^4} \\
\underline{(\tfrac{1}{8})Z^3 - (\tfrac{3}{8})Z^4} \\
\underline{(\tfrac{1}{8})Z^3 - (\tfrac{1}{16})Z^4 + (\tfrac{1}{16})Z^5} \\
- (\tfrac{5}{16})Z^4 - (\tfrac{1}{16})Z^5
\end{array}
$$

. . . from which we produce:

$$p(n) = 0, \tfrac{1}{2}, \tfrac{3}{4}, \tfrac{1}{8}, -\tfrac{5}{16}, -\tfrac{7}{32}, \tfrac{3}{64}, \cdots$$

. . . the inverse transform of the transfer function.

Stability in a System

Observe the oscillating behavior of p, in response to the unit impulse (see Figure 7–36).

Management policy in this simple sales-inventory system as portrayed by difference equation (7–14) has the effect of overreacting to a unit impulse (a unit of sales, followed by no sales thereafter).

If a system's response to a unit impulse is a series which does not

FIGURE 7–36

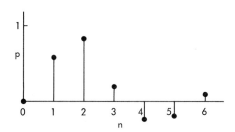

fall outside some finite range, that system is stable. If the effect of an impulse tends to vanish, as does that in Figure 7–36, the system is asymptotically stable.

If a system is asymptotically stable:

$$\underset{n\to\infty}{\text{Limit}}\ f(n) = \underset{z\to1}{\text{limit}}\ (z-1)f^T.$$

Extensions and Some Limitations of Flow Graph Analysis

Consider again the system in Figure 7–6. Nothing we've done so far in this chapter has equipped us to build a flow graph model of the inventory system under uncertainty. Furthermore, thus far we have confined ourselves to systems with one input (driver) and one output only. Flow graph analysis *can* be applied to systems with multiple inputs and outputs as is demonstrated in Supplement A at the end of this chapter.

We will now see that flow graph analysis can also be applied to probabilistic systems, but we will confine ourselves to a few comments about the use of the Z transform in studying the interaction of random variables with known distributions.

Let us assume that we have two warehouses from each of which the same product is withdrawn daily. We believe that the daily demand pattern on the two warehouses is as shown in Table 7–4.

TABLE 7–4

Warehouse No. 1		Warehouse No. 2	
Demand/day	*Probability*	*Demand/day*	*Probability*
0	.4	0	.4
1	.3	1	.5
2	.2	2	.1
3	.1		

We would like to determine the probability distribution for the demand on the two warehouses taken together. Clearly we are dealing with an interaction—the interaction of two random variables. But how shall we determine the nature of their interaction analytically?

Consider first how we would attack this problem if, instead of two probability distributions, we had two *vectors,* each of which was 10 days' demand on one or the other of the two warehouses, both representative of the random behavior specified by the two probability distributions. Thus:

A 10-day sample from Whse. No. 1:   0,0,0,1,2,0,1,3,0,0
A 10-day sample from Whse. No. 2:   0,1,1,0,1,2,1,0,0,1

Since the interaction we seek is their sum we model the two components in parallel:

Warehouse #1

Warehouse #2

The sum we seek, output g, is simply the *sum* of the elements of the two time series: 0,1,1,1,3,2,2,3,0,1.

We have achieved very little thus far, however. We wanted a probability distribution for the interaction of the two and all we have is a simulation sample of 10 elements.

What we seek is easily obtained. It develops that to produce the probability distribution for the sum of two random variables, given their individual probability distributions, we perform the convolution sum operation on their probability distributions. We proceed as though the daily demands were the values for n, and the probabilities the corresponding values for the two time functions. Schematically we have two systems in series, each with its own impulse response function, as shown below:

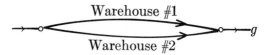

.4, .3, .2, .1   .4, .5, .1

Warehouse No. 1   Warehouse No. 2

If we employ the convolution sum operation we have:

	.4	.5	.1
.4	.16	.20	.04
.3	.12	.15	.03
.2	.08	.10	.02
.1	.04	.05	.01

Combined Demand	Probability
0	.16
1	.32
2	.27
3	.17
4	.07
5	.01

Had we shifted to the transform domain we would, of course, have produced the same result.

We have just seen how to determine the probability distribution for the *sum of random variables,* given their individual distributions. Notice, however, that the interaction of daily demand and lead time, in an inventory system, is not a simple sum of two random variables. Given the two distributions:

Daily Demand	Probability	Days Lead Time	Probability
0	.4	1	.25
1	.3	2	.50
2	.2	3	.25
3	.1		

. . . and a sample of their output, such as:

Days Lead Time: 1,2,2,1,3,2, ...
Demand: 0,1,0,2,1,3,0,0,1, . . .

. . . to determine the output string which is demand during lead time, we proceed as suggested below:

Lead Time: 1 2 2 1 3   2
Demand: 0,1,0,2,1,2,1,3,0,0,1, . . .
Demand during LT: 0,1,3,2,4,1, . . .

In this interaction between two random functions of time we seek a *random sum of a random variable.* The *number* of elements from the daily demand function to include in the next element of the demand during lead time function is itself a random variable.

The interaction of these two is most easily determined in the transform domain. We first form the transforms of each:

1. $p_1 = .4, \quad .3, \quad .2, \quad .1$
   $n = 0, \quad 1, \quad 2, \quad 3$
   $p_1^T = .4 + .3Z + .2Z^2 + .1Z^3$
2. $p_2 = 0, \quad .25, \quad .50, \quad .25$
   $n = 0, \quad 1, \quad 2, \quad 3$
   $p_2^T = 0 + .25 + .50Z + .25Z^2$

Now, the transform of their interaction, p_3^T is:

$$p_3^T = 0(.4 + .3Z + .2Z^2 + .1Z^3)^0$$
$$+ .25(.4 + .3Z + .2Z^2 + .1Z^3)^1$$
$$+ .50(.4 + .3Z + .2Z^2 + .1Z^3)^2$$
$$+ .25(.4 + .3Z + .2Z^2 + .1Z^3)^3$$
$$= .1960 + .2310Z + .2260Z^2 + .1797Z^3 + .0935Z^4 + .0477Z^5$$
$$+ .019Z^6 + .00525Z^7 + .0015Z^8 + .00025Z^9$$

Detaching the Zs and replacing the plus signs with commas we produce the demand during lead time distribution displayed in Table 6–6 of Chapter 6.

In mathematical statistics the transform of a probability function—such as those for daily demand and for lead time—is called its *generating function*. We have seen illustrations above of two ways in which probability functions may interact: one producing the sum of two random variables; the other the random sum of a random variable. Probability functions may interact with each other in still other ways, in dynamic systems. The nature of the interaction is, in most cases, more easily calculated via their generating functions; i.e., in the transform domain.

While we have now seen how the interaction of demand and lead time may be determined via their generating functions we have not seen how to portray their interaction in flow graph form, nor how to *reduce* components in such a system, as is implied by the schematic of Figure 7–6.

The difficulty lies in the algebra of linear systems. In our modeling of systems in flow graph form we are constrained to linear systems and while the *convolution sum* operation is a linear operation, the interaction of demand and lead time is not.

"Interaction" is, therefore, a general term, applicable to a number of kinds of systems interaction. In the chapter on queuing systems we will encounter yet another kind of interaction. In succeeding chapters we will explore other ways in which the transforms of functions can be employed in analyzing systems.

Other Network Approaches to Systems Analysis

We have employed graphs in a very particular way in this chapter, attaching a particular meaning to interconnected arrows and employing a special algebra (transform algebra) to express and analyze relationships. There are other ways of modeling systems in a graph context and the reader is referred to the bibliography at the end of this chapter for further study in this field.

SUPPLEMENT A

Flow Graph Modeling with Initial Conditions[4]

To see how we would flow graph model a system when initial conditions are specified, consider Exercise 8, Chapter 3. Keynes Co.

---

[4] It can be shown that the initial state, $f(0) = \lim\limits_{Z \to \infty} f^T$.

is experiencing exploding profitability and growth, with sales increasing at 20 percent per month, and diminishing cash. In the exercise we are asked to track the loss of cash. From the information given it is evident that sales during the month, SDM, cost of sales, COS, accounts receivable, AR, cash on hand, COH and inventory, VEN, are related as shown below in the component identification graph below.

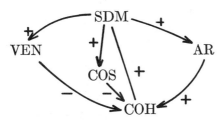

The component identification graph shows that cash on hand increases when accounts receivable and sales increase, and decreases when cost of sales and inventory increase.

Forty percent of sales are cash sales and the remainder is paid the following month. Cost of sales is 90 percent of sales. To keep inventory proportional to sales management augments the inventory at the end of each month so that it equals half that month's sales.

The difference equations which follow portray these relationships explicitly.

$$SDM(n) = 1.2SDM(n - 1)$$
$$AR(n) = .6SDM(n)$$
$$COS(n) = .9SDM(n)$$
$$VEN(n) = .5SDM(n)$$

Since the inventory at the end of period $n - 1$ will be $.5SDM(n - 1)$ and that at the end of period n will be $.5SDM(n)$, the inventory *adjustment* in period n will be:

$$VEN(n) = .5[SDM(n) - SDM(n - 1)].$$

With the following difference equation we can now express the way COH is related to those components which increase it and those which decrease it, as suggested by the component identification graph above:

$$COH(n) = \underbrace{COH(n - 1)}_{\substack{\text{Cash} \\ \text{previous} \\ \text{month}}} + \underbrace{AR(n - 1)}_{\substack{\text{AR col-} \\ \text{lected} \\ \text{this month}}} + \underbrace{.4SDM(n)}_{\substack{\text{Cash} \\ \text{sales this} \\ \text{month}}} - COS(n) - \underbrace{\Delta VEN(n)}_{\substack{\text{Inventory} \\ \text{adjustment} \\ \text{this month}}}$$

Replacing the elements on the right side of the equal sign with their SDM equivalents we have:

$$\begin{aligned}
\text{COH}(n) &= \text{COH}(n-1) + .6\text{SDM}(n-1) + .4\text{SDM}(n) \\
&\quad - .9\text{SDM}(n) - .5\text{SDM}(n) + .5\text{SDM}(n-1) \\
&= \text{COH}(n-1) - \text{SDM}(n) + 1.1\text{SDM}(n-1) \quad (1)
\end{aligned}$$

The corresponding flow graph for expression (1) is:

. . . which reduces to:

$$\frac{-1 + 1.1Z}{1 - Z}$$

$$\text{SDM}^T \longrightarrow\!\!\longrightarrow \text{COH}^T$$

Since $\text{SDM}(n) = 1.2\text{SDM}(n-1)$, $\text{SDM}^T = 1/(1 - 1.2Z)$

. . . and therefore:

$$\text{COH}^T = \left(\frac{1}{1 - 1.2Z}\right)\left(\frac{-1 + 1.1Z}{1 - Z}\right) = \frac{-1 + 1.1Z}{1 - 2.2Z + 1.2Z^2}$$

. . . which, by long division, becomes:

$$\text{COH}^T = -1 - 1.1Z - 1.22Z^2 \ldots.$$

However, at the moment we appear on the scene, Keynes' accounts are as follows:

$$\begin{aligned}
\text{SDM}(0) &= 300{,}000 \\
\text{COH}(0) &= 228{,}000 \\
\text{VEN}(0) &= 150{,}000 \\
\text{AR}(0) &= 180{,}000
\end{aligned}$$

To account for these initial conditions in our flow graph we will exploit a transform pair which we have not had occasion to use before. Consider first the following difference equation which follows from expression (1):

$$\text{COH}(n+1) = \text{COH}(n) - \text{SDM}(n+1) + 1.1\text{SDM}(n)$$

Solving for $\text{COH}(n)$:

$$\text{COH}(n) = \text{COH}(n+1) + \text{SDM}(n+1) - 1.1\text{SDM}(n)$$

. . . that is:

$$\begin{aligned}
\text{COH}(n+1) &\searrow \\
\text{SDM}(n+1) &\longrightarrow \!\!\!\!\bullet\!\!-\!\!\rightarrow \text{COH}(n) \\
-1.1\text{SDM}(n) &\nearrow
\end{aligned}$$

Referring to transform pair 5, Table 7–2:

$$COH(n + 1) \longrightarrow Z^{-1}[COH^{T} - COH(0)]$$
$$SDM(n + 1) \longrightarrow Z^{-1}[SDM^{T} - SDM(0)]$$

. . . and of course:

$$SDM(n) \rightarrow SDM^{T}$$
$$COH(n) \rightarrow COH^{T}$$

We therefore have, in the transform domain, the following flow graph:

$$Z^{-1}COH^{T} - Z^{-1}COH(0)$$
$$Z^{-1}SDM^{T} - Z^{-1}SDM(0) \longrightarrow \circ \rightarrow COH^{T}$$
$$-1.1SDM^{T}$$

. . . but this is equivalent to:

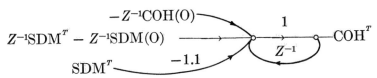

. . . which is equivalent to:

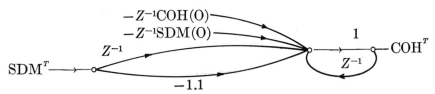

Reducing, we have:

$$SDM^{T} \underset{Z^{-1} - 1.1}{\overset{-Z^{-1}COH(0)}{\underset{-Z^{-1}SDM(0)}{\longrightarrow}}} \frac{1}{1 - Z^{-1}} COH^{T}$$

Expressing COH^{T} as the output we have:

$$COH^{T} = \left\{ -Z^{-1}[COH(0) + SDM(0)] + [SDM^{T}(Z^{-1} - 1.1)] \right\}$$
$$\times \frac{1}{1 - Z^{-1}}$$
$$= \frac{-1}{Z - 1}[COH(0) + SDM(0)] + SDM^{T}\left[\frac{Z^{-1} - 1.1}{1 - Z^{-1}} \right] \quad (2)$$

Now, recalling that:

$$COH(0) = 228{,}000$$

and

$$\mathrm{SDM}(0) = 300{,}000$$

. . . and since

$$\mathrm{SDM}(n) = 1.2\mathrm{SDM}(n - 1), \text{ from which}$$

$$\mathrm{SDM}^T = \frac{300{,}000}{1 - 1.2Z},$$

. . . we have:

$$\mathrm{COH}^T = \frac{-228{,}000}{Z - 1} - \frac{300{,}000}{Z - 1} + \frac{300{,}000}{1 - 1.2Z} \cdot \frac{Z^{-1} - 1.1}{1 - Z^{-1}}$$

$$= \frac{378{,}000}{1 - Z} - \frac{150{,}000}{1 - 1.2Z}.$$

We immediately identify the inverse transforms of the two terms above to produce:

$$\mathrm{COH}(n) = 378{,}000 - 150{,}000(1.2^n).$$

Incrementing n from 0 we have:

$$\mathrm{COH} = 228{,}000, \quad 198{,}000, \quad 162{,}000 \ldots \qquad (3)$$
$$n = \quad 0, \qquad\quad 1, \qquad\quad 2,$$

Note that transform equation (2) could be written:

$$\mathrm{COH}^T = \begin{bmatrix} \dfrac{-\mathrm{COH}(0) - \mathrm{SDM}(0)}{Z - 1} & \dfrac{Z^{-1} - 1.1}{1 - Z^{-1}} \end{bmatrix} \begin{bmatrix} \mathrm{UI}^T \\ \\ \mathrm{SDM}^T \end{bmatrix}$$

. . . revealing that in fact we have a system with *two* inputs, unit impulse UI and SDM, and one output, COH. The row vector is the counterpart of the transfer function. In a system with two or more inputs and two or more outputs the transform equation would be a matrix equation and the counterpart of the transfer function would be a matrix of transforms.

Clearly we could have produced output (3) with less effort by simulating, using expression (1). However, in Chapter 14 we will see how the Z transform can be used to decompose a dynamic system into its transient and steady state components, a revelation which cannot be easily obtained from simulation.

SUGGESTIONS FOR FURTHER STUDY

ASELTINE, JOHN A. *Transform Models in Linear Systems Analysis.* New York: McGraw-Hill Book Co., 1958.

HALL, A. D. *Methodology for Systems Engineering.* Princeton, N.J.: D. Van Nostrand Co., Inc., 1962.

HAMILTON, H. R. et al. *Systems Simulation for Regional Analysis: An Application to River-Basin Planning.* Cambridge, Mass. The M.I.T. Press, 1969.

HARARY, NORMAN, and CARTWRIGHT, DORWIN. *Structural Models.* New York: John Wiley & Sons, Inc., 1965.

KOENIG, H. E.; TOKAD, Y.; and KESAVAN, H. K. *Analysis of Discrete Physical Systems.* New York: McGraw-Hill Book Co., 1967.

MILSUM, J. H. (ed.). *Positive Feedback.* New York: Pergamon Press, Inc., 1968.

OYSTEIN, ORE. *Graphs and Their Uses.* New York: Random House, Inc., 1963.

SCHWARZ, R. J., and FRIEDLAND, B. *Linear Systems.* New York: McGraw-Hill Book Co., 1958.

EXERCISES

1. Refer again to expression **(7–1)** in which the convolution sum operation is employed to determine Smith's holdings in the nth year. Now refer to expression **(7–2)**, which shows the convolution of $(1/2)^n$ and $(1/3)^n$. Following expression **(7–2)** a "matrix format" is shown, via which the output of this convolution can be produced. Using the matrix format which is shown just after expression **(7–2)**, determine Smith's holdings through the fifth year.

Now determine Smith's holdings for the first five years by using transform algebra; that is: (1) construct the flow graph equivalent of the system in Figure 7–16(b); (2) determine its transform; and finally (3) return to the time domain and produce the time series which is Smith's holdings through the fifth year.

2. Derive the Z transform for the following time functions:

a) The unit impulse: 1,0,0,0, . . .
b) The unit step: $f(n) = 1$: 1,1,1,1, . . .
c) The unit ramp: $f(n) = n$: 0,1,2,3,4, . . .

3. Recalling the "place marker" function which transform variable Z performs, determine the time function for which the following is the transform:

$$7.2Z^3 + 0.5Z^0 - 35.1Z^2 - 16.9Z^1 + 197.6Z^6$$

4. The transform of a reduced system, developed in this chapter, proved to be: $Z/(1-Z)^3$. Since this can be written:

$$Z[1/(1-Z)][1/(1-Z)][1/(1-Z)]$$

. . . suggest the schematic for an *expanded* equivalent system, in flow graph form.

5. In this chapter we modeled the interaction between time series $(1/3)^n$ and time series $(1/2)^n$ by forming the convolution sum. Determine the nature of the interaction of these two systems in the *transform* domain.

6. Refer to Supplement A at the end of this chapter, and to the system of difference equations which specifies the system described in the supplement. Through simulation, determine—through the sixth time period—how the component "cash on hand" would respond to a unit impulse input from the component "sales during the month." Now *convolve* this time series (the impulse response), using the convolution sum operation, with the time series: Sales during the month $= 300,000(1.2)^n$.

Compare the behavior of cash on hand with that produced via transform algebra in Supplement A.

7. Components in the U.S. economic system may be aggregated into:

$$C = \text{Consumption}$$
$$I = \text{Investment}$$
$$Y = \text{Income}$$
$$G = \text{Government expenditures}$$

Their relationships may be grossly portrayed as shown in the following component identification graph:

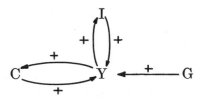

The relationships between the components may be portrayed more precisely by the following system of difference equations:

$$C(n) = 20 + .7Y(n-1) - .14Y(n-2)$$
$$I(n) = 2 + .1Y(n-1)$$
$$Y(n) = C(n-1) + I(n-1) + G(n-1)$$

It is desired to know how government expenditures, G, influence consumption, C. Construct the flow graph equivalent of the system of difference equations above, with G as the input and C the output. Reduce the system to an equivalent simpler system, then determine C which results from a unit impulse input from G. Now convolve this with the input:

$$G = \$100 \text{ million} \times (1.1)^n$$

. . . to determine the influence of increasing government expenditures on consumption.

How might a simulation model be employed to obtain this information? Build and run such a model, initializing the system at "reasonable" values for the various components.

chapter 8

Binomial and Poisson Processes

IN THIS CHAPTER we want to acquaint ourselves with the usefulness of the binomial distribution in a variety of decision situations. In addition we will see how the Poisson distribution is developed from the binomial distribution, we will acquaint ourselves with the properties of the Poisson distribution, and we will prepare for dealing in the next two chapters with problems resulting from queuing phenomena.

THE BINOMIAL PROBABILITY DISTRIBUTION

Many processes encountered in systems studies can be described in terms of a number of discrete trials, each of which has only two possible outcomes. The toss of a coin exemplifies the process; or the inspection of parts, each of which is determined to be either good or bad; or examination of accounts to determine if budgeted expenses were exceeded or not; or inquiry into a program of activities to determine if the programmed deadline of each component event was met or not.

A process of this character is said to be a Bernoulli process if, as with the toss of a coin:

1. There is no time variance to the occurrence of one or the other event—giving us no reason to believe that trials early in the day, for example, will differ from those late in the day.
2. The long-run outcome is known; thus in an infinite number of trials, heads will be tossed half the time.

The throw of a die can be a Bernoulli process. If we choose to designate the toss of snake eyes (two "ones") as "success" and the toss of anything *other than* snake eyes as "failure," then the process is clearly Bernoulli.

We know that the probability of snake eyes in 1 toss (or trial, as it is generally called) is 1/6. But suppose we want to know more. Specifically, suppose we would like to know the probability of 2 successes in 6 Bernoulli trials, given that the probability of success in 1 trial is 1/6. In our die experiment we would be asking specifically: "What is the probability of tossing 2 snake eyes in 6 consecutive tosses of 1 die?"

Let us let S = snake eyes and N = not snake eyes; that is, anything except snake eyes. We might, in 6 tosses, get 2 snake eyes in the following order: SSNNNN. From our knowledge of joint probabilities we know that the probability of tossing this particular pattern in 6 tosses of 1 die is:

$$(1/6)(1/6)(5/6)(5/6)(5/6)(5/6) = 625/46656.$$

However, we might also get 2 snake eyes in the order SNSNNN, and the probability of tossing this pattern is:

$$(1/6)(5/6)(1/6)(5/6)(5/6)(5/6) = 625/46656.$$

It is evident, therefore, that the probability of getting 2 snake eyes in any one particular pattern is 625/46656.

A quick survey will show that it is possible to get 2 snake eyes in 6 tosses in 15 different patterns.

SSNNNN	NSSNNN	NNSNSN
SNSNNN	NSNSNN	NNSNNS
SNNSNN	NSNNSN	NNNSSN
SNNNSN	NSNNNS	NNNSNS
SNNNNS	NNSSNN	NNNNSS

Since each pattern is equally likely (we infer this since we have no reason to believe otherwise), the probability of tossing 2 snake eyes in 6 tosses of 1 die, without regard to the pattern or order in which the 2 snake eyes occur, is: $(625/46656) \times (15)$.

We can now develop a general model. We will let:

p = Probability of "success" on 1 trial (then $1 - p$ = probability of "failure" on 1 trial);

n = Number of trials;

r = The number of successes whose probability we want to determine.

Then we would have, as in our snake eyes experiment,

$$(p \times p \times p \times \ldots \ldots p) \times (1 - p)(1 - p)(1 - p) \ldots (1 - p).$$

Now also, as in our snake eyes experiment, we will have r of the p's in the left-hand expression, and $n - r$ of the $(1 - p)$'s in the right-hand expression. Therefore the above expression becomes: $p^r \times (1 - p)^{n-r}$.

This gives us the probability of r successes in n trials, given that all the successes come at the first of the series of n trials. To get at the probability of r successes in n successive trials *without regard to the order in which the successes come*, we must multiply the above expression (as we did in our snake eyes experiment) by the number of ways in which r successes can occur in n trials. From our knowledge of permutations and combinations we know that this number is the binomial coefficient:

$$\frac{n\,!}{r\,!\,(n - r)\,!}$$

(in our snake eyes experiment this was 15).

Our general model[1] then becomes:

$$p(r) = p^r(1 - p)^{n-r} \times \frac{n\,!}{r\,!\,(n - r)\,!}.$$

This is the binomial probability distribution, and with this distribution model we can determine the probability of various numbers of successes in a given number of trials, knowing the probability of success in one trial.

Referring once again to our die experiment, we might determine —using our binomial model—the probability of various numbers of snake eyes in six tosses of one die. We might portray these probabilities graphically in a histogram like that shown in Figure 8–1.

The binomial probability distribution is used extensively in statistical quality control, and particularly in acceptance sampling. It is apparent from Figure 8–1 that the probability of our tossing *two or fewer* snake eyes in six tosses of one die is 15625/46656 + 18750/46656 + 9375/46656. In a similar fashion the probability of our encountering $d = 2$ or fewer defective parts in a sample of 100 parts, taken at random from a lot in which the known fraction defective is .02, would be:

---

[1] $p(r)$ means: the probability of r successes in n successive Bernoulli *trials*, given that the probability of success in one trial is p. Note that 0! is defined as 1.

$$P(d \le 2) = (.02)^0(.98)^{100-0} \times \frac{100\,!}{0\,!\,(100-0)\,!}$$
$$+ (.02)^1(.98)^{100-1} \times \frac{100\,!}{1\,!\,(100-1)\,!}$$
$$+ (.02)^2(.98)^{100-2} \times \frac{100\,!}{2\,!\,(100-2)\,!}$$
$$= 0.63.$$

FIGURE 8–1

Binomial Distribution

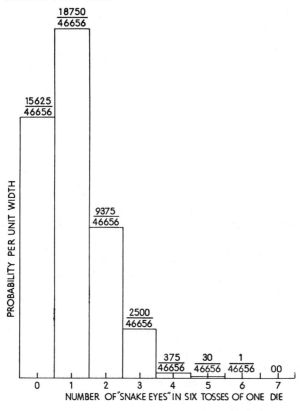

Controlling the quality of incoming parts in a manufacturing process is important. Inspecting *all* incoming parts is sometimes not desirable, as when the inspection process is destructive; it is frequently not economical, as when the cost of inspection is high and the consequences of passing defectives is low; and finally 100 percent inspection is not always 100 percent effective.

A commonly employed procedure, then, is to select at random from a lot whose quality is unknown a sample of size n, to inspect all the members of that sample, and to accept the lot from which the sample was taken if c or fewer defective parts are found.

Suppose that we had a plan in which the random sample is of size n, and we plan to accept the lot if we find c or fewer defectives and to reject it otherwise. Since each part is either good or defective our inspection process is a Bernoulli process, and it can be portrayed by the binomial probability distribution. If the actual quality of the lot is p (that is, the fraction defective is p, and therefore the probability that any one part is defective is p) then the probability that we will find c or fewer in a sample of size n is:

$$P(d \leq c) = (p)^0(1 - p)^{n-o} \times \frac{n\ !}{0\ !\ (n - 0)\ !}$$
$$+ (p)^1(1 - p)^{n-1} \times \frac{n\ !}{1\ !\ (n - 1)\ !}$$
$$.$$
$$.$$
$$+ (p)^c(1 - p)^{n-c} \times \frac{n\ !}{c\ !\ (n - c)\ !}$$

By using the model above and by letting the actual quality of the incoming product vary with the fraction defective increasing from, say, 0.02 through 0.08, we can gather data and plot a curve that portrays the relationship between the actual incoming quality and the probability of our accepting a lot, thus showing how well our sampling plan (i.e., $n = 100$, $c = 2$) discriminates between good and bad lots.

The model above is also useful in determining the optimum job shop order size, as we will see. To minimize the computation involved we would like to compose a FORTRAN program that will calculate $P(d \leq c)$ in the expression above. Let us begin by composing a program for determining $\dfrac{n\ !}{c\ !\ (n - c)\ !}$ in the expression:

$$P(c) = (p)^c(1 - p)^{n-c} \times \frac{n\ !}{c\ !\ (n - c)\ !}.$$

We *could* determine each of the three individual factorials, then form the desired product and quotient. However, $n\ !$ may be a very large number, exceeding the capacity of the computer. It must occur to us that perhaps we could do what is desired with logarithms.

Some Reminders about Logarithms

Recall that the logarithm of a number is the power to which some base (usually 10, or $e = 2.718$ . . .) must be raised to produce the original number. Thus 2 is the logarithm of 100 in the base 10 system since:

$$10^2 \overset{\text{the logarithm}}{=} \quad \text{the original number}$$

the
base

Any real number can be represented by its logarithm. That is, in the "logarithm domain" (to the base 10) 100 is 2, and 10,000 is 4.

Recall further that multiplying in the "arithmetic domain" is the equivalent of adding in the logarithm domain. Thus to multiply 100 by 1,000 we first represent these two factors by their logarithms:

Let 2 represent 100

and

" 3 " 1,000

. . . we then add these logarithm equivalents: $2 + 3 = 5$, and return to the arithmetic domain to produce the answer: 10,000. That is:

$$
\begin{aligned}
100 \times 1,000 = 10^2 \times 10^3 &= \text{antilog } (\log 100 + \log 1{,}000) \\
&= \text{antilog } (2 + 3) \\
&= \text{antilog } (5) \\
&= 10{,}000.
\end{aligned}
$$

Now, clearly:

$$
\begin{aligned}
4\,! = 4 \times 3 \times 2 \times 1 \\
= \text{antilog } (\log 4 + \log 3 + \log 2 + \log 1).
\end{aligned}
$$

Finally, since $1/n = n^{-1}$ we can write:

$$
\frac{n\,!}{c\,!\,(n-c)\,!} = \text{antilog } (\log(n\,!) - [\log(c\,!) + \log(n - c)\,!]).
$$

Let us assume that when the computer encounters the expression $\text{ALOG}(X)$ to the right of the equal sign in an algebraic instruction it replaces it with the logarithm of the quantity in parentheses (X, in this case) to the base of the natural logarithms, e. With the following statements we can cause the computer to calculate the logarithm of $N\,!$ and store it at address T1:

```
N = _____
T1 = 0.0
DO 1 J = 1,N
D = J
1   T1 = T1 + ALOG(D)
```

Let us store at address IC the value of c. With the following program segment we can also find the logarithms of $c!$ and $(n - c)!$:

```
IC = _____
T2 = 0.0
DO 2 J = 1,IC
D = J
2   T2 = T2 + ALOG(D)
L = N - IC
T3 = 0.0
DO 3 J = 1,L
D = J
3   T3 = T3 + ALOG(D)
```

Recognizing that $\dfrac{n!}{c!\,(n-c)!}$ may be a very large quantity, we may do well to postpone finding the antilog and instead continue using logarithms in solving for the desired probability. Notice that if

$$C1 = (p)^c(1 - p)^{n-c}$$

then:

$$\log(C1) = (c)\log(p) + (n - c)\log(1 - p)$$

It follows that we should be able to calculate and store at address C1 the logarithm of the first group of terms in our binomial model as follows:

```
S1 = IC
S2 = N
C1 = S1 * ALOG(P) + (S2 - S1) * ALOG(1.0 - P)
```

We can now calculate the logarithm of the probability of finding c defective parts in a lot of size n, when the actual fraction defective in the lot is p, by adding the program segment: C3 = C1 + T1 − (T2 + T3).

Another FORTRAN function is EXP(X). When the computer encounters this expression to the right of an equal sign it replaces it with the base of the natural logarithms (i.e., e) raised to the power expressed in the parentheses.

Since C3 in the FORTRAN statement above is the *logarithm* of our answer, our answer (the antilog of C3 and hence the probability of our encountering IC defective parts) can be calculated and stored at address PROB by adding the statement: PROB = EXP(C3).

Our total program at this stage, with the initializing statements gathered together at the beginning, appears as follows:

```
      IC = _____
      N = _____
      P = _____
      T1 = 0.0
      DO 1 J = 1,N
      D = J
    1 T1 = T1 + ALOG(D)
      T2 = 0.0
      DO 2 J = 1,IC
      D = J
    2 T2 = T2 + ALOG(D)
      L = N - IC
      T3 = 0.0
      DO 3 J = 1,L
      D = J
    3 T3 = T3 + ALOG(D)
      S1 = IC
      S2 = N
      C1 = S1 * ALOG(P) + (S2 - S1) * ALOG(1.0 - P)
      C3 = C1 + T1 - (T2 + T3)
      PROB = EXP(C3)
```

Since we want to know the probability of our encountering *c or fewer* defective parts we must now add to our model a component that will cause the computer to sum the probabilities calculated by the program above, as *c* varies from 0 through *c*. We can easily sum the probabilities from IC to 1. We simply place all the statements in our program above in the space left blank among the following statements:

```
      TPROB = 0.0
      DO 4 K = 1,KC
      IC = K
               .
               .
               .
    4 TPROB = TPROB + PROB
```

Now stored at TPROB is the probability desired *except* for the component:

$$(p)^o (1 - p)^{n-o} \times \frac{n\,!}{o\,!\,(n-o)\,!}$$

but since this term is simply $(1-p)^n$ we add the statement: TPROB = TPROB + (1.0 − P) ** N.

Our general model for determining the probability of encountering KC or fewer defectives in a random sample of size N, from a universe whose actual fraction defective is P, appears in Figure 8–2.

We could place this model in an appropriate DO loop, allow the actual incoming quality P to vary, and see how a given sampling

FIGURE 8–2

```
    KC = ___9___
    N = ___100___
    P = ___.02___
    TPROB = 0.0
    DO 4 K = 1,KC
    IC = K
    T1 = 0.0
    DO 1 J = 1,N
    D = J
  1 T1 = T1 + ALOG(D)
    T2 = 0.0
    DO 2 J = 1,IC
    D = J
  2 T2 = T2 + ALOG(D)
    L = N − IC
    T3 = 0.0
    DO 3 J = 1,L
    D = J
  3 T3 = T3 + ALOG(D)
    S1 = IC
    S2 = N
    C1 = S1 * ALOG(P) + (S2 − S1) * ALOG(1.0 − P)
    C3 = C1 + T1 − (T2 + T3)
    PROB = EXP(C3)
  4 TPROB = TPROB + PROB
    TPROB = TPROB + (1.0 − P) ** N
    WRITE (6,5)N,KC,P,TPROB
  5 FORMAT ( )
    STOP
    END
```

plan (set of values for N and KC, representing n and c, respectively) discriminates between good and bad lots. We will leave this for the exercises.

Exponentiation on the computer is a good deal slower than other algebraic operations. Our proposed program above can involve the computer in computation that may be rather time-consuming, particularly when n is a large number. We might reduce this rather drastically at a slight sacrifice in accuracy by employing Stirling's approximation of n ! :

$$n \ ! \approx e^{-n}(n)^n \sqrt{2\pi n}$$

When $n = 10$ Stirling's approximation of n ! differs from n ! by about 1.1 percent. As n increases, the error decreases so that for large values of n Stirling's approximation is quite dependable. Further use of Stirling's approximation will be reserved for the exercises at the end of the chapter.

Another use for the binomial probability distribution in decision making has to do with the determination of the optimum production lot size. An example will illustrate the problem.

Optimum Job Shop Order Size

Filling a customer's order requires delivery of $N = 100$ units of a particular product. Experience has shown that when the production process which makes this item is under control, the fraction defectives produced is $p = .04$. Setup cost to make the product is $S = \$300$ per setup, and the variable cost is $C = \$4$ per unit produced.

If with the first setup M units are produced and M minus the number of defectives D is greater than N, the excess is a loss. If $M - D$ is less than N it is necessary to set up again and produce $N - (M{-}D)$ units to make up the deficit. (Assume that zero defectives are produced on the makeup setup.)

We want to know how many units M should be ordered to minimize the expected cost of delivering $N = 100$ units.

There are two sets of costs. One set is the cost of the first setup to produce M units, $S + C \times M$. The other set is the expected cost associated with the second seutp. For any M there is an associated expected shortage. If a second setup is required it will be because $(M{-}D) < N$. The possible shortages (and hence the possible units required on the makeup setup) are:

$$100 - (M - D) = 1$$
$$100 - (M - D) = 2$$
$$100 - (M - D) = 3$$
$$\cdot$$
$$\cdot$$
$$100 - (M - D) = 100$$

Therefore:

when $D = M - 100 + 1$　the shortage will be 1;
" $D = M - 100 + 2$　"　"　"　" 2;
" $D = M - 100 + 3$　"　"　"　" 3;
.
.
" $D = M - 100 + 100$ "　"　"　" 100.

The expected shortage will be the sum of the products of (1) the possible shortages, and (2) their probabilities or:

$$\sum_{D=M-100+1}^{M} [100 - (M - D)]P(D)$$

where $P(D)$ is the probability of generating D defectives in a lot of M when the probability that any one is defective is $p = .04$. The expected setup cost for the second setup would be the cost of a setup times the probability that $M-D < 100$, or $D > M-100$, which we might express thus: $S \times P(D > M-100)$.

The expected cost associated with the second setup would therefore be:

$$S \times P(D > M - 100) + C \times \sum_{D=M-100+1}^{M} [100 - (M - D)]P(D)$$

and the expected total cost for both setups would be:

$$S + C \times M + S \times P(D > M - 100) + C \times \sum_{D=M-100+1}^{M} [100 - (M - D)]P(D)$$

　↑　　↑
Fixed　Varia-
cost　ble
　　cost　　　　Expected fixed　　　　　Expected variable
　　　　　　　　　cost　　　　　　　　　　cost

　└──────┬──────┘　└────────────────┬────────────────┘
Cost of first　　　　　　　　Cost of second
setup　　　　　　　　　　　setup

Our objective is to solve for that value M which minimizes the function above. Since the optimum value for M cannot be less than N we might begin with $M = 100$, evaluate the function, increment

M by 1, evaluate the function again, and continue until we find that further increases in M do not pay. The solution will be reserved for the exercises.

We have considerably simplified the job shop order size problem by assuming that no defects will be produced on the makeup setup. In fact, the problem is of the following character: How many should we order, knowing that if we fail to produce enough acceptable units, a second setup will be required, and we will again be confronted with the same problem—this time involving a smaller required output. The number we select to produce on the first setup and all subsequent possible setups cannot be determined in isolation but must consider the number to be produced in subsequent setups. Therefore we must search for an optimum combination of order sizes.[2]

THE POISSON DISTRIBUTION

Having some conversancy with the binomial distribution we can easily understand the Poisson distribution. We are interested in the Poisson distribution chiefly because of its importance in queuing systems. One or more random components in many queue systems can frequently be approximated by the Poisson distribution. We will find that distribution particularly useful as we try to assess the probability of varying numbers of customers arriving at a service facility, in a unit of time.

Let us begin by imagining a machine producing insulated wire in which defects are found to occur at random, but to average 1,000 defects per 1,000 feet of wire—or 1 defect per foot as a mean or expected number of defects per foot of wire.

We will try to develop a model to determine the probability of 2 defects in 1 foot of wire. To do this, let us imagine that we cut a 1-foot piece of the wire into 6 equal segments, each segment 2 inches long. Now the expected number of defects in all 6 pieces is 1. Yet, of course, we view 2 defects as a possibility, and we want to know what is the probability of 2 defects.

If we could be sure that one, but no more than one, defect could occur in *each* of our 6 pieces, we could then view the experiment as a Bernoulli process, corresponding precisely to our experiment with the die. In that experiment we knew that the expected number of

---

[2] D. J. White treats this problem in "Dynamic Programming & Systems of Uncertain Duration," *Management Science*, September 1965, p. 37.

snake eyes in 6 tosses was 1; and that the probability of a snake
eyes in one toss was 1/6. Similarly, with our 6 small pieces of wire,
the expected number of defects in all 6 pieces together is one, and
the probability of a defect in any one piece is 1/6.

By dividing our 1-foot length of wire into 6 equal pieces, and by
assuming that not more than 1 defect in any one piece is possible, we
make our wire-inspecting experiment a Bernoulli process, precisely
like the experiment with the toss of a die. In the toss of the die we
knew that the expected number of snake eyes in 6 tosses was 1. Similarly, the expected number of defects in our 6 pieces of wire is 1.

In the case of the die we knew that 2 snake eyes in 6 tosses is
possible; that 3 snake eyes is possible—or 4, 5, or 6—but no more.
In the die experiment a toss of the die was a trial; in the case of the
wire, inspection of one piece is a trial. In the case of the die snake
eyes was success in a trial; in the wire experiment encountering a
defect is success. And as in the die experiment, we know that 2 defects might be encountered among our 6 pieces of wire; 3 might be
encountered; or 4, 5, or 6; but no more than 6 (since we've assumed
that more than 1 defect in any one of our 2-inch pieces is impossible).

Thus by assuming that no more than one defect can occur in any
one of the six pieces, we have made a Bernoulli process out of our
inspection of the wire. The binomial distribution governs, and we
can easily calculate the probabilities of various numbers of defects.
Thus the probability of 2 defects in the 6 pieces is:

$$p(2) = (1/6)^2(5/6)^{6-2} \times \frac{6\ !}{2\ !\ (6-2)\ !}.$$

Clearly, however, the above is only an approximation of the real
probability of encountering 2 defects in our 1-foot piece of wire because of our assumption that each 2-inch piece has no more than
one defect. It should occur to us, however, that if instead of dividing
our 1-foot piece of wire into 6 pieces we divide it into 60 pieces, then
each piece is smaller, and hence our assumption that the process is
a Bernoulli process becomes more nearly valid. If we do this, and
then employ the binomial distribution to determine the probability
of 2 defects in our 1-foot piece, we have:

$$p(2) = (1/60)^2(59/60)^{60-2} \times \frac{60\ !}{2\ !\ (60-2)\ !}.$$

(Note that when we divide the 1-foot piece of wire into 60 rather
than 6 pieces we no longer have a process precisely like that of the

toss of the die. Whereas in 60 tosses of the die we can expect 10 snake eyes, in our 60 pieces of wire the expected number of defects is still only 1. The probability of any of our 60 pieces having a defect is therefore 1/60, and the probability of any 1 piece not having a defect is 59/60. However, the process is still thoroughly Bernoulli, and this is all that matters: our binomial distribution still governs, and we can use it to calculate the probabilities of various numbers of defects in our 1-foot length of wire, the maximum possible now being 60.)

If 60 pieces is a better basis for approximation, then it must occur to us that if we could divide the 1-foot piece of wire into *still smaller* pieces we would approach the point where more than 1 defect in any 1 piece is so unlikely that we could, with impunity, assume it to be impossible. Then our model would give us the real probability of 2 defects in a 1-foot piece of wire. Pursuing this logic, we would ask ourselves what value $p(2)$ approaches as n approaches infinity in the expression:

$$p(2) = \left[\frac{1}{n}\right]^2 \left[\frac{n-1}{n}\right]^{n-2} \times \frac{n!}{2!(n-2)!}.$$

It develops that as n approaches infinity the limit of this expression (and hence the probability of our encountering 2 defects in our 1-foot piece of wire) is:

$$p(2) = \frac{e^{-1}(1)^2}{2!},$$

where e is the base of natural logarithms. The 1s in the above expression represent the average or the expected number of defects in a unit length of wire (1 in our model), and so for the more general model we can write:

$$p(2) = \frac{e^{-\lambda}(\lambda)^2}{2!},$$

where $\lambda =$ the average number of defects *per unit* of length.

In *our* model we were looking for the probability of two defects, or successes; for a more general model we can write:

$$p(r) = \frac{e^{-\lambda}(\lambda)^r}{r!}. \tag{8-1}$$

Equation (8-1) portrays the Poisson distribution, and with it we can determine the probabilities of various numbers of defects, r, in a foot of wire—for example, given that the average number of defects in a foot of wire is λ. Such a distribution is shown in Figure 8–3.

We can also use the Poisson distribution to determine the probability of various numbers of arrivals at a service facility in a unit of time, given the expected or average number per unit of time. Thus Figure 8–2 might be viewed as giving us the probability of 1, 2, 3, and so on, customers arriving at our service facility in one hour, given that the average or expected rate of arrival is 1, 2, 3, or 4 customers per hour. We can go further, using this model, and determine the probabilities of various numbers of customers arriving in *any* period of time, the expected number of customers during any period of time, and the like.

This is predicated, of course, on the assumption that arrivals occur in a fashion characterized by the Poisson distribution. (Customers might arrive in some pattern other than Poisson. The fact is, however, that in a number of real situations, arrivals tend to approximate Poisson, and the Poisson distribution therefore is useful for other than purely theoretical purposes.)

Variance of the Poisson Process

One of the unique properties of the Poisson process is that its variance and its mean are equal. Therefore the standard deviation of a Poisson process is the square root of its mean. Since any Poisson process is uniquely specified by its mean (or its variance or standard deviation) the Poisson process is a one-parameter process.

The normal distribution, on the other hand, is a two-parameter distribution. Both the mean and the standard deviation (or variance) must be specified to distinguish one normal process from another.

The Poisson process is a discrete process. We would never use expression (8–1) to determine the probability of finding $2\frac{3}{4}$ defects in a foot of wire, or for finding the probability that $7\frac{1}{6}$ customers would arrive in an hour.

The Poisson distribution is also a "zero crossing" distribution. We never evaluate (8–1) for negative values of r; we never ask the probability of –4 customers arriving in a period of time.

Referring to Figure 8–3 it is apparent that the histogram which is the Poisson distribution becomes more skewed (flattened) as the mean increases. This should be expected since the variance equals the mean. Its histogram also begins to approach the bell shape of the normal distribution as the mean increases. However, the Poisson distribution would be unsuitable for approximating a process with a large mean and a *small* variance, even if that process seemed symmetrical about its mean (bell shaped).

Compound Probability Distributions

The Poisson probability function (expression **8–1**) is one of a group of discrete probability functions which can be expressed in closed form. A particular Poisson distribution could, of course, be expressed in tabular form. Consider, for example, the following compound probability problem.

A health center consists of two clinics, clinic A and clinic B. The probability distribution for arriving patients in clinic A is approximated by the following distribution:

A

Patients Arriving per Hour	*Probability*
0	.1
1	.4
2	.3
3	.1
4	.1

The arrival pattern at the other clinic is found to be approximated by the Poisson distribution with a mean of three patients per hour. We would like to know the probability distribution for the health center; that is, both clinics together.

Using expression (**8–1**) (or the next to last histogram in Figure 8–3) we have distribution B, below, for the second clinic.

B

Patients Arriving per Hour	*Probability*
0	.049
1	.149
2	.224
3	.224
4	.168
5	.101
6	.054
7	.021

Our problem is like that posed in Table 7–4, Chapter 7. To produce the compound distribution we *convolve* the two distributions as shown below.

Distribution A

	.1	.4	.3	.1	.1
.049	.004	.019	.014	.004	.004
.149	.014	.059	.044	.014	.014
.224	.022	.089	.067	.022	.022
.224	.022	.089	.067	.022	.022
.168	.016	.067	.050	.016	.016
.101	.010	.040	.030	.010	.040
.054	.005	.021	.016	.005	.005
.021	.002	.008	.006	.002	.002

(Distribution B labels the row values: .049, .149, .224, .224, .168, .101, .054, .021)

Summing the products in the diagonals we produce the compound distribution:

Total Patients per Hour	Probability
0	.004
1	.033
2	.095
3	.159
4	.190
5	.180
6	.139
7	.091
8	.050
9	.050
10	.007
11	.002

THE NEGATIVE EXPONENTIAL DISTRIBUTION

In our wire-inspecting experiment we observed that the number of defects encountered per unit length of wire was a random variable, Poisson distributed. What if we had observed, not the number of defects in successive units of length of wire, but rather the number of units of length of wire *between defects?* We would have found that the distance between defects is "negative exponentially distributed."

Whereas the variable whose probability is specified by the Poisson *probability function* is a discrete variable, the *density function* of the negative exponential distribution specifies a continuous variable. Whereas only a whole number of customers will arrive in an hour, the time between arrivals might be any nonnegative number.

This being the case we specify the negative exponential distribution by a density function, as we do the normal distribution. The density function of the negative exponential distribution is:[3]

---

[3] Where *e* is the base of the natural logarithms and is approximately 2.718.

FIGURE 8–3

Poisson Distributions

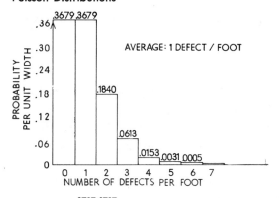

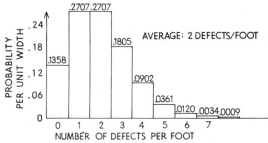

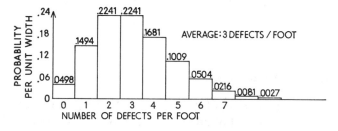

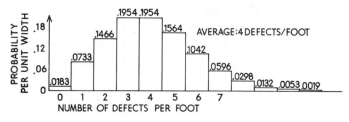

$$f(t) = \lambda e^{-\lambda t} \tag{8-2}$$

. . . with a mean value of $1/\lambda$.

The cumulative probability function for the negative exponential distribution is:

$$F(t) = e^{-\lambda t}. \tag{8-3}$$

The negative exponential distribution is the product of a Poisson process. If the number of customers arriving in successive units of time is a random variable, Poisson distributed, then the time between arrivals will be a random variable negative exponentially distributed. If the mean number of arrivals per hour is 6 (one every 10 minutes, on the average) then the mean time between arrivals will be 10 minutes: $\frac{1}{6}$ of an hour.

If the arrival pattern is Poisson with a mean of λ customers per unit of time, the mean time between arrivals will be $1/\lambda$ units of time.

Expression (8-3) gives the probability that the time between arrivals will exceed t units of time, given that the mean time between arrivals is $1/\lambda$ units of time. Thus if customers are arriving at a mean rate of 6 per hour, the probability that the time between arrivals will be greater than two hours is:

$$F(2) = e^{-(1/6)(2)} = e^{-1/3}.$$

THE GAMMA DISTRIBUTION

Like the negative exponential distribution the gamma distribution is the product of a Poisson process. Given a Poisson arrival process, if we record the time between the most recent arrival and the nth succeeding arrival, for each value of n we would have a different gamma distributed variable. The negative exponential distribution is therefore a special case of the gamma distribution; one in which n has a value of 1.

The Poisson, negative exponential and gamma distributions are all zero-crossing distributions: they do not generate negative values.

We observed in connection with the Poisson process that while, as its mean increases the histogram of the process assumes a bell-shaped form, we cannot approximate with the Poisson process a process with a large mean and small variance. Such a process can frequently be closely approximated by one or another gamma distribution, however. For this and other reasons the gamma distribution is useful in modeling many real world systems.

We will have more to say about the gamma distribution in the next chapter.

SUGGESTION FOR FURTHER STUDY

Schlaifer, Robert. *Analysis of Decisions under Uncertainty.* New York: McGraw-Hill Book Co., 1969.

EXERCISES

1. Stirling's approximation should be shown in correction 20, above.

Compose a FORTRAN program that will compare, for accuracy, Stirling's approximation of n ! with actual values of n ! as n varies from 1 through 10.

2. Using the model of Figure 8–2, determine the probability of accepting lots whose actual quality is $p = .02$, given the sampling plan: $n = 100$ and $c = 8$.

3. Plot a family of "Operating Characteristic" curves for sampling plans with acceptance number $c = 2$ and $n = 4$, 14, 24, 34, 44, 54, 64, 74, 84, and 94, as incoming quality varies from 0.00 through 0.10 by increments of 0.01. Plot actual incoming quality, p, on the horizontal axis and the probability of acceptance on the vertical axis. (Suitably modified, the program of Figure 8–2 may be used for generating the data required.)

4. A common inspection procedure for controlling outgoing quality is as follows. From a lot of N a sample of n is selected at random.

  a)   If c or fewer defectives are found:
  1) The defectives in the sample are replaced by good ones.
  2) The rest of the lot $(N - n)$ is passed without further inspection.
  b)   If more than c defectives are found the entire lot is inspected, and any and all defectives are replaced.

Since some defectives are replaced, this inspection procedure serves as a filter, and we can be sure that on the average the outgoing quality is superior to the incoming quality. For actual incoming quality with fraction defectives p the expected outgoing quality can be found as follows. When more than c defectives are found and the entire lot N is inspected, zero defectives are passed. When c or fewer defectives are found the expected *number of defectives* passed is: (the expected *number* passed when a lot is passed without 100 percent inspection) *times* (the probability a lot is passed without 100 percent inspection) or:

$$(N - n)p \times P(d \leq c)$$

where $P(d \leq c)$ is the probability that the number of defectives encountered in sample n is less than or equal to c.

Therefore the expected *fraction defectives* passed, *AOQ*, would be:

$$\text{Average Outgoing Quality, } AOQ = \frac{(N - n)p \times P(d \leq c)}{N}$$

Given a particular sampling plan (thus $n = 100$, $c = 2$), if we calculate *AOQ* as the actual incoming quality p varies from 0.00 to 0.08 we can plot a curve that portrays the expected behavior of our filter. For this particular inspection plan (i.e., $n = 100$, $c = 2$) the curve appears below. As we should expect, when the incoming quality is very good the outgoing quality is very good. As the incoming quality worsens, the outgoing quality worsens, but beyond some point, *AOQL*, the outgoing quality improves as we find ourselves performing 100 percent inspection more frequently.

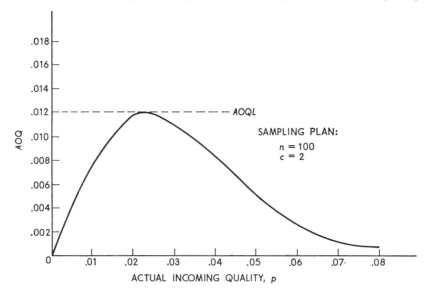

Associated with any sampling plan there is a maximum expected fraction defective outgoing quality or average outgoing quality limit, *AOQL*.

Compose a FORTRAN program that will find the value for n (the sample size) which, coupled with an acceptance number $c = 2$, will cause the *AOQL* to be 0.01, given $N = 1,000$.

5. Assume in acceptance sampling that we consider $AQL = .02$ to be good quality—quality we would like to have a low probability of rejecting (AQL suggests acceptable quality level). Assume that we consider $LTPD = .08$ to be bad quality—quality we would like to have a high

probability of rejecting (*LTPD* suggests lot tolerance percent defective). Specifically, suppose that we would like to have a probability of $a = .05$ of rejecting incoming lots with actual quality $AQL = .02$, and we would like to have a probability of $b = .10$ of accepting lots with actual quality $LTPD = .08$. Recalling the purpose of the model of Figure 8–3, we might conceive of the optimum sampling plan that would give this expected experience if we reason as follows.

First condition that must prevail:

$$1 - a = AQL^o(1 - AQL)^{n-o}\frac{n!}{o!(n-o)!}$$

$$+ AQL^1(1 - AQL)^{n-1}\frac{n!}{1!(n-1)!}$$

$$+ \ldots AQL^c(1 - AQL)^{n-c}\frac{n!}{c!(n-c)!}. \qquad (1)$$

Second condition that must prevail:

$$b = LTPD^o(1 - LTPD)^{n-o}\frac{n!}{o!(n-o)!}$$

$$+ \ldots LTPD^c(1 - LTPD)^{n-c}\frac{n!}{c!(n-c)!}. \qquad (2)$$

If we divide Expression (1) by $(1 - a)$ and Expression (2) by b, their *difference* will be zero, and we can write:

$$\left[\frac{AQL^o(1 - AQL)^{n-o}}{1 - a}\frac{n!}{o!(n-o)!} + \ldots \frac{AQL^c(1 - AQL)^{n-c}}{1 - a}\frac{n!}{c!(n-c)!}\right]$$

$$- \left[\frac{LTPD^o(1 - LTPD)^{n-o}}{b}\frac{n!}{o!(n-o)!}\right.$$

$$\left. + \ldots \frac{LTPD^c(1 - LTPD)^{n-c}}{b}\frac{n!}{c!(n-c)!}\right] = 0$$

or:

$$\frac{n!}{(1-a)b}\left\{\left[\frac{bAQL^o(1 - AQL)^{n-o}}{o!(n-o)!} + \ldots \frac{bAQL^c(1 - AQL)^{n-c}}{c!(n-c)!}\right]\right.$$

$$- \left[\frac{(1-a)LTPD^o(1 - LTPD)^{n-o}}{o!(n-o)!}\right.$$

$$\left.\left. + \ldots \frac{(1-a)LTPD^c(1 - LTPD)^{n-c}}{c!(n-c)!}\right]\right\} = 0.$$

But since $\dfrac{n!}{(1-a)b} \neq 0$, we can write:

$$\left[\frac{bAQL^o(1 - AQL)^{n-o}}{o!(n-o)!} + \ldots \frac{bAQL^c(1 - AQL)^{n-c}}{c!(n-c)!}\right]$$

$$- \left[\frac{(1-a)LTPD^o(1 - LTPD)^{n-o}}{o!(n-o)!}\right.$$

$$\left. + \ldots \frac{(1-a)LTPD^c(1 - LTPD)^{n-c}}{c!(n-c)!}\right] = 0$$

or more economically:

$$\sum_{z=0}^{c} \frac{bAQL^z(1 - AQL)^{n-z} - (1 - a)LTPD^z(1 - LTPD)^{n-z}}{z!(n-z)!} = 0. \quad (3)$$

We would like that combination of values for c and n which causes expression (3) to most closely approximate zero. *Note:* In the event that several combinations of c and n appear suitable we should choose that combination in which n is smallest, to minimize inspection costs.

Compose a FORTRAN program that will find an appropriate sampling plan (value for n and c).

6. Refer to the discussion of the optimum job shop order quantity, in this chapter. Compose a FORTRAN program that will cause the computer to determine and print out the expected costs associated with a production order for $N = 101, 102, 103 \ldots 130$ units, and identify the optimum order size for the first setup.

7. Autos passing a toll station are found to arrive at a mean rate of 13 per minute from 4:00 to 6:00 each afternoon, Monday through Friday. A study of the arrival pattern shows that it can be closely approximated by the Poisson distribution.

a)   What is the probability that 45 autos will arrive in a minute?
b)   What is the probability that from 43 to 48 will arrive in a minute?
c)   What is the probability that more than 10 seconds will elapse between an arrival and its immediate successor?
d)   What is the probability that between 10 and 20 seconds will elapse between an arrival and its immediate successor?

chapter 9

Basic Queuing Concepts

THE UNCERTAINTIES associated with queuing phenomena are attributable to randomness—or what seems to be randomness—in certain system parameters. Let us consider Pete's Two-Minute Auto Wash as an illustration.

PETE'S TWO–MINUTE AUTO WASH

Two minutes are required for washing each car in Pete's facility. There is only one wash facility, and it can accommodate only one auto at a time.

If customers arrived exactly at two-minute intervals no uncertainties would be associated with the operation of Pete's auto wash. If the system (i.e., the wash facility plus any customers waiting to enter the wash facility) began operations with six customers in it, there would always be exactly six customers in the system.

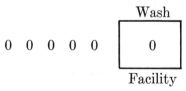

If the system began operations empty, there would always be one customer in the facility and zero customers in the queue. In either case the wash facility would be busy continually, and whatever state prevailed at the beginning of operations would continue.

However, Pete's customers do not arrive at exact two-minute intervals. Customers average two minutes between arrivals, but the arrival pattern is random with the following distribution.

Time between Arrivals (Minutes)	Relative Frequency (Percent)
1	40
2	30
3	20
4	10
	100

On the morning of June 1, no customers were in Pete's auto wash system when it opened for business at 9 A.M. Pete's first customer arrived one minute after time zero; i.e., one minute after 9 A.M., when operations began. The arrival times of the first and the succeeding five customers are shown in Table 9–1.

TABLE 9–1
Time Data of First Six Customers at Pete's Auto Wash

Customer Number	Time of Arrival	Time since Previous Arrival	Time Entered Wash Facility	Time Departed Wash Facility	Total Time in System (Minutes)
1	9:01	–	9:01	9:03	2
2	9:04	3	9:04	9:06	2
3	9:06	2	9:06	9:08	2
4	9:09	3	9:09	9:11	2
5	9:10	1	9:11	9:13	3
6	9:11	1	9:13	9:15	4

It is apparent from Table 9–1 that the first four customers entered the wash facility the moment they arrived. When customers five and six arrived the wash facility was occupied, and they were obliged to wait. During the first 15 minutes of operations the wash facility had been idle 3 minutes, and the average customer had spent 2½ minutes in the system.

During the first 15 minutes of operation the average time between arrivals was 2 minutes. Thus, even though customers arrived at the same average rate at which the wash facility could service them, customers waited (queues existed) 20 percent of the time, the wash facility was idle 20 percent of the time, and the average customer spent 2½ minutes in the system.

The randomness of the time between arrivals and the time required for service is responsible for the queuing phenomenon. In the schematic which follows 13 customers arrived at a service facility in a particular one-hour interval. The times required to service them varied from 1/100 hour to 1/5 hour, as shown. The mean time required for service during that hour was just under .06 hours. Thus customers were arriving at a mean rate of 16 per hour and they could be accommodated at a rate just above that. Yet by virtue of the random grouping of six customers early in the hour, each of whom required well in excess of the average time required for service, most of the arrivals spent some time in a queue.

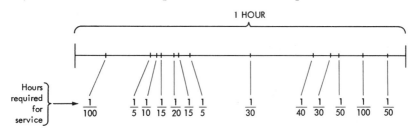

In business and economic systems the queuing phenomenon is omnipresent. At time machines are idle; at other times customers must wait. At times inventories are excessive, and stock sits idle; at other times needs go unsatisfied. At times an industry operates at half capacity, workers are unemployed, and capital is idle. At other times capacity is taxed, labor is critically short, and suppliers have large files of unfilled orders (back order queues).

Neither extreme is desirable, and a basic management decision involves a balance between the costs of idle men, facilities, and materials on the one hand, and the costs associated with a low level of service on the other hand. To make decisions of this type, management must know something about the behavior of a given queue system; that is, given some knowledge of the pattern of demand on a service facility (if the capacity of the facility to provide service is varied) management must know how the following are affected:

1. Queue lengths.
2. Percent utilization of the service facility.
3. Total system time (time spent waiting plus service time).

Management needs to know the expected or average data concerning the system attributes, but it also needs to know *more*. The following two waiting lines have the same average length (15 customers) but their differences are of considerable significance.

Waiting Line No. 1		Waiting Line No. 2	
Length	Relative Frequency (Percent)	Length	Relative Frequency (Percent)
5	10	5	1
10	20	10	10
15	40	15	78
20	20	20	10
25	10	25	1

In view of the prevalence of queuing phenomena and the importance of an understanding of these phenomena for the analysis of complex system, it is appropriate that we pursue some of the theory associated with queuing.

Kinds of Queue Systems

One queue system is distinguished from another by a number of attributes. Chief among them are:

1. The number of phases.
2. The number of channels.
3. The queue discipline.

Some of these attributes are illustrated below.

SINGLE–CHANNEL, SINGLE–PHASE SYSTEM:

Input ⟶ 0 0 0 0 ☐ ⟶ output

↑ Arriving customers   ↑ Service facility

SINGLE–CHANNEL, MULTIPHASE SYSTEM:

0 0 0 0 ☐ → 0 0 0 0 ☐ → 0 0 0 ☐ →

MULTICHANNEL, SINGLE–PHASE SYSTEM:

0 0 0 { ☐ ⟶ \
          ☐ ⟶

MULTIPHASE, MULTICHANNEL SYSTEM:

0 0 0 0 { ☐ →0 0 ☐ ⟶ \
          ☐ ⟶0 ☐ ⟶ 0 0 0 ☐ ⟶

Queue discipline has to do with whether arrivals are accommodated on a first-come, first-served basis or on the basis of some other priority rule.

In more complex queue systems customers may leave a facility, then circle back and reenter one passed through before, depending on their discovered needs and the capacity of the various facilities to accommodate those needs.

By the *behavior* of a queue system we mean the way arriving customers interact with its service facilities. The needs of the arriving customers and the capacity of the facilities to accommodate them determine the nature of this interaction.

By "customers" we mean entities whose arrival places demands on some facility. Customers may be arriving purchase orders; aircraft at an airport desiring to land or take off; patients in a clinic who, from time to time, ring for a nurse; or machines in a factory which, from time to time, fail and require maintenance.

Queuing Interaction

In Chapter 8 we observed that components in a system may interact in a number of different ways. The queuing phenomenon results from the interaction of the two components' random arrivals and random service time.

The arrival pattern depends on (1) the size of the universe of possible customers, which "generates" customers in need of attention; and (2) the level of their activity, which causes them to require service from time to time.

We will see in this chapter that the interaction between the two components in a queue system is different from the kinds of interaction we've dealt with before, such as the interaction between lead time and demand.

The Classical Elemental Queue System

In Chapter 8 we identified the "elemental system" in the context of flow graph analysis. The elemental *queue* system is a single-channel, single-phase system. In theory any queue system, however complex, can be broken down into a network of such systems.

In order to gain some insight into the nature of the interaction of random arrivals and random service time we will develop a special elemental queue system. By assuming that this system is entirely

Poisson we can simplify the analysis. By this we mean that we will assume that the time between arrivals is negative exponentially distributed and the time required for service is also negative exponentially distributed. Since the negative exponential distribution is a product of the Poisson process, our queue system will be thoroughly Poisson.

We will assume that the service facility can accommodate only one customer at a time (single channel) and that arrivals are serviced on a first-come, first-served basis (the queue discipline). From time to time queues will form before the service facility, and at times the service facility will be idle. We would like to develop a model to predict:

1. The probability of various numbers of customers in the *system* (i.e., in the queue or in the service facility) at any given moment.
2. The expected or average time a customer will spend in the system.
3. The probability that the service facility will be idle.

Let us begin by assuming that the service facility is so equipped that it *can* service, on the average, μ customers per unit of time. If the service facility is servicing μ customers per unit of time, on the average, then μ is also the expected number of departures from the service facility during each unit of time. (Observe that μ represents the average number of customers the service facility can service per unit of time, *assuming that the service facility is kept busy, and is not idle.* That is, the service facility could service, say, 15 customers per hour if the moment it completes service on 1 customer, another customer is immediately introduced into the facility. Clearly, if the facility can service 15 per hour but only 3 show up during an hour, it will not service 15 during that hour.)

We are now going to think of t as a *moment* in time. Perhaps t is 8 A.M. We begin observing our queue system at time t. We would like to develop a model for determining the probability of various numbers of customers *in* the system at this moment in time.

To do this, let us think beyond time t by a *fractional* part of one unit of time. This second moment in time with which we are going to concern ourselves is $t + \Delta t$, a fraction of one unit of time *after* time t.

Now let us assume, as we did in developing our Poisson model, that Δt is so small that while one arrival or one departure during interval of time Δt is possible, *more* than one arrival or departure during this fractional part of one unit of time is impossible.

Let us now designate p_n as the probability of n customers in the *system* at some moment in time, *n being equal to or greater than one.* We make this restriction so that we can use μ with confidence; since n is not zero the system (and hence the service facility) is not empty. Now, so long as the service facility always has a customer in it, we can assume that it will, in fact, average μ customers serviced per unit of time.

To get at the problem, let us first ask ourselves what is the probability that there will be n customers in the system at time $t + \Delta t$; that is: $p_n(t + \Delta t)$.

Now, n customers in the system at time $(t + \Delta t)$ can occur in four different mutually exclusive and collectively exhaustive ways.

Way One

We could have n customers in the system at time t; 0 arrivals during interval of time Δt; and 0 departures during interval of time Δt.

Assuming for the moment that $p_n(t)$ is the probability of n in the system at time t, the probability of n in the system at time $t + \Delta t$ can be got at by the following logic. We have assumed that no more than 1 arrival during interval Δt is possible. Therefore, we will have during time interval Δt either 1 arrival or 0 arrivals. The probability of 0 arrivals is 1 minus the probability of 1 arrival. The probability of 1 arrival is $\lambda \Delta t$.

Recall (Chapter 8) that in our wire experiment $\lambda = 1$; that is, the expected number of defects per unit length of wire was 1, and in our wire experiment Δt was 1/6 when we divided our 1 foot of wire into 6 pieces. The probability of 1 defect in Δt in our wire experiment was therefore $(1) \times (1/6)$. It would follow, in a similar way, that the probability of 1 arrival in Δt is $\lambda \Delta t$, and the probability of 0 arrivals during time interval Δt is $(1 - \lambda \Delta t)$.

Now if μ is the expected humber of customers serviced by the service facility during a unit of time, assuming that the facility is not idle, then μ is also the expected number of departures from the facility during a unit of time. Recall that *more* than 1 departure during Δt has been ruled out.

Therefore, as above, the probability of 1 departure from the system (and therefore from the service facility) during time interval

Δt is $\mu\Delta t$. And the probability of 0 departures is $(1 - \mu\Delta t)$. The probability of Way One, then, is: $p_n(t)(1 - \lambda\Delta t)(1 - \mu\Delta t)$.

Way Two

We could have $n - 1$ in the system at moment of time t; 1 arrival during interval of time Δt; and 0 departures during interval of time Δt. Reasoning as above, the probability of Way Two is: $p_{n-1}(t)$ $(\lambda\Delta t)(1 - \mu\Delta t)$.

Way Three

We could have $n + 1$ in the system at moment of time t; 0 arrivals during interval of time Δt; and 1 departure during interval of time Δt. Reasoning as above, the probability of Way Three is: $p_{n+1}(t)(1 - \lambda\Delta t)(\mu\Delta t)$.

Way Four

We could have n in the system at time t; and 1 arrival and 1 departure during interval of time Δt. The probability of this is: $p_n(t)$ $(\lambda\Delta t)(\mu\Delta t)$.

Now the probability of n in the system at moment of time $t + \Delta t$ is the sum of the probabilities of the four individual ways in which it might occur, or:

$$p_n(t + \Delta t) = p_n(t)(1 - \lambda\Delta t)(1 - \mu\Delta t) + p_{n-1}(t)(\lambda\Delta t)(1 - \mu\Delta t) \Big\} + p_{n+1}(t)(1 - \lambda\Delta t)(\mu\Delta t) + p_n(t)(\lambda\Delta t)(\mu\Delta t).$$

Expanding and collecting terms above, transposing $p_n(t)$ to the left side of the equation, dropping infinitesimals of the order $(\Delta t)^2$, and dividing by Δt, we have:

$$\frac{p_n(t + \Delta t) - p_n(t)}{\Delta t} = p_n(t)(-\lambda - \mu) + \lambda p_{n-1}(t) + \mu p_{n+1}(t).$$

Now recall that the above provisional model is somewhat invalid because we assumed that no more than one arrival or departure could occur during the interval of time Δt. Clearly, if as before we make Δt smaller, then our assumption becomes more tenable and our model improves in validity. Specifically, if we allow Δt to approach zero as a limit, the above expression becomes the differential equation:

$$\frac{dp_n(t)}{dt} = -(\lambda + \mu)p_n(t) + \lambda p_{n-1}(t) + \mu p_{n+1}(t). \qquad (9\text{--}1)$$

And now recall that the development above applies to the case where $n \geq 1$. To determine the special case in which $n = 0$, we simply reflect that when $n = 0$ the probability of $n - 1$ is 0, since less than zero customers in the system is impossible. Replacing $p_{n-1}(t)$ by 0 in (9–1), we have:

$$\frac{dp_0(t)}{dt} = -\lambda p_0(t) - \mu p_0(t) + \mu p_1(t).$$

Note that the second term on the right, $-\mu p_0(t)$, has to do with the expected number of departures from the system. This can be checked by once again following through our calculation of the probability of n being encountered in the system. If $n = 0$ the system is empty and there can be no departures. The second term therefore drops out, and our differential equation for the special case where $n = 0$ becomes:

$$\frac{dp_0(t)}{dt} = -\lambda p_0(t) + \mu p_1(t). \tag{9–2}$$

Observe the sense of (9–1) and (9–2). Since the left side is the derivative of the probability of various numbers of customers in the system, and since the derivative is (as shown on the right side of the equal sign) a function of time (i.e., t), it must follow that the probabilities of various numbers of customers in the system changes with time.

This might be expected. If we began our queue system empty at 8 A.M. tomorrow, it is less likely that there would be 10 customers in it at 8:01 than that there would be 10 customers in it at noon. We might further expect that after some time has elapsed (assuming the system continues to operate without interruption for, say, five days) the system would stabilize, so that the probability of finding n in the system at 8 A.M. on the fifth day is about the same as the probability of finding n in the system at 8 A.M. on the fourth day.

While the system is settling down to this stable condition it is said to be in the *transient state*. Once it has settled down, it is said to be in the *steady state*.

In many cases the transient state is very important. In many cases the steady state is very important, and the transient state is rather unimportant. For the moment we will concern ourselves with the steady state only.

By manipulating (9–1) and (9–2) we can develop the model toward which we set out at the beginning. Note first that if we concern ourselves only with the steady state, then the derivative (i.e., the rate of change through time) of the probability of various numbers of customers in the system is zero, and **(9–1)** becomes:[1]

$$(\lambda + \mu)p_n = \lambda p_{n-1} + \mu p_{n+1} \qquad (9\text{–}3)$$

similarly: **(9–2)** becomes:

$$\lambda p_0 = \mu p_1. \qquad (9\text{–}4)$$

From **(9–4)** it is apparent that:

$$p_1 = [\lambda/\mu]p_0. \qquad (9\text{–}5)$$

Solving **(9–3)** for p_{n+1}, we find:

$$p_{n+1} = \left[\frac{\lambda + \mu}{\mu}\right]p_n - \left[\frac{\lambda}{\mu}\right]p_{n-1}. \qquad (9\text{–}6)$$

Now we let $n = 1$; from **(9–6)** it follows that:

$$p_2 = \left[\frac{\lambda + \mu}{\mu}\right]p_1 - \left[\frac{\lambda}{\mu}\right]p_0. \qquad (9\text{–}7)$$

Substituting in this expression our value for p_1 **(9–5)**, we have:

$$p_2 = \left[\frac{\lambda + \mu}{\mu}\right]\left[\frac{\lambda}{\mu}\right]p_0 - \left[\frac{\lambda}{\mu}\right]p_0 = \left[\frac{\lambda}{\mu}\right]^2 p_0.$$

Now we let $n = 2$; again, from **(9–6)**, it follows that:

$$p_3 = \left[\frac{\lambda + \mu}{\mu}\right]p_2 - \left[\frac{\lambda}{\mu}\right]p_1.$$

From our knowledge of p_1 and p_2 **(9–5)** and **(9–7)**, we can manipulate the above to yield:

$$p_3 = [\lambda/\mu]^3 p_0.$$

If we continue we will find that:

$$p_4 = [\lambda/\mu]^4 p_0$$
$$p_5 = [\lambda/\mu]^5 p_0,$$

and by induction we infer that:

$$p_n = [\lambda/\mu]^n p_0. \qquad (9\text{–}8)$$

Now, from our knowledge of probabilities we know that as n increases without limit,

$$p_0 + p_1 + p_2 + p_3 \ldots \ldots + p_n = 1.$$

---

[1] Since the probability is now independent of time we can drop the subscript t, and p_n now means the probability of n customers in the system at any time *in the steady state*.

Therefore

$$p_0 + [\lambda/\mu]p_0 + [\lambda/\mu]^2 p_0 \ldots\ldots + [\lambda/\mu]^n p_0 = 1,$$

and

$$p_0 = \frac{1}{1 + [\lambda/\mu] + [\lambda/\mu]^2 + [\lambda/\mu]^3 + \ldots\ldots + [\lambda/\mu]^n}.$$

The denominator (above) is an infinite geometric series of the form: $a,\ ar,\ ar^2,\ ar^3\ \ldots$ where $a = 1$ and $r = \lambda/\mu$; and for all values of $r < 1$ the series converges, and its sum is:

$$s = \frac{a}{1 - r}.$$

Therefore our expression for p_0 (assuming that $\lambda/\mu < 1$) becomes:

$$p_0 = \frac{1}{\dfrac{1}{1 - [\lambda/\mu]}} = 1 - \lambda/\mu.$$

Now, having a value for p_0, we can solve for p_n from **(9–8)**:

$$p_n = [1 - \lambda/\mu][\lambda/\mu]^n. \qquad (9\text{–}9)$$

In **(9–9)** we have a general model for determining the probability of n customers in a single-channel queue system in the steady state wherein the mean arrival rate (i.e., λ) is less than the mean service rate (i.e., μ). The model we have developed is *the classical single-channel, single-phase queue system, having a Poisson input and a negative exponential service time distribution, in the steady state.*

Notice that the probability that we will find n customers in the system at any time is dependent *only* on the average or expected number of arrivals per unit of time, λ, *and* on the average time required to service one customer, $1/\mu$.

Notice, too, that if $\lambda/\mu = 1$ then **(9–9)** becomes zero. This makes little sense. And when $\lambda/\mu > 1$? Then, for all values of n, p^n is negative! Nor does this make much sense. It should be remembered that our model is restricted to the case where $\lambda/\mu < 1$. We will soon consider the case where $\lambda/\mu > 1$.

ANALYSIS OF THE SINGLE–CHANNEL QUEUE SYSTEM MODEL

We can more fully understand the behavior of this single-channel queue system, if we develop several other expressions to describe certain characteristics we are interested in.

Percent Idle Time and Percent Utilization

What portion of the time will the service facility be empty and the system therefore idle? This would be simply the probability that there will be zero customers in the system. From (**9–9**) we have:

$$p_0 = [1 - \lambda/\mu][\lambda/\mu]^0 = 1 - \lambda/\mu. \quad \text{% idle time}$$

And if the probability that the system is idle is: $1 - \lambda/\mu$, it follows that the fractional utilization of the full capacity of the service facility is:

$$1 - [1 - \lambda/\mu] = \lambda/\mu. \quad\quad\quad (9\text{–}10)$$

% utilization

Expected Number in the System

What is the expected number of customers in the system? This would be simply the probability of 1 in the system times 1, plus the probability of 2 in the system times 2, plus the probability of 3 in the system times 3, and so on, or:

$$
\begin{array}{lllll}
\text{For 1 in the system:} & [1 - \lambda/\mu][\lambda/\mu] \times 1 \\
+ \text{ " 2 " " " } & + [1 - \lambda/\mu][\lambda/\mu]^2 \times 2 \\
+ \text{ " 3 " " " } & + [1 - \lambda/\mu][\lambda/\mu]^3 \times 3 \\
+ \text{ " " " " " } & + \text{ " " " " } \\
+ \text{ " " " " " } & + \text{ " " " } \\
+ \text{ " " " " " } & + \text{ " " " } \\
+ \text{ " } n \text{ " " " } & + [1 - \lambda/\mu][\lambda/\mu]^n \times n \\
\ldots \text{as } n \to \infty
\end{array}
$$

This proves to be an infinite series of the form: $ar + 2ar^2 + 3ar^3 + \ldots nar^n$, in which a corresponds to $1 - \lambda/\mu$ and r corresponds to λ/μ. The sum of the series proves to be:

$$[a] \times \left[\frac{r}{(1 - r)^2}\right].$$

Therefore the sum of our series, and hence the expected number of customers in the system is:

$$[1 - \lambda/\mu]\left[\frac{\lambda/\mu}{(1 - \lambda/\mu)^2}\right] = \frac{\lambda}{\mu - \lambda}. \quad\quad (9\text{–}11)$$

Expected Number in the Queue

What is the expected number of customers waiting for service? Since the average or expected number in the system is the expected number in the service facility plus the expected number in the queue waiting for service, we reason that the expected number in the queue is the expected number in the system minus the expected number in the service facility.

But what is the expected number in the service facility? This would be:

1. The number in the service facility when it is busy times the probability that it is busy; plus
2. The number in the service facility when it is idle times the probability that it is idle.

Having already determined the probability that the system is busy and the probability that it is idle, we can write:

$$
\begin{array}{l}
1. \quad 1 \times (\lambda/\mu) = \\
2. \quad \underline{+0 \times (1 - \lambda/\mu)} = \underline{0} \\
 \text{Sum} \qquad\qquad = \lambda/\mu
\end{array}
$$

Now, since the expected number in the system (**9–11**) is: $\dfrac{\lambda}{\mu - \lambda}$, the expected number in the queue waiting for service is:

$$
\frac{\lambda}{\mu - \lambda} - \frac{\lambda}{\mu} = \frac{\lambda^2}{\mu(\mu - \lambda)}. \tag{9–12}
$$

Expected Time in the System

How much time must the average customer spend in the system; that is, waiting in line and being serviced? A moment's reflection will make it apparent that the expected number in the system is λ times the expected time in the system. Thus if 5 customers are arriving each hour on the average, and if each customer spends 2 hours in the system on the average, then there will be 10 customers in the system on the average. The expected time in the system, then, is the expected number in the system divided by λ, or:

$$
\frac{\dfrac{\lambda}{\mu - \lambda}}{\lambda} = \frac{1}{\mu - \lambda}. \tag{9–13}
$$

Expected Waiting Time

How much time must the average customer spend waiting in line for service? This would be simply the expected total time in the system less the expected time in the service facility. Since the expected time in the service facility is $1/\mu$, we have:

$$\frac{1}{\mu - \lambda} - \frac{1}{\mu} = \frac{\lambda}{\mu(\mu - \lambda)}. \qquad (9\text{--}14)$$

Probability of N in the Queue

The probability of n in the queue is simply the probability of $n + 1$ in the system. If n customers are in the queue, there are $n + 1$ in the system, 1 being in the service facility. (*Note:* This would apply only where $n > 0$; the probability of 0 in the queue is the probability of 0 in the system *plus* the probability of 1 in the system.)

We are now equipped to make some observations about the behavior of the single-channel queue system with Poisson arrivals. Let us explore what happens to the following attributes as the rate of customer arrivals approaches the rate at which the service facilities can accommodate them: (1) the expected time in the system, (2) the portion of time the system is idle, and (3) the probability of various numbers in the system.

We will assume that when the facility is busy our service facility is equipped to service customers at an average rate of 100 per hour ($\mu = 100$). Let us plot curves of the three system attributes, above, as the average rate of arrivals (λ) varies from 0 to 99 customers per hour.

As we should expect (see Figure 9–1), there is a variable probability of our encountering 1, 2, 3, 4, ... in the system; a peak is reached as the hourly arrival rate, λ, increases from 0, and the probability decreases as λ approaches the mean service rate μ.

The time we can expect the system to be idle (i.e., the probability of zero in the system) is a straight line, being 1.0 at $\lambda = 0$ and becoming quite small as λ approaches μ.

Since the probabilities of various numbers in the system sum to unity, at any point on the X axis the distance from the X axis to a corresponding point on the "Fraction Idle Time curve," plus the distances to each of the probability curves, will add to 1.0. Note that the expected time in the system increases rapidly as λ approaches 99.

The shape of the expected "Time in the System" curve is important. If customers are arriving at close to the rate at which they can be accommodated ($\lambda \approx \mu$) the time in the system is quite large. However, with a modest increase in the capacity to serve arriving customers (a modest decrease in λ/μ) time in the system drops off

FIGURE 9-1

Mean Capacity to Serve: $\mu = 100$ units per hour

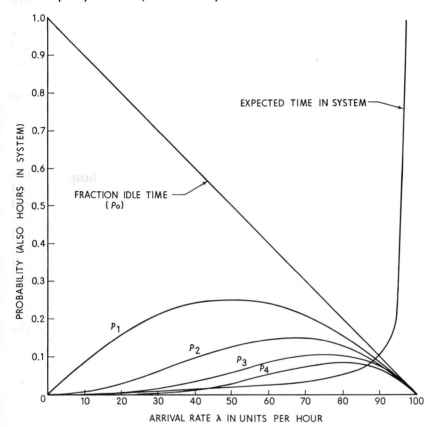

dramatically. On the other hand if λ is small compared to μ, even a substantial improvement in the capacity to serve yields only a slight decrease in time in the system.

Other ways to improve service—to decrease time in the system— are: (1) increasing the number of channels, and (2) pooling facilities. We will have some comments to make on these shortly.

The Probability of N as a Function of Time

In developing the single-channel, single-phase Poisson queue model above we assumed the steady state, thus simplifying the model considerably. Let us reconsider this question. Suppose that

λ were 99 and μ were 100. From expression (**9–12**) the expected queue length is:

$$\frac{\lambda^2}{\mu(\mu - \lambda)} = \frac{99^2}{100(100 - 99)} = 98.$$

If 98 is the expected queue, then a queue of 0 can be expected to be a rare event. If we start up a system of this sort at 8:00 *empty* the probability of finding 98 in the queue at 8:01 is surely less than the probability of finding 98 in it at 12:00.

The steady state is a condition which is assumed to prevail after the system has had time to settle down and approach its expected state. Note, however, that in the steady state, finding 0 in the queue is a possibility.

Except in the steady state, therefore, P_n is a function of time as well as λ and μ.

The Probability of an Arrival as a Function of the Queue Length

The single-channel, single-phase model above assumes that the population of potential customers is infinite. Model 9–9 would otherwise be inapplicable. Consider, for example, a hospital ward with one nurse and 10 patients. From time to time patients ring for the nurse. If most of the patients have rung for the nurse and she is waiting on one of them, with the others in the queue, the probability of an additional arrival in the next minute is small compared to the probability of an arrival in the next minute if the queue is 0.

Thus when the population of potential customers is small the probability of an arrival in the next time period is a function of the queue length as well as a function of λ and μ.

The Transient State and Truncation

In many real world systems the population of potential customers can be considered to be infinite. Yet even with an infinite population the probability of an arrival is a function of the queue length. Seeing a large queue, approaching customers will pass one filling station and go to another. Thus queues get truncated at some size when there are alternative facilities available.

In some situations the transient state is of more interest than the steady state: the opening of a new facility, the annual model changeover in the automobile industry, and so on. Some systems can never be expected to operate long enough to achieve a steady state.

So far, we have spoken of the case where the arrival rate is less than the rate at which customers could be served if the service facility were kept busy. What about the case where customers arrive at an average rate faster than the average rate at which they can be serviced? It is easy to conceive of a system wherein $\lambda > \mu$, and to perceive that in theory the system would have only a transient state, since over time the number of customers in the system would grow indefinitely.

In practice, systems in which $\lambda > \mu$ do not grow indefinitely. As the waiting line, and hence the required time in the system, grow larger, customers become impatient and will not wait. Or perhaps accommodating a longer line becomes costly, and the queue is not allowed to grow beyond a certain limit.

In this way systems in which $\lambda > \mu$ get truncated at some queue length, and we find that even with $\lambda > \mu$, queue systems *can* have a steady state.

OPTIMUM SYSTEM DESIGN

In our study of the inventory system we observed that the randomness of demand on the system forces us to seek an optimum service capability in which an occasional stock-out can be expected. The cost of maintaining this capability is the cost of holding in readiness—idle and on the shelf—an inventory of stock.

The queue system poses the same problem when the economics of the system are considered. If demand on the system were constant, our problem would be simple, and obliging customers to wait could be easily avoided. Randomness, however, forces us to seek an optimum service capability in which *some* waiting can be expected. The cost of maintaining this capability is the cost of holding—ready to serve but idle part of the time—a service facility.

Most queue systems are a great deal more complex than the single-channel system for which we have developed an analytical model. Service may not be on a first-come, first-served basis; we may have multiple channels; when a waiting line gets too long, arrivals may be shunted to a separate facility; and so on.

Decentralizing versus Pooling of Facilities

Machinists queue up for tools at a tool crib manned by one attendant in the factory depicted in the schematic which follows.

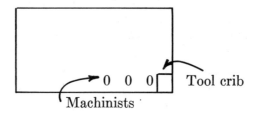

Service would be improved if a second tool crib were installed at the opposite corner of the factory floor. We could assume that about half the machinists would go to one of the tool cribs and half to the other. Thus the arrival rate at each would be about halved, the ratio λ/μ would be half as great as before and time in the system would be correspondingly reduced. On the other hand if the factory floor is large, at times we could expect to find a long queue at one tool crib and an idle service facility(attendant) at the other.

This undesirable condition could be eliminated by putting the two attendants in the one tool crib shown in the schematic. When one attendant is busy the other would be available to accommodate an arriving machinist. Pooling facilities in this fashion would constitute a two-channel, single-phase queue system and would be superior to two decentralized facilities in average time in the system per machinist.

Time in the system is not the only consideration in queue system design, of course. There are over 260 Conoco filling stations in the city of Denver. At times some have a waiting line while others are empty. Average time in the system would be reduced if one big station with a thousand pumps replaced the 260 stations, but the unwholesome consequence is obvious.

Formal Analysis versus Simulation

Model 9–9 and its derivatives is applicable only to the single-channel, single-phase queue system with Poisson arrival and negative exponential service time patterns. Formal analytical models also have been developed for simple multichannel systems. However, in spite of the rich body of literature on queuing theory the study of queuing systems via formal analytical models is restricted to very well-behaved and elementary systems. The vast majority of real world queue systems of interest consist of multichannel, multiphase components, varying priority rules and other complexities which make their study via formal analysis unrewarding. With the computer, however, we can build models with which we can simulate, and thus study, the behavior of extremely complex queue systems. In Chapter 10 we will explore how this might be done. First, however, we must equip ourselves to simulate a number of processes which are approximated in real queuing systems.

SUGGESTIONS FOR FURTHER STUDY

BUFFA, ELWOOD S. *Operations Management.* New York: John Wiley & Sons, Inc., 1968.

COOPER, ROBERT B. *Introduction to Queuing Theory.* New York: The Macmillan Co., 1972.

MORRIS, WILLIAM T. *Analysis for Materials Handling Management.* Homewood, Ill.: Richard D. Irwin, Inc., 1962.

SAATY, THOMAS L. *Elements of Queuing Theory.* New York: McGraw-Hill Book Co., Inc., 1961.

EXERCISES

(Where a computer program is called for in any of the following exercises, begin with a flow diagram.)

1. The base of Napierian or natural logarithms, designated e in mathematics, is defined as the limit of the expression $(1 + X)^{1/X}$, as X gets smaller and smaller and approaches 0.

We can discern something about the nature of this expression by giving X several values and determining the corresponding value of the above expression, thus:

$$\text{when } X = 2: (1 + X)^{1/X} = 1.73$$
$$\text{`` } X = 1: \text{ `` } = 2.00$$
$$\text{`` } X = \tfrac{1}{2}: \text{ `` } = 2.25$$

It is apparent that as we let X take a value equal to $\frac{1}{2}$ the value it had previously, the expression $(1 + X)^{1/X}$ becomes larger, but by smaller increments.

Write a FORTRAN program that will cause the computer to continue this process, printing out the values of this expression and the corresponding values for X, with each value of X equal to $\frac{1}{2}$ the preceding value of X, through $X = 1/2048$.

2. Compose a FORTRAN program that will provide data for plotting a curve of the expected number of customers in a single-channel queue system with Poisson arrivals and negative exponential service time (i.e., using the model **(9–11)** of Chapter 9) with a mean service rate, μ, of 1,000 units per hour, as the mean arrival rate, λ, varies from 0 units per hour through **999** units per hour. Plot the curve.

In what way does your curve differ from that of Figure 9–1?

3. The Youngstown Company produces a line of widgets in a two-stage process. Widgets emerge from the first stage in a Poisson-distributed fashion at a mean rate of 10.1 per hour (i.e., $\lambda = 10.1$). The second stage is capable of handling the output from the first stage at a mean rate of 10.4 per hour (i.e., $\mu = 10.4$).

Assume that there is no limit to the allowable size of the production bank between the two stages, that the cost associated with a bank of semifinished widgets between the two stages is $3 per widget per hour, and that idle time in stage 2 costs $250 per hour. Determine the optimum rate of production (λ) for stage 1, i.e., the rate that minimizes total cost.

4. On each trial a particular Zippo either lights or does not light. Whether it lights on a trial is independent of whether it lighted on the previous trial. In the long run it lights 90 percent of the time. Do successive efforts to light this Zippo constitute a Bernoulli process?

5. Given a single-channel queue system with an average of λ arrivals per hour and a mean capacity to serve μ per hour:

a) When λ is smaller than μ, queues will or will not form?
b) When λ equals μ, a queue will or will not form and grow indefinitely?
c) When λ is greater than μ, there is a steady state?

6. In a queue system like that described in Chapter 9, if the probability of encountering 10 customers in the system is .03, what is the probability of encountering 9 in the queue?

7. Write a FORTRAN program that will determine as economically as possible and as accurately as possible the sum of the series: $1/x + 2/x^2 + 3/x^3 + 4/x^4 \ldots n/x_n$, as n approaches infinity. (Assume that x is greater than 10 and that the computer will interpret any number smaller than 10^{-37} as 0.0.)

chapter 10

Process Generators

MENTION was made in Chapter 6 of *algebraic random number generators* and their use was described briefly. The simulation of random processes is of great importance to the systems analyst and it is appropriate that we give this topic more serious attention.

The Multiplicative Congruential Generator

Table 10–1 shows two lists of numbers. We immediately perceive upon examining the two lists that list 1 is ordered and that list 2 is

TABLE 10–1

List 1	List 2
1	4
2	8
3	5
4	10
5	9
6	7
7	3
8	6
9	1
10	2

not. It is important that we understand why we regard list 1 as ordered. We regard list 1 as ordered because the numbers appear in the sequence in which we normally recite them. But there are other sequences we have memorized—thus: 2, 4, 6 . . . ; 5, 10, 15, 20 . . . ; and so on.

Perhaps it would be more appropriate to say that a list of numbers is ordered if the relationship between one number and its predecessor number is constant throughout the list. Each number in list 1 is its predecessor plus 1. The recursive relationship which portrays the way the nth number in list 1 is related to the succeeding number is:

$$K_{n+1} = K_n + 1$$

. . . where K refers to the number and n to the position of K in the sequence.

List 3, below, is obviously not a random list of numbers and its recursive relationship is:

$$K_{n+1} = 2K_n + 1$$

List 3

1
3
7
15
31
63

It seems that we are endowing a list of numbers with orderliness if some recursive relationship can be found to generate any number in the list, given its predecessor.

The recursive relationship which relates the numbers in list 3 involved the algebraic operations *multiplication* and *addition*. Let us define a new algebraic operation which we will represent symbolically: $K(mod\ m)$, and which we will read, "K reduced modulo m." By this operation we mean, "Divide K by m and record the remainder." Thus if $K = 15$ and $m = 11$, we record 4. If $K = 123$ and $m = 5$ we record 3.

Let us now define a new recursive relation as follows:

$$K_{n+1} = (2K_n)(mod\ 11) \tag{10-1}$$

In (10–1), to obtain number K_{n+1} we multiply its predecessor, K_n, by 2, then reduce it modulo 11. Thus if our first number were 4:

$$K_2 = (2K_1)(mod\ 11) = 2 \cdot 4\,(mod\ 11) = 8$$

our second number is 8, and

$$K_3 = (2 \cdot 8)(mod\ 11) = 5$$

our third number is 5, and:

$$K_4 = (2 \cdot 5)(\text{mod } 11) = 10$$

our fourth number is 10, and:

$$K_5 = (2 \cdot 10)(\text{mod } 11) = 9 \text{ etc.}$$

Notice that we are generating the numbers in list 2, Table 10–1. Indeed list 2, which we have previously regarded as nonordered, is ordered! It might be presumptuous of us to deduce about *any* list of numbers that it is *not* an ordered list. For while the recursive relation which generated the list might not be obvious it might be presumptuous of us to assume that no such relation exists, however unlikely such a relation might seem.

Suppose that a list of random numbers is generated by selecting balls at random from a jar, and recording the numbers on the balls —stirring them after each selection. Would not such a list be thoroughly random? In the sense of Newtonian mechanics it would not, for each time a ball is selected its selection is the consequence of the state of the system (positions of the balls) before a ball is selected, plus a sequence of deliberate motions of our arm and fingers, and is thus entirely causal. In fact, one might argue, randomness is an attribute we endow a process with when we are unable to recognize order in the process, and hence unable to predict its state from period to period.

This being the case, so long as a list of numbers has the *appearance of randomness* it is suitable for our needs, and an algebraic random number generator will do nicely.

For generating random numbers algebraically the recursive relation employed to generate list 2 is unsatisfactory in that it will generate only 10 numbers before it begins to repeat itself—to cycle. Sooner or later any algebraic generator will generate the number it started with and hence repeat itself. This should not bother us so long as the cycle is large enough.

We can produce a generator with a large cycle, and with certain other attractive features, by careful choice of the two parameters a and m in expression (**10–2**).

$$K_{n+1} = (aK_n)(\text{modulo } m) \tag{10–2}$$

The recursive relation in expression (**10–2**) portrays the *multiplicative congruential* method for producing random numbers. Expression (**10–1**) portrays the multiplicative congruential method with

$a = 2$ and $m = 11$. For a binary computer it proves useful to let m be some power of 2. In fact, for a *good* generator—one whose output appears "truly random," one which is computationally efficient and which does not consume much memory space—parameters a and m should be selected as follows:

1. Let $m = 2^b$; that is, let m be a power of 2.
2. Let $a = 8t \pm 3$, where t is some positive integer ... *and* let a be approximately $2^{b/2}$.
3. Let K_0 be an odd integer. K_0 is the *first* number in the list of random numbers, sometimes called the "root" or "seed."

A generator so designed will produce numbers all of which will be less than or equal to 2^b. Its maximum period—the number of numbers it produces before cycling—will be 2^{b-2}.

For example, we might design a multiplicative congruential generator in which $b = 4$.

From (1), above: $m = 2^4 = 16$

From (2), $a \approx 2^{b/2} = 2^{4/2} = 4$, *and* $a = 8t \pm 3$. If $t = 1$, $a = 11$ or 5. Hence we select $a = 5$.

Our generator is therefore:

$$K_{n+1} = (5K_n)(\text{modulo } 16).$$

Rather arbitrarily letting $K_0 = 7$, we produce the following list, which cycles after producing $2^{b-2} = 4$ numbers:

	K	$K \times 5$	(*modulo 16*)
First number	7	35	3
Second number	3	15	15
Third number	15	75	11
Fourth number	11	55	7
Fifth number	7		

For a larger cycle one simply selects b accordingly. Thus with $b = 21$, $2^{b/2}$ is greater than 1 million, and at least 1 million numbers will be produced before the generator cycles.

Uniform Fraction Generators

The multiplicative congruential method produces "uniformly distributed" numbers. That is, within the range of numbers produced (never larger than m) each number is as likely to be generated as any other number. A "random fraction generator" would be a generator which produces numbers from 0 to 1. Since the largest number it will produce is $m = 2^b$, we could convert our multiplicative congruential generator to a *uniform fraction generator* by dividing each random number it produces by 2^b.

It would be convenient, in using an algebraic random fraction generator such as that above, to be able to call for execution of a sequence of instructions from any number of different positions in a computer program as need for a new random number arises. To make this possible we might exploit an additional FORTRAN convention of great convenience—the subroutine.

The Subroutine

A FORTRAN subroutine consists of a group of statements that are, in a sense, isolated from the rest of the program. By calling on the subroutine from any part of the main program, we can cause those statements that make up the subroutine to be executed, and then cause control to be transferred back to the position in the main program from which the subroutine was called. The advantages of this will soon become apparent.

The subroutine has the form:

SUBROUTINE _____ (___,___,___ .... ___)

and the executable statements   RETURN and END

A FORTRAN program may have a number of subroutines. In order to identify the subroutine being called, each is given a different name, which appears immediately after the word SUBROU–TINE at the beginning of the subroutine (indicated in the example above by the blank space). Any acceptable FORTRAN variable (nonsubscripted) may be used as a subroutine name.

As the example above would indicate, the subroutine name is also followed by other data (indicated by the blank spaces in parentheses). The computer ordinarily views variables and statement numbers *inside* a subroutine as different and distinct from variables and statement numbers *outside* a subroutine. Thus the variables TAC, J(M), and M12 might be used inside *and* outside a subroutine, and, in the absence of a provision specifying otherwise, the computer would assume that the variables TAC, J(M), and M12 inside and outside the subroutine (i.e., elsewhere in the main program or in other subroutines) are *not* the same variables even though they have the same names. Thus two or more values might be stored simultaneously for variables that have the same name, one arising from computations within the main program and the other(s) arising from computations in one or more subroutines.

While this arrangement has advantages, provision must be made for getting around it. Otherwise we would have no means for transferring a value from a subroutine to a main program, and vice versa, and therefore calling a subroutine would be valueless.

We provide for transferring values in and out of a subroutine by identifying—in the blanks inside the parentheses to the right of the subroutine name, separated by commas—a set of variables, thus:

SUBROUTINE SALES (TAC,J,M12)

We call a subroutine by a CALL statement; and we identify the specific subroutine we want to call by stating its name in the CALL statement. Then, for every variable appearing in the parentheses to the right of the subroutine name we must have a variable in parentheses to the right of the subroutine which we name in the CALL statement. Thus with the statement CALL SALES (TAC, J,M12), we could call the subroutine SUBROUTINE SALES (TAC,J,M12).

The computer will associate the variables named in the CALL statement with the variables named in the SUBROUTINE statement. The computer will regard the variables TAC, J(M), and M12 as being common to both the subroutine and the main program. In this way, the *values* these three variables get as a consequence of computation (which we have caused to be executed by calling the subroutine) will also be given to these same variables in the main program.

A useful flexibility is added by the fact that the computer associates the variables in the SUBROUTINE statement and the variables in the CALL statement by the order in which they appear rather than by their names. For example, we might have written the CALL statement CALL SALES (R,LPT,M7R), and the SUB-ROUTINE statement SUBROUTINE SALES (TAC,J,M12).

The computer would associate R with TAC,LPT(M) with J(M), and M7R with M12. Whatever value the variables TAC,J(M), and M12 received (as a consequence of the execution of the statements in the subroutine) would also be given, respectively, to the variables R,LPT(M) and M7R, in the main program. (By now it will have been observed that we do not include the subscript where a sub-scripted variable is referred to either in the CALL statement or in the SUBROUTINE statement.)

One more rule merits attention: *When values for subscripted variables are to be transferred from inside out, or from outside in, there must be a* DIMENSION *statement inside the subroutine specifying the space reserved for that variable. The* DIMENSION statement should follow the SUBROUTINE statement.

If we initialize A, B and TK, as shown below, each time SUB-ROUTINE RAND is called variable T will be given a new, positive fractional value.

Main Program

$$\begin{cases} A = 5.0 \\ B = 4.0 \\ TM = 2.0 ** B \\ TK = 7.0 \\ {—} {—} {—} \\ {—} {—} {—} \\ {—} {—} {—} \\ \text{CALL RAND (A,TM,TK,T)} \\ {—} {—} {—} \\ {—} {—} {—} \\ {—} {—} {—} \\ \text{STOP} \\ \text{END} \end{cases}$$

```
      SUBROUTINE RAND (A,TM,TK,T)
1     TK = A * TK
2     J = TK/TM
3     T = J
4     T = T * TM
5     T = TK − T
6     TK = T
7     T = TK/TM
      RETURN
      END
```

In statement 1, of the subroutine, the previous value of K, i.e., K_{n-1}, is multiplied by a. In statement 2 the number of integer multiples of m in a K_{n-1} is determined and stored first at J, then at T in statement 3.

In statement 4 the integer part of a K_{n-1}/m is determined and stored at T. This is then subtracted from $A \cdot K_{n-1}/m$ in statement 5 and the remainder is stored first at T then at TK in statement 6. In statement 7 K_n is divided by m to produce a fraction.

Since variables A,TM,TK, and T appear as arguments both in the CALL and in the SUBROUTINE statements they are both common to the main program and to the subroutine.

The *optimal* choice of parameters a and b and the appropriate "root"—value for K_0—are critically dependent upon the word length of the computer being used. A set of parameters optimal for a 32-bit word machine would not be appropriate for a 12-bit machine.

Much work has been devoted to the selection of parameter values for different machines.[1]

System Functions for Generating Random Numbers

In fact, building our own random number generator subroutine is seldom necessary. Just as most FORTRAN and BASIC compilers come equipped with commonly used system functions for extracting square roots, for finding logarithms and the like, most also include a random number generator. Thus when the computer encounters RANF(0) to the right of the equal sign in an algebraic instruction it replaces it with a random variable, uniformly distributed between 0 and 1.[2]

If the user wants something other than fractions—thus four-digit integers—he simply adds a bit of algebra. The following routine will generate 50 four-digit, uniformly distributed random integers and store them in the array I(N):

$$DO\ 4\ N = 1,50$$
$$4\ \ I(N) = RANF(0) * 10000.0.$$

Sometimes a random variable uniformly distributed between two extreme values is desired. To store at X a uniformly distributed random variable from 6 to 10, for example, we might write the following instruction:

$$X = 6.0 + .4 * RANF(0) * 10.0.$$

Nonuniform Random Number Generators

Consider the discrete free run time probability distribution shown in Table 10–2. Free run time is the period of time a machine

---

[1] See especially R. R. Coveyou and R. D. MacPherson, "Fourier Analysis of Uniform Random Number Generators," *Journal of the Association of Computing Machinery*, Vol. 14, No. 1 (January 1967).

[2] The "0" in parentheses is a dummy variable only. Other function names for random fraction generators, commonly found in higher level languages, include: RAND(0), RN(0), RND(X), and so on.

will run before requiring maintenance. Table 10–2 is a discrete approximation of the free run time of a particular machine. If we wished to simulate the free run time of this machine we could do so easily, in a computer simulation model, by calling upon our random fraction generator. We would simply interpret a fraction from 0 to .484 to mean a simulated FRT of 1 month; a fraction from .484 through .838 to mean a FRT of 2 months, and so forth, as suggested in Table 10–3.

TABLE 10–2

Free Run Time (Months)	Probability
1	.484
2	.354
3	.147
4	.015

TABLE 10–3

FRT	Probability	Range
1	.484	0– .484
2	.354	.484– .838
3	.147	.838– .985
4	.015	.985–1.0

With a suitable set of IF statements and using RANF(0) or its equivalent as an argument we could easily build a routine for generating random free run times faithful to the discrete function portrayed in Table 10–2.

Continuous versus Discrete Generators

unlimited Amt. of random #s   Limited Amt. of Random numbers

The probability distribution in Table 10–2 is a discrete distribution. Discrete approximations of real processes are useful but they are likely to be unrealistic. Table 10–2 states that the system might run for one month or for two months before it fails, but not for any period of time in between.

In most computer simulation experiments we are likely to employ *continuous* rather than discrete probability distributions. An important component of simulation theory has to do with the design of continuous process simulations. A thorough mastery of this subject involves the computer user in the study of mathematical statistics and is beyond the scope of this text. However, an intuitive appreciation of the means by which the model builder simulates continuous processes is rather easy to acquire.

The discrete probability distribution in Table 10–4 is portrayed graphically by the histogram in Figure 10–1. Observe that Table 10–4 differs from Table 10–3 only in the final column. The "piece-

TABLE 10–4

FRT	Probability	Range
1	.484	1.000–.516
2	.354	.516–.162
3	.147	.162–.015
4	.015	.015–.000

wise linear" curve in Figure 10–1 portrays the final column of Table 10–4 graphically. Thus segment "a" corresponds to the first row of the final column; segment "b" to the second row; and so on. Interpreting a random fraction to mean a free run time of 1, 2, 3, or 4 months—depending on where it falls in the range 1.000 to .000—is equivalent to locating that random fraction on the vertical axis in

FIGURE 10–1

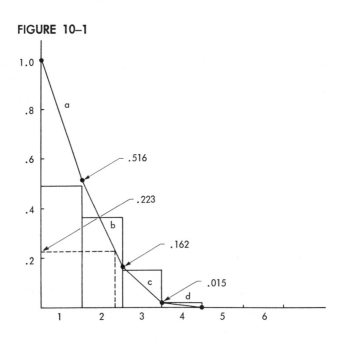

Figure 10–1, and finding the corresponding point on the horizontal axis.

For example, assume that we just generated .223, by calling on RANF(0). Moving opposite .223, on the vertical axis, to the piecewise linear curve we encounter segment "b," and drop down to two months free run time.

Just as the probability distribution of Table 10–4 (the histogram in Figure 10–1) is a discrete approximation of a continuous random process, the piecewise linear function in Figure 10–1 is an approximation of the *cumulative* probability for that process.

Now note that the histogram of Figure 10–1 can be closely approximated by the *density function* in Figure 10–2. Figure 10–1 specifies a random process which produces values of X between 0 and 4. The cumulative probability function for this continuous process, $F(X)$, produced by forming the definite integral of $f(X)$ from X to 4, proves to be:

$$F(X) = X^2/16 - X/2 + 1 \qquad 0 \le X \le 4. \qquad (10\text{–}3)$$

Expression (**10–3**) tells us the probability that the random process portrayed graphically in Figure 10–2 will generate a value greater

FIGURE 10–2

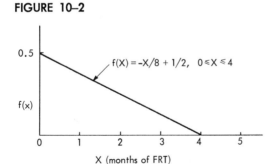

than or equal to X. Thus the probability that it will generate a value ≥ 2.3 is:

$$F(2.3) = (2.3)^2/16 - 2.3/2 + 1 = .18.$$

The probability that it will generate a value ≥ 0 is 1, and a value ≥ 4 is 0.

If we plot the function $F(X)$ we obtain the curve shown in Figure 10–3, which closely approximates the piecewise linear curve

FIGURE 10–3

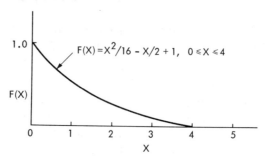

in Figure 10–1. Let's now call on our uniform random fraction generator, generate a fraction and interpret it as a value for $F(X)$, in Figure 10–3. For each value of $F(X)$ randomly generated we will find the corresponding value of X, on the horizontal axis.

For example, let us assume that RANF(0), called upon three times in succession, yielded the values in the first column of Table 10–5.

TABLE 10–5

$F(X)$	X
.015	3.51
.324	1.73
.050	3.10

For each of these values of $F(X)$ we find the corresponding value for X, shown in the second column of Table 10–5.

To facilitate finding values of X, given values for $F(X)$, we solve $F(X)$ for X, obtaining:

$$X = -4\sqrt{F(X)} + 4, \qquad 0 \le X \le 4. \qquad (10\text{–}4)$$

Now for a nonuniform random number generator whose output is faithful to the density function portrayed in Figure 10–2 we simply substitute RANF(0) for $F(X)$, in (10–4), and cause the function to be evaluated sequentially.

Since the random fraction generating routine which we call upon by RANF(0) can generate any positive fraction, the function $-4\sqrt{\text{RANF}(0)} + 4$ can generate any number 0 to 4, and in simulating the free run time of our machine we are not confined to the rather unrealistic set of integers, 1 through 4.

A Poisson Generator

Not concerned with generating negative values

The distribution portrayed by the density function in Figure 10–2 is of little real interest to us. It is not representative of random processes commonly encountered in real systems. On the other hand, many real systems do exhibit behavior which can be approximated by the Poisson distribution.

We know that the probability of a specific number of arrivals in a unit of time on the one hand (the Poisson distribution) and the probability of a specific amount of time between arrivals on the other hand (the negative exponential distribution) are related. Recall that

$$F(t) = e^{-\lambda t} \tag{10-5}$$

is the cumulative probability function for the negative exponential distribution. It tells us the probability that more than t units of time will elapse between arrivals. In designing a Poisson generator we are more interested in the time between arrivals than the number of arrivals per unit of time, and the cumulative probability function of the exponential distribution tells us about the distribution of time between arrivals.

To generate negative exponential distributed values for the time between arrivals, then, all we need to do is read a random fraction and determine the value for t, (**10–5**), that corresponds to it.

When we use this process we are, in effect, asking ourselves: "Given a value for the function $e^{-\lambda t}$, and a value for λ, what is the value of t?" That is, "What is t in terms of e and λ?" Solving for t in (**10–5**), we have:

$$t = -\frac{1}{\lambda} \times \log_e F(t).$$

For generating purposes $F(t)$ is our uniformly distributed random fraction. Therefore for a group of FORTRAN statements that will generate negative exponential distributed times between arrivals we can employ the instructions:

```
R = RANF(0)
T = (-1.0/TLMBDA) * LOG(R)
```

in which TLMBDA is the mean arrival rate of the Poisson process, in customers per unit of time. This might also be written:

$$\text{T} = (-1.0/\text{TLMBDA}) * \text{LOG}(\text{RANF}(0)) \tag{10-6}$$

A NORMALLY DISTRIBUTED VARIABLE GENERATOR

To equip ourselves for efficient systems simulation we also need a normal generator. Many processes, especially in business and economic systems, approximate the normal distribution, and to study the behavior of these processes we find ourselves in frequent need of a normal generator.

We could develop a normal generator by the same means used to develop the Poisson generator. However, the problem is a bit more difficult. The probability density function for the normal process is:

$$f(x) = \frac{1}{\sigma\sqrt{2\pi}} e^{-\frac{1}{2}\left[\frac{x-m}{\sigma}\right]^2}, \tag{10--7}$$

in which m is the mean, σ is the standard deviation, and x is the random variable.

We can translate (**10--7**) into the *cumulative density function* for the normal distribution, to get it in the form of (**10--5**), but solving for x in terms of the *cumulative probability* is quite another thing. Therefore, we cannot design a normal generator so easily as we designed our Poisson generator.

Using Simpson's rule we could approximate the cumulative probabilities of a sample "x or more" as x varies over, perhaps, $m \pm 3\sigma$. For use in a computer program we might then store these probabilities as a table of values in an array, and we might devise a scheme for calling for values of x by a random selection from the table. Through this means we could build a rather satisfactory normal generator, but this is somewhat complicated, and storing our table may consume a good deal of memory space.

A number of schemes have been employed to design an arithmetic function that would (approximately) generate normally distributed variables. A rather widely used generator of this sort will be presented, but without elaboration on why the variables it generates approximate the normal distribution.

This generator requires two different, uniformly distributed random fractions to generate one normal variable.[3] With two uniformly distributed fractions, $R1$ and $R2$, one generates a variable, V, which is normally distributed about a mean of 0, with a standard deviation of 1, thus:

$$V = (-2 \log_e R1)^{1/2} \times \cos 2\pi R2.$$

---

[3] For a discussion of this generator and how it *can* be used to generate two normal variables from two uniformly distributed variables, see Box and Muller, "A Note on the Generation of Normal Deviates," *Annals of Mathematical Statistics*, Vol. 28 (1958), p. 610–11.

To convert V to a variable $V1$, which is normally distributed about a mean of TMU, with a standard deviation SD, we simply exploit the relationship:

$$V1 = (V)SD + TMU.$$

Four FORTRAN statements suitable for generating a normally distributed variable, V1, about mean TMU, with standard deviation SD, would be:

```
R1 = RANF(0)       RNO(I)
R2 = RANF(0)
V  = (-2.0 * LOG  (R1)) ** 0.5 * COS  (6.283 * R2)
V1 = V * SD + TMU
```

or, more briefly,

V1 = (-2.0 * LOG (RANF(0)) ** 0.5 * COS (6.283 *
        RANF(0)) * SD + TMU   (10-8)

THE GAMMA DISTRIBUTION

In simulation studies we will also find ourselves in need of a gamma generator. While many real processes in business and economics approximate the normal process, many other processes do not. The normal process becomes particularly inappropriate when the ratio of the standard deviation to the mean of the process we want to simulate is larger than about $1/3$.

Suppose, for example, that we had reason to believe demand for a particular product was fluctuating about a mean of 50 units per week with a standard deviation of 50, giving us a value of 1 for the standard deviation to mean ratio. We know that about 68 percent of the variables generated by a normal process will fall between the mean minus 1 standard deviation, and the mean plus 1 standard deviation; and thus within the range from 0 to 100 for a normal process with mean of 50 and standard deviation of 50.

If we assume that the process generating our demand is normal then we must assume that about 32 percent of the variables generated by our demand generating process should fall outside the range 0 to 100. Furthermore, we would expect that half of these variables would fall short of this range, and thus that about 16 percent would be less than 0.

In most real business systems a negative demand does not occur. Where the ratio of the standard deviation to the mean is less than $1/3$, the actual demand generating process may in many real systems approximate the normal distribution rather closely. But where this ratio is much larger than 1/3 the normal distribution is not likely to be a good approximation of the real process.

The Poisson distribution in some cases may be a better approximation. The Poisson process has the virtue of generating no negative variables. However, the mean and the variance in the Poisson distribution are always equal. Clearly this restricts the usefulness of the Poisson distribution not only to those processes that have the Poisson curve form but also to those processes in which the ratio of the standard deviation to the mean is precisely the reciprocal of the square root of the mean.

The gamma distribution combines virtues of both the normal and Poisson distributions for processes that do not generate negative values. The probability density function of the gamma distribution is:

$$f(x) = \frac{\lambda^r x^{r-1} e^{-\lambda x}}{(r-1)!}.$$

The development of the gamma distribution somewhat parallels the development of the Poisson distribution. The Poisson distribution resulted from an effort to determine the probability of n successes (defects in our wire experiment) per unit length, given a mean of λ successes per unit of length. The exponential distribution results from an effort to determine the probability of x units of length from one success to the next in a Poisson process. The gamma distribution results from an effort to determine the probability of x units of length between one success and the rth succeeding success.

The gamma distribution has two parameters, r and λ, in a Poisson process. The mean and the standard deviation of a gamma process are related to these two parameters as follows:

$$\text{Mean} = r/\lambda.$$
$$\text{Standard deviation} = \sqrt{r}/\lambda.$$

From these relationships it follows that:

$$r = \text{mean}^2/\text{standard deviation}^2.$$
$$\lambda = \text{mean}/\text{standard deviation}^2.$$

Therefore a gamma distribution, like a normal distribution, can be uniquely specified by its mean and its standard deviation.

Figure 10–4 shows gamma probability distributions for the spe-

FIGURE 10–4

Gamma Probability Distribution for the Special Case where $\lambda = 1$

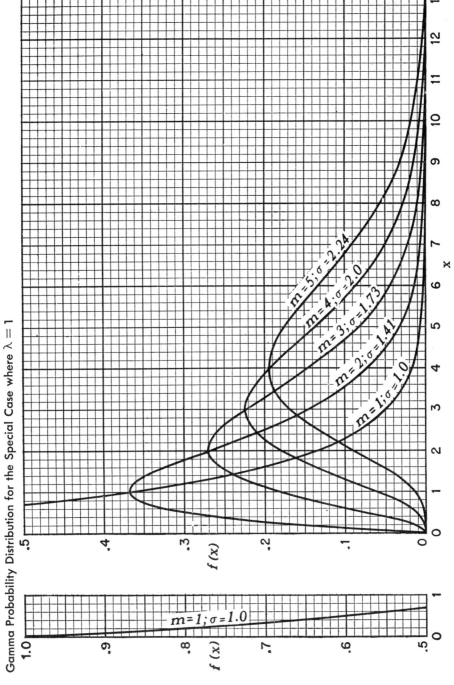

cial case in which $\lambda = 1$, and the mean varies from 1 through 5. In the gamma distribution the ratio of the standard deviation to the mean is the reciprocal of the square root of r. When this ratio is $1/3$ or smaller (i.e., when r is 9 or greater), the gamma distribution closely approximates a normal distribution with the same mean and standard deviation.

A GAMMA GENERATOR

Designing a gamma generator poses greater complexity than designing a normal generator. A scheme for generating gamma distributed variables, in the form of a FORTRAN subroutine, will be presented without elaboration on why the variables generated approximate the gamma distribution (see Figure 10–5). Variables common to the subroutine and the main program are TMU and SD, representing the mean and the standard deviation, respectively. Each time the subroutine is called, G gets a new value. These values will be gamma distributed with mean TMU and standard deviation SD. As in the case of our normal generator, a uniformly distributed random fraction generator is called into play to generate gamma distributed variables. The generator of Figure 10–5 is restricted to those cases where $r = (\text{mean/standard deviation})^2$ is an integer.

FIGURE 10–5

A Subroutine for Generating Gamma
Distributed Variables

```
SUBROUTINE GAMMA (TMU, SD, G)
IR = (TMU/SD) ** 2
TLMBDA = TMU/SD**2
T = 1.0
DO 1 J = 1, IR
1   T = T * RANF(0)
G = - LOG(T)/TLMBDA
RETURN
END
```

OTHER GENERATORS

A convenient exponential generator, the great majority of whose generated variables, V, fall between 0 and 5 times the mean, TMU, is:

$$V = |TMU \times \log_e R|$$

where R is a uniformly distributed random fraction, and the vertical lines mean "absolute value," i.e., "without regard to sign." Two FORTRAN statements suitable for this might be:[4]

```
R = RANF(0)
V = ABS(TMU * LOG(R))
```

or, more briefly:

$$V = ABS(TMU * LOG(RANF(0))) \qquad (10\text{-}9)$$

By adding a statement to (**10-5**) we can construct a "log-normal" generator:

$$V2 = 2.718 ** V1 \qquad (10\text{-}10)$$

In (**10-10**) the natural logarithm base, e, is raised to powers that are normally distributed, but the distribution of V2 is skewed, with a mean of: $e^{(TMU+\frac{1}{2}SD^2)}$ and a standard deviation of: $e^{(2TMU+2SD^2)} - e^{(2TMU-SD^2)}$.

SUGGESTIONS FOR FURTHER STUDY

GORDON, GEOFFREY. *System Simulation.* Englewood Cliffs, N.J.: Prentice-Hall, Inc., 1969.

NAYLOR, BALINTFY, BURDICK, AND CHU. *Computer Simulation Techniques.* New York: John Wiley & Sons, Inc., 1966.

SCHLAIFER, ROBERT. *Probability and Statistics for Business Decisions,* chaps. 10, 13, 14, and 17. New York: McGraw-Hill Book Co., 1963.

EXERCISES

(Where a computer program is called for, begin with a flow diagram.)

1. A "Fibonacci sequence" results when we begin with a number, N; add to it N + 1, yielding N1; then add to N + 1, N1, yielding N2; then add to N1, N2, yielding N3; then add to N3, N2, yielding N4; and so on, thus:

2	N
3	N + 1
5	N1
8	N2
13	N3
21	N4, etc.

---

[4] ABS( ) means absolute value.

The numbers 121393 and 414229 are 2 successive numbers in a Fibonacci sequence. We might design a random number generator, based on a Fibonacci sequence, beginning with these two numbers. To more nearly guarantee randomness, we might select as our random numbers (assuming we want a two-digit random number list) the third and fourth digits, counting from right to left.

Thus our first random number would be 56, 121393 + 414229 = 535622, and we drop all but the third and fourth digits, counting from the right.

Our second random number would be 98, 414229 + 535622 = 989851, and we drop all but the third and fourth digits, counting from the right.

Write a FORTRAN program that will enable us to get a two-digit random interger based on a Fibonacci sequence, beginning with 121393 and 414229, by calling SUBROUTINE FIBONA.

2.   Using the system function associated with your computer for generating uniformly distributed random fractions, compose a FORTRAN program that will generate 4,000 two-digit random integers, and will keep a record and print out the frequency with which each of the various two-digit numbers generated appeared.

3.   Using the normal generator described in Chapter 10:

    a)   Compose a FORTRAN program that will generate 4,000 three-digit integers, randomly distributed about a mean of 163 with standard deviation of 40, and will keep a record and print out the frequency with which the various three-digit integers appeared.

    b)   Repeat the above, using the Poisson generator described in Chapter 10, with a mean of 103.

    c)   Repeat the above, using the log-normal generator described in Chapter 10 and the normal parameters specified in (*a*) above.

    d)   Plot curves of the distributions generated in (*a*), (*b*), and (*c*).

4.   Employ the normal generator described in Chapter 10 using a mean of 67 and a standard deviation of 20, to generate 4,000 three-digit integers. Compose a FORTRAN program that will determine the mean of the 4,000 integers thus generated, and their variance.

5.   Random variable X exhibits a behavior that can be approximated by the following density function:

$$Y = -\tfrac{1}{2}X + 1 \qquad 0 \leq X \leq 2$$

Compose a FORTRAN subroutine that will employ a uniform fraction generator to generate values for X which conform to this density function.

6.   *Monte Carlo Simulation for Determining Equipment Reliability.* A piece of production equipment has been constructed by assembling three component machines. When *any* component machine breaks down the system of three machines is down.

Free run time probability distributions for each of the three machines —the time each machine can be expected to run before breaking down and requiring service—have been provided by the manufacturers of the machines, and are as shown below.

Determine the free run time probability distribution for the *system*.

	Free Run Time (Months)	Probability	Appropriate Range of One-Digit Integer Random Number List
Machine 1	3	.4	0–3
	4	.3	4–6
	5	.2	7–8
	6	.1	9
Machine 2	2	.3	0–2
	3	.4	3–6
	4	.2	7–8
	5	.1	9
Machine 3	4	.1	0
	5	.3	1–3
	6	.4	4–7
	7	.2	8–9

A hand solution of the problem is suggested below.

Procedure:

1) Load MACH boxes with approximate mean free run time of each machine.
2) Identify machine(s) with lowest remaining free run time.
3) Give that free run time an extra score in the SCORE array.
4) Subtract value in box with lowest free run time from all 3 MACH boxes (that is, "advance clock").
5) Generate new free run time for machine(s) with zero free run time remaining.
6) To (2), above.

Compose a FORTRAN program that will apply Monte Carlo simulation to this problem, and will generate and print out a free run time probability distribution for the *system*.

chapter 11

Simulation of Queuing Systems

Now THAT we have equipped ourselves with a variety of process generators, we are in a position to study the behavior of rather complex systems in which processes similar to these seem to be operative. To see how these generators might be employed, let us undertake the design of a computer model for simulating queuing systems. Once again we will begin by designing a rather elementary model, one involving a single-channel and a single-service facility. However, we will carefully design the model in a rather particular manner so that it can be applied, with minor modifications, to quite complex queuing systems. We will design our model around a specific queue system, and then move to the more general model.

SINGLE–CHANNEL QUEUE SYSTEM SIMULATION

In this single-channel queue system, arrivals are Poisson distributed with a mean arrival rate of 2.0 customers per hour. Arrivals are serviced on a first-come, first-served basis in a service facility that can accommodate only one customer at a time. Service time is exponentially distributed with a mean of one-third hour per customer.

We wish to determine the behavior of the system by simulating experience with 1,000 customers, beginning at time 0 with the system empty.

Two events can occur that change the "state" of the system:

1. Customers arrive in the system.
2. Customers whose service has been completed depart from the service facility.

To simulate the system's performance let us use two subroutines in a FORTRAN program. We will make a comparison in the main program between (1) the *time* after time zero when the next arriving customer is "destined to arrive," and (2) the *time* after time zero when the next departure is "destined to occur." The earlier of the two events will determine which of the two subroutines will be called for determining the new state of the system.

Data will be accumulated during the simulation to determine the following:

1. The percent utilization of the service facility (the percent of the total time the facility is busy).
2. The probabilities of queues of varying lengths forming before the service facility.
3. The average or expected time in the system per customer.

Variables employed in the FORTRAN program will be as follows:

TIME: always has the value of the hour of the most recent change in the state or status of the system.

TNARV: has the value of the hour of the next arrival.

TNDPR: has the value of the hour of the next departure.

QUE: has a value equal to the length of the queue.

STATUS: indicates the state of the service facility. When STATUS is 0.0 the facility is empty; when STATUS is 1.0 the facility is occupied.

CUMUTL: has a value equal to the total number of hours since time zero that the service facility has been busy (cumulative utilization).

CUSERV: has the value of the number of customers who have been served and have departed from the service facility since time zero.

CUMQUE: is a one-dimension subscripted variable which holds the cumulative record of hours during which the queue has been of various lengths. Thus: CUMQUE(1) holds the number of hours the queue has had 0 customers in it since time 0; CUMQUE(2) holds the number of hours the queue has had 1 customer in it since time 0; CUMQUE(3) holds the number of hours the queue has had 2 customers in it since time 0; CUMQUE(19) holds the number of hours the queue has had 18 customers in it since time 0 (assume that the queue will never exceed 18).

Figure 11–1 is a flow diagram for a computer program that could be employed to simulate the system using the variables defined.

FIGURE 11–1

Flow Diagram for Single-Channel Queue System

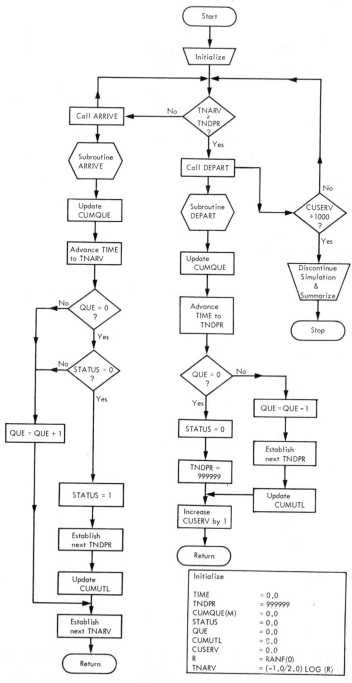

Notice that in initializing the system we make TNDPR very large in order to assure that the first status disturbing event is an arrival (a departure being impossible, since the system begins empty). Let us design a subroutine to interpret and record the effect of an arrival on the system.

The Arrival Subroutine

Since an arrival, like a departure, is a status disturbing event, we should begin by updating the variable, CUMQUE. Recalling the use of the variable TIME, we know that whatever the status of the queue *prior* to our current arrival it has had that status since TIME, or for TNARV minus TIME hours. Updating CUMQUE means that we must add this increment of time to that cumulative record of time during which the queue has had length QUE. We can do this with the following statements:

M = QUE
CUMQUE(M + 1) = CUMQUE(M + 1) + TNARV − TIME

Now we can reset TIME to reflect the hour of our most recent status disturbing event: TIME = TNARV.

Next we would do well to determine whether our new arrival enters the service facility or the queue. Recalling that the variable STATUS has a value of 0 if the facility is empty and a value of 1.0 if it is occupied, we can determine whether our arrival enters the queue or the facility by two IF statements:

IF (QUE − 1.0)1,3,3   ·
1   IF (STATUS − 1.0)2,3,3

If as a result of these two statements control passes to statement 2, it means that the queue had length zero and the service facility was empty. Under these conditions, our new arrival would enter the facility immediately on arriving, and we would want to add a statement to indicate that the facility is now occupied: 2 STATUS = 1.0.

Since a customer just entered the facility (at hour TIME), the stage is set for a departure to occur at some future hour. Since service time is known to be exponentially distributed, with a mean of one-third hour we can use our Poisson generator to determine the increment of time, T, which will be required to service the customer who just entered the facility. With the following statements we can determine T and calculate the hour this customer is "destined to depart" from the facility, TNDPR:

$$T = -1.0/3.0 * ALOG(RANF(0))$$
$$TNDPR = TIME + T$$

Knowing the magnitude of this added increment of time T with which the facility is "destined" to be occupied, we can update CUMUTL, our cumulative record of the hours the facility is utilized: CUMUTL = CUMUTL + T.

We must now make provision for the event: "Our current arrival arrived to find the service facility occupied." In this event our two IF statements, toward the beginning of our arrive subroutine, would send control to statement 3. We should add a statement to increase the length of QUE: 3   QUE = QUE + 1.0.

Finally we must set the stage for our next arrival by giving the variable TNARV a new value. Knowing that the arrival pattern is Poisson distributed, with a mean of 2.0 customers per hour, we can use our Poisson generator to determine the increment of time "destined to elapse" before our next arrival and determine his hour of arrival, TNARV, by the statement:

$$4 \quad TNARV = -1.0/2.0 * ALOG(RANF(0)) + TIME$$

Our arrive subroutine would appear as follows:

```
    SUBROUTINE ARRIVE (QUE,STATUS,TNDPR,
        CUMUTL,TNARV,CUMQUE,TIME)
    DIMENSION CUMQUE(20)
    M = QUE
    CUMQUE(M + 1) = CUMQUE(M + 1) + TNARV - TIME
    TIME = TNARV
    IF (QUE - 1.0)1,3,3
1   IF (STATUS - 1.0)2,3,3
2   STATUS = 1.0
    T = -1.0/3.0 * ALOG(RANF(0))
    TNDPR = TIME + T
    CUMUTL = CUMUTL + T
    GO TO 4
3   QUE = QUE + 1.0
4   TNARV = -1.0/2.0 * ALOG(RANF(0)) + TIME
    RETURN
    END
```

The Depart Subroutine

As with our arrive subroutine, we should begin by updating CUMQUE and by resetting TIME:

```
M = QUE
CUMQUE(M + 1) = CUMQUE(M + 1) + TNDPR - TIME
TIME = TNDPR.
```

Next, let us make provision for the event: "A customer departs from the service facility at a time when the queue is zero":

```
      IF (QUE - 1.0)1,2,2
    1 STATUS = 0.0
      TNDPR = 999999.0
```

In the program segment above we set STATUS at zero, since the service facility is now empty, and we give the variable TNDPR a very large value to assure that the next status disturbing event is *not* a departure (now an impossibility).

Now let us deal with the case where the departure that caused our depart subroutine to be called occurs when the queue is not zero. Clearly the departure will reduce the queue by one: 2 QUE = QUE $-$ 1.0.

Since a new customer has just entered the service facility we would do well to determine how long an increment of time, T, this customer will be in the facility, and to use this information to update CUMUTL and to determine the time of our next departure, TNDPR:

```
      T = (-1.0/3.0 * ALOG(RANF(0)))
      TNDPR = TIME + T
      CUMUTL = CUMUTL + T
```

Having just serviced an additional customer, we should update CUSERV:

```
    3 CUSERV = CUSERV + 1.0
```

Our depart subroutine would appear as follows:

```
      SUBROUTINE DEPART (QUE,STATUS,TNDPR,
         CUMUTL,CUMQUE,TIME,CUSERV)
      DIMENSION CUMQUE(20)
      M = QUE
      CUMQUE(M + 1) = CUMQUE(M + 1) + TNDPR - TIME
      TIME = TNDPR
      IF (QUE - 1.0)1,2,2
```

```
1  STATUS = 0.0
   TNDPR = 999999.0
   GO TO 3
2  QUE = QUE - 1.0
   T = (-1.0/3.0) * ALGO(RANF(0))
   TNDPR = TIME + T
   CUMUTL = CUMUTL + T
3  CUSERV = CUSERV + 1.0
   RETURN
   END
```

The Main Program

Our main program will consist of: (1) initializing statements, (2) our calling routine, and (3) some procedure for summarizing and printing out results of our simulated experience.

Let us turn first to the calling routine. Our calling routine must compare TNARV and TNDPR, and call the subroutine that interprets the effect on the system of whichever of these two status disturbing events occurs earlier. These statements should meet our needs:

```
2  IF (TNARV - TNDPR)3,4,4
3  CALL ARRIVE (QUE,STATUS,TNDPR,CUMUTL
      TNARV,CUMQUE,TIME)
   GO TO 2
4  CALL DEPART (QUE,STATUS,TNDPR,CUMUTL,
      CUMQUE,TIME,CUSERV)
   IF (CUSERV - 1000.0)2,5,5
```

By the addition of the final statement in the above program segment we provide for terminating the operating routine when the servicing of 1,000 arrivals has been simulated.

Let us assume that 1,000 arrivals have been serviced and that we are ready to interpret the results of our simulation. The variable TIME holds the hour of departure of the 1,000th customer and hence the total simulated time. The percent utilization of the service facility can be determined by 5 PCUTIL = (CUMUTL/ TIME) * 100.

To find the average time a customer spent in the system we could divide the total number of customer hours spent in the system by 1,000. Total customer hours in the system would be total customer hours spent in queues plus total customer hours spent in the service facility. Total customer hours spent in queues would be:

1 × total hours the queue length was 1
+ 2 × total hours the queue length was 2
+ 3 × total hours the queue length was 3, etc.

We could calculate total customer hours in queues thus:

```
    HRSNQ = 0.0
    DO 6 M = 1,19
    H = M
6   HRSNQ = HRSNQ + H * CUMQUE(M + 1)
```

And total customer hours spent in the service facility is simply CUMUTL.

Average time in the system would therefore be: AVTIS = (HRSNQ + CUMUTL)/1000.0.

Since we are interested in the probabilities of queues of varying lengths, we might convert the contents of the array CUMQUE to probabilities in this way:

```
    DO 7 M = 1,20
7   CUMQUE(M) = CUMQUE(M)/TIME
```

With suitable WRITE and FORMAT statements we can provide for printing out the desired data:

```
    WRITE (6,8) PCUTIL,AVTIS
8   FORMAT(1H0,42HPERCENT UTILIZATION OF SERVICE
    FACILITY = ,F10.6,2X,43HAND AVERAGE TIME IN
    SYSTEM PER CUSTOMER = ,F10.2)
    DO 10 M = 1,19
    L = M − 1
    WRITE (6,9) L, CUMQUE(M)
9   FORMAT(1H0,15HPROBABILITY OF ,I2, 2X,
    21HCUSTOMERS IN QUEUE = ,F10.8)
```

Our total program, with the initializing statements added and with comment statements interspersed to facilitate interpretation, would appear as shown in Figure 11–2.

The results of the simulation (our printout) follow.

PERCENT UTILIZATION OF SERVICE FACILITY =
                              67.496540
AVERAGE TIME IN THE SYSTEM PER CUSTOMER =
                                1.03 HOURS

PROBABILITY OF 0 CUSTOMERS IN QUEUE =   0.55110
PROBABILITY OF 1 CUSTOMERS IN QUEUE =   0.13431

FIGURE 11-2*

```
      DIMENSION CUMQUE(20)
C INITIALIZE SYSTEM AT TIME ZERO
      TIME=0.0
      TNDPR=999999.9
      DO 1 M=1,20
    1 CUMQUE(M)=0.0
      STATUS=0.C
      QUE=0.0
      CUMUTL=0.0
      CUSERV=0.C
      R=FURNB(0)
      TNARV=-1.0/2.0*ALOG(R)
C CALL UPON TIMING ROUTINE
    2 IF (TNARV-TNDPR)3,4,4
    3 CALL ARRIVE (QUE,STATUS,TNDPR,CUMUTL,TNARV,CUMQUE,TIME)
      GO TO 2
    4 CALL DEPART (QUE,STATUS,TNDPR,CUMUTL,CUMQUE,TIME,CUSERV)
C TERMINATE SIMULATION IF ONE THOUSAND ARRIVALS HAVE BEEN SERVICED
      IF (CUSERV-1000.0)2,5,5
C DETERMINE PERCENTAGE UTILIZATION OF SERVICE FACILITY
    5 PCUTIL=CUMUTL/TIME*100.0
C DETERMINE FROM CUMQUE CUSTOMER-HOURS SPENT IN QUEUES
      HRSNQ=0.0
      DO 6 M=1,19
      H=M
    6 HRSNQ=HRSNQ+H*CUMQUE(M+1)
C ADD CUSTOMER-HOURS IN FACILITY AND DETERMINE AVERAGE TIME IN SYSTEM
      AVTIS=(HRSNQ+CUMUTL)/1000.0
C CONVERT CONTENTS OF CUMQUE TO PROBABILITIES
      DO 7 M=1,20
    7 CUMQUE(M)=CUMQUE(M)/TIME
C WRITE PCUTIL ANDAVTIS
      WRITE (6,8) PCUTIL,AVTIS
    8 FORMAT (1H0,45HPERCENTAGE UTILIZATION OF SERVICE FACILITY = ,F10.6
     1,2X,42HAND AVERAGE TIME IN SYSTEM PER CUSTOMER = ,F5.2)
C PRINT PROBABILITIES OF QUEUES OF VARYING LENGTHS
      DO 10 M=1,19
      L=M-1
      WRITE (6,9) L,CUMQUE(M)
    9 FORMAT (1H0,15HPROBABILITY OF ,I2,2X,21HCUSTOMERS IN QUEUE = ,F10.
     17)
   10 CONTINUE
      STOP
      END


      SUBROUTINE ARRIVE (QUE,STATUS,TNDPR,CUMUTL,TNARV,CUMQUE,TIME)
      DIMENSION CUMQUE(20)
C UPDATE CUMQUE, RESET TIME
      M=QUE
      CUMQUE(M+1)=CUMQUE(M+1)+TNARV-TIME
      TIME=TNARV
C CHECK QUEUE LENGTH AND STATE OF SERVICE FACILITY
      IF (QUE-1.0)1,3,3
    1 IF (STATUS-1.0)2,3,3
    2 STATUS=1.0
C ESTABLISH TIME IN SERVICE FACILITY AND TIME OF NEXT DEPARTURE
      T=-1.0/3.0*ALOG(FURNB(0))
      TNDPR=TIME+T
C UPDATE CUMUTL
      CUMUTL=CUMUTL+T
      GO TO 4
C INCREASE QUEUE LENGTH
    3 QUE=QUE+1.0
C ESTABLISH TIME OF NEXT ARRIVAL
    4 TNARV=-1.0/2.0*ALOG(FURNB(0))+TIME
      RETURN
      END


      SUBROUTINE DEPART (QUE,STATUS,TNDPR,CUMUTL,CUMQUE,TIME,CUSERV)
      DIMENSION CUMQUE(20)
C UPDATE CUMQUE, RESET TIME
      M=QUE
      CUMQUE(M+1)=CUMQUE(M+1)+TNDPR-TIME
      TIME=TNDPR
C CHECK QUEUE LENGTH
      IF (QUE-1.0)1,2,2
    1 STATUS=0.0
      TNDPR=999999.9
      GO TO 3
C DECREASE QUEUE LENGTH
    2 QUE=QUE-1.0
C ESTABLISH TIME IN SERVICE FACILITY AND TIME OF NEXT DEPARTURE
      T=-1.0/3.0*ALOG(FURNB(0))
      TNDPR=TIME+T
C UPDATE CUMUTL AND CUSERV
      CUMUTL=CUMUTL+T
    3 CUSERV=CUSERV+1.0
      RETURN
      END
```

* Like RANF(0), the function FURNB(0) produces a uniformly distributed random fraction.

PROBABILITY OF 2 CUSTOMERS IN QUEUE =   0.09515
PROBABILITY OF 3 CUSTOMERS IN QUEUE =   0.06547
PROBABILITY OF 4 CUSTOMERS IN QUEUE =   0.06206
PROBABILITY OF 5 CUSTOMERS IN QUEUE =   0.02601
PROBABILITY OF 6 CUSTOMERS IN QUEUE =   0.02588
PROBABILITY OF 7 CUSTOMERS IN QUEUE =   0.01626
PROBABILITY OF 8 CUSTOMERS IN QUEUE =   0.01197
PROBABILITY OF 9 CUSTOMERS IN QUEUE =   0.00492
PROBABILITY OF 10 CUSTOMERS IN QUEUE =   0.00425
PROBABILITY OF 11 CUSTOMERS IN QUEUE =   0.00262
PROBABILITY OF 12 CUSTOMERS IN QUEUE =   0.00000

This single-channel queue system appears to be a rather elementary system. Most queue systems in business and economics consist of multiple facilities, multiple channels, and multiple queues. The queue discipline may vary from channel to channel; the service times, arrival patterns, and other parameters of each of the individual subcomponent queue systems may vary. However, in a very real sense most complex systems may be thought of as many component subsystems, each of which bears some similarity to the others. By virtue of this basic uniformity we can use the construct of Figure 11–2 to simulate and to study the behavior of highly complex systems that are composed of many different component subsystems, each with different attributes.

We can do this by using one-, two-, and three-dimension subscripted variables to store attributes of the component subsystems where we used zero-dimension subscripted variables in Figure 11–2. Thus the variables TIME, TNDPR, STATUS, QUE, CUMUTL, CUSERV, and TNARV might be converted to one-dimension subscripted variables. Position 1 in each of these subscripted variables could refer to component queue system 1; position 2 in each of these subscripted variables could refer to component system 2; and so on. The main program, then, would serve to inquire not simply which occurs next—an arrival or a departure—but rather which of many possible arrivals and many possible departures occurs next. When the component queue system (involved with the event "destined" to occur next) is identified, the appropriate position in our set of arrays would be called into play. Execution of the statements in either the arrival subroutine or the departure subroutine would then involve interpreting the effect of an arrival or a departure on the particular component subsystem for which some status disturbing event just occurred.

In this scheme the variable CUMQUE could be made a two-dimension subscripted variable to hold records of all queues.

MULTIPLE–SERVICE FACILITIES

Let us suppose that we have a single-channel queue system with three, rather than one, service facilities, as portrayed in Figure 11–3.

FIGURE 11–3

As before, let us assume that arrivals at service facility 1 are Poisson distributed, with a mean arrival rate of 2.0 customers per hour, and that service time in each of the three service facilities is exponentially distributed with a mean service time of one-third hour per customer.

We can think of this system as three component subsystems, each consisting of a service facility and its queue of customers waiting for service. The status of each subsystem is disturbed, as before, by either of two possible events: an arrival or a departure. Clearly, however, a departure from subsystem 1 is an arrival at subsystem 2, and a departure from subsystem 2 is an arrival at subsystem 3. Therefore, the moment TNDPR for subsystem 1 is determined, TNARV for subsystem 2 is established, and, similarly, the moment TNDPR for subsystem 2 is determined, TNARV for subsystem 3 is established.

In these circumstances we are obliged to call on our Poisson generator only for establishing the time of the next arrival at subsystem 1. This special characteristic of our multiple-service facility system would require only a few modifications in the program of Figure 11–2.

Variables for the model of Figure 11–2 could be redefined, enabling us to simulate the multiple facility model of Figure 11–3 as follows:

TIME(1) . . . always has the value of the hour of the most recent change in the status of subsystem 1.

TIME(2) . . . always has the value of the hour of the most recent change in the status of subsystem 2.

TIME(3) . . . always has the value of the hour of the most recent change in the status of subsystem 3.

TNARV(1) . . . has the value of the hour of the next arrival in subsystem 1.

TNARV(2) . . . has the value of the hour of the next arrival in subsystem 2.

TNARV(3) . . . has the value of the hour of the next arrival in subsystem 3.

TNDPR(1) . . . has the value of the hour of the next departure from
subsystem 1.

TNDPR(2) . . . has the value of the hour of the next departure from
subsystem 2.

TNDPR(3) . . . has the value of the hour of the next departure from
subsystem 3.

QUE(1) . . . has a value equal to the length of the queue of subsystem 1.

QUE(2) . . . has a value equal to the length of the queue of subsystem 2.

QUE(3) . . . has a value equal to the length of the queue of subsystem 3.

STATUS(1) . . . indicates the status of the service facility in subsystem 1.

STATUS(2) . . . indicates the status of the service facility in subsystem 2.

STATUS(3) . . . indicates the status of the service facility in subsystem 3.

CUMUTL(1) . . . has a value equal to the total number of hours since
time zero that the service facility of subsystem 1 has
been busy.

CUMUTL(2) . . . has a value equal to the total number of hours since
time zero that the service facility of subsystem 2 has
been busy.

CUMUTL(3) . . . has a value equal to the total number of hours since
time zero that the service facility of subsystem 3 has
been busy.

CUMQUE(1,1) . . . holds the number of hours the queue of subsystem 1
has had zero customers in it since time zero.

CUMQUE(1,2) . . . holds the number of hours the queue of subsystem 1
has had one customer in it since time zero.

CUMQUE(2,1) . . . holds the number of hours the queue of subsystem 2
has had zero customers in it since time zero.

CUMQUE(2,2) . . . holds the number of hours the queue of subsystem 2
has had one customer in it since time zero.

.

.

.

and so on.

We might think of our computer model as consisting of three *sets* of subroutines, one set pertaining to each of the three subsystems. Associated with each set is a separate clock (the various positions of TIME(N)) and means for keeping a cumulative record of the operations of the subsystem to which each subroutine set pertains.

Our timing mechanism in the main program will now be obliged to search (for the smallest value) the time stored in the N positions of the variables TNARV(N) and TNDPR(N).

MULTIPLE CHANNELS

Suppose that we have a system like that of Figure 11–4. Let us assume that customers departing from subsystem 1 enter subsys-

FIGURE 11–4

tems 2, 3, or 4, and that the distribution between these three subsystems is random, with equal probabilities. That is: one third go to subsystem 2, one third go to subsystem 3, and one third go to subsystem 4.

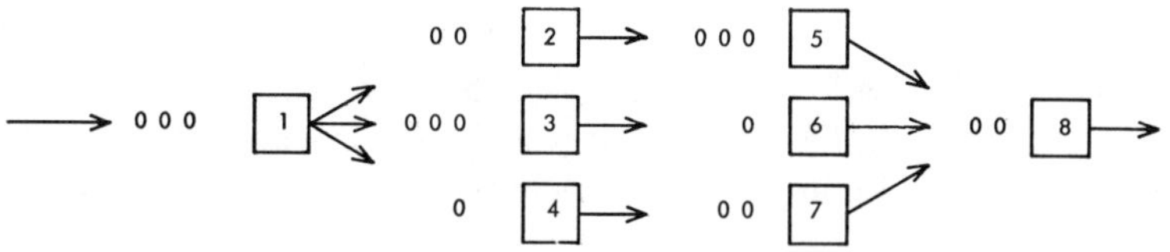

Here also we can employ a slightly modified version of the model of Figure 11–2. We envision a two-subroutine set for each of the eight subsystems, with a clock and an operating experience recording routine for each subsystem. The only innovation required is some scheme for determining whether a departure from subsystem 1 is an arrival at subsystem 2, at subsystem 3, or at subsystem 4. This we could do easily with a suitably designed generator.

Our previous examples have been rather simple in that service times at the various service facilities all have had the same distribution parameters. Suppose that service times are all normally distributed but that other parameters of the distributions are different. We might also deal rather easily with this problem. We could introduce a second subscripted variable, which we might call PARAM(M,N)—to hold the means and the standard deviations of the various distributions—with

PARAM(1,1) . . . holding the mean of the service time distribution of subsystem 1.

PARAM(1,2) . . . holding the standard deviation of the service time distribution of subsystem 1.

PARAM(2,1) . . . holding the mean of the service time distribution of subsystem 2.

PARAM(2,2) . . . holding the standard deviation of the service time distribution of subsystem 2.

But how would we proceed if the service time at one service facility were normally distributed, while the service time distribution at another service facility were constant, or perhaps Poisson or Gamma distributed?

One way to deal with this added complexity would be to provide a set of special service time generating subroutines, with one subroutine for each different class of service time distributions. Thus we might have a service time generating subroutine for all facilities whose service time distribution is normal and another for those whose service time distribution is Poisson. We could also construct a special subroutine for a facility whose service time is constant, or perhaps one characterized by a discrete distribution of some unique form.

With such a general arrangement we might do our service time calculating in the main program rather than in a subroutine (as called for in Figure 11–2). Once the subsystem for which a departure has just occurred has been identified, we could cause the appropriate service time generating subroutine to be called for determining the time of departure of the next customer in that service facility.

In trying to conceptualize the requirements for adapting our model of Figure 11–2 to the systems portrayed in Figures 11–3 and 11–4, we found ourselves thinking of subsystem service facilities and their associated queues. Focusing our attention on a subsystem, we found that we could simulate its behavior by a few modifications of the model of Figure 11–2, that we could relate that subsystem to the other subsystems in the total system, and that we could accumulate records of data relating to the operating experience of each subsystem by specifying:

1. The distribution of service time in the subsystem's service facility.

2. The position of the subsystem in the flow of customers.

The initial subsystem and the final subsystem are unique, however. The time of the next arrival for the initial subsystem is not determined by the time of departure from a predecessor subsystem; rather, customers arriving from outside the total system are generated by some specified process. Also, the time of departure of a customer from the final subsystem does not determine the time of arrival at a succeeding subsystem, but rather signals permanent departure of the customer from the total system.

Our conceptual scheme, therefore, involves:

1. Generation of customers from outside the system.
2. A flow of customers through a specified sequence of subsystems, each of which involves a service facility and a queue.
3. Departure of customers from the system.

SPECIALIZED SIMULATION LANGUAGES

Widespread simulation of complex systems, especially those containing queues, has led to the creation of several "problem-oriented" languages. This means that a language is designed to simplify the modeling of certain situations or problems. In contrast, a "procedure-oriented" language facilitates machine processing of data without special concern for the kind of problem under investigation. FORTRAN, for example, is procedure oriented. Two analysts modeling the same system, both using FORTRAN, would most likely produce grossly dissimilar models. However, if both used GPSS, their models would be very similar in the way the system was represented and written up as a computer program.

GASP and SIMSCRIPT, described in this section, and GPSS the subject of Chapter 12, are also known as "high-order" languages. This refers to the availability of subroutines for event processing, timing, and record keeping. FORTRAN is high order relative to machine language. Analogously, GASP, SIMSCRIPT, and GPSS are high order in relation to FORTRAN. It will become apparent that special languages eliminate the need to program many details as well as the overall program logic. They are indeed high order, problem *and* user oriented.

A special language gives the analyst a particular view of the world. Although he may model systems with different technologies, their models share a common structural logic. The analyst conforms his model to the systems concept implicit in the language. In return he achieves substantial savings during model construction and computer programming. Offsetting these are the relative loss of modeling freedom, higher machine processing costs, and of course, the time necessary to learn the language. When the system is complex and the analyst faced with many experiments, he typically decides the added costs are acceptable. Studies of comparative costs of simulation procedures with different languages and machines have been carried out. At this time decisions to employ special languages reflect convenience and acceptance of underlying concepts, and only secondarily reprogramming and machine costs.

GASP

This is the newest of the three languages considered here. Modest claims are made for it—successful applications are reported for novices using fairly small machines. It is FORTRAN based and can be implemented on a variety of computer systems without serious problems.

The systems concept in GASP is about the same as proposed in our first chapters. A system is a set of *entities* that interact. Properties or *attributes* of an entity describe it. Attributes take numerical values, and when all like attributes have the same value the state of the system is described. *Relationships* explain the effect one attribute has on another. The notions of *environment* and *boundaries* are conventionally defined.

Statically, the system is specified in terms of entities, attributes, and relationships. System dynamics are modeled in terms of *activities* and *events* that occur through time. By definition, events produce changes in attribute values. Events are significant milestones of activities. Generally, the beginning and end of an activity will be explicitly modeled as events.

In the following we discuss certain features of GASP that would be involved in modeling Pete's Two-Minute Auto Wash.

First of all, two entities and their attributes are set up.

Entity	*Attributes*
1. Customers	Arrival rate
	Number in the system
2. Server	Service rate
	Status (busy or idle)

Two events cause changes in the state of the system.

Event	*Attributes*
1. Arrival of *i*th customer	Time
2. End of service of *i*th customer	Time

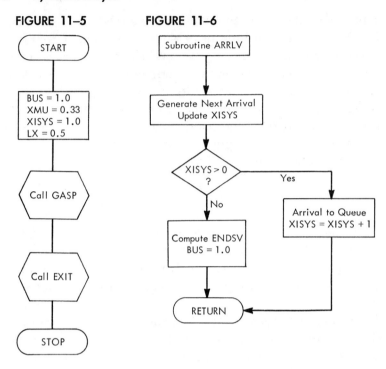

FIGURE 11–5

FIGURE 11–6

Note that events are described by their attributes. Also that only those events necessary to develop estimates of the system's behavior as earlier modeled are included here.

To simulate Pete's Auto Wash in GASP we need to write a main program, a so-called events subroutine, and subroutines for each kind of event.[1] The main program serves to initialize non-GASP variables—attributes of server and customers. By way of clarification "customers" is a single kind of entity although of course there will be many customers in the course of the simulation.

Initial conditions are slightly changed from those in the original illustration. It is assumed that one customer is in the system at time 0 when the simulation starts. His service is due to end at 0.2. Therefore the servers will be busy (BUS = 1.0) and the number in the system (XISYS) will initially be one. XMU is the mean service time, and XL is the mean interarrival time. The main program looks like Figure 11–5.

---

[1] See the example of the single-channel queue in A. Alan B. Pritsker and Phillip J. Kiviat, *Simulation with Gasp II* (Englewood Cliffs, N.J.: Prentice-Hall, Inc., 1969), pp. 116–33.

Subroutine GASP controls the simulation. It initializes non-GASP variables and stores information about key events. It establishes two files—one for the set of events, another for the set of customers. GASP then directs the processing of events, creating and filing them as necessary. It records changes in system attributes and finally causes a summary report to be printed.

For control purposes data about three events must be furnished as part of initialization.

1. Arrival of first customer—time 0.
2. End of service of initial customer—time 0.2 (customer in system at time 0).
3. End of simulation—time 333. This approximates minimum time to process 1,000 customers.

After the first arrival, subsequent arrivals and their service times are generated in event subroutines ARRLV and ENDSV in a manner logically the same as in our original FORTRAN program. Subroutine ARRLV is diagrammed in Figure 11–6. Each time an arrival occurs, the subroutine determines the time of the next arrival and files the information about the event.

The other subroutines determine the end of service of a customer, ENDSV, or the end of the simulation, ENDSM. Each time a new event is processed its code is read in a subroutine called EVNTS. The event is either an arrival, end of service, or end of simulation.

Virtually all other programming is provided by GASP. The user may write optional output subroutines but GASP's standard or summary report prints means and variances for waiting time, time in the system, number in the system, and utilization of server.

A diagram of a typical GASP program, applicable to the single-channel model, is shown in Figure 11–7. It provides for multiple runs as well as additional output from a user written report generator called OTPUT.

SIMSCRIPT

Another simulation language is SIMSCRIPT.[2] Like GASP, SIMSCRIPT is another kind of shorthand. Many data manipulations required in simulating the effect on a system of a status dis-

---

[2] A programming manual for SIMSCRIPT is Harry N. Markowitz, Bernard Hauser, and Herbert W. Karr, *SIMSCRIPT: A Simulation Programming Language* (Englewood Cliffs, N.J.: Prentice-Hall, Inc., 1963).

FIGURE 11–7

A Typical GASP Program*

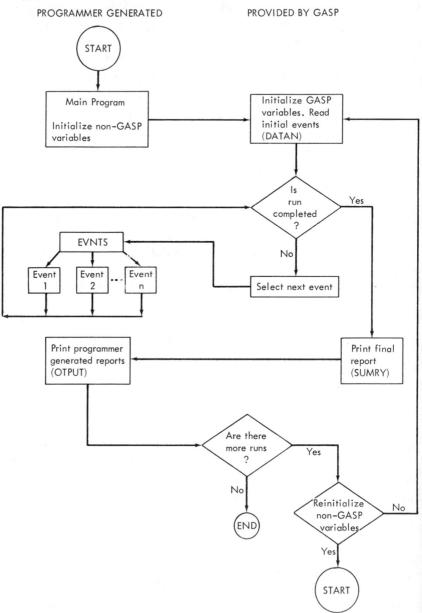

* A. Alan B. Pritsker and Phillip J. Kiviat, *Simulation* with GASP II (Englewood Cliffs, N.J.: Prentice-Hall, Inc., 1969), p. 19.

turbing event can be called into play by only one or a few SIM-SCRIPT statements.

SIMSCRIPT is a FORTRAN based language, but it has its own logic structure and its own set of programming conventions. Like GASP, SIMSCRIPT emphasizes the status of the system and the events that modify that status. SIMSCRIPT defines a system's status in terms of its "entities," their "attributes," and the "sets" to which they belong (or which they "own").

There are two kinds of entities in SIMSCRIPT—temporary and permanent entities. Temporary entities might correspond to "customers," as we have employed the term in this book. Permanent entities might correspond to our use of the term "service facilities."

Thus, in a machine shop, a machine group or a department through which work orders flow might be a "permanent entity," and orders themselves might be "temporary entities."

In the machine shop setting, an "attribute" of a department might be service time in that department; an order might be a temporary entity; and attributes of an order might include the date of the order or its sequence (routing) through the shop.

In a typical machine shop a work order may also be part of a "set" of work orders. Thus, work orders No. 2071, No. 34, and No. 056 may be the three jobs required for processing customer order No. A–274–6.

SIMSCRIPT provides for defining "entities" (temporary and permanent) by both their "attributes" and the "sets" to which they belong or which they "own." Customer order No. A–274–6 "owns" work orders 2071, 34, and 056. Similarly, a department might "own" a queue.

A SIMSCRIPT program is divided into a number of segments. An initial segment is the "definition" segment, in which the various kinds of temporary and permanent entities, their attributes, and "sets" are identified.

Events in SIMSCRIPT occur *within* the system (*endogenous events,* as when a work order is completed and departs from a department) or from *without* the system (*exogenous events,* as when a customer order arrives after having been "generated" by the market process). Events in SIMSCRIPT are status disturbing incidents in the same sense as we have used the term in this textbook.

In addition to the definition segment of a SIMSCRIPT program, one also uses a variety of routines. Thus we may have a routine for describing the effect on the system of a receipt of a customer's order, another routine for describing the arrival of a work order at a particular department, and another for describing the effect on the system of a departure from the system itself. These routines are analogous to the subroutines of our model in Figure 11–2.

Another SIMSCRIPT program segment is the report generator. This segment provides for summarizing results of the simulation and printing them out.

Like GASP, SIMSCRIPT has a variety of functions built into its compiler to simplify the job of the programmer. For simulating complex queuing systems, SIMSCRIPT has many advantages over FORTRAN. The most noteworthy advantages are simplicity and flexibility for the programmer in accommodating varied flow patterns and queue disciplines, and the conservation of computer memory space.

SUGGESTIONS FOR FURTHER STUDY

BUFFA, ELWOOD S. *Operations Management.* New York: John Wiley & Sons, Inc., 1968.

GORDON, GEOFFREY. *System Simulation.* Englewood Cliffs, N.J.: Prentice-Hall, Inc., 1969.

IBM Reference Manual for General Purpose Systems Simulator III (1966).

MARKOWITZ, HARRY N.; HAUSER, BERNARD; and KARR, HERBERT W. *Simscript: A Simulation Programming Language.* Englewood Cliffs, N.J.: Prentice-Hall, 1963.

NAYLOR, THOMAS H. *Computer Simulation Experiments with Models of Economic Systems.* New York: John Wiley & Sons, Inc., 1971.

PRITSKER, A. ALAN B.; and KIVIAT, PHILLIP J. *Simulation with GASP II.* Englewood Cliffs, N.J.: Prentice-Hall, Inc., 1969.

WYMAN, FORREST PAUL. *Simulation Modeling.* New York: John Wiley & Sons, Inc., 1970.

EXERCISES

1. Assume that customers arrive in a queue system in a fashion characterized by the Poisson distribution. Arrivals are serviced on a first-come, first-served basis in a service facility that can accommodate only one customer at a time, and service time is normally distributed with mean of 0.34 hours per customer and standard deviation 0.08. Employ the model in Figure 11–2 to determine the maximum mean arrival rate that could be tolerated without a queue length of 19 or more customers occurring more than 10 percent of the time.

2. Super Service, Inc., operates a truck fleet maintenance and repair service. Arriving trucks enter one of eight service areas, depending on the service they require. Service is on a first-come, first-served basis, and only one truck at a time can be accommodated in each service area.

Each service area operates independently of the others, although arriving trucks are occasionally obliged, on departing from one service area (after having been repaired), to enter another before leaving Super Service's facilities entirely.

In spite of this reentry characteristic, arrivals at all service areas are Poisson distributed. Service time at all service areas is normally distributed. Currently the mean arrival rate at the service area is as follows:

Service Areas	Mean Arrival Rate (Hour)
1	.43
2	.16
3	.14
4	.10
5	.09
6	.08
7	.05
8	.05

The mean service time at the service areas, and the associated standard deviations, are as follows:

Service Areas	Service Time Mean (Hours)	Standard Deviation
1	2.0	1.1
2	5.8	3.1
3	6.2	2.7
4	6.1	4.1
5	10.9	5.2
6	11.2	6.9
7	9.0	5.8
8	18.7	13.0

Compose a model along the pattern of Figure 11–2 for simulating the behavior of the Super Service system.

Super Service management anticipates that demand on the system will increase in the months ahead and is interested in forecasting when their present space facilities will become inadequate.

Super Service can accommodate *occasional* overloads by renting space in adjoining properties to hold trucks waiting for service. Management feels, however, that it is time to expand when demand reaches a level where their own space facilities are inadequate more than 20 percent of the time.

Super Service is presently equipped to accommodate 85 trucks awaiting service. If, as management forecasts, the mean arrival rate at each of the 8 service areas increases 0.24 percent per week, how many weeks does Super Service have to prepare additional storage space?

Suggestion: Use a modified version of the model in Figure 11–2, but use subscripted variables. For example:

QUE(1):   holds the length of the queue before service area 1.
QUE(2):   holds the length of the queue before service area 2, etc.

TMU(1):   holds the mean service time at service area 1.
SD(1):   holds the standard deviation associated with TMU(1).

CUMQUE(1,1):   holds the cumulative hours that the queue before service area 1 has had 0 trucks in it.
CUMQUE(1,2):   holds the cumulative hours that the queue before service area 1 has had 1 truck in it, etc.
CUMQUE(2,1):   holds the cumulative hours that the queue before service area 2 has had 0 trucks in it.
CUMQUE(2,2):   holds the cumulative hours that the queue before service area 2 has had 1 truck in it, etc.

3. Stored in the N positions of subscripted variables TNARV(N) and TNDPR(N) are floating-point numbers representing hours after time zero in which the next status disturbing event at each of N subsystems in a queue system are destined to occur. Compose a program segment that will cause the computer to search these two arrays, and identify the variable and the position of that variable in which the smallest number is stored.

4. Construct a program, using a modified version of the model in Figure 11–2, for simulating the multiple-channel, multiple-service facility system portrayed in Figure 11–4. Assume the following:

a) Arrivals at subsystem 1 are Poisson-distributed with a mean of 1.42 customers per hour.
b) Service time in subsystems 2, 4, 6, and 7 are normally distributed, with means of 1.9, 1.4, 1.6, and 1.8 hours per customer, respectively, each with a standard deviation equal to $\frac{1}{3}$ its mean.
c) Service time in subsystems 3, 5, and 8 are uniformly distributed as follows:

Subsystem	Mean (Hours per Customer)	Range
3	1.1	0.6 through 1.6
5	1.3	0.7 " 1.9
8	0.2	0.1 " 0.3

Simulate operations during the processing of 500 arrivals. Arrange to have printed out:

a) Percent utilization of each of the eight service facilities.

b) Average time in each subsystem, per customer.

c) The probabilities (based on this sample of 500) of encountering 0 through 18 customers in each of the 8 queues.

5. Using the appropriate models developed at the end of Chapter 9, check how closely the percent utilization, average time in the system, and probabilities of various numbers in the queue of our simulation study (Figure 11–2) approximate values that we would expect given a mean arrival rate of two per hour and mean service time of one-third hour.

6. Spence Airfreight Company flies cargo from airport A to airport B. During peak traffic hours, planes arrive at airport B in a fashion which, it has been found, can be approximated by the normal distribution with mean of $3\frac{1}{3}$ minutes between arrivals and standard deviation of 1 minute.

In good weather planes in the stack above airport B can be brought in at a rate of 30 per hour, Poisson distributed, and in bad weather at a rate of 20 per hour, Poisson distributed.

When a plane in the stack above airport B reaches its minimum landing reserve of fuel it is permitted to land without waiting its turn. Users, however, are urged not to rely on this priority rule in determining their fuel loading prior to departure for airport B. (Before Spence planes depart from airport A the weather at airport B is checked.)

Spence wants to know how much fuel in excess of the minimum landing reserve its planes that arrive at airport B should enter the stack with, in (*a*) good weather, and (*b*) bad weather, so that Spence planes will not have to request immediate landing priority more than 5 percent of the time. Using the model of Figure 11–2, suitably modified, determine *in hours of flight time* the desired arrival fuel under each of the two weather conditions.

7. In the manufacture of widgits ovens are shared by several assemblers. An assembler spends 30 minutes ± 5 minutes (uniformly distributed in this range) assembling the raw widgit. If an oven is free he then places the raw widgit in the oven and fires it, taking 8 minutes ± 2 minutes (uniformly distributed). If an oven is NOT free the assembler waits in the queue until it is. While waiting in the queue and while waiting for his raw widgit to be fired the assembler does nothing.

Assemblers are paid $3.75 per hour and each oven costs $80 per day whether used or not.

Profit per widgit is $5 but the market can take no more than 275 widgits per day.

Build a model to simulate this queue system and test a variety of assembler-oven combinations, in search of that number of assemblers and that number of ovens which maximizes daily profit.

chapter 12

GPSS: A Special-Purpose Language for Modeling Queuing Systems[1]

INTRODUCTION

IN CHAPTER 9, basic queuing concepts were introduced with the eventual objective of teaching you how to build computer models to simulate queuing systems. Then, in the first part of Chapter 11, a FORTRAN model was presented for a single-channel queuing system. Building that model required a considerable amount of care. To say this another way, although it is "simple" to visualize a single-channel queuing system, it is not necessarily simple to model the system on a computer in FORTRAN. Before such a model can be built, the various events which can occur in the system must be identified. Cause and effect relationships among these events have to be determined, and the effect each type of event has on the state of the system must be clarified. Then, to reflect these events in a computer model, the model has to be "taught" how to allow these events to occur. Among other things, the events must be "timed" so that they occur in the proper chronological sequence. In other words, the computer model must be able to move itself forward through simulated time. In addition, the model must be designed to collect various statistics describing system behavior. In fact, the major motivation for building such a model is to gain insight about

---

[1] This chapter was written by Thomas J. Schriber, professor of Management Science in the Graduate School of Business Administration at the University of Michigan. Portions of this material are taken from a book written by Professor Schriber (see reference 3 in the last section of this chapter). As part of the book, these portions have been copyrighted by Professor Schriber, and are reproduced here with his permission.

the system's properties. This is done by gathering data on the system when it is "forced to perform" in simulated fashion.

If modeling rather simple queuing systems in FORTRAN requires care, think of how demanding it must be to model highly complicated queuing systems in FORTRAN. For example, imagine building a FORTRAN model to simulate airplane traffic at a major airport. The level of detail in such a model can be overwhelming. The result is that building these models in FORTRAN becomes a costly, time-consuming, and error-breeding activity. For these reasons, there has been considerable motivation to develop special-purpose computer languages especially designed for modeling queuing systems. The designers of such a language have the advantage of knowing that it will be used specifically for queuing-type problems. This makes it possible to incorporate common aspects of queuing problems into the language itself. The effect is to automate some of the burdensome "housekeeping" tasks which the analyst himself would otherwise have to worry about.

For example, because simulated time elapses as events occur in queuing systems, it is natural to build a "timing routine" into any special-purpose language for modeling these systems. Consider the benefit to be derived from such a built-in timing routine. Suppose that a queuing system has been modeled in a special-purpose language, and that the model is being run on a computer. When the state of the system has been brought up to date at a given simulated time, the timing routine then "automatically" advances the simulation clock to the next earliest time at which another event is to occur in the model. There is no need for the analyst to keep track of the "times of future events." There is also no need to specify how to search lists of "future event times" to find out which event should occur next. Thanks to its built-in timing mechanism, the underlying program supplied for use with the special-purpose language "knows how" to keep lists of future event times. It also "knows how" to advance the simulation clock to the next earliest of these times, and then cause the analyst-supplied logic for the corresponding event to be performed. Quite apart from the timing routine, the special-purpose language very likely also "knows how" to automatically gather statistics describing system behavior, and how to print out fixed-format summaries of these statistics at the conclusion of a simulation. As a result, having been freed from these mechanical details, the analyst using such a language can devote himself to more important aspects of the problem at hand.

As suggested above in the context of queuing problems, it is generally true that special-purpose languages can be a blessing for the analyst working in specific problem areas. For those whose work involves the modeling of queuing systems, a number of these special-purpose languages have been developed. The best known, most easily learned, and most frequently used of these is "GPSS." GPSS stands for "General-Purpose Simulation System." It is a special-purpose language originally developed by Geoffrey Gordon and others working for the International Business Machines Corporation (IBM). Historically, the language had its beginnings as early as the late 1950s. It has moved through several stages during the intervening years, and is now at the point where it is available in a number of different versions to users of IBM computers.[2] The most frequently used of these versions is GPSS/360, so named because it can be used with computers in IBM's "System/360" family. The most recently announced version of GPSS is called GPSSV. It has certain features not contained in GPSS/360, but has been designed so that GPSS/360 is "upwardly compatible" with it. That is, a model prepared in the GPSS/360 language can be run on any computer on which GPSS V can be run.

The purpose of this chapter is to provide you with an introduction to the GPSS language. The language elements to be described are contained both in GPSS/360, and in GPSS V. You will consequently be learning a part of the "latest" available version of the language.

Here is the plan for the chapter. The plan consists of three parts.

1. We will proceed slowly and carefully at first, with the objective of bringing you to the point of understanding certain GPSS language features fairly well. After introducing a minimum number of language elements in this way, we will study a GPSS model for the single-channel queuing system. The "system" to be simulated will be a small barber shop, in which only one barber works. You will thereby not only see a "complete" GPSS model, but will see the GPSS equivalent for the single-channel queuing model presented in Chapter 11. Hence, you can conveniently compare and contrast the GPSS approach with the FORTRAN approach for a given problem. A computer exercise is even suggested after this

---

[2] GPSS is also available for use on the hardware of manufacturers other than IBM. For example, the language can be used on Univac 1108 computers, and on certain Honeywell-GE computers. And, at this writing, the Norden Division of the United Aircraft Corporation is developing a version of GPSS for the Control Data Corporation's 6000-series computers.

first computer model is presented, so that you yourself can try your hand with GPSS in a simplified setting, if this appeals to you.

2.   We will then see how servers who work "side by side" can be modeled in GPSS. Using this feature of the language, a complete GPSS model will then be presented for a three-man barber shop. This will give you a chance to see how easy it is to convert a "one-man barber shop" to a "three-man barber shop" in GPSS. (In a good special-purpose language, it should be possible to "re-configure" models of systems with this kind of relative ease.) Furthermore, the three-man barber shop is highly similar to the "multiple-channel" queuing system you considered earlier via Figure 11–4 in Chapter 11. Hence, you will again have a chance to compare and contrast "the GPSS way" with "the FORTRAN way."

3.   In the next to last section of the chapter, another barber shop computer model will be considered. This model will incorporate considerably more "realism" into the barber shop than will have been done in the first two computer models. Its purpose is to show you how relatively easy it is to add increasing degrees of realism to GPSS models. Although key features of the model's logic will be briefly discussed, no attempt will be made to have you completely understand all aspects of the GPSS elements built into the model. The model will serve, then, principally to increase your overall feeling for the language. Finally, in the last section of the chapter, sources of additional information will be provided for those who would like to study GPSS in further detail.

APPROACH TO MODEL BUILDING IN GPSS

It has been indicated that GPSS is a special-purpose computer language for modeling queuing systems. Actually, GPSS is both a computer language *and* a computer program. As a language, it has a well-defined vocabulary and grammar with which certain types of system models can be unambiguously described. As a computer program, it interprets a model described in the GPSS language, thereby making it possible to conduct experiments with the model on a computer. Without such interpretation, the computer would not be able to directly act out, or simulate, the system represented by the model. The computer program which performs this interpretation is only of indirect interest to us here. Nevertheless, there will be occasion to make reference to it from time to time. For this purpose, the program will be referred to as the "GPSS Processor," or simply as the "Processor."[3]

A GPSS model of a system may be expressed either as a Block Diagram, or as the punch card equivalent of a Block Diagram. The model builder usually begins his work by constructing a Block Diagram of the system he intends to simulate. The punch card version of the Block Diagram is then prepared and presented to the computer for implementation. Model conceptualization most often takes place at the Block Diagram level. After a Block Diagram has been developed, the process of producing its equivalent as a deck of punched cards is then straightforward and mechanical.

A Block Diagram is a collection of characteristically shaped figures (Blocks) connected by directed line segments. There is a set of more than 40 Blocks which GPSS makes available to the model builder. The shapes of these Blocks are pre-defined. The distinction among shapes eases the process of becoming familiar with a model by studying its Block Diagram. The various shapes have no significance, *as such,* in the punch card version of the model.

Models are built by selecting certain Blocks from the available set and arranging them in a diagram so that, at the time of model implementation, they (that is, their images) interact meaningfully with one another. The logical requirements of the system being modeled dictate which Blocks are used in constructing the model. When the model is implemented, it is the interaction among the Blocks which is analogous to (simulates) the interaction of elements in the real system being modeled.

The silhouette of a typical GPSS Block Diagram is shown in Figure 12–1. Ten different Blocks can be identified in the figure. Several of them appear more than one time. Detailed information that would typically appear in the Blocks has been deliberately deleted. The intent here is to provide a first glimpse of a Block Diagram for the sake of perspective.

It is now possible to repeat the "plan" for this chapter, interpreting the plan in terms of GPSS Blocks. After some additional preliminary considerations, the properties of a basic subset of Blocks,

---

[3] Recall that FORTRAN is also both a computer language and a "computer program," that is, a compiler. The FORTRAN compiler translates a program written in FORTRAN into an equivalent program expressed at the level of machine language. The GPSS Processor, however, does *not* translate a GPSS model into the machine-language equivalent. Instead, it "interprets" a GPSS model in ongoing fashion as a simulation proceeds. In this sense, then, the FORTRAN compiler and the GPSS Processor differ from each other to a considerable extent.

FIGURE 12–1

The Silhouette of a Typical GPSS Block Diagram

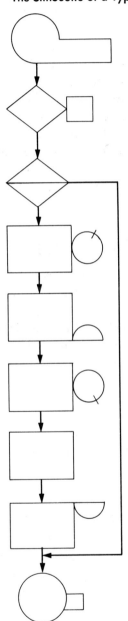
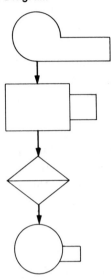

consisting of seven Blocks in total, will be taken up. The particular seven-Block subset is chosen to make it possible to build a complete GPSS model for a simple version of the single-channel queuing system (one-man barber shop). Then an additional two Blocks will be considered, and their use in scaling up the single-channel model to a multiple-channel model (three-man barber shop) will be shown. Finally, an additional three Blocks will be considered in the context of a more complicated variation of the three-man barber shop. It will be seen, albeit in simple fashion, that as the model builder's "Block vocabulary" grows, he can build models of increasingly complicated systems. Those who continue their study of GPSS beyond the "12-Block introduction" given here will find that when the entire set of Blocks has been mastered, rather sophisticated models can be built in GPSS with relative ease.

TRANSACTIONS: DYNAMIC ENTITIES IN GPSS MODELS

Lines with arrowheads were used in the flowcharts presented earlier in this book to represent a time-ordered series of steps to be followed in performing procedures. Expressing this differently, it can be said that "control moves from box to box" (or, from instruction to instruction) in the flowcharts shown in Chapters 1 through 11. The directed line segments in the Figure 12–1 Block Diagram also suggest movement. In GPSS, however, the concept of "control moving from Block to Block" is not entirely valid, and must be discarded. The directed line segments in a GPSS Block Diagram represent paths along which *units of traffic* move. Each unit of traffic is termed a *Transaction*. Transactions, then, are dynamic (that is, moving) entities in a GPSS model. They move from Block to Block as a GPSS simulation proceeds.

When a simulation first begins, no Transactions exist in a GPSS model. As the simulation proceeds, Transactions enter the model at certain times, according to the logical requirements of the system being modeled. Similarly, Transactions leave the model at certain times during the course of a simulation. In general, then, there are many Transactions in a model. Nevertheless, only one of these Transactions moves forward at a time.

After it is set into motion, a Transaction moves from Block to Block along whichever path it is in. Each Block can be thought of as a point at which a subroutine can be called. When a Transaction "enters" a Block, the corresponding subroutine is executed. This forward motion is continued until any one of three possible circumstances arises:

1. The Transaction moves into a Block whose purpose is to hold it there for a prescribed length of time.
2. The Transaction moves into a Block whose purpose is to remove it from the model.
3. The Transaction *attempts* to move into the next Block in its path, but that Block refuses to let it enter. In this case, the Transaction is held at the Block preceding the one refusing entry. Later, it will repeat its attempt to gain entry to the next Block. As model conditions change, one of the subsequent attempts will, in general, be successful. The Transaction can then resume its movement in the model.

After a Transaction comes to rest for one of the three reasons explained, the forward motion of another Transaction in the model is initiated.[4] Eventually it, too, comes to rest, and the forward motion of yet another Transaction begins. It is in this fashion that execution of a GPSS model proceeds. Recall that each successful entry of a Transaction into a Block results in a call on a subroutine. Model execution, then, consists of a series of subroutine calls which result from movement of Transactions.

Given this much information, certain inferences can now be drawn from Figure 12–1. For example, two Blocks in the figure are "sinks"; that is, the path on which they lie does not extend beyond them. These two Blocks, identical in shape, must have the purpose of removing from the model Transactions which enter them. Similarly, there are two Blocks in the figure which are "sources"; that is, no path leads into them. These Blocks must represent points at which Transactions are brought into a model. Finally, it can be noted that Figure 12–1 consists of two separate, free-standing segments. In general, "a" GPSS model can consist of many free-standing segments. As a simulation proceeds, "activity" occurs in the segment containing the currently moving Transaction. When it comes to rest, the next Transaction set into motion may happen to be in a different model segment, resulting in a switch of the "action" to that segment. The concept of free-standing Block Diagram segments, then, is entirely valid in GPSS.

---

[4] It is beyond the scope of this chapter to indicate the *order* in which Transactions are moved, one after the other. It must be taken on faith here that the order followed is logically sound in the context of the system being modeled.

Until now, the discussion of Transactions has been completely abstract. An attempt has been made to answer the question, "What *is* a Transaction?" but there has been nothing said to answer the parallel question, "What *meaning* do Transactions have?" The "meaning" of Transactions is determined by the model builder. This is done by establishing an analogy, or correspondence, between Transactions and elements of the real world system being modeled. These analogies are never "declared" to the GPSS Processor. They exist only in the mind of the analyst who builds the model. Of course, each model must be built in a way consistent with the analogies the analyst has in mind.

Some examples of possible analogies between Transactions and elements of real systems appear in Table 12–1. In a model of a

TABLE 12–1

Examples of Possible Interpretations for Transactions

System	System Element Represented by a Transaction
Barber shop	Customer
Highway	Car
Maintenance shop	Part
Inventory control	Demand
Supermarket	Shopper

barber shop, for example, a Transaction might represent a customer. In the real system, the customer arrives at the shop, joins a waiting line, waits until his turn comes, then uses the services of the barber and leaves. The customer can clearly be thought of as a "unit of traffic" moving through the barber shop. In a GPSS model of the shop, various Blocks must be used to represent such occurrences as a customer's arrival (entry of a Transaction), a customer's use of the barber, a customer's departure (removal of a Transaction), and so on. Movement of a Transaction from Block to Block in the model is then analogous to movement of a customer from stage to stage in the barber shop.

These analogies between Transactions and real system elements will be brought into sharper focus as properties of the GPSS language are unfolded.

THE SIMULATION CLOCK

Time passes as various events occur in real systems. A customer arrives at a barber shop. Later, his turn comes and the barber begins to cut his hair. Still later, the haircut is finished and the customer leaves. If such events are to be represented in a simulation model, they must occur against a background of simulated time. As a consequence, the GPSS Processor automatically maintains a clock to record "what time it is."

While the GPSS Processor is "reading in" a model, it specifically looks for those Blocks which act as a "source" of Transactions. Each time it finds one of these source-Blocks, the Processor takes steps to determine the future time when a Transaction is first "destined to arrive" at the model via that Block. This amounts to "prescheduling" future times of Transaction arrivals. When this reading in and prescheduling has been accomplished, the simulation clock is then automatically set to the earliest time that a Transaction is to enter the model. This Transaction (and others, if any, which have been prescheduled to arrive at the same time) is then brought into the model. Then, it (or they, one by one) is moved through as many Blocks as possible. Eventually, there is nothing else which is to occur in the system at this first clock reading. The GPSS Processor then advances the clock to the time when the next event, or series of events, is scheduled to take place. These events, as represented by Transaction movement through Blocks, are then caused to occur. When there are no more Transaction movements left to perform at this second clock reading, the clock is again advanced, and so on. It is in this manner that the passage of time is simulated.

A numeric example will help explain the process just described in general terms. Suppose that a one-man barber shop opens for business at 8:00 A.M., and that the first few events on a given day are as shown in Table 12–2. When a model of the shop is read in by the

TABLE 12–2

A Possible Sequence of Events in a One-Man Barber Shop

Sequence in Which the Event Occurs	The Event Itself	Real Time of Occurrence	Simulated Time of Occurrence*
1	The barber opens the shop	8:00 A.M.	0
2	Customer 1 arrives and goes into service	8:22 A.M.	22
3	Customer 2 arrives	8:29 A.M.	29
4	Customer 3 arrives	8:33 A.M.	33
5	Customer 1 is finished	8:47 A.M.	47
6	Customer 2 goes into service	8:47 A.M.	47
7	Customer 4 arrives	9:07 A.M.	67

* Expressed in minutes, relative to a starting point of zero at 8:00 A.M.

GPSS Processor, arrival of the first customer-Transaction via a corresponding source-Block is prescheduled. Per Table 12–2, assume that the arrival time of this first customer turns out to be 22 simulated minutes after the shop is opened, i.e., turns out to be 8:22 A.M. Now if there are no other source-Blocks in the model, no events can then possibly occur until simulated time 22. The Processor therefore sets the simulation clock to a value of 22, and causes customer 1 to arrive (a customer-Transaction enters the model). Finding he does not have to wait for the barber, the customer immediately gets into the barber's chair (the customer-Transaction moves forward, Block by Block, until it enters a Block which deliberately holds it, to simulate haircutting time). Per the information in Table 12–2, no further events are to take place until time 29. The Processor consequently advances the clock to 29, and causes customer 2 to arrive (another customer-Transaction enters the model). This customer has to wait for the barber, who is already in the process of giving a haircut (the customer-Transaction is denied permission to move into the Block whose execution simulates the act of capturing the barber). Nothing else is to happen at time 29. The Processor therefore moves the clock to 33, causes customer 3 to arrive (yet another customer-Transaction enters the model), and so on.

It should be clear by now how intimately the reading of the simulation clock is related to the sequence of events which can, in general, occur in a simulation model. One of the advantages of GPSS is that it automatically updates the simulation clock as required by the logic described with the model. There is no need for the analyst to explicitly arrange for this clock maintenance.

There are several important features of GPSS and the GPSS clock which will now be stated, point by point.

1. The GPSS clock registers only *integer* values. This means that events can only occur at "whole" time values in GPSS models.
2. The unit of time which the clock registers is determined by the analyst. However, the time unit chosen is never "declared" to the Processor. It is expressed implicitly in terms of the time data built into the model. If all time data are expressed in minutes, then the minute is the implicit unit of time. Or, if all time data are in milliseconds, then the unit of time is the millisecond. The analyst is responsible for deciding the smallest time unit required to realistically reflect real system events in his

model. He must then take care to express all his time data in terms of this smallest unit.

In the Table 12–2 barber shop example, the time unit is implied to be one minute. This means it would not be possible for a customer to arrive at, say, the 47th second after 8:51 A.M. in the corresponding model. If it is necessary to have arrivals occur "to the nearest second" in a model, then the implicit time unit cannot be larger than one second.

3. GPSS is a "next event" simulator. That is, after a model has been fully updated at a given point in simulated time, the clock is advanced to the nearest time at which one or more next events are scheduled to occur. *Potential* clock readings are "jumped over" when no events are to take place at those times. This means that execution time requirements are independent of the implicit time unit chosen by the analyst.

Finally, care should be taken to distinguish between "simulated time," and "real time." When the simulation clock is advanced to a next reading, that reading "remains constant" while the model is updated. Nevertheless, *real* time passes as the updating occurs. It may require hours of real time to move models of some systems (such as models of computer systems) through only minutes of simulated time. On the other hand, experiments equivalent to weeks, months, or even years of simulated time can often be conducted in only seconds of real time on a computer. This ability to "compress time" is one of the potential advantages of experimenting with systems by simulating them on a computer.

GENERAL DETAILS ASSOCIATED WITH A GPSS BLOCK DIAGRAM

The Figure 12–1 Block Diagram silhouette is repeated in Figure 12–2, where the general Block details have been filled in. Each Block carries with it information falling into three categories.

1. Location

Each Block occupies a specific Location in a Block Diagram. Strictly speaking, Locations are designated numerically. The first Block in a model occupies Location 1, the second Block occupies Location 2, and so on. Fortunately, it is not necessary for the model builder to provide Location Numbers. When the GPSS Processor reads in the punched card version of a model, it assigns the Location Numbers in the order in which the cards for the various Blocks have been placed in the card deck.

It frequently happens that the analyst wants to know which Locations are occupied by certain Blocks in a model. This information may be required so the Blocks in question can be referenced from one or more other Blocks. When this need arises, it would be tedious to "count Blocks" to predict the Location Numbers ultimately to be assigned by the GPSS Processor. Rather than counting, the analyst has the option of providing *symbolic Location Names* for the Blocks of interest. When such symbolic names are used, the Processor later supplies absolute Location Numbers in their place.

Symbolic names are composed of from three to five alphanumeric characters, with the restriction that the first three be alphabetic. Examples of valid and invalid symbolic Location Names are shown in Table 12–3.

TABLE 12–3

Examples of Valid and Invalid Names
for Block Locations

Valid	*Invalid*
BYPAS	BY25
BLOK1	2AND
OUT	NO4
JOE23	A2B
FLO2M	P

Normally, the analyst only assigns a symbolic name to the Location occupied by a Block when it is logically necessary to refer to that Block from other parts of the model. In Figure 12–2, for example, the Location occupied by one of the two "TERMINATE" Blocks in the model has been symbolically named BYBYE. The Location Name is written just above and to the left of the TERMINATE Block, and is enclosed in parentheses. (The parentheses are not part of the name.) Note how the Location BYBYE is referenced at another Block in the model (i.e., at the "TEST" Block). The name BYBYE is supplied at the horizontal exit from the TEST Block to indicate one of the Locations which Transactions entering the TEST Block might move to next. The "other exit" from the

TEST Block is shown as a vertical path leading into the "QUEUE" Block. The QUEUE Block is "sequential" to the TEST Block. It is usually not necessary to provide Location Names for Blocks which Transactions can only reach "sequentially," that is, along a path leading from the preceding Block. This is why no Location Name appears with the QUEUE Block (or, for that matter, with any Blocks except the one TERMINATE Block) in Figure 12–2.

2. Operation

The "Operation" of a Block is a "verb" suggestive of the task the Block accomplishes. Each Block type is characterized by its own, predefined verb. The Operations GENERATE, GATE, TEST, QUEUE, ENTER, DEPART, ADVANCE, LEAVE, LOGIC, and TERMINATE all appear in Figure 12–2. When the punch card version of a Block Diagram is prepared, each Block Operation must be specified.

Some GPSS Blocks make use of "Auxiliary Operators." An Auxiliary Operator is represented in general with the letter X. As indicated by the presence of Xs in Figure 12–2, then, the use of Auxiliary Operators is involved at "GATE" Blocks, "TEST" Blocks, and "LOGIC" Blocks.

3. Operands

The various Blocks have Operands associated with them. A Block's Operands provide the specific information on which the Block's action is based. The Operands may be conveniently thought of as supplying values which are used in calls on subroutines.

The number of Operands each Block has depends on the type of Block. No GPSS Block uses more than seven Operands. Most use only one or two. The Operands are represented *in general* as A, B, C, D, E, F, and G. The Operands are shown only in this general fashion in Figure 12–2. In fact, because no more than two Operands per Block will be discussed in this chapter, only the general Operand representations A and B appear in the figure.

For some Blocks, certain Operands must always be specified, whereas others are optional. In some cases, when optional Operands are not explicitly provided, the Processor assumes "default values" to be in effect.

FIGURE 12–2

A Repetition of Figure 12–1, with General Block Details Shown

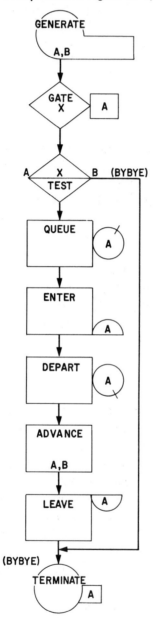
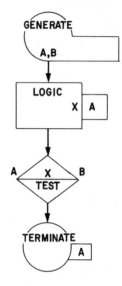

BRINGING TRANSACTIONS INTO A MODEL:
THE GENERATE BLOCK

The GENERATE Block can be thought of as a "door" through which Transactions enter a model. In fact, the GENERATE Block is the Block-type referred to earlier as a "source-Block." There is no limit to the number of different GENERATE Blocks a given model can contain.

Now, it is usually the analyst's intention to have Transactions come into a model at different points in simulated time. The time between two consecutive Transaction arrivals at a given GENER–ATE Block is termed "interarrival time." The interarrival-time concept used in the Chapter 11 single-channel queuing model is applicable here. Indeed, the approach used in GPSS to arrange for Transaction arrivals is identical to the one taken in arranging for customer arrivals in Chapter 11. That is, when a Transaction enters a model through a GENERATE Block, the Processor predetermines its successor's time of arrival by sampling from an interarrival-time distribution, then adding the sampled value to the current clock reading. When that future time is reached, another Transaction is brought into the model through that GENERATE Block, *its* successor's time of arrival is then prescheduled, and so on.

In the Chapter 11 single-channel queuing model, the analyst had to supply the logic necessary to support this prescheduling procedure. In GPSS, the Processor conducts the various required prescheduling steps automatically, as part of the operation of the GENERATE Block. The analyst is consequently relieved of a number of otherwise burdensome details.

In fact, almost all the analyst does in using a GENERATE Block is supply the specifications for the interarrival-time distribution to be in effect at that Block. The required information is expressed through the Block's A and B Operands. In GPSS, all possible interarrival-time distributions are divided into two categories:

1. Uniformly distributed interarrival times.
2. All other interarrival-time distributions.

In short, a "special case" is made of what is perhaps the simplest of all nontrivial distributions, the uniform. To express more complicated (and realistic) interarrival-time distributions in GPSS, the model builder must resort to Function definition. The way

Functions are defined and used at GENERATE Blocks will be illustrated in the last computer model in this chapter. For now, only uniformly distributed interarrival times will be considered.

The GENERATE Block, with its A and B Operands in their usual positions, is shown in Figure 12–3. As indicated, the A

FIGURE 12–3

The GENERATE Block and Its A and B Operands

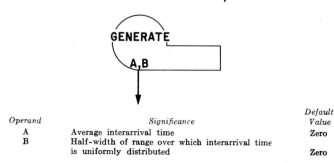

Operand	Significance	*Default Value*
A	Average interarrival time	Zero
B	Half-width of range over which interarrival time is uniformly distributed	Zero

Operand specifies the *average* time between consecutive arrivals of Transactions at the GENERATE Block. The B Operand provides the *half-width* of the range over which the interarrival time is understood to be uniformly distributed. When the Operands are supplied as *constants,* they *must* be *nonnegative* integers. In fact, there is only one Block in the entire GPSS Block vocabulary for which a decimal point can be included as part of an Operand. In all other circumstances, it is an error to include decimals when expressing Block Operands.

Figure 12–4 provides a specific example of the GENERATE Block. The A and B Operands are 5 and 3, respectively. The interarrival time, then, is uniformly distributed over the range 5 ± 3,

FIGURE 12–4

A GENERATE Block with Specific
A and B Operand Values

GENERATE

5,3

i.e., over the *integers* 2, 3, 4, 5, 6, 7, and 8. Recall that the GPSS clock only registers *integer* values. For this reason, Transactions can only be brought into a model at integer-valued points in time. This explains why 5 ± 3 describes the closed interval of integers from 2 to 8, rather than the continuum of all values between 2 and 8. In this example, then, interarrival time can take on any one of seven different values. Because the values are uniformly distributed, each occurs with a relative frequency of ⅐th.

To illustrate prescheduling, suppose that a Transaction arrives at the Figure 12–4 GENERATE Block at simulated time 15. After this Transaction has moved to the next Block in the model, the GPSS Processor draws a sample from the 5 ± 3 interarrival-time distribution. The sampled value is, say, 7. The Processor then schedules arrival of the next Transaction *at that GENERATE Block* at future time 15 + 7, or 22. When that Transaction appears at the GENERATE Block and moves to the next Block, the time of *its* successor's arrival will then have to be prescheduled. In short, a "boot-strapping" technique is used to arrange for Transaction arrivals. Again, note the similarity between the approach used here, and that used to preschedule customer arrivals in the Chapter 11 single-channel queuing model.

As suggested in Figure 12–3, values for the A and/or B Operands do not have to be provided explicitly at a GENERATE Block. When no values are specified, "default" values of zero are assumed by the Processor. Figure 12–5 shows an example in which the de-

FIGURE 12–5

A GENERATE Block with
No Explicit B Operand

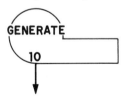

fault option has been taken with the B Operand. The A Operand is 10. Because a value of zero is assumed for the B Operand, the interarrival times are uniformly distributed over the integers 10 ± 0. That is, interarrival times are always exactly 10. This is an example, then, of deterministic (i.e., nonrandom) interarrival times.

The GENERATE Block actually has seven Operands associated with it. GENERATE Block Operands C through G make it possible for the model builder to do such things as specify the maximum number of Transactions which are to enter a model through the GENERATE Block in question, and so on. However, use of these Operands is optional. Because these additional Operands are not of direct interest to us here, details surrounding their meaning and use will not be considered.

PUNCH CARDS CORRESPONDING TO BLOCKS IN GPSS BLOCK DIAGRAMS

The three types of information carried by Blocks have already been described. Corresponding to this information, there are three fields laid out on the punch card used for Block representation. The card columns making up each of these fields are shown in Table 12–4.

TABLE 12–4

Punch Card Fields in Which Block
Information Is Entered

Card Columns	Block Information
2–6	Location
8–18	Operation
19–71	Operands

The symbolic Location Name (if any) of a Block must be punched in consecutive columns anywhere within the field consisting of columns 2 through 6. The Block's Operation is entered in consecutive columns in the field beginning with card column 8. The Operands must be punched in order in a field beginning with column 19. They must be entered in consecutive card columns and be separated from one another by commas, *without any intervening blanks.*

A coding sheet showing punch card images for the GENERATE Block examples in Figures 12–4 and 12–5 appears in Figure 12–6. Note that "explanatory comments" have been entered in Figure 12–6 beginning (arbitrarily) in column 25. The same comments

FIGURE 12–6
Punch Card Images for the GENERATE Blocks in Figures 12–4 and 12–5

LOCATION	OPERATION	A,B,C,D,E,F →
	GENERATE	5,3 PUNCHCARD IMAGE FOR FIGURE 12.4
*		
	GENERATE	10 PUNCHCARD IMAGE FOR FIGURE 12.5

could also be entered on the punch cards themselves. This is because *the first blank column* encountered in the Operands field causes the GPSS Processor to terminate its scan of that punch card. Explanatory comments can consequently be included toward the end of each punch card for purposes of model documentation.

Note that column 1 is not part of the Location field. When an *asterisk* is entered in column 1, the Processor ignores the entire card. This provides further possibilities for documenting models with lengthy comments, and/or leaving space between distinct model segments. In this spirit, a "blank card" has been inserted between the two examples in Figure 12–6.

The Figure 12–6 examples have nothing entered in the Location field. This is consistent with the fact that, in Figures 12–4 and 12–5, the GENERATE Blocks have not been given a Location Name. Had such a name been supplied for either of those GENERATE Blocks, the name would have been entered somewhere between card columns 2 through 6, inclusive, in the corresponding Block image in Figure 12–6.

REMOVING TRANSACTIONS FROM A MODEL: THE TERMINATE BLOCK

Transactions are removed from a model whenever they move into a TERMINATE Block. TERMINATE Blocks always accept Transactions which seek to move into them. There may be any number of TERMINATE Blocks in a model.

The TERMINATE Block, with its A Operand in its usual position, is shown in Figure 12–7. As indicated, the A Operand is a *Termination Counter decrement*. That is, it is the amount by which a special counter, called the *Termination Counter,* is to be decremented each time a Transaction moves into the TERMINATE

FIGURE 12–7

The TERMINATE Block and Its A Operand

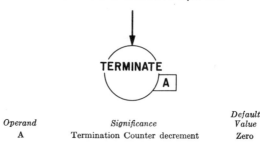

Operand	Significance	Default Value
A	Termination Counter decrement	Zero

Block. When the analyst chooses not to provide a TERMINATE Block A Operand, a default value of zero is in effect. Movement of Transactions into such TERMINATE Blocks then does not decrease the value of the Termination Counter.

What *is* the Termination Counter? It is a computer memory location in which a positive integer value is stored at the time a simulation run is begun. As the simulation proceeds, Transactions move into TERMINATE Blocks from time to time, resulting in decrementation of this counter. *As soon as the counter has been decremented to zero, the simulation stops.*

Note carefully that, although there may be many TERMINATE Blocks in a model, there is *only one* Termination Counter. It is this Termination Counter which will be decremented whenever a Transaction moves into *any* TERMINATE Block in a model.

As already indicated, the Termination Counter is supplied with its initial value at the time a simulation begins. The GPSS Processor starts the simulation when it encounters a START Card in the punch card version of a model. *It uses the A Operand on the START Card as the initial value for the Termination Counter.*

The general format for the START Card is displayed in the upper part of Figure 12–8. As shown, the word START is punched in the *Operation field* on the card. The A Operand, as usual, is entered beginning in column 19. The lower part of Figure 12–8 shows a specific example of a START Card in which the A Operand has a value of 1.

Now consider an example in which the TERMINATE Block and START Card are used in harmony to control the duration of a simulation run. Suppose that a model builder has chosen one minute as the implicit time unit in a model. He wants to run the model

FIGURE 12–8

Format for the START Card

LOCATION	OPERATION	A,B,C,D,E,F
	START	A	THE START CARD, AND ITS A OPERAND
*			
	START	1	A START CARD WITH AN A OPERAND OF 1

through eight hours of simulated time, and then have it shut off. This is the approach he might use:

1. He includes in the model the two-Block segment shown in Figure 12–9.
2. At all other TERMINATE Blocks in the model, *he defaults on the A Operand.* This means that terminations occurring at those Blocks during the simulation do not cause the Termination Counter to be decremented.
3. He punches 1 as the A Operand on the START Card.

FIGURE 12–9

A Two-Block Segment Which Shuts Off
a Run at Simulated Time 480

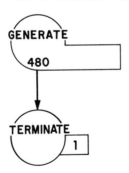

The A Operand of 1 on the START Card causes the Processor to give the Termination Counter an initial value of 1 when the simulation is started. As the simulation proceeds, Transaction terminations that occur from time to time at *other* TERMINATE Blocks in the model have no effect on the Termination Counter. Then, at simulated time 480, a Transaction enters the model through the

Figure 12–9 GENERATE Block. The Transaction moves immediately into the sequential TERMINATE Block, causing the underlying TERMINATE Block subroutine to be executed. Because the TERMINATE Block has an A Operand of 1, 1 is consequently subtracted from the Termination Counter. This has the effect of decreasing the Termination Counter's value from 1 to 0. As a result, the Processor shuts off the simulation.

This use of a "Termination Counter" may seem like a strange way to implement run control in a model. Nevertheless, it is the *only* way to control the duration of a run in a GPSS model.

Now suppose that, to accomplish the *same* objective stated in the preceding example, the analyst uses this approach:

1. He includes in the model the two-Block segment shown in Figure 12–10.
2. At all other TERMINATE Blocks in the model, he defaults on the A Operand.
3. He punches 480 as the A Operand on the START Card.

FIGURE 12–10

An Alternative Two-Block Segment Which
Shuts Off a Run at Simulated Time 480

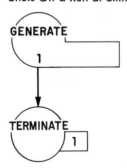

Note that, at the Figure 12–10 GENERATE Block, the interarrival time is 1. That is, Transactions arrive there at times 1, 2, 3, 4, . . . , 478, 479, and 480. Upon arrival, each of these Transactions moves to the next Block, where it is removed from the model and the Termination Counter is decreased by 1. When the 480th Transaction moves into the Figure 12–10 TERMINATE Block, then, the Termination Counter has already been decremented to 1. The 480th

Transaction causes it to be decreased from 1 to 0, and the simulation stops.

The approach shown in the first example is *much better* than that just shown. The reason is simple. Although both approaches are logically sound, the latter requires 480 executions of the GENER–ATE and TERMINATE Blocks in Figure 12–10, whereas the former only requires 1 execution of each Block in Figure 12–9. Of course, each Block execution consumes computer time. The latter approach is inferior, then, because it consumes about 480 times as much computer time as the former approach.

ENTITIES TO SIMULATE SINGLE SERVERS: FACILITIES

Consider the concept of entities whose purpose is to perform "service upon demand." Such entities might either be people, or things. For example, these people provide service on demand.

a)   A barber.
b)   A gas station attendant.
c)   A repairman.
d)   An insurance agent.

In a similar sense, these things are designed to provide service on demand.

a)   A card punch.
b)   A pencil.
c)   A parking space.
d)   An opera glass.
e)   A crane.

Whether people or things, entities such as those listed above will be referred to as "servers." As understood here, servers are characterized by two properties of interest.

1.   Each server can only respond to *one demand for service at a time.* If a new service demand arises when the server is already providing service, then the new demand must either (*a*) wait its turn for the server, or (*b*) go elsewhere.[5]

---

[5] There is a third possibility. If the new demand is "important enough," it can *interrupt* the server at the expense of the earlier demand. This interrupt capability can be modeled in GPSS, but discussion of this alternative is beyond the scope of this introduction.

2.   When a server has been engaged, time elapses while the service demanded is performed. This time is termed *service time*.

In GPSS, the term "Facility" is a synonym for "server." Just as there can be many servers at different points in a system, there can be many Facilities in a GPSS model. *Names* are given to Facilities, making it possible to distinguish among them. The names are supplied by the model builder, instead of being predefined. Names can be either *numeric*, or *symbolic*.

When Facilities are named numerically, *positive whole numbers* must be used. The largest number which is valid equals the maximum number of different Facilities allowable in a model. This, in turn, depends on the amount of computer memory available. Usually, anywhere from 35 to 300 different Facilities can be included in a single GPSS model.

When Facilities are named symbolically, the same set of rules that applies for naming Block Locations must be followed. As previously discussed, symbolic names are composed of from three to five alphanumeric characters, with the restriction that the first three be alphabetic. Examples of valid and invalid names for Facilities, both numeric and symbolic, are shown in Table 12–5.

TABLE 12–5

Examples of Valid and Invalid
Names for Facilities

Valid	*Invalid*
CRANE	IT
26	26KEY
CPU	OS
SURVR	−5
1	94528

It was pointed out earlier that the abstract concept of "Transaction" has meaning, from the analyst's point of view, in terms of the analogies he draws between Transactions and elements in the real system being modeled. The same observation holds for Facilities. A modeler might choose, for example, to let Facility 9 represent a repairman in a maintenance system. Or, the Facility named CPU might be chosen to represent a central processing unit in a computer system, and so on. The process of drawing analogies between abstract concepts in GPSS, and their real system equivalents, is an inherent part of modeling in the GPSS language.

ENGAGING AND DISENGAGING FACILITIES: THE SEIZE BLOCK AND THE RELEASE BLOCK

Suppose that we want to use a server. In doing so, we go through this series of steps.

1. We wait our turn, if necessary. Of course, waiting takes place over an *interval* of time.
2. When our turn comes, we engage the server. It might also be said that we "capture," or "seize," the server. The event "seize the server" occurs at a *point* in time.
3. We hold the server in a state of capture while the service demanded is performed. The service is performed over an *interval* of time.
4. When the demanded service has been performed, we disengage the server. It might also be said that we "release" him. The event "release the server" occurs at a *point* in time.

As would be expected, this same series of steps is followed when simulating the use of a server in GPSS. The GPSS implementation of steps (2) and (4) will now be considered. The means of providing step (3), and the possibility of gathering statistics for the step (1) waiting process, are then taken up in the following sections.

In GPSS, the entities which place demands on Facilities for service are *Transactions*. It is the nature of Transactions that they tend to move forward in a model, Block by Block. Suppose that, as its next activity, a Transaction is to seize a Facility (i.e., capture a server). The Transaction accomplishes this objective by moving (or *attempting* to move) into a particular Block associated with the Facility of interest. The Block has these features:

1. If the Facility is already in use, the Transaction is denied entry to the Block, i.e., it is not permitted to seize the Facility at this time, but must wait its turn. This "denial of permission" to enter a Block brings the moving Transaction temporarily to rest, as was described earlier.
2. If the Facility is not in use, the Transaction is permitted to enter the Block. Movement of a Transaction into a Block causes the underlying Block subroutine to be executed. A consequence of the subroutine execution is to change the status of the Facility from "not in use" to "in use."

The Block which has these properties is the SEIZE Block. This Block and its A Operand are shown in Figure 12–11.

FIGURE 12–11

The SEIZE Block and Its A Operand.

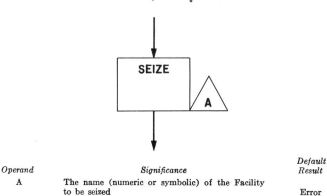

Operand	Significance	Default Result
A	The name (numeric or symbolic) of the Facility to be seized	Error

Just as movement of a Transaction into a SEIZE Block simulates capturing a server, movement of the same Transaction into another particular Block simulates releasing the server. The purpose of this other Block, of course, is to change the status of the previously captured Facility from "in use" to "not in use." The Block which has this purpose is the RELEASE Block. The Block and its A Operand are shown in Figure 12–12.

FIGURE 12–12

The RELEASE Block and Its A Operand

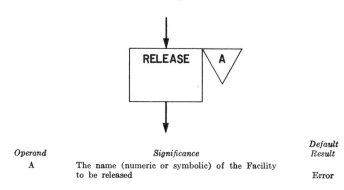

Operand	Significance	Default Result
A	The name (numeric or symbolic) of the Facility to be released	Error

The RELEASE Block never denies entry to a Transaction seeking to enter it. On the other hand, it would clearly be illogical for a Transaction to attempt to release a Facility not already in use. If such an attempt is made, the GPSS Processor outputs an error message and terminates execution of the model. Furthermore, if the Transaction seeking to release the Facility is not the very same one which has it "in use," an error message is outputted and execution of the model stops.

It is not necessary to declare the existence of particular Facilities to the GPSS Processor before referring to them at SEIZE Blocks. The very fact that they are referenced at SEIZE Blocks causes the Processor to recognize their existence. By the same token, recall that when Transactions were discussed, nothing was said about declaring their existence to the Processor before attempting to bring them into a model. In short, the Processor automatically provides Transactions and Facilities (and other GPSS entities not yet discussed) as required by the logic in a model. Whereas Transactions lead a transient existence, however, all Facilities referenced in a model exist throughout the course of a simulation.

When a single server is modeled, it may be important to collect information summarizing the server's experiences during the simulation. For example, answers to questions like the following are often of interest.

a) What fraction of the time was the server busy?
b) How many different times was the server captured?
c) What was the average holding time per capture of the server?

One of the nice features of the GPSS language is that answers to the above questions are *automatically* provided for each Facility which is used in a model. These answers, or statistical summaries, are printed out by the Processor at the end of a simulation. Such summaries are frequently of considerable use to the analyst.

In concluding this section, note that the events "engage a server" and "disengage a server" are complementary. The latter event reverses the effect produced by the former. The SEIZE and RE-LEASE Blocks, then, can be thought of as a complementary pair. Many other GPSS Blocks exist in "complementary pairs." One member of the pair always has the effect of "undoing," or "reversing," the effect of the other pair member. In most cases, the "characteristic shapes" of complementary Blocks are mirror images of each other with respect to a horizontal axis. This makes the shapes easier to remember. Figure 12–13 shows the SEIZE and RELEASE Blocks in a mirror-image perspective.

FIGURE 12–13

The SEIZE and RELEASE Blocks as Mirror Images

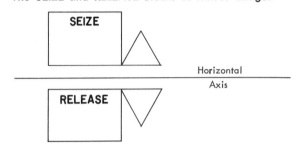

PROVIDING FOR THE PASSAGE OF TIME: THE ADVANCE BLOCK

Assume that a Transaction has just moved into a SEIZE Block, thereby capturing a Facility. After executing the Block subroutine, the Processor immediately attempts to move the Transaction into the next sequential Block. There are very few restrictions on what this next Block might be. For example, it could be another SEIZE Block, referencing another Facility. This would make sense logically if it were necessary, say, to engage both a repairman *and* a particular tool before a certain type of service could be performed. If the repairman and the tool were simulated with a pair of Facilities, the Transaction would have to simultaneously hold both in a state of capture before its demand for service could be met.

Usually, though, a Transaction captures a Facility with the objective of immediately receiving service from it. As noted in the preceding section, time passes while the service is performed. While this time is passing, the Transaction should cease its forward motion in the model. Only after the service time has elapsed should it move on into a RELEASE Block to disengage the server.

The ADVANCE Block is provided in GPSS to accomplish the task of freezing a Transaction's motion for a prescribed length of time. The "prescribed length of time" is usually a random variable. This is consistent with the experience that service time usually varies from one service to the next.

The information required to describe the applicable service time distribution is expressed through the ADVANCE Block's A and B Operands. The various possible service time distributions are divided into two categories:

1. Uniformly distributed service times.
2. All other service time distributions.

In short, as with the GENERATE Block, a "special case" is made of the uniform distribution. Expressing more complicated distributions requires the use of GPSS Functions. For now, only uniformly distributed service times will be considered.

Figure 12–14 shows the ADVANCE Block with its A and B

FIGURE 12–14

The ADVANCE Block and Its A and B Operands

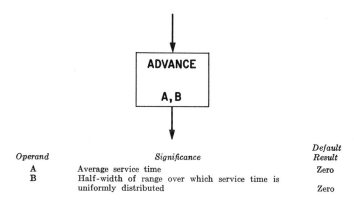

Operand	Significance	Default Result
A	Average service time	Zero
B	Half-width of range over which service time is uniformly distributed	Zero

Operands. As indicated, the A Operand supplies the *average* time that Transactions entering the Block are held there. The B Operand provides the half-width of the range over which the holding times are understood to be uniformly distributed.

Figure 12–15 shows an ADVANCE Block with A and B Operands

FIGURE 12–15

An Advance Block with Specific A and B Operand Values

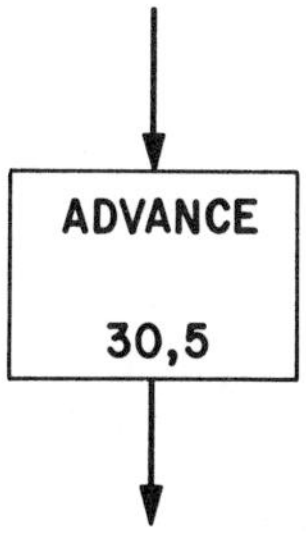

```
       │
       ▼
┌─────────────┐
│   ADVANCE   │
│             │
│    30,5     │
└─────────────┘
       │
       ▼
```

of 30 and 5, respectively. For each Transaction moving into that Block, the range of possible holding times varies over the integers from 25 to 35, inclusive. Suppose that a Transaction moves into the Block at time 134 and, executing the Block subroutine, the Processor draws a sample of 31 from the 30 ± 5 distribution. The Transaction will then be delayed at the Block until future time 134 + 31, or 165. At that time, the Processor will attempt to move it into whatever is the next sequential model Block.

The ADVANCE Block never refuses entry to a Transaction. Any number of Transactions can be held there simultaneously. Whenever a Transaction moves into such a Block, the underlying subroutine is executed again and a customized holding time is computed. The newcomer, then, is in no way influenced by the presence of other Transactions in the Block.

The classical SEIZE–ADVANCE–RELEASE pattern is shown in Figure 12–16. A Transaction moving down the indicated path

FIGURE 12–16

An Example of the SEIZE–ADVANCE–RELEASE Sequence

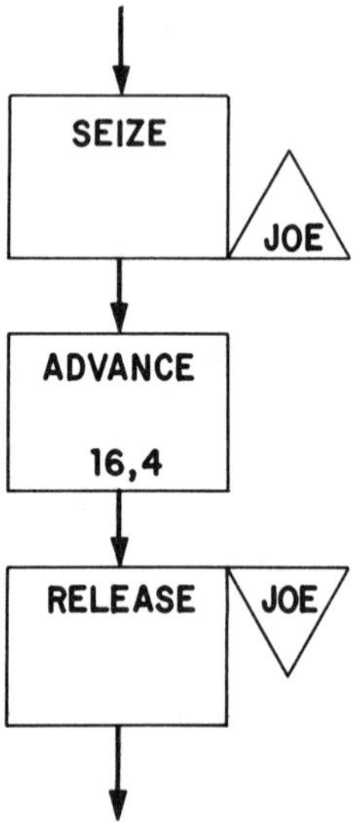

eventually will capture the Facility symbolically named JOE, hold it for 16 ± 4 time units, and then release it. After the Transaction enters the RELEASE Block and that subroutine has been executed, the Processor will attempt to move it into the next Block in the model. Meantime, with execution of the RELEASE subroutine completed, the next Transaction intending to use the Facility named JOE will be able to capture it.

Do not form the conclusion from the Figure 12–16 example that ADVANCE Blocks can only be placed after SEIZE Blocks in a GPSS model, or that RELEASE Blocks must follow them. ADVANCE Blocks can actually be put *anyplace* in a model. The GPSS Processor will not object. Of course, the choice of their locations should be defensible on logical grounds.

WHEN WAITING OCCURS: WHERE AND WITH WHAT PRIVILEGES TRANSACTIONS WAIT

Suppose that a Transaction arrives at the Figure 12–16 model segment and finds that the Facility named JOE is already in a state of capture. The Transaction is denied permission, then, to move into the SEIZE Block. Two questions arise.

1. While the Transaction "waits" for the Facility, *where* does it wait?
2. If two or more Transactions are waiting for the Facility when it again becomes available, which of the waiting Transactions will be permitted to capture it next?

The answer to the first question is that the Transaction waits *in the Block preceding the SEIZE*. Does this mean that the effect of the Transaction's having entered that preceding Block has not yet taken place? Not at all. Remember that, when a Transaction moves "through" a Block, the sequence of events is (*a*) the Block subroutine is executed as soon as the Transaction moves *into* the Block, then (*b*) the Processor attempts to move the Transaction into the next Block. It is entirely possible for a Transaction to come to rest in a Block after it has caused that Block's subroutine to be executed. *This* type of "coming to rest" is "involuntary"; the Transaction would prefer to keep moving forward in the model, if system conditions permitted. Contrast this with a Transaction "voluntarily" coming to rest in an ADVANCE Block.

The answer to the second question touches on the concept of *queue discipline*. "Queue" is a synonym for "waiting line." The queue discipline exercised by a server is the *rule* he follows in determining whom to serve next, given that two or more demands for service await him. In our normal activities, we usually encounter "first-come, first-served" queue discipline. The person who has been waiting the longest for the server captures him next. This is the queue discipline which is implemented by the GPSS Processor as the "default" case. That is, in the absence of special provisions which the model builder might otherwise make, a first-come, first-served queue discipline is "automatic" in GPSS. When the analyst does choose to make special provisions, it is possible to model arbitrarily complicated queue disciplines in the language. In this introduction, however, only the default case will be of interest to us.

GATHERING STATISTICS WHEN WAITING OCCURS: THE QUEUE BLOCK AND THE DEPART BLOCK

Almost by definition, queuing systems involve "constrained resources." A resource is "constrained" when there simply isn't enough of it to always respond immediately to the demands made on it. For example, the barber in a one-man barber shop is a "constrained resource." If he is already busy when the next customer arrives (that is, when a new demand arises for his services), then the new arrival must wait his turn. In fact, it is this very waiting which produces waiting lines, or *queues*, and gives rise to the term *queuing systems*.

Consider our own experience when we use a "constrained resource," and "go through a line" in the process. Three steps can be identified.

1. We join the waiting line. That is, we "queue up." Queuing up is an event which occurs at a point in time.
2. We wait our turn. The waiting occurs over an *interval* of time.
3. We depart the waiting line. The departure is an event which occurs at a *point* in time.

Now, it is frequently of interest to gather "statistics" which summarize the waiting process implied above in step (2). These summary statistics provide answers to questions such as these.

a) How many entries were there to the (potential) waiting line?
b) How many of these entries were actually forced to wait, in contrast with being able to capture the server immediately?
c) What was the maximum number waiting at any one time?
d) What was the average number waiting?
e) Of those who had to wait, how much time did they spend in the queue on average?

A special-purpose language designed for modeling queuing systems should provide the capability of collecting this kind of statistical information with relative ease. GPSS provides such a capability through the so-called *Queue entity*. When the model builder uses the GPSS Queue entity at points in a model where constrained resources are simulated, the GPSS Processor responds by automatically collecting summary statistics describing the waiting (if any) which occurs at those points.

The Queue entity is similar to the Facility entity in several general ways. As with Facilities, there can be many different Queues in a model. This is because waiting usually can occur at many different points in a system. By using a different Queue at each point of potential waiting, a separate set of statistics describing waiting-line behavior can be gathered at each individual point. Of course, to distinguish among different Queues, *names* must be supplied for them by the model builder. The naming conventions are the same as for Facilities. Names can either be numeric, or symbolic. If numeric, they must be positive integers. If symbolic, they must be composed of from three to five alphanumeric characters, with the first three being alphabetic.

As is true for Facilities, the analyst incorporates Queues into a model by making use of a pair of complementary Blocks. The complementary Block pair for the Queue entity is used to simulate the events (1) and (3) above. When a Transaction moves into the first member of the Block pair, the event "join a waiting line" is simulated. Similarly, when a Transaction moves into the second Block pair member, the event "depart a waiting line" is simulated. The Blocks corresponding to the "join" and "depart" events are the QUEUE and DEPART Blocks, respectively. These two Blocks are shown with their A Operand in Figure 12–17.

As indicated in Figure 12–17, the A Operand is used at the QUEUE and DEPART Blocks to indicate the name of a particular Queue (that is, the name of a particular waiting line). Whenever a Transaction moves into the QUEUE Block, the "content" of the referenced Queue is increased by 1. Similarly, whenever a Transaction moves into the DEPART Block, the referenced Queue has its "content" decreased by 1. This Queue "content" can be thought of in simple terms as a record of the number of Transactions which are "in a state of waiting." At the end of a simulation, the GPSS Processor automatically prints out information summarizing the values this "content" statistic assumed during the course of the simulation.

Now consider an example of placement of the QUEUE and DE–PART Block pair in a model. Referring again to Figure 12–16, it

FIGURE 12–17

The QUEUE and DEPART Blocks, with Their A Operand

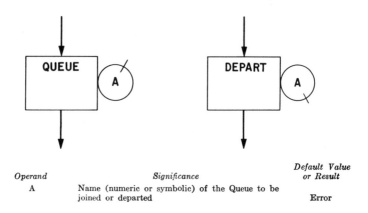

Operand	Significance	Default Value or Result
A	Name (numeric or symbolic) of the Queue to be joined or departed	Error

is clear that involuntary waiting might occur in connection with use of the Facility named JOE. Suppose that statistics are to be collected for this waiting process. A Queue is introduced into the model segment by sandwiching the SEIZE Block between the QUEUE–DEPART Block pair, as shown in Figure 12–18. The symbolic name LINE has been given to the Queue. Subject to the previously mentioned naming rules, this choice of a Queue name is of course arbitrary.

Just how does the Figure 12–18 model segment work in practice? Suppose that a Transaction moves into the model segment at a time when the Facility JOE is not in a state of capture. The Transaction enters the QUEUE Block, that subroutine is executed, and the content of the Queue named LINE is increased by 1. The Processor then immediately attempts to move the Transaction into the SEIZE Block. Because JOE is "available," the attempt is successful. The SEIZE subroutine is performed, and the status of the Facility JOE is changed from "not in use" to "in use." The Transaction then immediately moves into the DEPART Block. That subroutine is executed, and the content of the Queue named LINE is decreased by 1. Continuing its forward motion, the Transaction next moves into the ADVANCE Block. A holding time is computed by the Processor by sampling from the 16 ± 4 distribution, and the Transaction temporarily comes to rest. All of this has happened at a particular reading of the GPSS clock. This means that, although the Transaction joined the Queue named LINE, it spent zero units

of simulated time as a resident of that Queue. In GPSS, this phenomenon is described by saying that the Transaction was a "zero
entry" to the Queue. Such "zero entries" can occur for the simple
reason that the SEIZE Block is sandwiched between the QUEUE–
DEPART Block pair. In other words, all Transactions capturing
the Facility JOE must move through the QUEUE and DEPART
Blocks in the process, even if the Facility is available at the time
they arrive to attempt the capture.

Now suppose that while the Facility JOE is in a state of capture,
another Transaction moves into the Figure 12–18 model segment.
Entering the QUEUE Block, it causes the content of the Queue

FIGURE 12–18

Repetition of the Figure 12–16 Model Segment,
with a Queue Included

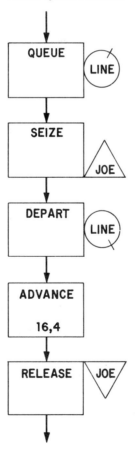

named LINE to be incremented by 1. The Transaction then immediately tries to enter the SEIZE Block. Permission to enter is denied, however, because the Facility JOE is "in use." The would-be capturer consequently comes to rest, "involuntarily," in the QUEUE Block. Later, when the current user of the Facility finishes its use, the waiting Transaction will again try to enter the SEIZE Block. This time, the attempt will be successful. Having resumed its forward motion, the new capturer will then move into the DEPART Block, decrementing the content of the Queue LINE by 1. For the situation described, these "increment" and "decrement" steps occur at different points in simulated time. This means that a "nonzero entry" to the Queue has taken place. The Processor knows, of course, how long this "nonzero entry" was "in the waiting line," and takes this into account in computing summary statistics to describe the experience of Transactions which moved through the waiting line.

In the Queue statistics it maintains, the Processor distinguishes between "zero entries," and "nonzero entries." The nature of these statistics will be examined by means of the one-chair barber shop model to be presented after the next section.

As indicated above, a Transaction is recorded as being "in a state of waiting" as soon as it enters a QUEUE Block, thereby causing the underlying subroutine to be executed. Being "in a state of waiting" does not require being "in a QUEUE Block," however. That is, after it has caused the QUEUE Block subroutine to be executed, a Transaction can *in general* continue its movement in a model. Independent of where the Transaction is, and despite the fact that it may be "on the move," a Transaction which has moved through a QUEUE Block continues to be "in a state of waiting," statistically speaking, until it eventually moves into a corresponding DEPART Block. In GPSS, then, residence in a Queue is a matter of *records,* and is not necessarily the same thing as being "physically present in a line." In real systems, it is also quite possible to be in a waiting line as a matter of record, without actually being physically present in a line. As a simple example of this, consider a shopper who "takes a number" when she enters a meat market. When that number is called, it will be her turn to be served. If the shopper judges that her number won't come up for a while, she might go next door to a bakery, wait her turn for service there, be served, and then return to the meat market to continue waiting there. As a matter of record, she has been in the meat market all the time, without always being physically present in the store.

DOCUMENTATION PATTERN FOR COMPUTER MODELS

In this chapter, three computer models are provided to illustrate selected features of GPSS. A consistent documentation pattern is followed in presenting these models. These are the components of the documentation:

1. *Statement of the Problem*
   This component provides a sufficiently detailed description of the problem so that a GPSS model for the system described can be built and run.

2. *Approach Taken in Building the Model*
   This section attempts to explain how the task of interpreting the problem in the context of GPSS was approached. The intention is to explain the rationale behind the particular approach used. For the relatively simple models presented here, the "approach" is not that demanding. For more difficult problems, this is usually not true.

3. *Table of Definitions*
   The importance of using analogies in building GPSS models is clear. Good model documentation includes a description of the analogies chosen by the analyst. The Table of Definitions is a listing of the various GPSS entities used in the model, with a brief explanation of their interpretation as elements in the system being modeled. The implicit time unit chosen by the analyst appears at the head of this table. Then the interpretation given to Transactions appears. After that, alphabetical order is followed for the other entities and their interpretations.

4. *The Block Diagram*
   In a sense, the Block Diagram *is* the model. An unadorned Block Diagram can be difficult for someone other than the model builder to follow. For this reason, *annotations* are placed adjacent to the Blocks in the diagram. Annotations are brief comments which indicate what the Block simulates, or helps to simulate, in the system being modeled.

5. *Extended Program Listing*
   As the GPSS Processor reads in the punch card version of a model, these three steps are performed (among others).
   a) A Location Number is assigned to each Block in the model.
   b) A Card Number is assigned to each punch card in the deck.
   c) For each card, this information is copied to the printer.
   (i) Block Number (if the card is a Block image).

(ii)   Information punched in the Location, Operation, and Operands fields in the card, including comments, if any.

(iii) Card Number (number of the position this card occupies in the deck).

The result is a Processor-produced listing of the original program. Actually, because numeric Block Locations and Card Numbers are included in this listing, but are not entered on the original cards themselves, this listing is better described as an "extended program listing." The extended listing is included in model documentation because it implicitly answers the sometimes asked questions "where do the cards go?" and "exactly what definition has been used for this or that feature of the model?"

6. *Program Output*

Selected portions of the printout produced when the simulation is run are shown to display what the model-builder receives for his efforts, and to serve as the basis for discussion.

7. *Discussion*

The discussion of a computer model may involve *model logic, model implementation,* and *program output.*

Model Logic. When appropriate, features in the Block Diagram are discussed to relate them to facets of the problem itself, or to the particular approach taken for interpretation of the problem in a GPSS context.

Model Implementation. The punch card version of a model contains cards corresponding to Blocks, but it also contains cards supplying other information. For example, the START Card must be included as part of the model implementation. There is no "Block" in a Block Diagram which corresponds to the START Card. Similarly, other possibilities exist for including information in the card deck which does not appear directly in the Block Diagram. When the occasion demands, this information will be singled out in the extended program listing and discussed.

Program Output. In general, the program output is important in the sense that it hopefully provides "answers" to the questions posed in the original problem. For our purposes here, however, the principal use of the output will be to show the kinds of statistical information which the GPSS Processor gathers when a GPSS model is run.

COMPUTER MODEL 1: A ONE–MAN BARBER SHOP

1. Statement of the Problem

The interarrival time of customers at a one-man barber shop is uniformly distributed over the range 18 ± 6 minutes. Service time for haircuts is 16 ± 4 minutes, uniformly distributed. Customers coming to the shop get their hair cut, first-come, first-served, then leave. Model the shop in GPSS, making provisions to collect data on the waiting line. Then run the model through eight hours of simulated time. Interpret the output produced by the model in the context of the barber shop.

2. Approach Taken in Building the Model

This model is easily constructed as a single-sequence of Blocks, excepting the run-control component. The order in which the Blocks appear corresponds to the sequence of stages through which customers move in the real system. Customers arrive; if necessary, they wait their turn; then they engage the barber, get their hair cut, release the barber, and leave. Except for the GENERATE and TERMINATE Blocks, this sequence has already been displayed and discussed in Figure 12–18.

To control the duration of the run, a two-Block "timer segment" can be used. In Figure 12–9, a segment accomplishing the objective required here was presented and discussed, under the assumption that the implicit time unit in effect is one minute. That segment will be used for this model.

3. Table of Definitions

TABLE 12–6

Table of Definitions for Computer Model 1

Time unit: 1 Minute

GPSS Entity	Interpretation
Transactions	
Model Segment 1	Customers
Model Segment 2	The "owner" of the barber shop, who arrives at simulated time 480 to "close up the shop"; alternatively, the "timer-Transaction" which comes into the model at simulated time 480 to shut off the simulation
Facilities	
JOE	The barber
Queues	
LINE	The Queue used to collect statistics on the waiting experience of customers

4. Block Diagram

FIGURE 12–19

Block Diagram for Computer Model 1

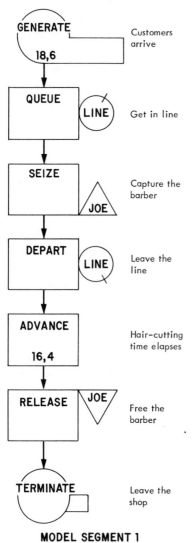
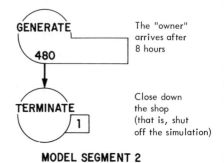

5. Extended Program Listing

FIGURE 12–20

Model as Submitted, and Corresponding Extended Program Listing

(a) Coding Sheet for Punch Card Version of the Model

LOCATION	OPERATION	A,B,C,D,E,F	COMMENTS
	SIMULATE		
*			
*	MODEL SEGMENT 1		
*			
	GENERATE	18,6	CUSTOMERS ARRIVE
	QUEUE	LINE	GET IN LINE
	SEIZE	JOE	CAPTURE THE BARBER
	DEPART	LINE	LEAVE THE LINE
	ADVANCE	16,4	HAIR-CUTTING TIME ELAPSES
	RELEASE	JOE	FREE THE BARBER
	TERMINATE		LEAVE THE SHOP
*			
*	MODEL SEGMENT 2		
*			
	GENERATE	480	THE "OWNER" ARRIVES AFTER 8 HOURS
	TERMINATE	1	CLOSE DOWN THE SHOP
*			(THAT IS, SHUT OFF THE SIMULATION)
*			
*	CONTROL CARDS		
*			
	START	1	START THE SIMULATION
	END		RETURN CONTROL TO THE OPERATING SYSTEM

(b) Extended Program Listing Produced for the Model in (a)

BLOCK NUMBER	*LOC	OPERATION	A,B,C,D,E,F,G	COMMENTS	CARD NUMBER
		SIMULATE			1
	*				2
	*	MODEL SEGMENT 1			3
	*				4
1		GENERATE	18,6	CUSTOMERS ARRIVE	5
2		QUEUE	LINE	GET IN LINE	6
3		SEIZE	JOE	CAPTURE THE BARBER	7
4		DEPART	LINE	LEAVE THE LINE	8
5		ADVANCE	16,4	HAIR-CUTTING TIME ELAPSES	9
6		RELEASE	JOE	FREE THE BARBER	10
7		TERMINATE		LEAVE THE SHOP	11
	*				12
	*	MODEL SEGMENT 2			13
	*				14
8		GENERATE	480	THE "OWNER" ARRIVES AFTER 8 HOURS	15
9		TERMINATE	1	CLOSE DOWN THE SHOP	16
	*			(THAT IS, SHUT OFF THE SIMULATION)	17
	*				18
	*	CONTROL CARDS			19
	*				20
		START	1	START THE SIMULATION	21
		END		RETURN CONTROL TO THE OPERATING SYSTEM	22

6. Program Output

FIGURE 12–21

Selected Program Output for Computer Model 1
(a) Clock Values and Block Counts

```
RELATIVE CLOCK          480   ABSOLUTE CLOCK        480
BLOCK COUNTS
BLOCK CURRENT    TOTAL
  1         0      27
  2         1      27
  3         0      26
  4         0      26
  5         1      26
  6         0      25
  7         0      25
  8         0       1
  9         0       1
```

(b) Facility Statistics

FACILITY	AVERAGE UTILIZATION	NUMBER ENTRIES	AVERAGE TIME/TRAN	SEIZING TRANS. NO.	PREEMPTING TRANS. NO.
JOE	.860	26	15.884	3	

(c) Queue Statistics

QUEUE	MAXIMUM CONTENTS	AVERAGE CONTENTS	TOTAL ENTRIES	ZERO ENTRIES	PERCENT ZEROS	AVERAGE TIME/TRANS	$AVERAGE TIME/TRANS	TABLE NUMBER	CURRE CONTE
LINE	1	.160	27	12	44.4	2.851	5.133		

$AVERAGE TIME/TRANS = AVERAGE TIME/TRANS EXCLUDING ZERO ENTRIES

7. Discussion

Model Logic. In the Figure 12–19 Block Diagram, note that no A Operand has been provided with the TERMINATE Block in Model Segment 1. Recall that the "default value" for the TERMI-NATE Block's A Operand is zero. This means that whenever customer-Transactions leave the barber shop, they do *not* cause the Termination Counter to be decremented. Hence, condition (2) associated with Figure 12–9 is satisfied; that is, the two-Block segment shown in Model Segment 2 in Figure 12–19 (which is simply a repetition of Figure 12–9) serves to shut off the simulation at simulated time 480.

In the model presented here, no provision is made for "removing customers from the barber shop" when the simulation shuts off at time 480. If the barber were to be true to the model, he would simply have to "walk out of the shop" at the end of his eight-hour day. Conversely, if the model were to be true to the barber, it would simulate locking the door after eight hours, but would not shut off until all customers already in the shop at that time had been serviced. In the last computer model in this chapter, it will be seen how this latter approach can be implemented in GPSS.

The model shown here also fails to make any provision for the barber to take a lunch break at noon, or coffee breaks at midmorning and midafternoon. In short, the barber in this model works eight consecutive hours, then stops. It is, of course, possible to incorporate "breaks" into GPSS models. The possibilities for doing this will not be discussed in this chapter, however.

Model Implementation.   The coding sheet from which the punch card version of the model was prepared is shown in Figure 12–20(a). The corresponding extended program listing produced by the Processor appears in Figure 12–20(b). Notice how the Processor has augmented the original information in producing the extended program listing. The "extensions" consist of the "Block Number" and "Card Number" columns appearing at the extreme left and right, respectively, in Figure 12–20(b). Inspection of the Block Number column shows that Block Numbers have been assigned, in sequence, to each punch card representing a Block image. In the Card Number column, note that each card in the deck has been assigned a sequence number.

"Comments" have been used liberally to document the model. Cards 2, 3, 4, 12, 13, 14, 17, 18, 19, and 20 in Figure 12–20(b) are comments cards which set off the model segments and the Control Card segment. An asterisk (*) has been entered in column 1 on each of these cards. The Block-image punch cards also carry comments in the Operands field. These comments are identical to the annotations written next to the corresponding Blocks in the Figure 12–19 Block Diagram.

Card 1 in Figure 12–20(b) is the SIMULATE Card. If the analyst is submitting a deck to have a run made, this card usually must be the first one the Processor encounters when it reads in the deck. The card consists of the single word SIMULATE, punched in the Operation field. If the SIMULATE card is absent, the Processor checks the deck for violations of the language rules, but makes no run with the model.

As stated earlier, the Processor starts the simulation when it finds a START Card in the model. A START Card has been placed, then, at the end of the model (Card 21). A 1 has been entered as the A Operand on the START Card. This causes the Processor to initialize the Termination Counter with a value of 1 when the simulation starts. This value will then not be decremented to 0 until simulated time 480, when a Transaction enters the model through the Model Segment 2 GENERATE Block and moves into the sequential TERMINATE Block.

After a simulation shuts off, the computer session is not necessarily finished. Many additional options remain open to the analyst. Whether or not these options are exercised, the analyst eventually reaches the point at which all instructions for the run have been included in the card deck. At this point, he puts in an END Card. This card instructs the Processor to return control to the operating system. The END Card appears after the START Card in Figure 12–20(*b*). It consists of the word END, punched in the Operation field.

The order of the cards *within a model segment* is critical, but the relative ordering of model segments within the card deck is not. For example, the timer segment could have been placed ahead of the major segment in Figure 12–20 without having any effect on the model.

Program Output. It is not evident by examining the Block Diagram or the extended program listing how any output is produced by the model. As suggested earlier, at the end of a simulation the GPSS Processor *automatically* prints out an extensive set of information pertaining to the model. This information includes statistics for each of the various entities used, i.e., for Facilities and Queues (and other entity types which have not been discussed).

A portion of the output produced by running the Figure 12–20(*a*) model is shown in Figure 12–21. Figure 12–21(*a*) shows "clock values" and "Block Counts." As indicated in the top line of that figure, there are *two* simulation clocks, the "Relative Clock" and the "Absolute Clock." The distinction between these two clocks need not be explained here. It is enough to note that both clocks show values of 480 in Figure 12–21(*a*). This simply means that the simulation shut off at simulated time 480.

Immediately under the "clock line" in Figure 12–21(*a*) are shown the "Block Counts." This information appears in three columns, "Block Numbers" (labeled simply as BLOCK in the figure), "Current Count" (shown as CURRENT), and "Total Count" (shown as TOTAL). The Block Numbers correspond to those shown in Figure 12–20(*b*). The "Current Count" is the count of Transactions "in" the corresponding Blocks at the time the simulation shut off. The "Total Count" is a count of the total number of Transactions which entered the corresponding Blocks during the simulation, *including* those that are still in the Block (if any). For example, the Total Count at Block 1 is 27, meaning that 27 Transactions entered the model through the Location 1 GENERATE Block. Similarly, the Total Count at Block 2 is 27, meaning that 27 Transactions moved into the QUEUE Block in Location 2. The Current Count at Block 2 is 1, meaning that 1 Transaction is still in the QUEUE Block, i.e., 1 customer was waiting for the barber when the model shut off. At the Block in Location 5, the ADVANCE Block, the Current Count is 1 and the Total Count is 26. That is, 26 customers have captured the barber; of the 26, 1 still has him captured (i.e., has not yet moved into the RELEASE Block). The Total Counts at the SEIZE and RELEASE Blocks are 26 and 25, respectively, which is consistent with the ADVANCE Block Counts.

In Figure 12–21 parts (*b*) and (*c*) show the statistics gathered for the Facility JOE and the Queue LINE. The Facility statistics are shown again in Figure 12–22, where the columns have been num-

FIGURE 12–22

Interpretation of the Information Shown in Figure 12–21(b)

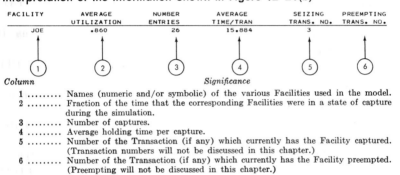

FACILITY	AVERAGE UTILIZATION	NUMBER ENTRIES	AVERAGE TIME/TRAN	SEIZING TRANS. NO.	PREEMPTING TRANS. NO.
JOE	.860	26	15.884	3	

Column	Significance
1	Names (numeric and/or symbolic) of the various Facilities used in the model.
2	Fraction of the time that the corresponding Facilities were in a state of capture during the simulation.
3	Number of captures.
4	Average holding time per capture.
5	Number of the Transaction (if any) which currently has the Facility captured. (Transaction numbers will not be discussed in this chapter.)
6	Number of the Transaction (if any) which currently has the Facility preempted. (Preempting will not be discussed in this chapter.)

bered for ease of reference. The table appearing in the lower part of Figure 12–22 indicates the significance of the entries in the various columns. Similarly, in Figure 12–23, the Queue statistics have been

FIGURE 12–23

Interpretation of the Information Shown in Figure 12–21(c)

QUEUE	MAXIMUM CONTENTS	AVERAGE CONTENTS	TOTAL ENTRIES	ZERO ENTRIES	PERCENT ZEROS	AVERAGE TIME/TRANS	$AVERAGE TIME/TRANS	TABLE NUMBER	CURRENT CONTENTS
LINE	1	.160	27	12	44.4	2.851	5.133		1

Column	Significance
1	Names (numeric and/or symbolic) of the various Queues used in the model.
2	Largest value the record of Queue content ever assumed.
3	Average value of the Queue content.
4	Total number of entries to the Queue.
5	Total number of entries to the Queue which experienced no waiting ("zero entries").
6	Percentage of total Queue entries which experienced no waiting.
7	Average time that each Queue entry spent waiting in the Queue (zero entries are *included* in this average).
8	Average time that each Queue entry spent waiting in the Queue (zero entries are *excluded* from this average).
9	Name (numeric and/or symbolic) of the GPSS table in which the distribution of Queue residence time is being tabulated (the GPSS table entity is not discussed in this chapter).
10	Current value of the Queue content.

repeated with column numbers included. The table at the bottom of that figure indicates the meaning of the various Queue statistics. The tables in Figures 12–22 and 12–23 should be studied, making reference to the output immediately above them in the process. Note these features of the information provided in those figures for the Facility JOE and the Queue LINE.

1. JOE was in use 86 percent of the time (AVERAGE UTILIZATION = .860).

2. JOE was captured 26 times (NUMBER ENTRIES = 26). This is consistent with the previously noted Total Count of 26 for the SEIZE Block.

3. The average holding time per capture of JOE was 15.884 minutes (AVERAGE TIME/TRAN = 15.884).

4. Transaction number 3 had JOE in a state of capture when the simulation shut off (SEIZING TRANS. NO. = 3). The fact that JOE was "in use" when the simulation shut off is consistent with the previously noted Current Count of 1 at the ADVANCE Block. As for Transaction "numbers," they will not be discussed here.

5. There was never more than one customer in the Queue LINE (MAXIMUM CONTENT = 1).

6. The average number of customers in the waiting line was .160 (AVERAGE CONTENTS = .160).

7. The total number of entries to the waiting line was 27 (TOTAL ENTRIES = 27).

8. Included among the 27 total entries to the waiting line were 12 "zero entries" (ZERO ENTRIES = 12).

9. Of the total entries to the waiting line, 44.4 percent of them were "zero entries" (PERCENT ZEROS = 44.4).

10. The average residence time in the waiting line per entry (*including* zero entries) was 2.851 minutes (AVERAGE TIME/TRANS = 2.851).

11. The average residence time in the waiting line per *nonzero entry* was 5.133 minutes (SAVERAGE TIME/TRANS = 5.133).

12. At the time the simulation shut off, there was 1 Transaction in the waiting line (CURRENT CONTENTS = 1). This is consistent with the previously noted Current Count of 1 at the QUEUE Block.

It is evident, then, that the GPSS Processor automatically produces a "lot" of statistics describing the behavior of a system modeled in the GPSS language. The analyst does not have to tell the Processor "how" to maintain and compute such information. He also does not have to provide FORMAT statements telling how this information is to be printed out. Quite apart from these "blessings," it must also be admitted that the GPSS model itself for the one-man barber shop (that is, for a single-channel queuing system) is much easier to build than was the FORTRAN equivalent. It may be edifying at this point to pause, and compare the GPSS Block Diagram in Figure 12–19 with the flowchart for the equivalent FORTRAN model, as shown in Figure 11–1 in Chapter 11.

EXTERNAL CONTROL CARDS REQUIRED TO RUN GPSS MODELS

After the punch card version of a GPSS model has been prepared, the resulting card deck must be placed within an appropriate control card sequence before the model can be run. These external control cards have nothing to do with the logic of the model itself. Instead, they provide information specifying the user's account number, indicating that the task to be performed requires use of the GPSS Processor, and so on. When the GPSS model has had the applicable control cards placed around it, the resulting "job" can then be submitted for running on a computer.

Figure 12–20 shows only the punch card images (and Processor-supplied extensions) of the GPSS model for the one-man barber shop; no external control card images are shown in the figure. The control cards which are appropriate for a job depend on the computer installation at which the job is to be run. For this reason, no attempt is made here to provide specific details about these external control cards. It is assumed that this kind of information can be obtained from the computing center at which the GPSS modeling is to be accomplished.

A SUGGESTED EXERCISE

The objective of this chapter is to provide you with some fundamental insights into GPSS as a special-purpose computing language. There is no intention here to bring you to the point of active mastery of even a small portion of the language. Nevertheless, GPSS *is* easily learned and, apart from that, *is* "fun" to use. If you have a GPSS Processor available on your computing system, you might want to experience this fact for yourself by performing the following experiment. First of all, find out what "external control cards" are necessary to run a GPSS model on your system. Then, punch up and run the one-man barber shop presented in Figure 2–20(a). In the "automatically produced" output you get back from your run, find and identify the clock values, Block Counts, and Facility and Queue statistics as presented in Figure 2–21. Then do the following. Change the interarrival time distribution in your model from 18 ± 6 to 17 ± 6. (This only involves changing one card in the model.) Submit the modified model for running. Examine the Facility and Queue statistics produced in the output. Compare such things as server utilization, maximum Queue content, the number of zero entries to the Queue, and the average residence time in the Queue with the corresponding statistics in Figure 2–21. Then, modify the model again by changing the interarrival time distribution to 16 ± 6. (After this change, the rate of customer arrivals will equal the rate at which the barber can provide haircuts.) Then run the model with this modification, and again inspect the various Facility and Queue statistics in the output. Compare the observed statistics with those which you would intuitively expect under the indicated circumstances.

ON THE QUESTION, "DO YOU NOW UNDERSTAND HOW GPSS WORKS?"

You have now seen a complete GPSS model for the single-channel queuing system, and have been shown that "the model works." The single-channel queuing model is probably the simplest nontrivial GPSS model that it is possible to build. Furthermore, every effort has been made to discuss the GPSS elements used in the model in such a way that the model will, in some sense, be "understandable" to you. Nevertheless, your feeling right now probably is that there is a bit of "black magic" involved somewhere. There is very little to the model that meets the eye. In fact, the entire model consists of only nine Blocks. And yet, fairly complicated logical conditions are handled, and fairly complicated computations are performed, when the model is run. The truth of the matter is that you have only been told *what* GPSS does, not *how* it does it. Before a model builder can really feel comfortable with GPSS, it is necessary to "get under the skin of the Processor" and follow its moves as it performs a simulation, step by step. *Then* comes the understanding. In an extended treatment of the language, it therefore makes good sense at this juncture to consider in closer detail just how the GPSS Processor "does its thing." Space limitations do not permit such a detailed treatment here. (For such a treatment, see Thomas J. Schriber, *Simulation Using GPSS* cited in "Suggestions for Further Study" in the last section of this chapter.) This is not inconsistent with this chapter's objective, which is simply to make you aware of GPSS, and give you a feeling for the flavor of the language. The point being made here, is that you shouldn't be too surprised if you don't feel completely comfortable about this matter of "how GPSS works."

We have now reached "part 2" of the plan for this chapter as described earlier. In part 2, we will learn about the capability for simulating "side-by-side" servers in GPSS, and then study a computer model which uses this capability to scale computer model 1 up from a one-man barber shop to a three-man barber shop.

ENTITIES TO SIMULATE PARALLEL SERVERS: STORAGES

Two or more servers often work side-by-side, performing a similar service. Such servers can either be people, or things. Here are some examples of two or more people in the category of side-by-side, or parallel, servers.

a)   Barbers.
b)   Supermarket checkout girls.
c)   Beauty shop operators.
d)   Clerks at a tool crib.
e)   Ticket-takers at the theatre.

Here are some examples of things which perform a similar service, and which might be available in quantities of two or more.

a)   Tugs for berthing and de-berthing ships at a harbor.
b)   Overhead cranes for moving heavy castings from molds to machines.
c)   Parking places in a parking lot.
d)   A supply of a particular type of spare part, sitting on a shelf.
e)   Card punches in a computing center.

A Facility can be used in GPSS to simulate a *single* server. Two or more side-by-side servers could be simulated in a GPSS model, then, with two or more Facilities located "side-by-side," i.e., in parallel. Indeed, it is sometimes necessary to use parallel Facilities to model parallel servers. This is the approach usually taken when the individual servers are *heterogeneous*, that is, are characterized by different properties, such as performing service at different rates. Many times, however, parallel servers are assumed to be *homogeneous*. This means, roughly speaking, that such servers share a common set of properties. For example, the rate at which barbers cut hair in a barber shop may not depend on the particular barber involved.

GPSS provides a special entity for simulating homogeneous parallel servers. The name "Storage" is used for this entity. As is true for Facilities and Queues, there can be many different Storages in a model. The analyst supplies names to distinguish among the various Storages he uses. The naming convention used for Facilities and Queues also applies to Storages. Names can be numeric or symbolic. When numeric, they must be positive, whole numbers. When symbolic, names are composed of from three to five alphanumeric characters, with the restriction that the first three be alphabetic.

The *number of servers* which each particular Storage simulates must be defined in the model by the model builder. In this sense, one speaks of the *capacity* of a Storage. The method for defining Storage capacity and using the Storage entity is described in the next section.

USING PARALLEL SERVERS: THE ENTER BLOCK
AND THE LEAVE BLOCK

The approach to simulating the use of a parallel server with a Storage is similar to that for simulating use of a single server with a Facility. The entities which place demands on Storages for service are Transactions. Assume that a Transaction wants to capture one of the servers being simulated with a Storage. The Transaction does this by moving (or *attempting* to move) into a particular Block related to the Storage. The Block has these features.

1. If no server is currently available, the Transaction is denied entry to the Block.
2. If a server is available, the Transaction is permitted to enter the Block. This causes the underlying Block subroutine to be executed. As a consequence, the status of the Storage is updated.

   Whereas a Facility is either "in use" or "not in use," the status of Storages is somewhat more complicated. The *extent* to which a Storage is in use must be considered. The number of parallel servers who are currently captured is termed the *content* of the

Storage. The number of servers not currently captured is the *remaining capacity*. Of course, the sum of current content and remaining capacity equals the number of parallel servers simulated with the Storage.

The Block which has the features indicated above is the ENTER Block. It is shown with its A Operand in Figure 12–24. The A Op-

FIGURE 12–24

The ENTER Block and Its A Operand

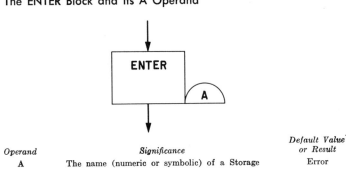

Operand	Significance	Default Value or Result
A	The name (numeric or symbolic) of a Storage	Error

erand is the name of the Storage simulating the parallel servers in question.

Movement of a Transaction into an ENTER Block, then, simulates the act of capturing a parallel server. In complementary fashion, movement of a Transaction into another particular Block simulates the act of "uncapturing" a parallel server. The Block which accomplishes this is the LEAVE Block. It is shown with its A Operand in Figure 12–25. When a Transaction moves into the LEAVE

FIGURE 12–25

The LEAVE Block and Its A Operand

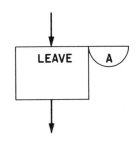

Operand	Significance	Default Value or Result
A	The name (numeric or symbolic) of a Storage	Error

Block, the current content of the Storage named by the A Operand is decreased by 1, and the remaining capacity is simultaneously increased by 1. The LEAVE Block never denies entry to a Transaction. An error condition results if execution of the LEAVE Block subroutine causes the current content of the referenced Storage to become negative. If this happens, an error message is outputted and the simulation is stopped.

The capacity of each Storage in a model is defined by use of *Storage Capacity Definition Cards*. In the form to be discussed here, a separate card is used for each Storage. Table 12–7 shows the card

TABLE 12–7

Card Format for the Single-Storage Capacity Definition Card

Punch Card Field	*Information Supplied in the Field*
Location	The name (numeric or symbolic) of a Storage
Operation	Literally, the word STORAGE
Operands	
A	The capacity of the Storage

format. Like most other GPSS cards, the Storage Capacity Card is divided into the Location, Operation, and Operands fields. Entered in the Location field is the number or symbolic name of the Storage. The Operation field contains the word STORAGE. The A Operand, which must be supplied as a nonnegative integer constant, specifies the capacity of the Storage. Two examples are shown in Figure 12–26, where the Storages 7 and GUYS are defined to have capacities of 5 and 3, respectively.

FIGURE 12–26

Examples Showing Use of the Table 12–7 Card Format

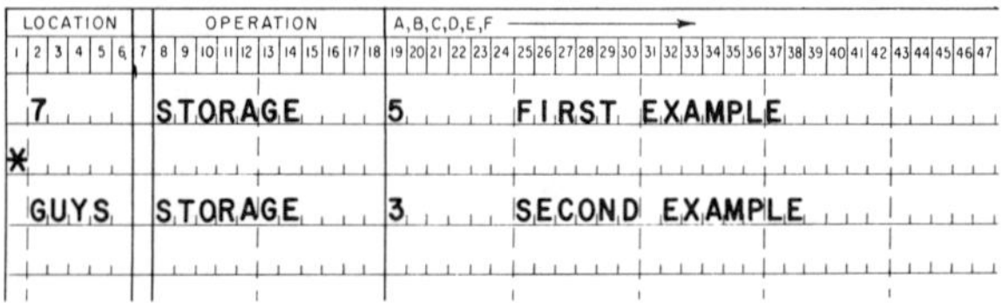

Although it is not strictly necessary to do so, it is good practice to place Storage Capacity Definition Cards at an early point in the card deck, after the SIMULATE Card, but before the first card which is a Block image.

It is natural to wonder what difference there is, if any, between a Facility and a Storage whose capacity has been defined to be 1. There are actually two differences, but they need not concern us here. For our purposes, a Storage with a capacity of 1 behaves just like a Facility.

As would be expected, the GPSS Processor automatically maintains a set of statistics for each Storage included as part of a GPSS model. These statistics are highly similar to those automatically maintained for each Facility in a model. An example of these Storage statistics, as they appear in the printout produced at the end of a simulation, will be shown as part of the documentation for computer model 2.

ONE–LINE, MULTIPLE–SERVER QUEUING SYSTEMS

Probably the most frequently occurring pattern for incorporating the Storage entity into GPSS models is that shown by means of a specific example in the Figure 12–27 model segment. Each Transaction which moves through the segment uses one of the parallel servers simulated with the Storage symbolically named GUYS. Whenever one of these servers is captured, he is held in the state of capture for 16 ± 4 time units. Notice, then, that one and the same distribution is used for the determination of service time, independent of "which server" has just been captured. Not one of the side-by-side servers consequently has any individuality in terms of being characterized by a service-time distribution differing from that of his fellow servers. This is one of the ways in which the servers simulated with a Storage are "homogeneous."

The Figure 12–27 model segment fails to reveal how many parallel servers the Storage GUYS simulates. That information can be obtained only by inspecting the Capacity Definition Card for the Storage, as it would be found in the extended program listing for the associated model.

Of course, whether the Storage GUYS simulates 1, or 2, or 3, or however many parallel servers, the servers themselves represent a "constrained resource" in the system being modeled. This means that not every Transaction which attempts to move into the ENTER Block will be successful on its first try. The ENTER Block has

FIGURE 12–27

A Frequently Occurring Pattern for
Modeling with Storages in GPSS

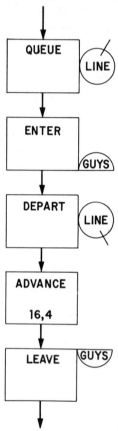

consequently been sandwiched between a QUEUE–DEPART Block
pair in Figure 12–27, on the assumption that the model builder
wants the GPSS Processor to gather statistics describing the behavior of the waiting line at that point. The symbolic name given to
the particular Queue involved is LINE.

Two aspects of the queuing system modeled with the Figure
12–27 Block sequence merit discussion. The first involves the way
a user selects a server; the second involves the way *a server selects
a user.*

Quite often, when parallel servers are involved, a *separate wait-*

ing line forms ahead of each server. When a would-be user arrives he surveys the situation and, if he must wait, then decides which line to join. In this sense, the user discriminates in his selection of a server. *Such discrimination is not possible when parallel servers are simulated with a Storage.* As has been mentioned, the servers a Storage represents have no individual identity. There is consequently no way to associate a separate waiting line with each server. In essence, then, a would-be user waiting at a Storage necessarily takes the attitude, "when my turn comes, I'll take whichever server is available." This is equivalent to having only one waiting line ahead of the parallel servers. When a would-be user arrives and finds he must wait, he simply joins the line. After reaching the head of the line, he goes to whichever server is free next. This situation is illustrated in Figure 12–28 for the specific case of three parallel servers. Note the strong similarity between Figure 12–28, and Figure 11–4 in Chapter 11.

FIGURE 12–28

Schematic Illustration of a One-Line, Multiple-Server Queuing System

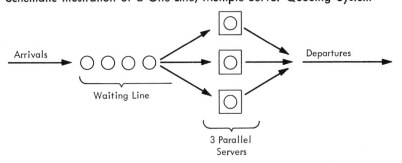

Interestingly enough, although the users cannot discriminate in the Figure 12–27 model segment, the servers can. That is, depending on the queue discipline which is being modeled, it is not necessarily true that the servers provide service on a first-come, first-served basis. As pointed out earlier, a variety of other queue disciplines can be modeled in GPSS if the model builder makes special provisions to bring them about. In the absence of such special provisions, the "automatic" queue discipline in GPSS, first-come, first-served, is the one in effect. It is this discipline which is implied in the Figure 12–27 model segment.

The one-line, multiple-server scheme is frequently used in real situations. This tends especially to be true when the items waiting for service are inanimate and, for all practical purposes, identical. This would be the case, for example, for parts moving from work station to work station on a production line. Even though the work stations might be manned by two or more people working in parallel, work would very likely be fed to them from a single line.

The one-line, multiple-server queuing system is rather frequently used, too, when those waiting for service are people, not things. In a barber shop, for example, all those waiting to get a haircut are usually understood to be in a single line. Whenever one of the barbers becomes free, he simply says, "who's next?" The understanding is that the customer who has been waiting the longest is the one who is "next."

Quite often, when parallel servers are involved, a separate waiting line does form ahead of each server. Modeling this *multiple-line, multiple-server* queuing system is substantially more complicated than modeling the one-line, multiple-server scheme. A *queue selection criterion* must be introduced, for example. When a new arrival comes, this criterion is then used to determine which waiting line the arrival should join. The possibility of *line jumping* should also be allowed. When a line is moving too slowly, those toward the end of the line may choose to jump to another line. Although multiple-line, multiple-server queuing systems can be modeled in GPSS, the details involved will not be taken up here.

COMPUTER MODEL 2: A THREE–MAN BARBER SHOP

1. Statement of the Problem

The interarrival time of customers at a three-man barber shop is uniformly distributed over the range 6 ± 2 minutes. Service time for haircuts is 16 ± 4 minutes, uniformly distributed and independent of the particular barber involved. Customers coming to the shop get their hair cut first-come, first-served, then leave. This implies that a one-line, multiple-server queuing system is used in the shop. Model this situation in GPSS, making provisions to collect data on the waiting line. Then run the model through eight hours of simulated time. Interpret the output produced by the model in the context of the barber shop.

2. Approach Taken in Building the Model

Given the availability of the GPSS Storage entity, and the fact that the three barbers are "homogeneous," simple modification of computer model 1 results in a model for a barber shop as described. Here is a list of the changes required in computer model 1 to bring about the desired effect.

1. Change the A–B Operands on the customer-Transaction GEN–ERATE Block from 18 and 6 to 6 and 2, respectively.
2. Replace the SEIZE Block with an ENTER Block.
3. Replace the RELEASE Block with a LEAVE Block.
4. Include a Capacity Definition Card in the model for the Storage referenced at the ENTER–LEAVE Block pair.

In fact, if the Storage involved is symbolically named GUYS, then Figure 12–27 can be thought of as showing the "heart" of the modified model after changes (2) and (3) above have been accomplished.

3. Table of Definitions

TABLE 12–8

Table of Definitions for Computer Model 2

Time unit: 1 Minute

GPSS Entity	*Interpretation*
Transactions	
Model Segment 1	Customers
Model Segment 2	The "owner" of the barber shop, who arrives at simulated time 480 to "close up the shop"
Storages	
GUYS	A Storage which, with a defined capacity of 3, is used to simulate the three barbers who work in parallel at the barber shop
Queues	
LINE	The Queue used to collect statistics on the waiting experience of customers who are resident in the barber shop's one waiting line

4. Block Diagram

FIGURE 12–29

Block Diagram for Computer Model 2

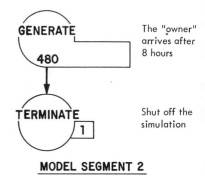

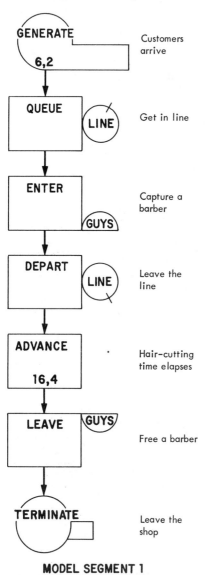

5. Extended Program Listing

FIGURE 12-30

Extended Program Listing for Computer Model 2

```
BLOCK
NUMBER  *LOC    OPERATION  A,B,C,D,E,F,G              COMMENTS              CARD
                SIMULATE                                                   NUMBER
          *                                                                  1
          *     STORAGE CAPACITY DEFINITION                                  2
          *                                                                  3
        GUYS    STORAGE    3              PROVIDE 3 BARBERS                   4
          *                                                                  5
          *     MODEL SEGMENT 1                                              6
          *                                                                  7
  1             GENERATE   6,2            CUSTOMERS ARRIVE                    8
  2             QUEUE      LINE           GET IN LINE                         9
  3             ENTER      GUYS           CAPTURE A BARBER                   10
  4             DEPART     LINE           LEAVE THE LINE                     11
  5             ADVANCE    16,4           HAIR-CUTTING TIME ELAPSES          12
  6             LEAVE      GUYS           FREE A BARBER                      13
  7             TERMINATE                 LEAVE THE SHOP                     14
          *                                                                 15
          *     MODEL SEGMENT 2                                             16
          *                                                                 17
          *                                                                 18
  8             GENERATE   480            THE "OWNER" ARRIVES AFTER 8 HOURS  19
  9             TERMINATE  1              SHUT OFF THE SIMULATION            20
          *                                                                 21
          *     CONTROL CARDS                                               22
          *                                                                 23
                START      1              START THE SIMULATION               24
                END                       RETURN CONTROL TO THE OPERATING SYSTEM  25
```

6. Program Output

FIGURE 12-31

Selected Program Output for Computer Model 2

Clock Values and Block Counts

```
RELATIVE CLOCK      480   ABSOLUTE CLOCK       480
BLOCK COUNTS
BLOCK CURRENT   TOTAL
  1     0        76
  2     0        76
  3     0        76
  4     0        76
  5     2        76
  6     0        74
  7     0        74
  8     0         1
  9     0         1
```

Storage Statistics

STORAGE	CAPACITY	AVERAGE CONTENTS	AVERAGE UTILIZATION	ENTRIES	AVERAGE TIME/TRAN	CURRENT CONTENTS	MAXIMUM CONTENTS
GUYS	3	2.454	.818	76	15.500	2	3

Queue Statistics

QUEUE	MAXIMUM CONTENTS	AVERAGE CONTENTS	TOTAL ENTRIES	ZERO ENTRIES	PERCENT ZEROS	AVERAGE TIME/TRANS	$AVERAGE TIME/TRANS	TABLE NUMBER	CURRENT CONTENTS
LINE	2	.091	76	58	76.3	.578	2.444		

$AVERAGE TIME/TRANS = AVERAGE TIME/TRANS EXCLUDING ZERO ENTRIES

7. Discussion

Model Implementation. In the Figure 12–30 extended program listing, note how the four changes mentioned in the "Approach Taken in Building the Model" section have been implemented.

Scanning the extended program listing from top to bottom, note
(a) the presence of a Capacity Definition Card for the Storage
named GUYS [Card 5]; (b) the new values for the A–B Operand
pair for the GENERATE Block image [Block Number 1]; (c) replacement of the SEIZE Block (in computer model 1) with an EN-
TER Block [Block 3]; and (d) replacement of the RELEASE
Block (in computer model 1) with a LEAVE Block [Block 6]. Except for these changes, then, computer model 2 is essentially a repetition of computer model 1.

Program Output.   Figure 12–31 displays the clock values and
Block Counts, Storage statistics, and Queue statistics produced by
the Processor when the Figure 12–30 model was run. In part (a) of
the figure, note that the Total Count at the Block in Location 1
(that is, the customer-Transaction GENERATE Block) is 76. This
means that 76 customers came to the barber shop during the course
of the simulated day. With an average interarrival time of 6, the
long-run average number of customers coming to the shop each day
would be 80 (480 divided by 6 equals 80). Hence, the number of arrivals on this simulated day was somewhat on the low side.

The Current Count at Block 2 (the QUEUE Block) is 0. This
means that no customers were waiting for a barber at the end of the
simulation. The Current Count at Block 5 (the ADVANCE Block)
is 2, meaning that two customers were "getting haircuts" when the
owner of the shop came along and shut off the simulation. By the
same token, this means that one barber was "available" when the
simulation ended.

The statistical summary for the Storage GUYS is shown in part
(b) of Figure 12–31. Eight pieces of information appear for the
Storage (including its name). Its analyst-defined CAPACITY is 3.
Its AVERAGE CONTENTS during the simulation was 2.454. This
means that, on average, 2.454 customers were getting haircuts during the course of the simulated day. Or, to put it differently, it
means that on average 2.454 barbers were "in use" during the day.
The corresponding AVERAGE UTILIZATION for the three barbers is .818 (2.454 divided by 3 equals .818). The ENTRIES to
the Storage GUYS (that is, the number of different times that one
or another of the parallel servers was captured) during the day to-
taled 76. The average holding time per capture of a server (AVER-
AGE TIME/TRAN) was 15.5 minutes. Of course, because the service time distribution is 16 ± 4, the long-run average holding time
would be 16 minutes. The barbers worked "somewhat fast," then,

on this simulated day. Note that the combination of (a) fewer customers than "expected," and (b) faster haircuts than "expected," have resulted in a Storage utilization statistic which is smaller than "expected." In the long run, the barbers would be busy a total of 1,280 minutes each day (80 customers per day times 16 minutes per customer equals 1,280 minutes of barber "in use" time per day). That corresponds to a total daily "in use" time of 426⅔ minutes per barber, and this in turn corresponds to an "expected" barber utilization of 88.75 percent.

The Storage statistics show that, at the time the simulation shut off, the CURRENT CONTENTS of the Storage was 2. That is, two of the parallel servers were in a state of capture at the time the model shut off. This is consistent with the Current Count of 2 at the ADVANCE Block in Location 5.

Finally, the MAXIMUM CONTENTS of the Storage at any time during the simulated day was 3. This simply means that there were times during the day when all three servers simulated by the Storage were "in use." We can infer that anyway from the AVERAGE CONTENTS information. In many instances, though, the MAXIMUM CONTENTS value will be less than the CAPACITY of the Storage; unless the Processor provided the MAXIMUM CONTENTS information in the output, there would then be no way to know what this maximum content value was.

Part (c) of Figure 12–31 shows the statistics for the Queue LINE. The MAXIMUM CONTENTS shows that there were never more than two customers waiting for service. In fact, the PER-CENT ZEROS information shows that about three customers out of four did not have to wait at all to be served.

It is interesting to compare the Queue statistics for the one-man barber shop [Figure 12–21(c)] with those for the three-man barber shop. The service-time distribution is the same in both models. Furthermore, the 6 ± 2 interarrival-time distribution for computer model 2 has been produced by dividing 3 (for 3 times as many barbers) into the 18 ± 6 distribution used in computer model 1. Would the typical waiting experience be the same after these changes have been made? No. When there are three barbers, the probability of finding a barber free is greater than when there is only one barber of like kind, even though only one third as many customers use that barber. This contention is clearly shown by comparison of the corresponding Queue information. Some of the key comparative statistics are summarized in Table 12–9. It is evident in the table that

TABLE 12–9

Comparison of Selected Queue Statistics for Computer Models 1 and 2

	Average Contents	Percent Zeros	$Average Time/Trans
One-man shop	.160	44.4	5.133
Three-man shop	.091	76.3	2.444

(*a*) fewer people were in line in the three-man shop, on average, than in the one-man shop, (*b*) the chances of not having to wait at all were greater in the three-man shop than in the one-man shop, and (*c*) those who did have to wait, waited a shorter time in the three-man shop than in the one-man shop. In general, it would be dangerous to draw conclusions from such small comparative samples, i.e., from samples based only on a one-day simulation. In this instance, though, simple logic indicates that the *direction of the differences* in these comparative statistics corresponds to the direction which would be "expected" in the long run.

Finally, in the Figure 12–31 Queue statistics, note that there is no entry in the CURRENT CONTENTS column. This means that the current content of the Queue was zero when the simulation shut off. ("Zero" prints as a "blank" in this case.) For this model, this is consistent with the Current Count of 0 at the QUEUE Block (the Location 2 Block).

This concludes "part 2" of the plan for this chapter. "Part 3" consists of only two sections. In the first of these sections, we will study computer model 3, which simulates a three-man barber shop characterized by (*a*) nonuniform distributions, (*b*) a customer "balking" feature, and (*c*) closing up of the barber shop under realistic conditions. Then, in the last section, several references to further sources of information about GPSS will be given.

COMPUTER MODEL 3: A THREE–MAN BARBER SHOP WITH NONUNIFORM INTERARRIVAL AND SERVICE TIMES, CUSTOMER BALKING, AND A REALISTIC CLOSEUP FEATURE

1. Statement of the Problem

The interarrival time of customers at a three-man barber shop takes on values between four and eight minutes, inclusive, with the relative frequencies shown in Table 12–10(a). The time required to service these customers ranges between 12 and 20 minutes, inclusive, with the relative frequencies shown in Table 12–10(b). A one-line, multiple-server queuing system is used in the shop.

TABLE 12–10

Distributions of Interarrival Times and Service Times for Computer Model 3

Interarrival Time (Minutes)	Relative Frequency (Percent)	Service Time (Minutes)	Relative Frequency (Percent)
4	10	12	3
5	20	13	7
6	40	14	12
7	20	15	17
8	10	16	22
		17	17
(a) Interarrival-Time Distribution		18	12
		19	7
		20	3
		(b) Service-Time Distribution	

Experience shows that whenever a *potential* customer arrives at the shop and finds that all three barbers are busy, and there is already someone in the waiting line, the potential customer goes away, and does not return later. That is, customers "balk" when the waiting line is of length one, and go elsewhere for service.

Furthermore, after eight hours of operation, the shop does not necessarily immediately "close up." At the end of the eighth hour, the "shade is pulled down" over the door to the shop, and the door is locked. This means that no new arrivals are allowed to enter the shop. Nevertheless, the shop remains "open" in the sense that any customers already inside at lockup time receive service before the barbers quit for the day.

Model this barber shop in GPSS, collecting data on the waiting line in the process. Then simulate with the model for a typical eight-hour day. Interpret the output produced by the model in the context of the barber shop. In particular, at what time were the barbers finally able to quit for the day, and how many customers "balked" because of conditions in the shop, and went elsewhere for service?

2. An Approach Leading to Solution

The "heart" of the requested GPSS model takes the form of the QUEUE–ENTER–DEPART–ADVANCE–LEAVE–TERMINATE Block sequence used in computer model 2. The features of GPSS required to model (*a*) nonuniform interarrival and service times, (*b*) the customer "balking" feature, and (*c*) realistic close-up conditions have not been discussed, however. Instead of including discussion of these features now, the discussion is deferred to part (7) of the model documentation. You should now briefly scan the Table of Definitions, the GPSS Block Diagram for the model, and the Extended Program Listing. Then turn to part (7) for commentary on how the conditions described in the problem statement have been incorporated into the model presented here.

3. Table of Definitions

TABLE 12–11

Table of Definitions for Computer Model 3

Time unit: 1 Minute

GPSS Entity	*Interpretation*
Transactions	
Model Segment 1	Customers
Model Segment 2	The "owner" of the barber shop, who arrives at simulated time 480 to "pull down the shade and lock the door," and then remains to finish "closing up the shop" when the last remaining customer has been served
Functions	
IAT	The symbolically named GPSS Function used to describe the customer interarrival-time distribution
STIME	The symbolically named GPSS Function used to describe the service-time distribution
Logic Switches	
LOCK	The symbolically named GPSS Logic Switch used to simulate the "locked" or "not locked" state of the door into the barber shop
Storage	
GUYS	A Storage which, with a defined capacity of three, is used to simulate the three barbers who work in parallel at the barber shop
Queues	
LINE	The Queue used to collect statistics on the waiting experience of customers who are resident in the barber shop's one waiting line

4. Block Diagram

FIGURE 12-32

Block Diagram for Computer Model 3

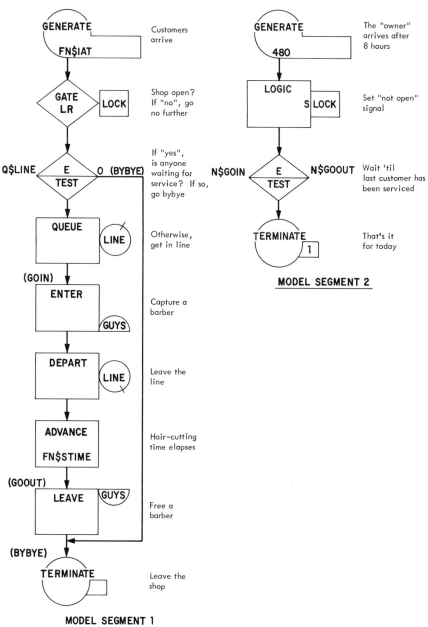

MODEL SEGMENT 1

MODEL SEGMENT 2

5. Extended Program Listing

FIGURE 12–33

Extended Program Listing for Computer Model 3

```
BLOCK                                                                     CARD
NUMBER  *LOC   OPERATION  A,B,C,D,E,F,G              COMMENTS            NUMBER
               SIMULATE                                                    1
        *                                                                 2
        *      FUNCTION DEFINITIONS                                       3
        *                                                                 4
        IAT    FUNCTION   RN1,D5       INTERARRIVAL-TIME DISTRIBUTION      5
        .1,4/.3,5/.7,6/.9,7/1.0,8                                         6
        STIME FUNCTION   RN2,D9        SERVICE TIME DISTRIBUTION           7
        .03,12/.1,13/.22,14/.39,15/.61,16/.78,17/.9,18/.97,19/1.0,20      8
        *                                                                 9
        *      STORAGE CAPACITY DEFINITION                               10
        *                                                                11
        GUYS   STORAGE    3            PROVIDE 3 BARBERS                  12
        *                                                                13
        *      MODEL SEGMENT 1                                           14
        *                                                                15
   1           GENERATE   FN$IAT       CUSTOMERS ARRIVE                  16
   2           GATE LR    LOCK         SHOP OPEN?  IF "NO", GO NO FURTHER 17
   3           TEST E     Q$LINE,0,BYBYE  IF "YES", IS ANYONE WAITING FOR 18
        *                              SERVICE?  IF SO, GO BYBYE         19
   4           QUEUE      LINE         OTHERWISE, GET IN LINE            20
   5    GOIN   ENTER      GUYS         CAPTURE A BARBER                  21
   6           DEPART     LINE         LEAVE THE LINE                    22
   7           ADVANCE    FN$STIME     HAIR-CUTTING TIME ELAPSES         23
   8    GOOUT LEAVE      GUYS          FREE A BARBER                     24
   9    BYBYE TERMINATE                LEAVE THE SHOP                    25
        *                                                                26
        *      MODEL SEGMENT 2                                           27
        *                                                                28
  10           GENERATE   480          THE "OWNER" ARRIVES AFTER 8 HOURS 29
  11           LOGIC S    LOCK         SET "NOT OPEN" SIGNAL             30
  12           TEST E     N$GOIN,N$GOOUT  WAIT 'TIL LAST CUSTOMER        31
        *                              HAS BEEN SERVICED                 32
  13           TERMINATE  1            THAT'S IT FOR TODAY               33
        *                                                                34
        *      CONTROL CARDS                                             35
        *                                                                36
               START      1            START THE SIMULATION              37
               END                     RETURN CONTROL TO THE OPERATING SYSTEM 38
```

6. Program Output

FIGURE 12–34

Selected Program Output for Computer Model 3

(a) Clock Values and Block Counts

```
RELATIVE CLOCK        495  ABSOLUTE CLOCK        495
BLOCK COUNTS
BLOCK CURRENT    TOTAL   BLOCK CURRENT    TOTAL
   1      1        82      11      0        1
   2      0        81      12      0        1
   3      0        81      13      0        1
   4      0        80
   5      0        80
   6      0        80
   7      0        80
   8      0        80
   9      0        81
  10      0         1
```

(b) Storage Statistics

STORAGE	CAPACITY	AVERAGE CONTENTS	AVERAGE UTILIZATION	ENTRIES	AVERAGE TIME/TRAN	CURRENT CONTENTS	MAXIMUM CONTENTS
GUYS	3	2.606	.868	80	16.125		3

(c) Queue Statistics

QUEUE	MAXIMUM CONTENTS	AVERAGE CONTENTS	TOTAL ENTRIES	ZERO ENTRIES	PERCENT ZEROS	AVERAGE TIME/TRANS	$AVERAGE TIME/TRANS	TABLE NUMBER	CURR CONTE
LINE	1	.084	80	61	76.2	.524	2.210		

$AVERAGE TIME/TRANS = AVERAGE TIME/TRANS EXCLUDING ZERO ENTRIES

7. Discussion

Model Logic

Nonuniform Interarrival Times and Service Times. Cards 5 and 6 in the Figure 12–33 extended program listing show the definition of a GPSS Function which describes the interarrival-time distribution presented in the problem statement in Table 12–10(*a*). For convenience, that Function definition is repeated in Figure 12–35 as

FIGURE 12–35

Coding Form Representation of Cards 5 and 6 in the Figure 12–33 Extended Program Listing

```
LOCATION  OPERATION  A,B,C,D,E,F
 IAT      FUNCTION   RN1,D5          INTERARRIVAL-TIME DISTRIBUTION
.1,4/.3,5/.7,6/.9,7/1.0,8
```

it would appear on a coding form. Note the following features of the first card in Figure 12–35.

a) The Operation field contains the word FUNCTION. (This tells the Processor that this card is the first in a series of two or more being used to define a Function.)

b) The Location field contains the analyst-supplied *name* of the Function being defined. In this case, the Function is being given the symbolic name IAT (for *i*nter*a*rrival *t*ime).

c) The A Operand gives the name of a predefined random number generator in GPSS (RN1) which is to be used as the Function's *argument*. That is, each time the Function named IAT is "called," the Processor is to draw a sample from random number stream 1 (i.e., RN1), then "convert" the sample value into an *equivalent* value from the nonuniform distribution which the Function defines. RN1 itself returns a value drawn at random from the population uniformly distributed between 0.000000 and 0.999999, inclusive. That is, RN1 is a *uniform* random number generator which generates a "random fraction" as its value. The procedure followed by the Processor to "convert" the random fraction from RN1 into an equivalent value from the nonuniform distribution *is identical to* that described in Chapter 10 of this book in the section entitled "Nonuniform Random Number Generators." That is, a table-lookup procedure is used.

d) The B Operand, "D5," tells first of all that the values returned by the Function are *discrete* (the "D" is for "discrete"), and secondly that the Function can take on any one of five different values.

Now note the second card in Figure 12–35. This card contains five ordered pairs of points. The ordered pairs are separated from each other by a slash (/). The *second member* of each ordered pair specifies one of the values which the Function can assume. The *first member* of each ordered pair specifies the *cumulative probability* with which the Function assumes the corresponding second-member value. For example, the first ordered pair in Figure 12–35 is ".1,4." This means that 10 percent of the time, the Function takes on a value of 4. The second ordered pair is ".3,5." This means that 30 percent of the time, the Function takes on a value *less than or equal* to 5. But we know from the first ordered pair that, of the "30 percent," 10 percent of the time the assumed value is 4; the other 20 percent of the time, then, the assumed value must be 5. This is consistent with a relative frequency of 20 percent for the value 5, as specified in Table 12–10, and so on, for the remaining ordered pairs appearing on the second card in Figure 12–35.

These mechanical details now being discussed will not be of much interest to you. What *should* interest you, however, are these following conclusions which can be inferred from the above observations.

1. A straightforward mechanical process is involved in defining discrete, nonuniform distributions in GPSS.

2. Predefined uniform 0–1 random number generators are built into GPSS. (There are actually eight such generators, named RN1, RN2, RN3, . . . , RN7, and RN8.) The model builder specifies which one of these he wants used as the "argument" for each Function with which he describes a nonuniform distribution.

3. The information needed to define a nonuniform distribution consists essentially of the cumulative probability values for the distribution. These values are needed by the Processor so that it can perform a table-lookup each time the Function is "called."

4. Although the relative-frequency information in Table 12–10 is

"symmetric," the symmetry is arbitrary. That is, the symmetry has in no way influenced the mechanics followed in defining the nonuniform distribution. The same simple procedure could consequently be used to incorporate empirically observed distributions into GPSS models.

Now consider the way the Function symbolically named IAT is used in the model to simulate the customer arrival process. The customer-Transaction GENERATE Block takes the form "GEN–ERATE FN\$IAT" (see Card 1 in the Figure 12–33 extended program listing). The A Operand, then, "points to," or "calls," the Function symbolically named IAT. (The fact that the call takes the form "FN\$IAT" need not concern us here.) There is no B Operand; that is, the model builder has defaulted on the B Operand. Recall that the default value for the B Operand is 0. This means that the interarrival-time distribution appears to the Processor to be "uniformly distributed" over the interval "FN\$IAT±0." To put it differently, when another sample is needed from the interarrival-time distribution, the Processor fetches a sample from the Function IAT and then uses the Function's value, "plus or minus zero," as *the* interarrival time in that instance. This means that the Function's returned value is used directly, in unmodified fashion. But because the Function returns values *at random*, the interarrival times are really random. In particular, they follow the nonuniform distribution which has been "built into" the Function via its definition.

What has just been said about Function definition and Function "calls" in terms of interarrival times also applies to nonuniform service times. The Function symbolically named STIME (see Cards 7 and 8 in Figure 12–33) is defined to describe the nonuniform service-time distribution; and the Function is "called" via the A Operand at the ADVANCE Block where service time is simulated (see Block 7 in Figure 12–33). It should be clear that, relative to simulating nonuniform interarrival times, there is really nothing "different" about simulating nonuniform service times in GPSS.

The Customer "Balking" Feature. According to the problem description, *potential* customers fail to remain for service at the barber shop if there is already one customer in the waiting line. This condition has been reflected in the Figure 12–32 Block Diagram by (*a*) making use of a predefined property of waiting lines in GPSS, and (*b*) making use of what is called a "transfer-mode TEST Block."

First of all, consider the idea of predefined properties of waiting lines in GPSS. The Queue statistics printed out at the end of a simulation *are available to be used as data during the simulation.* These data values are referred to as "Standard Numerical Attributes" in GPSS. For each GPSS entity (such as Queues, Facilities, and Storages), there are many of these "Standard Numerical Attributes." The *names* of these attributes are predefined. The *values* of these attributes are simply whatever values are currently in effect when that data is accessed. For example, at the Model Segment 1 TEST Block in Figure 12–32, "Q$LINE" is the predefined named of the Standard Numerical Attribute whose value is the *current content* of the Queue named LINE. When a Transaction enters that TEST Block, then, and the underlying subroutine is executed, one of the values used by the subroutine is the current content of the Queue LINE.

Now consider the idea of a transfer-mode TEST Block. The TEST Block in Model Segment 1 is just such a Block. For convenience, the Block is repeated in Figure 12–36. When a Trans-

FIGURE 12–36

Repetition of the Transfer-mode TEST Block from Model Segment 1 in Figure 12–32

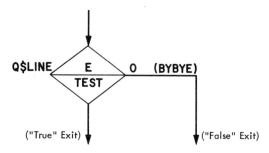

action enters the Figure 12–36 TEST Block, the test "is Q$LINE equal to 0?" is conducted. This fact can almost be "read" from the information associated with the TEST Block. The "E" in the Block means "equal to," and the "0" to the right of the Block is the value against which "Q$LINE" is being compared for equality. In other words, the Transaction entering the TEST Block causes a test to be performed to see if "the waiting line is empty." If the condition tested is *true,* the testing Transaction moves to the sequential Block in the model; that is, it moves into the QUEUE Block (the customer stays for service). If the tested condition is *false,* however, the testing Transaction moves to the *nonsequential* Block in the Location named BYBYE. (Note how the symbolic name BYBYE appears on the horizontal exit from the Test Block.) That is, the Transaction transfers to the TERMINATE Block in Model Segment 1 and leaves the model (the customer does not stay for service).

The Realistic Close-up Conditions. When close-up time arrives, the "owner" of the barber shop is to (*a*) "pull down the shade and lock the door," to signal that the shop is not open for new business, then (*b*) wait until all in-shop customers, if any, have been served before shutting off the simulation. This means that there are two aspects of the close-up procedure which must be incorporated into the model.

Consider first of all the aspect of "pulling down the shade and locking the door." The method used in the model to do this makes use of the so-called *Logic Switch entity* in GPSS. Logic Switches are much like the switches we are familiar with in our everyday experience, such as light switches, for example. A given Logic Switch is either "off" or "on." Instead of using the terms "off" and "on," however, the terms "Reset" and "Set" are used in GPSS as meaning "off" and "on," respectively. To say that a given Logic Switch is "Reset," then, is the same as saying that it is "off."

Now, the setting of a Logic Switch can be tested by a Transaction at a so-called "GATE" Block. The term "gate" is a convenient one. The GATE Block can be thought of much in the way that we think of the term "gate" in our normal experience. A "gate" is either open or closed. Similarly, a GPSS GATE Block is either open or closed. If it is closed, it will not let a Transaction pass through it. If it is open, it will.

As it turns out, a Logic Switch can be used to control the "open" or "closed" condition of a GATE Block. When a given Logic Switch is "off," for example, this can have the effect of causing a given GATE to be "open"; similarly, if the same Logic Switch is then turned "on," this has the effect of shutting the given GATE.

All the pieces necessary for "pulling down the shade and locking the door" have now been described. Referring to the Block Diagram segment in Figure 12–32, note the presence of a GATE Block following the customer-Transaction GENERATE Block. Before customer-Transactions enter the model, they must "pass through the gate." Using different words to say the same thing, when a Transaction enters the model at the Model Segment 1 GENERATE Block, it tries to move forward into the Block "GATE LR LOCK." This forces the Processor to test the Logic Switch named LOCK for a "Reset" condition (the "LR" stands for "*Logic Switch Reset*"). If the "Reset" condition is *true,* the gate is open, and the Transaction passes through. If the "Reset" condition is *false,* the gate is closed, and the customer-Transaction is forced to remain in the GENER-ATE Block.

At the beginning of a simulation, any Logic Switches used in a model are initially "Reset," by default. This means that the Model Segment 1 GATE Block is "open" at the start of the simulation. But now notice what happens at simulated time 480. In Model Segment 2, the "owner-Transaction" comes into the model at that time, and moves into the "LOGIC" Block. This Block has the purpose of modifying the setting of a Logic Switch. In particular, when the Block "LOGIC S LOCK" is executed, the Logic Switch named LOCK is thrown into a "Set" position (the "S" stands for "Set"). This has the effect of "closing the gate" in Model Segment 1. Hence, from simulated time 480 forward, no additional customer-Transactions are permitted to enter the barber shop.

Finally, there is the matter of having the "owner-Transaction" wait until all in-shop customers, if any, have been served before shutting off the simulation. This is accomplished by (*a*) making use of a predefined property of *Blocks* in GPSS, and (*b*) making use of what is called a "refusal-mode TEST Block."

Just as Facilities, Queues, and Storages have properties known as "Standard Numerical Attributes," so too do Blocks have such properties. One such Block property is the "Total Count" at the Block. We already know that a Block's Total Count equals the number of Transactions which have entered the Block "so far," and that Total and Current Block Counts are printed out at the end of a simulation. They are also available during a simulation. To get the Total Count at a Block, the model builder must put a symbolic Location Name on that Block, and then use the predefined Standard Numerical Attribute "N\$sn," where "sn" stands for the Block's Location Name, in general. For example, the Model Segment 1 ENTER Block in Figure 12–32 has been given the symbolic Location Name GOIN (for "go-in" to a barber's chair). The standard Numerical Attribute "N\$GOIN" consequently has the Total Count at that ENTER Block as its value. Similarly, the symbolic Location Name GOOUT (for "go-out" of a barber's chair) has been given to the LEAVE

Block in Model Segment 1. This means that "N\$GOOUT" has the Total Count at that Block as its value.

By now, you can probably see "what's up" with the owner-Transaction in Model Segment 2. After this Transaction makes the scene and moves through the LOGIC Block, thereby "closing the gate" on newly arriving customers, it encounters a TEST Block. That Block is repeated in Figure 12–37. From what we already know about

FIGURE 12–37

Repetition of the Refusal-Mode TEST Block from
Model Segment 2 in Figure 12–32

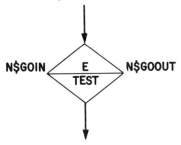

TEST Blocks, we can "read" the condition being tested from Figure 12–37. The test is: "Is the Total Count at the ENTER Block equal to the Total Count at the LEAVE Block?" When this condition is *true,* the testing Transaction is permitted to move through the TEST Block. When this condition is *false,* the testing Transaction is *not permitted to move anywhere;* instead, it hangs up on the TEST Block. (It is actually held in the Block preceding the TEST Block until the condition tested becomes true.) Notice that no "nonsequential exit" is shown, diagrammatically, leading from the Figure 12–37 TEST Block; also notice the absence of any Location Name associated with that Block, "pointing to" a nonsequential Block. We conclude, then, that TEST Blocks can either be used in "transfer mode," or in "refusal mode," in GPSS. You have an example of each mode in Figure 12–32.

Now, what about this matter of "equality of Block Counts"? When the owner-Transaction arrives at the end of the day, he cannot get through the refusal-mode TEST Block to shut off the simulation (by moving into the TERMINATE Block) until the number of customers who have captured a barber (that is, the number of Transactions which have moved into the ENTER Block) equals the number who have "uncaptured" a barber (that is, the number of Transactions which have moved into the LEAVE Block). But this condition only becomes true when all customers have left the shop. Hence, the shop can't be closed until all the customers who were in the shop at time 480 have managed to get their hair cut.

Program Output

Figure 12–34 shows selected program output produced by computer model 3. Note these features of the Clock values and Block Counts in part (*a*) of that figure.

1. The shop didn't close until simulated time 495 (the Relative and Absolute Clock values are 495). This means that 15 minutes of "overtime" were involved in that day's operation of the barber shop.
2. Only one customer balked, choosing not to remain for service. (The Total Count at Block 3, the transfer-mode TEST Block in Model Segment 1, is 81; and the Total Count at Block 4, the QUEUE Block, is 80. Hence, of the 81 Transactions which entered the TEST Block, 80 moved to the sequential Block, and only 1 "went BYBYE.")
3. The Current Counts at the Blocks making up the "heart" of the barber shop are all zero, meaning that the shop was "empty" when the simulation shut off.
4. The Current Count at the customer-Transaction GENERATE Block (the Location 1 Block) is 1, meaning that after time 480, one customer-Transaction came along, found the GATE Block closed, and as a result was hung up in the GENERATE Block when the simulation ended.

Features of the Storage and Queue statistics in Figure 12–34 will not be commented upon. You can provide an interpretation for these statistics, following the procedure used in discussion of the computer model 2 statistics.

EPILOGUE

You no doubt recognized the Block Diagram for computer model 3 as being the one used for the "silhouette" in Figure 12–1, and for the fleshed-out silhouette in Figure 12–2. This means, then, that we have now "come full circle" with this introductory treatment of GPSS. The idea was to go slowly at first, to give you a chance to digest some fundamental ideas about the language. Then, at the very end, things speeded up a bit in terms of computer model 3. Even at that, you may feel that computer model 3 makes reasonably good sense. If you do, and if you think you want to learn more about GPSS, you should look further into the language. As mentioned earlier, GPSS is actually "fun" to use; in fact, it may be more fun to use GPSS than to use any other computer language available at this time. Quite apart from this, the language is also most useful as a tool for investigating some weighty problems involving systems analysis and design. There can be a very real "real world" payoff associated with its use. Indeed, there are now at least several large corporations which "won't build anything" involving queuing systems until the proposed design has been simulated first on a computer. For such simulation, GPSS is very frequently the language used for the modeling involved.

To learn more about GPSS consult the references in the Suggestions for Further Study at the end of this chapter. With regard to those references the following observations will be helpful. Item (1) contains IBM's introductory treatment of GPSS/360. Item (2) is the GPSS/360 "bible," containing what can be called "bit-level information" about the language. Both of these items are necessarily rather terse, and are really only "easy to read" for the person who is already quite well checked out on computers in general, and GPSS in particular. This leaves a need for material written with the true beginner in mind. Item (3) attempts to meet that need by moving through many of the elements of GPSS/360 in what is hopefully a logical way. It also makes frequent use of fully documented computer models to show the use of these elements in context. In fact, there are 27 such computer models in item (3). The first of these is a single-channel queuing model which is almost identical to computer model 1 in this chapter. From there, of course, things get progressively more complicated. By the time a person has worked his way through to the end of item (3), he should have achieved active mastery of GPSS/360. He will then also be able to study items (1) and (2) with relative ease. Finally, he will be able to use a computer language which very likely will remain available, in one form or another, for at least the next ten or twenty years.

SUGGESTIONS FOR FURTHER STUDY

GPSS/360 Introductory User's Manual (published by IBM; Form Number GH20–0304).

GPSS/360 User's Manual (published by IBM; Form Number GH20–0326).

A GPSS Primer, by Thomas J. Schriber (currently available in softbound from Ulrich's Books, Inc., Ann Arbor, Michigan; to be published in hardbound in 1974 by John Wiley & Sons, Inc. under the tentative title *Simulation Using GPSS*).

chapter 13

Management Planning Models

Two MODELS of particular value for management decision making, and whose development has been greatly stimulated by progress in the computer sciences, have to do with planning. One deals with projects that are, relatively speaking, *one-time* undertakings and that involve a large number of component subprojects sequentially interrelated. The other model has to do with short-term forecasting of processes that are relatively repetitive.

A study of these models will help us to develop further skills in computer modeling and will help us to equip ourselves for dealing with large-scale *systems* studies.

The first of these models is concerned with network analysis, and is most extensively described in current literature as PERT (Program Evaluation and Review Technique) and as CPM (Critical Path Method) analysis.

CPM and PERT evolved independently. CPM was developed in 1957 by Morgan R. Walker of Du Pont and James E. Kelly of Remington Rand. PERT was developed in connection with the Polaris weapons system and was first described in an article by Malcolm, Roseboom, Clark, and Fazar in *Operations Research,* September 1959. Although each of these two techniques has its own modeling language, they differ in only one really fundamental respect: *Whereas CPM endeavors to determine the expected times of completion of the total project and times of completion of the subprojects of which it is composed, PERT goes further and endeavors to estimate variances associated with these expected times of completion.*

Therefore PERT deals more explicitly with the problem of uncertainty, and CPM becomes a kind of subset of PERT in which only expected values are used in the planning process. We will concern ourselves only with PERT.

PERT NETWORK ANALYSIS

Consider the network of Figure 13–1. In this network a numbered circle corresponds to a significant *completion event,* such as (*a*) an

FIGURE 13–1

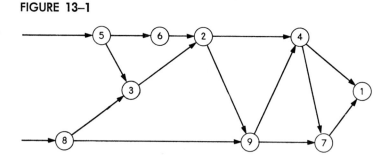

assembly completed, (*b*) a budget prepared, or (*c*) a component tested.

An arrow, on the other hand, corresponds to an *activity,* such as (*a*) manufacture fuselage, (*b*) brief executive committee, or (*c*) prepare plans and specifications.

In the pictorial representation of Figure 13–1 the tail of the arrow represents the beginning of the activity and its head represents the ending of the activity. The PERT network is simply the interrelated system of activities and completion events, in which a completion event can be both the terminus of one or more activities and the necessary conditions for the commencement of one or more other activities.

It seems appropriate to speak of events as *completion* events, even though some events may not *seem* to represent the terminus of an activity (such as events 5 and 8 in Figure 13–1). However, to the network analyst and the program planner all events are better thought of as the completion of something, since all events are not "beginning" events (thus event 1 in Figure 13–1).

PERT network analysis has as its objective the manipulation of data relative to an interrelated system of activities and completion events so as to yield estimates concerning:

1. The earliest expected time of occurrence of completion events.
2. The latest allowable time of occurrence of completion events.
3. The critical path of the network.
4. The probabilities of events occurring "on schedule."

For all but elementary networks, analysis "by hand" is too costly to justify. Equipped with a computer model, however, we can analyze and study the behavior of highly complex networks.

Before beginning the design of a computer model for network analysis we would do well to perform an analysis by hand, both to acquaint ourselves with several conventions we should observe and to acquaint ourselves with what has become rather standard PERT methodology.

First, we need time estimates for activities. In business and industry there is little certainty, so we must deal with probabilities. In network analysis we need two parameters for each time-consuming activity—a mean and a variance. A number of schemes may be employed to arrive at a mean and a variance for the amount of time required for an activity. One that enjoys rather widespread acceptance involves three estimates of the amount of time required for the activity:[1]

1. A most likely amount of time, which we will label m.
2. An optimistic estimate of amount of time, which we will label a.
3. A pessimistic estimate of amount of time, which we will label b.

To arrive, by this scheme, at the mean or expected amount of time required for the activity, which we will label t_e, we give the most likely amount of time a weight of 4, and the optimistic and pessimistic estimates of the amount of time a weight of 1 each. The mean or expected amount of time for the event, t_e, becomes:

$$t_e = \frac{a + 4m + b}{6}.$$

In this scheme the variance, v, associated with this mean is:

$$v = \left(\frac{b - a}{6}\right)^2.$$

---

[1] The defense for this method of determining the mean and variance of the amount of time required for an activity is dealt with in a number of works on network analysis. See especially Robert W. Miller, *Schedule, Cost and Profit Control with PERT* (New York: McGraw-Hill Book Co., 1963), Chap. II.

Let us assume that the expected times (in weeks) for the activities portrayed in the network of Figure 13–1, and their associated variances, have been determined and that they are as shown in Figure 13–2.

FIGURE 13–2

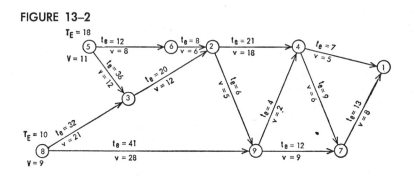

Let us also assume that estimates have been made of the amount of time required for whatever activities precede events 5 and 8, and that estimates have been made of the variances associated therewith. As shown in Figure 13–2, T_E (the earliest expected time of occurrence of completion event 5) is 18 weeks. This may best be thought of as 18 weeks after time 0, the time when the program of activities and events portrayed by our network actually gets underway.

The earliest expected time of occurrence of completion event number 8 is 10 weeks. The variances associated with the earliest expected times of occurrence of completion events 5 and 8 are 11 and 9, respectively.

We would now like to use these data to determine the earliest expected times of occurrence, T_E, and their associated variances, V, for all the *events* in the network. The calculation of these values involves simply a traverse through the network. We reason thus:

The activity that connects events 5 and 6 cannot *begin* until 18 weeks after time 0 (i.e., until after the occurrence of completion event 5, whose earliest expected time of occurrence is 18 weeks after time 0).

Since the activity that connects events 5 and 6 is expected to take 12 weeks, the earliest expected time of occurrence for event 6 is 30 weeks (18 weeks + 12 weeks) after time 0.

We calculate the variance for event 6 by adding the variance associated with its immediate predecessor event (i.e., event 5) and the variance associated with the expected time required for the activity that connects event 6 to its immediate precedessor event. Thus the variance, V, associated with the T_E for event 6 is 19 $(11 + 8)$.

Now that we have determined T_E for event 6, we might move on and determine T_E for event 2—6's immediate successor event. At once it occurs to us, however, that we cannot determine the earliest expected time of occurrence for event 2 solely on the basis of knowledge about event 6, because event 2 has another immediate predecessor event, namely, event 3. The T_E for event 3 and the t_e for the activity that connects 2 to 3 may pose the constraint that determines the earliest expected time of occurrence of event 2.

Having no knowledge of the T_E for event 3, we are obliged to abandon event 2 for the moment and to determine T_E for event 3. Event 3 has two immediate predecessor events—5 and 8. To determine T_E for event 3 we simply calculate T_E for event 3 on the basis of its dependence on event 5; then calculate T_E for event 3 on the basis of its dependence on event 8, and reason that the earliest expected time of occurrence of event 3 is the *larger* of the two.

T_E for event 3, based on event 5, is 54; and T_E for 3 based on 8 is 42. Therefore event 5 governs. T_E for event 3 is 54 weeks, and its associated variance is 23.

Equipped now with knowledge about event 3, we can return to event 2. Proceeding as with event 3, we find that event 3 governs for event 2, and that T_E for event 2 is 74 weeks, with an associated variance of 35.

If we continue this process we determine the T_E for each event, as shown in Table 13–1.

TABLE 13–1

Event Numbers

	⑧	⑤	③	⑥	②	⑨	④	⑦	①
T_E:	10	18	54	30	74	80	95	104	117
V:	9	11	23	19	35	40	53	59	67
T_L:	22	18	54	66	74	91	95	104	117
Slack:	12	0	0	36	0	11	0	0	0

Since the T_E for event 1, the final completion event, is 117 weeks, the earliest expected time of completion for the full program of activities represented by the network is 117 weeks after time 0, with a variance of 67.

We now want to determine T_L for each event. We define T_L to mean the latest expected time at which a completion event can be allowed to occur without disturbing the T_E of the final event of the network. Its meaning will become more apparent as we proceed. Let us begin with event 1 and work our way back toward time 0.

If we do not want to disturb the T_E of event 1, clearly we must cause event 7 to occur not later than 104 weeks after time 0 (117 − 13). The latest expected time of occurrence of event 7, i.e., T_L for event 7, is therefore 104 weeks after time 0.

In the same fashion, T_L for event 4 is 95 weeks after time 0.

Event 9 has two immediate successor events. T_L for event 9 then would be the *smaller* of the T_Ls determined from basing T_L for event 9 first on one and then the other of its two immediate successor events. If event 7 were 9's only immediate successor, T_L for event 9 could be as late as 92 weeks after time 0 (104 − 12). But since the latest expected time we can allow event 4 to occur without disturbing T_E for event 7 is 95 weeks after time 0, and since the activity connecting event 4 to event 9 is expected to require 4 weeks, event 9 cannot be allowed to occur later than 91 weeks after time 0 (95 − 4). Event 4 therefore governs, and T_L for event 9 is 91.

Continuing in this way, we calculate T_L's for all the events in our network as shown in Table 13–1.

While in the preceding development we spoke of T_E and T_L as the earliest and latest times after time 0 that an event can occur, it should be recognized that there are variances associated with these values for T_E and T_L, and therefore that T_E and T_L are *expected* values.

Interpretation

If we assume that the distribution for our final event—of which T_E and V are two parameters—approximates a normal distribution, we can calculate the probability of our final completion event's occurring at any time short of or in excess of T_E for event 1 by our knowledge of the normal distribution. For example, approximately 68 percent of the sample of a normal distribution falls within the mean minus 1 standard deviation and the mean plus 1 standard deviation; therefore approximately 32 percent falls outside this range. Furthermore, approximately 16 percent falls below the mean minus 1 standard deviation. Therefore, the probability that the final event will occur sooner than 108.8 weeks after time 0 is 0.16 $(117 - \sqrt{67} = 108.8)$.

A major value in network analysis arises from its usefulness in pointing up improvement opportunities. Suppose, for example, that the program of activities represented by the network in Figure 13–2 is a crucial component of a larger project for which time is of the essence. Suppose it is extremely important that event 1 occur not later than 117 weeks after time 0. At this moment it is apparent that the probability of event 1's occurring by 117 weeks after time 0 is only 0.5.

If we were anxious to increase the probability of event 1's occurring by 117 weeks after time 0, how should we go about it? Clearly, we would want to shorten the t_e and perhaps reduce the associated variance of one or more of the network's time-consuming activities. But all the network's activities do not present equally attractive improvement opportunities. Some are critical, and others are not.

It should be apparent that for those events that are critical their T_Es and their T_Ls are the same. That is, the latest expected time these events can be *allowed* to occur is also the earliest expected time that they *can* occur. For these events we say there is no "slack," or that their slack is 0.

By subtracting each event's T_E from its T_L we obtain the slack, as shown in Table 13–1. Slack is largest for event 6. Under present expectations, even 6 is not expected to occur sooner than 30 weeks after time 0 and cannot be allowed to occur later than 66 weeks after time 0—a slack of 36 weeks.

Event 6, therefore, is not critical. The time required for the activity that connects event 6 to event 5 could increase to 48 weeks without disturbing the expected time of occurrence of the final event.

On the other hand, event 2 *is* critical, and an increase of one week in the time required for the activity that connects events 2 and 3 will increase the expected time of occurrence of the final event by one week.

The Critical Path

The critical path through a network is made up of those events that have zero slack and the activities that connect them. In the network of Figure 13–2 the events in the critical path are: 5,3,2,4,7, and 1.

If we wish to decrease the T_E of our final event we must focus our attention on the events in the critical path and the activities that connect these events.

An optimum crash program designed to decrease T_E for the final event would involve a search for the most economical means of reducing the expected times required for the activities in the critical path.

The usefulness of the computer quickly becomes apparent. If we were to obtain cost data on which to base such a search we would almost certainly find that the more we reduce a t_e for any particular activity, the more costly it becomes to reduce it further. Thus while the most economical way to reduce T_E for our final event by one week might be to cut a week from the activity that connects critical events 5 and 3, the most economical way to salvage a second week might be to cut from the activity that connects critical events 2 and 4.

The problem is compounded by the fact that as we shorten t_es we must be alert to what happens to the makeup of the critical path. As we shorten t_es we may reduce the slack associated with non-critical events and thrust them into the critical path.

Clearly in a network involving several hundred events, or even several dozen, this repetitive process of searching for improvement opportunities and checking for changes in the makeup of the critical path can become a massive process of data manipulation.

Let us develop a general computer model for network analysis. First, however, an additional word about the network in Figure 13–2 is appropriate. Notice that in this network no event has more than two immediate predecessor events, and no event has more than two immediate successor events. Clearly an event in a program of the kind that business and industry continually develop can usefully be considered the completion or the beginning of more than two activities.

In the development that follows we will assume, however, that no event will ever have more than two immediate predecessor events, and that no event will ever have more than two immediate successor events.

By adopting this restriction the development of a general computer model is made easier. Meantime, however, we do not really make our model less general since, in fact, by introducing "dummy" events we could convert a network in which events had more than two successors and more than two predecessors into one in which events had no more than two of each. The two network segments below, for example, are the same.

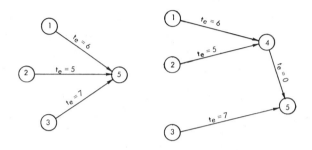

A COMPUTER MODEL FOR NETWORK ANALYSIS

The Determination of T_E

In analyzing a critical path network by hand, we proceed from one event to another by visual observation of the arrows that connect the events in a pictorial representation of the network. At the outset we identify the final completion event, and then we scan the network backward, toward time zero, until we finally come on an event whose T_E is known. On encountering an event whose T_E is known, we wend our way forward again, calculating the T_Es of succeeding events until we finally have the T_Es of the immediate predecessors of the final event, whereupon we can determine the T_E of the final event itself. Proceeding in this way, we frequently find ourselves at a junction of two activities that culminate in the same completion event. In these circumstances we are frequently obliged to abandon our forward progress and to retreat in search of an event whose T_E is known; then we can return later to the junction and proceed forward again.

The computer cannot "see" a pictorial representation of a network; but through use of associative memory we can tie our events together in computer memory in a fashion precisely analogous to our use of arrows in a pictorial representation.

To see how this might be done, reason that all events, except those earliest events for which a T_E is given at the outset, may have one or two immediate predecessor events. Where an event has two immediate predecessor events, let us arbitrarily designate one of them (either one) as that event's first immediate predecessor event and the other as its second immediate predecessor event. When an event has only one immediate predecessor event, we will call it that event's first immediate predecessor.

We would like now to conceive of some scheme for storing all the initial data we have about the network in computer memory in such a way that the following data, applicable to each event, can be retrieved by reference to a common address in core memory:

1. The number of the event's first immediate predecessor.
2. The t_e associated with the event's first immediate predecessor.
3. The v associated with the event's first immediate predecessor.
4. The number of the event's second immediate predecessor.
5. The t_e associated with the event's second immediate predecessor.
6. The v associated with the event's second immediate predecessor.
7. The T_E of the event, where known.
8. The V associated with the event's T_E, where known.

With this kind of data grouping, we can wend our way through the complete network, regardless of which event we start with. That is, the entire network will be tied together through associative memory.

Let us use a two-dimension subscripted variable for this memory storage purpose. Let us call this variable EVENT, and let us store:

in EVENT (1,M) all the data relative to event number 1,
in EVENT (2,M) " " "   "   "   "   " 2,
in EVENT (3,M) " " "   "   "   "   " 3,
etc.

Then for any one event—event N, for example—let

EVENT(N,1) hold, as a floating-point constant, the number of event N's first immediate predecessor.

EVENT(N,2) hold the t_e associated with N's first immediate predecessor.

EVENT(N,3) hold the v associated with N's first immediate predecessor.

EVENT(N,4) hold the number of event N's second immediate predecessor.

EVENT(N,5)   hold the t_e associated with N's second immediate predecessor.

EVENT(N,6)   hold the v associated with N's second immediate predecessor.

EVENT(N,7)   hold the T_E of event N.

EVENT(N,8)   hold the V associated with event N's T_E. (If the T_E and the V of event N are unknown, we will initialize positions 7 and 8 at zero.)

It will be useful if we adopt a practice of giving the final completion event the number 1. All other events can be given any numbers we choose, without regard to the order in which the events may occur: (To conserve memory space, however, we will want to keep these numbers as small as possible; therefore the number of the event with the largest number should equal the total number of events.)

Now, clearly, we could start with event number 1, our final event, and search backward—inquiring if an event's T_E is known by examining the contents of the proper position of the variable EVENT (N,M)—until we find an event whose T_E is known (much as we do in the analysis of a network by hand). However, to avoid duplication of effort it would be wise to keep track of our path of travel as we search, so that we can trace our path as we move forward, calculating T_Es. Let us use the one-dimension subscripted variable PATH for this purpose. We will let

PATH(1)   hold the number of the final event (event number 1).

PATH(2)   hold the number of the next event we inquire into, in search of an event whose T_E is known.

PATH(3)   hold the number of the next event we inquire into, in search of an event whose T_E is known. And so on.

All positions of PATH(K) might best be initialized at zero. As we work our way backward, toward time zero we can replace the zeros with the numbers of the events we have inquired into, and then as we work our way forward we can return these positions to zero, and thus empty them as we retrace our steps.

For the moment let us focus our attention solely on the construction of a computer program that will digest the initial data we have concerning our network and will calculate and store the T_Es of all the events in the network. Essentially we will want to compose a computer program that will do what is broadly called for in the flow

FIGURE 13–3

Flow Diagram for Determining T_Es in a Network
(IP = immediate predecessor)

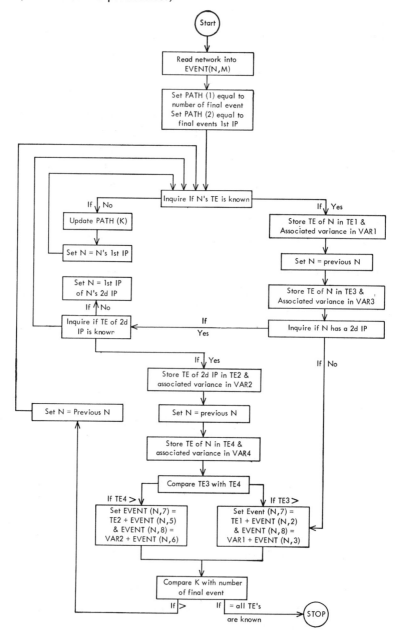

FIGURE 13-4

Program Segment for Calculating and
Storing T_Es for All Events

```
      NTOTAL=0.
100   READ(5,1)NUMBER,(EVENT(NUMBER,N),N=1,8)
1     FORMAT(I6,8F6.0)
      NTOTAL=NTOTAL+1
      IF(NUMBER-999)100,2,2
2     NTOTAL=NTOTAL-1
      K=1
      PATH(K)=1.
      K=K+1
      PATH(K)=EVENT(1,1)
      N=EVENT(1,1)
3     IF(EVENT(N,7))4,4,5
4     K=K+1
      PATH(K)=EVENT(N,1)
      N=EVENT(N,1)
      GO TO 3
5     TE1=EVENT(N,7)
      VAR1=EVENT(N,8)
      K=K-1
      N=PATH(K)
      TE3=TE1+EVENT(N,2)
      VAR3=VAR1+EVENT(N,3)
      IF(EVENT(N,4))6,6,7
6     EVENT(N,7)=TE1+EVENT(N,2)
      EVENT(N,8)=VAR1+EVENT(N,3)
      GO TO 11
7     K=K+1
      PATH(K)=EVENT(N,4)
      N=EVENT(N,4)
      IF(EVENT(N,7))4,4,8
8     TE2=EVENT(N,7)
      VAR2=EVENT(N,8)
      K=K-1
      N=PATH(K)
      TE4=TE2+EVENT(N,5)
      VAR4=VAR2+EVENT(N,6)
      IF(TE3-TE4)9,9,10
9     EVENT(N,7)=TE2+EVENT(N,5)
      EVENT(N,8)=VAR2+EVENT(N,6)
      GO TO 11
10    EVENT(N,7)=TE1+EVENT(N,2)
      EVENT(N,9)=VAR1+EVENT(N,3)
11    IF(K-1)13,13,12
12    K=K-1
      N=PATH(K)
      GO TO 3
13    CONTINUE
```

diagram of Figure 13–3. (In addition to reading in initial data relative to the events themselves, we should provide for counting and storing, in the variable NTOTAL, the number of events read into the network.)

A computer program suitable for calculating and storing the T_Es of all events appears in Figure 13–4.

The Determination of T_L

In determining the value of T_L for an event we will want to proceed much as we did in determining the value of T_E. However, to determine an event's T_L we need to know the identity of its immediate *successor* events and the t_es associated with these successors. We did not provide this information as part of the input data applicable to each event at the beginning of our program. We might do well to record those data now.

Let us add these data in the array EVENT(N,M). We will let

EVENT(N,9)   hold the number of N's first immediate successor.
EVENT(N,10) hold the t_e associated with N's first immediate successor.
EVENT(N,11) hold the number of N's second immediate successor.
EVENT(N,12) hold the t_e associated with N's second immediate successor.

These positions had best be initialized at zero at the beginning of our program.

Whether we designate an event the first immediate successor or the second immediate successor is unimportant. Also, it will become apparent that it is of no consequence if event A is considered event B's first immediate *predecessor*, while B is considered event A's second immediate *successor*.

We might begin with event number 1 (the final event), record its status as an immediate successor in either position 9 and 10 or 11 and 12 of its first immediate predecessor, and record its status as an immediate successor in either position 9 and 10 or 11 and 12 of its second immediate predecessor, then go to event number 2 and repeat this process, proceeding in this fashion until every event's status as an immediate successor of one or more other events is fully recorded.

We need a computer program that will do what is called for in the flow diagram of Figure 13–5. Figure 13–6 presents such a program.

We are now equipped to calculate the T_Ls for all the events in the network. The data we will need are stored as follows:

EVENT(N,1)   holds the number of N's first immediate predecessor.
EVENT(N,4)   holds the number of N's second immediate predecessor.
EVENT(N,9)   holds the number of N's first immediate successor.
EVENT(N,10) holds the t_e associated with N's first successor.
EVENT(N,11) holds the number of N's second immediate succesor.
EVENT(N,12) holds the t_e associated with N's second successor.

We will want to design a program segment that will calculate for each event its T_L and store it in position, EVENT(N,13).

FIGURE 13–5

Flow Diagram for Recording Identity of Immediate Successor (IS) Events

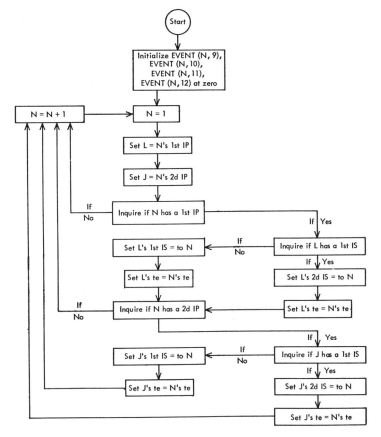

A procedure such as that employed in the flow diagram of Figure 13–7 should do this for us. Notice that we will keep track of events we abandon, in pursuit of an event with a known T_L, in the array PATH(K), much as before when we were calculating each event's T_E. However, the record we store in PATH(K) will never be very long. If we employ the procedure suggested in Figure 13–7, and if we begin our inquiry with the final event, then we will find ourselves simply calculating the T_L of each event's immediate predecessors before proceeding toward time zero. Thus the procedure suggested in Figure 13–7 essentially duplicates the procedure we would employ in a hand solution.

FIGURE 13–6

Program Segment for Recording
Identity of Immediate Successors
of Each Event

```
DO 14 N=1,NTOTAL
EVENT(N,9)=0
EVENT(N,10)=0
EVENT(N,11)=0
EVENT(N,12)=0
14 EVENT(N,13)=0
DO 22 N=1,NTOTAL
L=EVENT(N,1)
J1=EVENT(N,4)
IF(L)22,22,15
15 IF(EVENT(L,9))16,16,17
16 EVENT(L,9)=N
EVENT(L,10)=EVENT(N,2)
GO TO 18
17 EVENT(L,11)=N
EVENT(L,12)=EVENT(N,2)
18 IF(J1)22,22,19
19 IF(EVENT(J1,9))20,20,21
20 EVENT(J1,9)=N
EVENT(J1,10)=EVENT(N,5)
GO TO 22
21 EVENT(J1,11)=N
EVENT(J1,12)=EVENT(N,5)
22 CONTINUE
```

In Figure 13–8 is a computer program that should do what is required. By the time of completion (computer execution) of this added segment to our total program, the T_Es of all events and the T_Ls of all events will have been stored in the appropriate positions of array EVENT(N,M).

Now that T_Es and T_Ls have been determined, calculating slack is a simple matter:

DO 39 N = 1,NTOTAL
39   EVENT(N,14) = EVENT(N,13) − EVENT(N,7).

For purposes of interpretation it will be useful if we provide for having the computer print out values for T_E, slack, and variance in order of earliest T_Es. With a few added statements we can cause to be stored in the various positions of J(L) the numbers of the various events in our network, with the event with the smallest T_E in position 1, the event with the next smallest T_E in position 2, and so on:

DO 40 M = 1,NTOTAL
40   E(M) = EVENT(M,7)
DO 43 L = 1,NTOTAL
A = E(1)
K = 1
DO 42 M = 2,NTOTAL
IF(E(M) − A)41,42,43

FIGURE 13-7

Flow Diagram for Determining T_Ls in Network (IS = Immediate Successor)

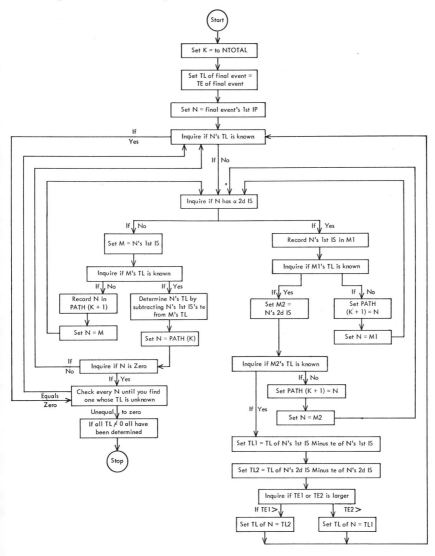

41 A = E(M)
    K = M
42 CONTINUE
    J(L) = K
43 E(K) = 9999.9

FIGURE 13–8

Program Segment for Calculating T_Ls
of Each Event

```
      K=NTOTAL
      FVFNT(1,13)=EVENT(1,7)
      N=FVENT(1,1)
 23   IF(EVFNT(N,13))24,24,29
 24   IF(EVENT(N,11))25,25,31
 25   M=FVENT(N,9)
      IF(EVENT(M,13))26,26,27
 26   K=K+1
      PATH(K)=N
      N=M
      GO TO 24
 27   FVFNT(N,13)=FVENT(M,13)-FVENT(N,10)
 28   N=PATH(K)
      IF(N)29,29,23
 29   DO 30 N9=1,NTOTAL
      N=N9
      IF(FVFNT(N,13))24,24,30
 30   CONTINUE
      GO TO 38
 31   M1=FVENT(N,9)
      IF(EVENT(M1,13))32,32,33
 32   K=K+1
      PATH(K)=N
      N=M1
      GO TO 24
 33   M2=FVFNT(N,11)
      IF(EVFNT(M2,13))34,34,35
 34   K=K+1
      PATH(K)=N
      N=M2
      GO TO 24
 35   TL1=FVENT(M1,13)-FVFNT(N,10)
      TL2=EVENT(M2,13)-FVFNT(N,12)
      IF(TL1-TL2)36,36,37
 36   EVENT(N,13)=TL1
      GO TO 28
 37   FVENT(N,13)=TL2
      GO TO 28
 38   CONTINUE
      DO 39 N=1,NTOTAL
 39   FVFNT(N,14)=EVENT(N,13)-FVENT(N,7)
```

With a suitable WRITE and FORMAT statement combination we can cause our printout to appear as we want. In Figure 13–9 is a complete program for analyzing a PERT network, composed of our previously designed program segments, including our sorter, above, and with our input data added. Notice that it does not matter in what order the input data deck is introduced. We have made provision for a final dummy card, referring to fictitious event number 999, to indicate that we have come to the end of the deck and the data relative to all events have been read into the array EVENT(N,M). The dummy card should, of course, be placed at the bottom of the data deck, but the cards presenting data relative to all other events in the network may be shuffled in any fashion.

Notice that in the DIMENSION statement we have made provision for only 100 events. To increase the capacity of the program to handle larger networks (limited only by computer memory space

FIGURE 13-9

```
      DIMENSION EVENT(100,20),PATH(100),E(100),J(100)
      DO 600 K=1,100
600   PATH(K)=0.
      NTOTAL=0.
100   READ(5,1)NUMBER,(EVENT(NUMBER,N),N=1,8)
1     FORMAT(I6,8F6.0)
      NTOTAL=NTOTAL+1
      IF(NUMBER-999)100,2,2
2     NTOTAL=NTOTAL-1
      K=1
      PATH(K)=1.
      K=K+1
      PATH(K)=EVENT(1,1)
      N=EVENT(1,1)
3     IF(EVENT(N,7))4,4,5
4     K=K+1
      PATH(K)=EVENT(N,1)
      N=EVENT(N,1)
      GO TO 3
5     TE1=EVENT(N,7)
      VAR1=EVENT(N,8)
      K=K-1
      N=PATH(K)
      TE3=TE1+EVENT(N,2)
      VAR3=VAR1+EVENT(N,3)
      IF(EVENT(N,4))6,6,7
6     EVENT(N,7)=TE1+EVENT(N,2)
      EVENT(N,8)=VAR1+EVENT(N,3)
      GO TO 11
7     K=K+1
      PATH(K)=EVENT(N,4)
      N=EVENT(N,4)
      IF(EVENT(N,7))4,4,8
8     TE2=EVENT(N,7)
      VAR2=EVENT(N,8)
      K=K-1
      N=PATH(K)
      TE4=TE2+EVENT(N,5)
      VAR4=VAR2+EVENT(N,6)
      IF(TE3-TE4)9,9,10
9     EVENT(N,7)=TE2+EVENT(N,5)
      EVENT(N,8)=VAR2+EVENT(N,6)
      GO TO 11
10    EVENT(N,7)=TE1+EVENT(N,2)
      EVENT(N,8)=VAR1+EVENT(N,3)
11    IF(K-1)13,13,12
12    K=K-1
      N=PATH(K)
      GO TO 3
13    CONTINUE
      DO 14 N=1,NTOTAL
      EVENT(N,9)=0
      EVENT(N,10)=0
      EVENT(N,11)=0
      EVENT(N,12)=0
14    EVENT(N,13)=0
      DO 22 N=1,NTOTAL
      L=EVENT(N,1)
      J1=EVENT(N,4)
      IF(L)22,22,15

15    IF(EVENT(L,9))16,16,17
16    EVENT(L,9)=N
      EVENT(L,10)=EVENT(N,2)
      GO TO 18
17    EVENT(L,11)=N
      EVENT(L,12)=EVENT(N,2)
18    IF(J1)22,22,19
19    IF(EVENT(J1,9))20,20,21
20    EVENT(J1,9)=N
      EVENT(J1,10)=EVENT(N,5)
      GO TO 22
21    EVENT(J1,11)=N
      EVENT(J1,12)=EVENT(N,5)
22    CONTINUE
      K=NTOTAL
      EVENT(1,13)=EVENT(1,7)
      N=EVENT(1,1)
23    IF(EVENT(N,13))24,24,29
24    IF(EVENT(N,11))25,25,31
25    M=EVENT(N,9)
      IF(EVENT(M,13))26,26,27
26    K=K+1
      PATH(K)=N
      N=M
      GO TO 24
27    EVENT(N,13)=EVENT(M,13)-EVENT(N,10)
28    N=PATH(K)
      IF(N)29,29,23
29    DO 30 N9=1,NTOTAL
      N=N9
      IF(EVENT(N,13))24,24,30
30    CONTINUE
      GO TO 38
31    M1=EVENT(N,9)
      IF(EVENT(M1,13))32,32,33
32    K=K+1
      PATH(K)=N
      N=M1
      GO TO 24
33    M2=EVENT(N,11)
      IF(EVENT(M2,13))34,34,35
34    K=K+1
      PATH(K)=N
      N=M2
      GO TO 24
35    TL1=EVENT(M1,13)-EVENT(N,10)
      TL2=EVENT(M2,13)-EVENT(N,12)
      IF(TL1-TL2)36,36,37
36    EVENT(N,13)=TL1
      GO TO 28
37    EVENT(N,13)=TL2
      GO TO 28
38    CONTINUE
      DO 39 N=1,NTOTAL
39    EVENT(N,14)=EVENT(N,13)-EVENT(N,7)
      DO 40 M=1,NTOTAL
40    E(M)=EVENT(M,7)
      DO 43 L=1,NTOTAL
      A=E(1)
      K=1
```

```
      DO 42 M=2,NTOTAL
      IF(E(M)-A)41,42,42
41    A=E(M)
      K=M
42    CONTINUE
      J(L)=K
43    E(K)=9999.9
      WRITE(6,44)
44    FORMAT(1H1,9HEVENT NO.,7X,2HTE,7X,5HSLACK,7X,8HVARIANCE)
      DO 45 L=1,NTOTAL
      N=J(L)
45    WRITE(6,46)N,EVENT(N,7),EVENT(N,14),EVENT(N,8)
46    FORMAT(1H ,2X,I3,8X,F6.1,4X,F6.1,7X,F6.1)
      STOP
      END
```

3	8.	32.	21.	5.	36.	12.	0.	0.
7	4.	9.	6.	9.	12.	9.	0.	0.
4	2.	21.	18.	9.	4.	2.	0.	0.
2	6.	8.	6.	3.	20.	12.	0.	0.
5	0.	0.	0.	0.	0.	0.	18.	11.
8	0.	0.	0.	0.	0.	0.	10.	9.
6	5.	12.	8.	0.	0.	0.	0.	0.
1	4.	7.	5.	7.	13.	8.	0.	0.
9	2.	6.	5.	8.	41.	28.	0.	0.
999	0.	0.	0.	0.	0.	0.	0.	0.

available) we would want to increase the space reserved for the various variables mentioned in the DIMENSION statement.

Notice also that in the DIMENSION statement we have made provision for storing for each event, not just 14 bits of information, but rather 20. Later we may want to read in additional information concerning the cost of shortening the t_es associated with the immediate predecessors of each event. By doing this we could add a program segment that would cause the computer to determine the most economical means for reducing the time required for completion of the total network of events—that is, for reducing the T_E of the final event.

Data Deck

A further word about the input data, as arranged in the program of Figure 13–9, would be appropriate. As suggested previously, *all* the data required for fully analyzing the network can be read into the computer if the essential data about each event are read into the computer *in association with* that event. In the program of Figure 13–9 we provide for punching on one card all the data pertaining to an event, and thus we will have as many data cards as we have events (plus one for the final dummy event). Each of the data fields is six columns wide; provision is made for punching the number of the event as an integer constant in the first field, and for punching all other data relative to that event in the remaining columns as floating-point constants.

In the second data field is punched the number of the event's first immediate predecessor. In the third data field is punched the t_e associated with the event's first immediate predecessor. In the fourth field is punched the variance associated with this t_e. In the fifth field is punched the number of the event's second immediate predecessor. In the sixth field the t_e associated with the event's second immediate predecessor is punched, and in the seventh field the variance associated with this t_e.

Where an event has no second immediate predecessor, a zero is punched in the fifth, sixth, and seventh data fields.

In the eighth field is punched the T_E of the event, when that is known, and in the ninth field is punched the variance associated with that T_E.

Where an event's T_E and variance are unknown, zeros are punched in the fifth, sixth, and seventh data fields.

The solution to the network of Figure 13–2, as analyzed by the program in Figure 13–9, appears in Table 13–2.

TABLE 13–2

Event No.	TE	Slack	Variance
8	10.0	12.0	9.0
5	18.0	.0	11.0
6	30.0	36.0	19.0
3	54.0	.0	23.0
2	74.0	.0	35.0
9	80.0	11.0	40.0
4	95.0	.0	53.0
7	104.0	.0	59.0
1	117.0	.0	67.0

Formal Analysis versus Simulation

It is appropriate that we return again to the question of analysis versus simulation.

The PERT framework is a system model. The components in the system of interacting components—which the PERT network models—are the time-consuming activities, each represented by an arrow. The interdependence of the components is represented by the network structure.

The behavior of the PERT system is a consequence of (1) the network structure, and (2) the interaction of the components' random activity times.

It should be apparent that we only partially model this interaction between PERT components. In fact our analysis introduces an optimistic bias. This fact is apparent when we refer again to Figure 13–2 and to Table 13–1. Clearly the critical path and the T_E for the final event (event 1) would be as shown in Table 13–1 even if all the activities NOT in the critical path were removed! Let us imagine that the entire network consisted only of the activities in the critical path: 5–3–2–4–7–1.

The earliest expected time of completion of event 1 would, of course, be 117 weeks. Now, imagine that we introduce the time-consuming activities which are not in the critical path. The introduction of these activities can do nothing to reduce the 117 week expected time to completion. However, their introduction could cause the expected time to completion to exceed 117 weeks.

In calculating T_E for event 1 as we did—by considering only the activities in the critical path—we ignored interaction between components in the critical path and those not in the critical path, and thus introduced an optimistic bias.

Via simulation we might overcome this bias. We might proceed as follows:

1. Generate, using the appropriate activity time mean and variance, a "time consumed" for each activity in the entire network.
2. Identify the T_E for event 1, associated with this simulated conduct of the whole project.
3. Return to Step 1.

After enough simulated runs the "true" T_E could be determined by averaging the simulated T_Es. In simulating we defer to the interaction between each time-consuming activity component and all the others, rather than limiting ourselves to modeling only the interaction between activities in the critical path.

This procedure (simulation) is seldom employed in PERT analysis. Other assumptions which are made tend to make this flaw in the model relatively insignificant. Furthermore, in a network of several hundred components, simulation becomes unwieldy.

PERT Component Interaction and the Convolution Sum

We have observed that components in a system may interact in many different ways. The interaction of two random components in a PERT network connected in series could be determined by forming the convolution sum of their discrete probability distributions (refer again to "Extensions and Some Limitations of Flow Graph Analysis," at the end of Chapter 8). Thus we might construct a PERT network as a flow graph, and then systematically reduce it to an equivalent single-component system with known discrete probability distribution. But the systems analyst is obliged to compromise accuracy and elegance in favor of computational economy, and the conventional PERT network procedure is better suited to the needs of the large-scale project planner.

Limited Resources

Let us assume for the moment that the variances associated with the time-consuming activities in a network are zero, and thus that we are employing CPM rather than PERT. If the resources that were considered to be essential when activity times were estimated are in fact available when needed, then our planning process is complete once we have identified the critical path. It is apparent from the network of Figure 13–2 and Table 13–2 that if the project is to be completed in 117 weeks then we should observe the following schedule for *critical* activities.

Activity*	Required Start Time	Required Finish Time
–5	Time 0	18
5–3	18	54
3–2	54	74
2–4	74	95
4–7	95	104
7–1	104	117

* Activity –5 refers to the activity whose completion is event 5; activity 5–3 refers to the activity that connects event 5 and event 3, and so on.

What of those activities that are *not* in the critical path? The following schedule for these activities is clearly a feasible schedule (in the sense that it does not threaten completion of the project in 117 weeks):

Activity	Required Start Time	Required Finish Time
–8	Time 0	10
8–3	10	42
5–6	18	30
6–2	30	38
8–9	10	51
2–9	74	80
9–4	80	84
9–7	80	92
4–1	95	102

In the schedule proposed above for *noncritical* activities it is assumed that each of the noncritical activities will be started as soon as possible. Thus activities 8–3 and 8–9 are both begun 10 weeks after time 0. Similarly activities 9–4 and 9–7 are both begun 80 weeks after time 0. With this schedule, during the period from time 18 to time 30 we will have four activities underway at the same time, specifically, critical activity 5–3 and noncritical activities 8–3, 5–6, and 8–9, as portrayed in Figure 13–10. But since noncritical activity 8–9 *can* be begun as late as time 50 we could easily reduce the number of activities scheduled from time 18 to time 30 by postponing noncritical activity 8–9.

FIGURE 13–10

Two Feasible Schedules for the Network of Figure 13–2

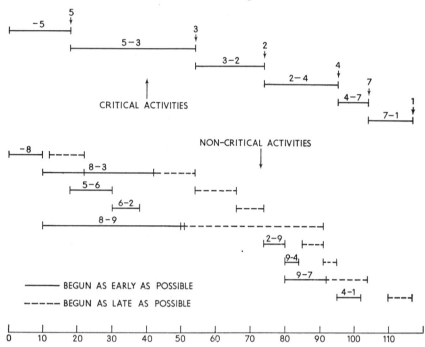

If we schedule all the noncritical activities as late as possible (as portrayed by the dashed lines in Figure 13–10) we have another feasible schedule. Between the two extreme schedules portrayed in Figure 13–10 there exist an infinite number of feasible schedules, and hence other opportunities to reduce the number of concurrent activities surely exist.

If resources are unlimited we need not be concerned, but resources are seldom unlimited. If we consider the availability of resources in varying time periods and the amount of resources required for each activity, it should be possible for us to identify a schedule that is superior from some standpoint. Thus we may want to minimize the maximum resources required at any moment in time. Or we may want to smooth the operation so that the level of resource utilization fluctuates least.

A number of algorithms have been developed for accomplishing this purpose, such as ASTRA (General Electric's "Automatic Scheduling with Time-Integrated Resource Allocation"), GRASP ("General Resource Allocation & Scheduling Procedure" of the Serice Bureau Corporation), and RAMPS ("Resource Allocation and Multiproject Scheduling" of C–E–I–R). In general these algorithms begin with the determination of the critical path, give first priority in scheduling to those activities in the critical path, then give priority in scheduling the noncritical activities to those activities with the least slack (or float). For further study in the use of network analysis in resource allocation the reader is referred to the bibliography at the end of this chapter.

SHORT–TERM FORECASTING

PERT network analysis is a particularly important part of the planning process when the system is characterized by a number of dissimilar, nonrepetitive activities or projects. For short-range planning, when the system is characterized by a more repetitive process, statistical forecasting techniques are particularly useful. In preparation for building "total system" models we should acquaint ourselves with some of these techniques.

We have already dealt rather fully with processes—phenomena that change in some continuous way through time. The compound interest model, $S = P(1 + R)^N$, describes a discrete, deterministic process in which the amount of growth during a period of time is a function of size: the amount of interest added during a period depends on the size of P at the beginning of that period. When interest is compounded continuously we have a continuous, deterministic process.

The Poisson model,

$$p(r) = \frac{e^{-\lambda}(\lambda)^r}{r!},$$

describes a discrete, stochastic process in which positive integer variables are distributed according to a particular pattern called the Poisson distribution.

The following model—the probability density function of the normal distribution,

$$f(x) = \frac{1}{\sigma\sqrt{2\pi}} e^{-\frac{1}{2}\left[\frac{x+m}{\sigma}\right]^2}$$

—describes a continuous stochastic process in which variables (i.e., x) ranging from minus infinity to plus infinity are distributed "symmetrically" about a mean, m.

Determining the precise output of a deterministic process at some specific future moment in time is simply a matter of computation. Thus, given our initial deposit at time zero and the interest rate, we can calculate precisely the magnitude of our deposit after some specified period of time has elapsed.

Determining the precise output of a stochastic process at some specific future moment in time is impossible; for example, we cannot determine precisely what the nth variable—which either a Poisson or a normal process is generating—will be. We can, of course, use our knowledge of a specific stochastic process to determine the probabilities associated with a variety of possible outputs and to determine expected values, and hence to improve the quality of our decisions. We did this in our discussion of the inventory problem under uncertainty and in our study of queuing systems.

In our study of the inventory problem under uncertainty (Chapter 6) we were dealing with a stochastic process which was *given*. Thus, it was assumed in the Brown Electronics Company model that daily demand was being generated by a stochastic process with the following probability distribution:

Demand per Day (Units)	Probability
0	.4
1	.3
2	.2
3	.1

Using Monte Carlo simulation, we combined our knowledge of this process with our knowledge of the process that was assumed to generate lead time for Brown Electronics Company to determine the distribution of the process generating demand during lead time.

In a similar way, in our study of queuing systems (Chapters 9 and 11) we used our knowledge of the process that was assumed to generate customer arrivals and our knowledge of the process that was assumed to generate service time in a service facility to determine the distribution of the process generating queues, total time in the system per customer, and so on.

In these studies we have always assumed that the parameters of the processes we dealt with were known and that they were constant.[2]

Our task, given this knowledge, was to determine specific things about the behavior of the systems we were studying so as to provide a basis for sound decision making.

---

[2] Or, if not constant, that their rate of change was known, and hence that their values at any moment in time could be determined.

What if we know that the process is constant, but we do not know *all* the parameters? Suppose, for example, we are quite confident that the daily demand in a particular market system is being generated by a normal process, and that that process is constant in the sense that the mean and standard deviation do not change through time; but suppose that we do not know the values of the mean and the standard deviation. If we wanted to study, through simulation, the behavior of the system of which this daily demand generator is an element, we would want to try to determine the mean and the standard deviation. The mean, by definition, is the simple arithmetic average of the variables generated. We could estimate the mean demand of this process by taking the average of the daily demands after the system has operated for a large number of days. The mean, so determined, might be the true mean of the process generating our daily demands; then again, it might not be. The larger our sample of days of observation the more closely our sample mean should approximate the true mean.

By analysis of the same sample data we could also estimate the standard deviation of the process, and the larger the sample, the more closely our sample standard deviation should approximate the real standard deviation.

If one found himself dealing with a process that was constant in this sense, the logical course would be to employ all past daily demand observations in estimating the unknown parameters. Each day a new estimate could be made on the basis of a new sample—a sample larger than its predecessor by one observation. As time passes, the accuracy of the estimates should improve. However, life is not so simple. Most real systems are characterized by processes whose parameters are unknown and changing. In these conditions, estimating the parameters of a process on the basis of current and past observations is useful, but since one or more of the parameters may be changing, observations in the remote past are relatively useless.

We are not prepared to disregard all past observations, of course, because only by averaging can we prevent random fluctuations (noise) from entirely obscuring the parameters of the underlying process. If we assume that change in one or more of the parameters of the process is itself a somewhat orderly process—and we do this when we perceive order rather than complete chaos in our environment—we assert that information from the recent past is quite significant. In fact, we tend to assume that in the short run the process is a constant process with unchanging parameters.

Forecasting in this sense is a matter of estimating what future observations will be (i.e., what the parameters of the process are), assuming that the underlying process continues as it has in the recent past.

Essentially the averaging of past data is a smoothing process which has as its purpose the filtering out of random fluctuations, or noise, in order to reveal the parameters of the underlying process. We get more filtering when we use more observations. But the larger the sample, the older some of it will be. The more heavily we rely on data from the remote past, the more we discount data in the recent past. This means that changes in the process are detected less quickly.

The basic question in smoothing is: What degree of reliance on past data will maximize the advantages of quick response to process change on the one hand, and the advantages of noise filtration on the other hand?

The Moving Average

One smoothing process useful for forecasting involves the moving average. With the moving average, one simply employs the most recent n observations to calculate an average, which is the forecast for the next period. Suppose, for example, that the following data represent recent daily demand in a given market system.

Date	Actual Demand
Jan. 1	46
" 2	54
" 3	53
" 4	46
" 5	58
" 6	49

We might average these six observations as a means of arriving at a forecast for demand on January 7:

$$\frac{46 + 54 + 53 + 46 + 58 + 49}{6} = 51.$$

Suppose that on January 7 actual demand proved to be 54, meaning our forecast error was 3. Our new moving average—our forecast for January 8—would now involve the six demand data from January 2 to January 7, inclusive:

$$\frac{54 + 53 + 46 + 58 + 49 + 54}{6} = 52.3.$$

Our thought process in the above can be summed up in the following way.

On January 6 we forecast that demand on January 7 would be 51. On January 7 demand actually proved to be 54, and we therefore underestimated the demand by 3. We do not believe that the inaccuracy in our estimate is attributable solely to a change in the process generating our demand, i.e., that the mean of that process rose from 51 to 54 in 1 day. Nor do we believe that the inaccuracy is attributable solely to random fluctuations, i.e., that the process has not changed. Lacking any thoroughly satisfactory way of sorting out what portion of the inaccuracy can be attributed to each of these elements, we will assume that the January 7 excess of the actual demand over our estimate of that demand is partly attributable to:

1. The fact that the mean of the demand-generating process was possibly already higher than our estimate of it on January 6.
2. The fact that the mean of the demand-generating process actually *rose* from January 6 to January 7.
3. Random fluctuations in the demand-generating process which have caused the actual demand on January 7 to be above the true mean.

In these circumstances, we reason, let us raise our previous estimate of the mean of the process to something less than the actual demand on January 7.

Now let us go back to January 6 and again forecast the demand for January 7, using the moving average again; but this time let us use only the three most recent observations to determine the forecast—those observations pertaining to January 4, 5, and 6. We would have:

$$\frac{46 + 58 + 49}{3} = 51.$$

If we continue to conform to this new sample size, on January 7 we would make a new forecast, thus:

$$\frac{58 + 49 + 54}{3} = 53.6.$$

With this smaller sample our thought process is much the same as before, except that this time we have allowed ourselves to be more heavily influenced by our actual demand experience on January 7. When we used a six-day sample each of the six demand observations got equal weight in our moving average. Therefore old data received a weight of $\frac{5}{6}$, and our current observation (the demand on January 7) got a weight of $\frac{1}{6}$.

When we used a three-day sample, each of the three demand observations also got equal weight in our moving average, but the old data received a weight of only $\frac{2}{3}$, whereas our current observation received a weight of $\frac{1}{3}$.

Our choice of the number of periods to use in a moving average is a measure of the relative importance we attach to old versus current data. Clearly if we feel the process is changing slowly we should adopt a large sample and get greater noise filtering with little sacrifice in change response. On the other hand, if we feel the process is changing rapidly we should adopt a small sample and get greater change response.

In forecasting with the moving average the accuracy of the forecast is dependent on the number of observations, and the optimum number of observations depends on the rate of change in the process.

Exponential Smoothing

For two reasons the moving average as a forecasting system is not so attractive as it might be.

disadvantage of moving average.

1. With the moving average all data in the sample are weighted equally. If more recent data is more valid than older data, why not give it greater weight?
2. Estimating by the moving average requires that we retain a good deal of data, carrying it along with us from forecast period to forecast period.

In computer work, carrying data along can be inconvenient. Admittedly in the moving average we could shorten our calculations a bit. Thus in the example above, involving six observations, we could arrive at our new forecast by adding to the old forecast one sixth of the new observation and subtracting one sixth of the oldest observation. But we still must keep all six observations stored and must update the record with each new forecast. If our optimum sample is believed to be several hundred observations, or more (as it sometimes is), this could be rather inconvenient.

Exponential smoothing gets around these disadvantages. In exponential smoothing we assign weights to observations in indirect proportion to their age, thus being faithful to our conviction that in a changing process recent data is more valid than older data. Furthermore, in exponential smoothing we need only the current forecast, a smoothing constant, and the new observation in order to determine the new forecast thus eliminating the need for carrying large lists of past data.

In exponential smoothing, the new forecast is the old forecast plus a fraction of the difference between the new observation and the old forecast. The fraction by which the difference between the new observation and the old forecast is discounted is called the smoothing constant, generally designated by the Greek letter *alpha, α.*

We might employ exponential smoothing to get day-to-day demand forecasts from the demand data employed earlier when we discussed the moving average. Let us assume that our smoothing factor is 0.3, and that on December 31 our forecast for demand on January 1 was 51. Our daily demand forecasts for these and succeeding days would be as shown in Table 13–3.

TABLE 13–3

Date	Smoothed Exponential Forecast of Next Day's Demand (i.e., the Forecast of the Mean of the Process)	Actual Demand	Forecast Error (i.e., Actual Demand Less Forecast Demand)
Dec. 31	51.0	—	—
Jan. 1	49.5	46	−5.0
" 2	50.9	54	4.5
" 3	51.5	53	2.1
" 4	49.9	46	−5.5
" 5	52.3	58	8.1
" 6	51.3	49	−3.3
" 7	52.1	54	2.7

When we forecast we are really estimating what we believe to be the mean (or, as we shall see shortly, the variance or standard deviation) of the process we believe is currently generating our demand.

We will let $f(n)$ represent the forecast *calculated in period n* and $AD(n)$ the actual demand in period n. Notice, in the table above, that:

$$f(n) = f(n-1) + \alpha[AD(n) - f(n-1)] \qquad (13\text{--}1)$$

. . . where $\alpha = .3$.

Expression (**13–1**) might also be written:

$$f(n) = \alpha AD(n) + (1 - \alpha)f(n - 1). \qquad (13\text{–}2)$$

Note carefully the subscripts in expression (**13–2**). They indicate that the forecast in period n is a function of actual demand in period n. It is as though the new forecast, $f(n)$, is calculated at the end of period n, just after the actual demand in period n, $AD(n)$, becomes known. The schematic, which follows, in which $\alpha = \frac{1}{2}$, makes this apparent.

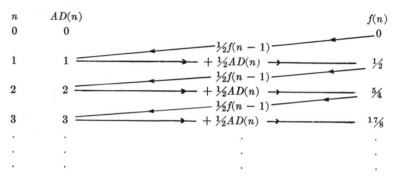

The flow graph model of 13–2 is:

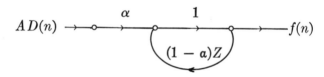

or:

$$AD(n) \longrightarrow \!\!\!\!\!\!\!\!\!\! \frac{\alpha}{1 - (1 - \alpha)Z} \longrightarrow \!\!\!\!\!\!\!\! f(n)$$

. . . and our exponential smoothing transfer function is:

$$\frac{\alpha}{1 - (1 - \alpha)Z}.$$

We can deal with this more easily if we let $k = 1 - \alpha$, from which $\alpha = 1 - k$ and our transfer function becomes:

$$\frac{1 - k}{1 - kZ} = \frac{1}{1 - kZ} - \frac{k}{1 - kZ}.$$

By reference to transform Table.8–2 we find the inverse transform to be:

$$k^n - k \times k^n = k^n(1 - k)$$

Replacing k with $1 - \alpha$ we have, in closed form, the impulse response of our exponential smoothing system:

$$(1 - \alpha)^n(1 - [1 - \alpha]) = \alpha(1 - \alpha)^n$$

. . . which expands to the series:

$$\alpha, \alpha(1 - \alpha), \alpha(1 - \alpha)^2, \alpha(1 - \alpha)^3, \ldots \qquad (13\text{-}3)$$

Time function (13–3) is our exponential smoothing system's response to a unit impulse. Let us now see how this sytem will respond to the following input:

$$AD(0), AD(1), AD(2), AD(3), \ldots \qquad (13\text{-}4)$$

The response we seek is produced most easily by simply forming the convolution sum of (13–3) and (13–4), as shown below.

	α	$\alpha(1-\alpha)$	$\alpha(1-\alpha)^2$	$\alpha(1-\alpha)^3$ ...
$AD(0)$	$\alpha AD(0)$	$\alpha(1-\alpha)AD(0)$	$\alpha(1-\alpha)^2AD(0)$	$\alpha(1-\alpha)^3AD(0)$
$AD(1)$	$\alpha AD(1)$	$\alpha(1-\alpha)AD(1)$	$\alpha(1-\alpha)^2AD(1)$	$\alpha(1-\alpha)^3AD(1)$
$AD(2)$	$\alpha AD(2)$	$\alpha(1-\alpha)AD(2)$	$\alpha(1-\alpha)^2AD(2)$	$\alpha(1-\alpha)^3AD(2)$
$AD(3)$	$\alpha AD(3)$	$\alpha(1-\alpha)AD(3)$	$\alpha(1-\alpha)^3AD(3)$	$\alpha(1-\alpha)^3AD(3)$

Summing the terms in the diagonals we have the time series:

$n = 0$ $n = 1$ $n = 2$

$\alpha AD(0), \; \alpha(1 - \alpha)AD(0) + \alpha AD(1), \; \alpha(1 - \alpha)^2AD(0) + \alpha(1 - \alpha)AD(1) + \alpha AD(2),$

$n = 3$

$\alpha(1 - \alpha)^3AD(0) + \alpha(1 - \alpha)^2AD(1) + \alpha(1 - \alpha)AD(2) + \alpha AD(3), \ldots$

Notice that in any period n, the actual demand in that period gets a weight of α, the demand in the preceding period gets a weight of $\alpha(1 - \alpha)$, the demand in the period preceding that gets a weight of $\alpha(1 - \alpha)^2$, and so on, as shown in Table 13–4.

TABLE 13–4

($\alpha = .3$)

	Weight
Current observation	0.3
Observation 1 period old	0.21
" 2 " "	0.147
" 3 " "	0.103
" 4 " "	0.072

Since α is a fraction it is apparent that actual demand data, in exponential smoothing, are weighted in inverse proportion to their age. With exponential smoothing we are faithful to our conviction that more recent data deserve more weight.

In exponential smoothing the discounting of past observations is geometrically proportional to their ages, so that *some* weight is given to even the most remote observation. With a moving average involving n past observations, all observations more remote than the $n$thmost remote observation get a weight of 0. However, by proper selection of the smoothing constant, α, it is possible to get essentially the same results (i.e., a forecast with the same variance from actual observations) from exponential smoothing that one gets from the moving average. Let us develop this relationship.

FIGURE 13–11

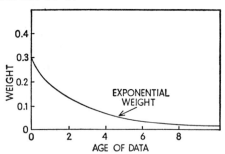

In a moving average the age of the current observation is 0, the age of the one before that is 1, the age of the one before that is 2, and so on. In a moving average of n observations each of the n observations gets the same weight $(1/n)$ regardless of its age. Let us define the average age of the n observations employed in a moving average thus:

$$\text{Average Age} = \frac{0 + 1 + 2 + \ldots n - 1}{n} = \frac{n - 1}{2}.$$

In exponential smoothing, older data gets less weight, but a concept of average age analogous to the definition above for the moving average might be as follows:

$$0 \times \alpha + 1\alpha \times (1 - \alpha) + 2\alpha \times (1 - \alpha)^2 \ldots .$$

The sum of the above terms, as the number of observations approaches infinity, is: $(1 - \alpha)/\alpha$.

We might now define an exponential smoothing system as being equivalent to an n observation moving average if the average ages of their observations are the same, or:

$$\frac{n-1}{2} = \frac{(1-\alpha)}{\alpha}.$$

Solving for α, we get:

$$\alpha = \frac{2}{n+1}.$$

We can use the expression above to determine the smoothing constant required if we want our smoothed exponential forecasts to be equivalent to forecasts obtained by using a moving average involving n observations. Several smoothing constants and the values for n in an equivalent moving average system are shown in Table 13–5.

TABLE 13–5

Smoothing Constant, α	Corresponding Number of Observations in a Moving Average, n
0.05	39
0.10	19
0.15	12
0.20	9
0.25	7
0.30	5.7
0.35	4.7
0.40	4
0.45	3.4
0.50	3

The variance of the estimates will be approximately the same whether one uses the moving average or exponential smoothing, provided the sample size n and smoothing constant α are related as shown in Table 13–5.[3]

Judgment is required in real forecasting systems. When a process we are trying to estimate generates an unusually large observation, or perhaps what seems to be an unnaturally long series of larger than forecast observations, when do we deduce that a new mean has developed? In an exponential smoothing system we exercise

---

[3] This analogy applies only where the process is constant. Thus we could not eliminate seasonal variation from 12 monthly observations by using a smoothing constant of 0.15, whereas we could eliminate seasonal variation from these observations by using a moving average involving $n = 12$ observations.

subjective judgment in selecting the smoothing constant. If we think the process is quite stable we employ a low smoothing constant and get better noise filtering from our system. On the other hand, if we think we detect a real change in the process we might switch to a larger smoothing constant to get quicker response.

We might identify these process changes by observing the errors in our forecasts (Table 13–3). If the process is perfectly stable and our forecast is reasonably close to the true mean, then the sum of our forecast errors should approach zero. That is, overestimates in one period will be canceled out by underestimates during nearby periods. If as our forecasting system continues to operate we keep a running sum of our forecast errors, we can detect process changes.

Observing the forecast errors is useful for another reason. It enables us to forecast another process parameter—the variance or standard deviation from the mean. This parameter is particularly important to us in inventory policy making. In Chapter 6 we learned how a knowledge of the probability of various possible demands during lead time could be used to calculate expected stockouts associated with a variety of order points, and thus we found a way to balance expected stock-out costs with expected holding and ordering costs to find the optimum inventory policy.

Many real processes approximate theoretical processes whose properties we understand rather thoroughly—the normal, Poisson, Gamma, and others.

If an analysis of the data generated by a process we are trying to estimate suggests to us that it is a reasonable approximation of the normal process, for example, a forecast of the mean and the standard deviation could be translated into estimates of the cumulative probabilities associated with a variety of reorder points, since the normal distribution is completely described by these two parameters.

The variance is defined as the arithmetic average of the squares of the difference between individual observations and the mean of the observations. The standard deviation is the square root of the variance.

If the process we are estimating is stable, the forecast errors are the difference between individual observations and the mean of the individual observations. To estimate the variance of the process, then, we might simply square our forecast errors as they are revealed, keep a running record of the most recent ones, and interpret their arithmetic mean to be the variance of the process.

This would be an estimate of the variance on the basis of a moving average. We have already concluded, however, that the moving average is inferior—in some ways—to exponential smoothing. Why not also estimate the variance by exponential smoothing? Each new period our estimate of the variance can be the product of our smoothing constant and the old estimate of the variance:[4]

$$VAR_{new} = \alpha(\text{Forecast Error})^2 + (1 - \alpha)VAR_{old}.$$

The Tracking Signal

We now have an exponential smoothing system for estimating both the mean and the variance of the process, and we are obliged to carry along with us from period to period only the old estimates and the smoothing constant.

We are not prepared to discard all other data, however. As mentioned earlier, we can discern process changes by continuing surveillance over our forecast errors. In a stable process their cumulative sum should be zero.

If we find that our forecast errors do not sum to zero, but rather to some growing positive value, our estimate of the mean is lagging actual observation. If our forecast errors sum to a growing negative value, our estimate of the mean is lagging actual observation in the opposite direction. In the first case the true mean of the process may have increased. In the second it may have decreased.

If our only record of past forecast errors is embedded in a smoothed exponential forecast of the variance, then positive or negative buildup cannot be discerned.

For tracking purposes we might therefore carry with us the sum of the forecast errors. Experience can show us that if the average of our forecast errors exceeds our estimate of the standard deviation (in either direction) by some specified value, which we call a tracking signal, the probability of a change in the process is high enough to warrant increasing our smoothing constant.[5]

---

[4] It is necessary, of course, to begin the process of estimating the variance of the process with an initial estimate of the variance, as we are obliged to do with the mean itself.

[5] In a normal process if the sum of the forecast errors exceeds (in either direction) about 4.6 times the standard deviation, one could have a 95 percent confidence that a nonrandom bias is present in the forecast. Thus a good tracking signal might be in the neighborhood of 4 or 5 times the estimate of the standard deviation.

Noise Filtering versus Change Response

By reference to expression (13–2) it is apparent that with a smoothing constant of 1 our new forecast, each period, is simply the current demand datum. With a smoothing constant of 0, at the other extreme, our new forecast is the old forecast.

With a larger smoothing constant we get very good response to change but very little noise filtering. On the other hand with a small constant we get a great deal of noise filtering but little change response.

In fact, however, no matter how close to 1 our smoothing constant is, simple exponential smoothing will always lag a trend. In Table 13–5 all noise (random fluctuation) has been eliminated. The actual demand function is a unit ramp—a constant trend increasing one unit each period. The line marked f_1 is the exponentially smoothed forecast. It is apparent that the forecast lags behind the actual demand, AD, by a constant 1 unit. If the smoothing constant were 1, rather than ½, the forecast would still lag behind the actual demand.

If we had good reason to believe that a trend was operative in the actual demand time series we would like to project ourselves onto the trend line, rather than lagging it consistently. Double smoothing is a scheme for doing this.

Double-Exponential Smoothing

Recall again that in simple-exponential smoothing the forecast, each period, is the previous forecast plus some fractional part of the amount by which we missed it (expression 13–1). Where a trend is operating, we lag continually with such a system (Figure 13–12). To project ourselves onto the trend line, consider that in simple exponential smoothing we *smooth* the actual demand. Suppose that we employ a new forecasting system which smooths our *forecast*. Just as the forecast, in a trend, lags the actual demand, our new forecast will lag the forecast which it smooths. We will refer to the forecast which smoothes the actual demand as the *single-smoothed forecast,* f_1, and that which smoothes the single-smoothed forecast as the double-smoothed forecast, f_2. Heretofore we've employed single-exponential smoothing and now we are considering double-exponential smoothing:

Single-Exponential Smoothing:

$$f_1(n) = \alpha AD(n) + (1 - \alpha)f_1(n - 1) \qquad (13\text{--}5)$$

Double-Exponential Smoothing:

$$f_2(n) = \alpha f_1(n) + (1 - \alpha)f_2(n - 1). \qquad (13\text{--}6)$$

In Figure 13–5, f_1 is seen to lag actual demand by 1 unit and f_2 lags f_1 by 1 unit. To project ourselves to the trend line—i.e., to cause that forecast which is calculated in period n to be precisely the actual demand in period $n + 1$—we calculate the forecast $f(n)$ as follows:

$$f(n) = 2f_1(n) - f_2(n - 1) \qquad (13\text{--}7)$$

Thus, using the fourth period as an example (Figure 13–12):

$$f(4) = 2f_1(4) - f_2(3)$$
$$= 2 \times 3 - 1 = 5$$

. . . and therefore $f(4)$ equals $AD(5)$ precisely.

FIGURE 13–12

Double-Exponential Smoothing

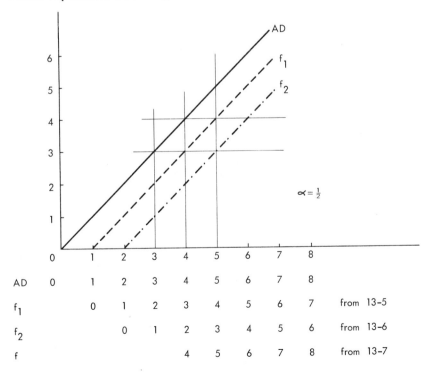

AD	0	1	2	3	4	5	6	7	8	
f_1		0	1	2	3	4	5	6	7	from 13–5
f_2			0	1	2	3	4	5	6	from—13–6
f					4	5	6	7	8	from 13–7

Note that the new forecast in double smoothing is neither the single-smoothed forecast nor the double-smoothed forecast, but rather is a function of the two.

We have seen that via double-exponential smoothing we can track perfectly a constant trend without noise. But how will such a forecasting system deal with a noisy signal on the one hand, and a *change* in the *trend* on the other? Perhaps even more important, how will such a forecasting system deal with a process which has a constant mean?

One way to approach these questions is via simulation. Another way might be to assess analytically how the transform of our double-exponential smoothing forecasting system will interact with a variety of input signals. We will reserve these questions for the exercises.

SUGGESTIONS FOR FURTHER STUDY

BROWN, ROBERT GOODELL. *Smoothing, Forecasting and Prediction of Discrete Time Series.* Englewood Cliffs, N.J.: Prentice-Hall, Inc., 1963.

EVARTS, HARRY F. *Introduction to PERT.* Boston: Allyn and Bacon, Inc., 1964.

MILLER, ROBERT W. *Schedule, Cost and Profit Control with PERT.* New York: McGraw-Hill Book Co., Inc., 1963.

EXERCISES

Using the normal generator described in Chapter 11, test a variety of forecasting schemes via simulation, as called for in exercises 1 through 3 below. In each case generate 30 actual demand data.

1. Simulate a demand process with a constant mean of 50 units and a standard deviation of 16 units. Forecast the process via:

a)   The moving average, with 8 data per forecast.
b)   Simple exponential smoothing with $\alpha = 0.3$. Let $f(0) = 50$.
c)   Double exponential smoothing with $\alpha = 0.3$. Let $f_1(0) = f_2(0) = 50$.

Plot curves of the actual demand and the three forecasts, all on the same graph.

2.   Repeat 1(*b*) and 1(*c*), above, this time with $\alpha = 0.05$.

3.   Repeat exercise 1, but this time let the mean of the normal process being simulated increase by 2 units each period, starting at 50. Let the standard deviation remain constant at 16. Then repeat with

$$\alpha = .05.$$

4. Design a self-tracking, single-smoothed forecasting system in which the exponential smoothing constant remains at 0.1, *except* when the cumulative sum of the forecast errors rises to 4 times the standard deviation within 60 observations, at which point (1) the smoothing constant changes to 0.25 and (2) the cumulative sum of the forecast errors is reinitialized at 0. Provide for returning the smoothing constant to 0.1 when the cumulative sum of the forecast errors fails to increase from 0 to 4 times the standard deviation within 60 observations.

Test the forecasting system with a normal generator, generating daily demand with a standard deviation of 16 and a mean initialized at 50. Provide for the mean of the generator to remain at 50 for the first 100 days, followed by a period of 100 days in which the mean increases by 2.0 each day, followed by a period of 100 days in which the mean decreases by 2.0 each day.

Arrange for a printout of the standard deviation of the forecast errors, in addition to other data required, and interpret the results.

5. Compare a double-smoothed forecasting system, without tracking signal, to the system you have designed in exercise 4.

6. In estimating a process, if one calculates a single-, double-, and triple-smoothed mean (as called for in exercise 1) from period to period, and if at the end of each period he compares the forecast errors of each of these forecasts, presumably he should base his buying or producing decisions in succeeding periods on that forecast whose forecast error in the current period was least.

Design a forecasting system on this basis and test it in the way called for in exercise 4. Let the smoothing constant equal 0.1.

Repeat the above, this time causing the mean of the demand-generating process to increase by 1.0 percent each period—thus by a constant *rate* rather than by a constant increment. Interpret the results.

7. Knudson Construction Company has contracted with the government to undertake a particular project. Knudson forecasts that the project will require 100 weeks' time to complete, with an associated standard deviation of 20 weeks. A $5 million bonus is due Knudson if the project is finished in 80 weeks, and a $2 million penalty is to be levied if it is not finished within 140 weeks.

Knudson thinks that the cost, RC, associated with reducing the 100 week forecast by the nth week is portrayed by the exponential relationship:

$$RC_n = \$100^{1+.15n}$$

Thus the cost of reducing the mean completion time to 99 weeks is:

$$\$100^{1+.15}$$

the cost of reducing the mean completion time to 98 weeks is:

$$\$100^{1+.15} + \$100^{1+.30}$$

the cost of reducing the mean completion time to **97** weeks is:

$$\$100^{1+.15} + \$100^{1+.30} + \$100^{1+.45}$$

and so on.

Knudson wants to know how profitable it would be to shorten the mean completion time; that is, at what point as the mean completion time is reduced by successive outlays does the gain in expected bonus (consider the penalty a negative bonus) prove insufficient to compensate for the added reduction cost?

Note that with the mean completion time = 100 weeks the expected bonus is:

$$\$5 \text{ million} \times .16 - \$2 \text{ million} \times .023 = \$.854 \text{ million.}$$

With the mean completion time = 90 weeks:

$$(90 - 80)/20 = \tfrac{1}{2} \text{ (standard deviation).}$$

Compose a FORTRAN program that will determine how many weeks Knudson could profitably shorten the mean completion time. (Note that we are assuming the standard deviation of the completion time does not change.)

8. Assume that the network of Figure 13–2 and the data in Table 13–1 pertain to a construction project, and that an agency of the federal government is buyer. Assume that a bonus of $5 million is offered if the total project is finished in 108.8 weeks or less. The contractor figures that with an expenditure of $1 million he can cause T_E of event 1 to be 108.8 weeks with a variance of 67 weeks. Determine whether the expenditure would be justified and determine the expected advantage, if any, in the expenditure.

9. Prepare a data check for introducing into the program of Figure 13–9 the data portrayed in the network below. Employ the program of Figure 13–9 to analyze this network and to print out data similar to that in Table 13–2.

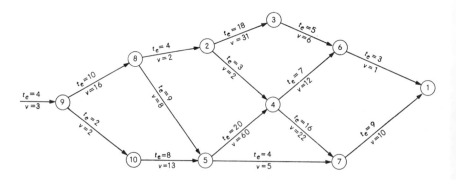

10. Referring to Figure 13–10 and the network of Figure 13–2, assume that each activity requires manpower only and that the manpower requirements for the various activities are as follows:

Activity	Manpower Required	
–5	10	⎫
5–3	13	
3–2	6	Critical activities
2–4	20	
4–7	24	
7–1	8	⎭
–8	3	⎫
8–3	7	
5–6	14	
6–2	18	
8–9	9	Noncritical activities
2–9	6	
9–4	19	
9–7	7	
4–1	15	⎭

Assume that idle men are never kept on the payroll, that excess manpower is laid off immediately, and that inadequacies are accommodated by immediate hirings.

a) Plot a curve showing level of resource employment through time, assuming that noncritical activities are scheduled as soon as possible. Determine the number of man-hirings and man-firings with this schedule.

b) Plot a curve showing level of resource employment through time, assuming that noncritical activities are scheduled as late as possible. Determine the number of man-hirings and man-firings with this schedule.

c) Conceive of a new schedule that will minimize the maximum manpower resources required during the course of the project, and plot its curve. Determine the number of man-hirings and man-firings with this schedule.

d) Assume now that resources are limited and that only 24 men are available at any one time during the course of the project. Notice that some previously noncritical activities are now critical activities, and that completing the total project within 117 weeks is impossible. Assume that an activity will *not* be begun unless the required number of men are available, and once an activity is begun it cannot be discontinued until it is completed. Allocate the available resources according to the rule: the activity with the least float gets first priority, the activity with the next least float gets next priority, and so on. Plot a curve of level of resources with this schedule. Determine the number of man-hirings and man-firings with this schedule.

chapter 14

Matrix Methods

In THE ANALYSIS of many system problems matrix methods prove to be a great deal more concise and efficient than the methods of scalar algebra. In this chapter we will consider computer strategies for solving systems of linear equations, for inverting matrices, for forming the products of matrices, and finally to the simplex algorithm of linear programming. As we begin each of these we will demonstrate the need for them by an illustrative example. It is assumed that the reader is familiar with matrix operations, but should the need arise a quick reference to Appendix C may prove useful.

THE NEED FOR A SIMULTANEOUS LINEAR EQUATION SOLVER

In a variety of system problems we find ourselves in need of a routine for solving systems of linear equations. The need arises in curve fitting, in the use of Lagrange multipliers in the search for optima, in geometric programming, and in many others. In input-output analysis we are likely to find ourselves obliged to solve much larger systems of equations, and it is this sort of system problem that we will now consider.

INPUT–OUTPUT ANALYSIS

Input-output analysis as an industry forecasting tool requires rather exhaustive classification of many sectors of an economic system and careful estimation of their interdependence. The underlying theory, however, can best be portrayed by a gross consolidation of all sectors into a very few. Let us assume that when the entire economy of country X is classified into three sectors, agriculture, industry, and services, and the total output in a year of each sector is evaluated in monetary terms, and finally when the value of the *output* of each which goes into each of the others is evaluated, the following input-output table results.

Table 14–1 should be interpreted thus, using the output of the

TABLE 14–1

Billions of Dollars of Value

From	Agriculture	To Industry	Services	Consumers' Consumption	Total
Agriculture 1		2.25	.2	1.55	5
Industry 2		6	1	16	25
Services 2		3	1.8	15	20
				32.55	

industrial sector as an example: industry output $25 billion in total value, of which $2 billion went to the agriculture sector as an input, $1 billion went to the services sector as an input, and 6 billion went back into the industry sector itself as an input. This accounts for $9 billion of industry's output. The remaining $16 billion of industry's output went directly to consumers.

If we add the columns in Table 14–1 we get the figures shown in the fourth row of Table 14–2.

The totals do not add up to the totals in the final *column* of

TABLE 14–2

Billions of Dollars of Value

From	Agriculture	To Industry	Services	Consumers' Consumption	Total
Agriculture 1		2.25	.2	1.55	5
Industry 2		6	1	16	25
Services	.2	3	1.8	15	20
Totals 3.2		11.25	3.0	32.55	
Sector income 1.8		13.75	17.0 ⟶ 32.55		
5.0		25.0	20.0		

Table 14–2. The differences, entered in the fifth row of Table 14–2, represent sector income—the amount input from (and paid to) those in the economy who contributed their labor or capital.

It is apparent from Tables 14–1 and 14–2 that each sector is dependent on the others and on itself. Clearly, then, an increase in consumer consumption of, say, agricultural output will require an increase in output from the industrial sector and the services sector as well as from the agriculture sector. Since an increase in output from agriculture will require an increase in output from industry and services, however, an increase in agriculture output over and above the increase in consumer demand for agriculture products will be required, because agriculture is also an input to industry and services. An increase in industry and services to accommodate the increase in agriculture will occasion a further increase in industry and services, and agriculture itself, occasioning a further increase in . . . and so on.

To get at the required output of each of the sectors, given that an increase of some specified magnitude is expected in consumer demand for the products of any one sector, let us proceed as shown below.

Examine Table 14–3 which shows us the fractional part of the

TABLE 14–3

	Agriculture	Industry	Services
Agriculture 1/5		2.25/25	.2/20
Industry 2/5		6/25	1/20
Services 2/5		3/25	1.8/20

total *output* of each sector that can be attributed to *input* from each sector.

To interpret Table 14–3 let us use the industry sector as an example. Table 14–3 says: Since industry contributed $2 billion of value to the agriculture sector and the value of the output of the agriculture sector was $5 billion, industry accounted for 2/5 of the value of agriculture output. Similarly, industry contributed $6 billion to itself, meaning that 6/25 of the value of the output of industry was input from the industry sector. Finally, 1.8/20 of the value of the output of the service sector was input from the service sector.

In decimal form our coefficients appear as shown in Table 14–4.

TABLE 14-4

	Agriculture	Industry	Services
Agriculture 2		.09	.01
Industry 4		.24	.05
Services .... .04		.12	.09

Now, let:

X_1 = Value of agriculture output.
X_2 = Value of industry output.
X_3 = Value of services output.
C_a = Consumers' consumption of agricultural output.
C_i = Consumers' consumption of industry output.
C_s = Consumers' consumption of services output.

From Table 14-4 we can now state the following relationships:

$$.2X_1 + .09X_2 + .01X_3 + C_a = X_1$$
$$.4X_1 + .24X_2 + .05X_3 + C_i = X_2 \qquad (14\text{-}1)$$
$$.04X_1 + .12X_2 + .09X_3 + C_s = X_3$$

which should be interpreted to mean, using the *first* equation as an example, the total value of the output of the agriculture sector, X_1, accounts for 20 percent of the value of the agriculture sector itself, 9 percent of the value of the output of the industry sector, and 1 percent of the value of the output of the service sector *plus* the value of the agriculture sector consumed by consumers.

If we replace the unknowns on the left of the equal sign in the first equation by their values as given in Table 14-1, we would, of course, find that the equality holds:

$$.2(5) + .09(25) + .01(20) + 1.55 = 5.$$

If we rearrange the terms of the set of equations above (that is, 14-1), and place on the right side of the equal sign only the unknowns C_a, C_i, and C_s, we have the system shown in (14-2):

$$- .8X_1 + .09X_2 + .01X_3 = -C_a$$
$$.4X_1 - .76X_2 + .05X_3 = -C_i \qquad (14\text{-}2)$$
$$.04X_1 + .12X_2 - .91X_3 = -C_s.$$

Now if we replace C_a, C_i, and C_s with the values shown in Table 14-1, and solve these three equations in three unknowns for X_1, X_2, and X_3, we have, as we would expect:

$$X_1 = 5$$
$$X_2 = 25$$
$$X_3 = 20.$$

Suppose, now, that in the period ahead we expect the transaction matrix (Table 14–4) to remain the same, but we anticipate an increase in consumers' consumption of agriculture products from \$1.55 to 2.05 billion. What will be the required output of each sector? To get at the answer we simply substitute for C_a, C_i, and C_s in (14–2), above, the values:

$$C_a = 2.05$$
$$C_i = 16$$
$$C_s = 15$$

and solve the three equations in three unknowns.

If we are to deal with more realistic and hence more useful input-output analyses we must be equipped to solve systems of many equations in an equal number of unknowns, since we will want to subdivide the economy into many interdependent sectors. Therefore we would do well to equip ourselves with an algorithm for solving M equations in M unknowns, where M is quite large. Equipped with an algorithm that can be translated efficiently into a computer program we will have an economical scheme for forecasting the impact on a sector of the economy (one particular industry, perhaps) given forecasts of consumer demands in the period ahead.

Solving Systems of Linear Equations

Given two equations in two unknowns, such as

$$2X + 4Y = 80 \tag{14–3}$$
$$3X + 2Y = 60,$$

our usual procedure is to multiply one equation through by some constant, so that when it is added to the other equation, one unknown disappears. Thus we might multiply the second equation through by -2, yielding:

$$2X + 4Y = 80$$
$$-6X - 4Y = -120$$

Adding the two equations, we obtain:

$$-4X + 0Y = -40.$$

from which $X = 10$.

Returning now to the first equation, if $X = 10$, $Y = 15$.

Notice that we *could* express our solution thus:

$$X + 0Y = 10 \qquad\qquad (14\text{--}4)$$
$$0X + Y = 15.$$

We can say that system of equations (14–3) is equivalent to system of equations (14–4) in that they have the same *solution set;* that is, the same set of values of X and Y will satisfy the equalities in both system (14–3) and system (14–4). The advantage in system of equations (14–4) is, of course, that in system (14–4) we can read off the solution set (the values of X and Y) directly. In a sense we might say that solving a system of several linear equations in the same number of unknowns is a matter of finding a new system of equations that is equivalent (has the same solution set) but has the form:

$$1X_1 + 0X_2 + 0X_3 + \ldots\ldots = C_1$$
$$0X_1 + 1X_2 + 0X_3 + \ldots\ldots = C_2$$
$$0X_1 + 0X_2 + 1X_3 + \ldots\ldots = C_3$$

$$.$$
$$.$$
$$.$$

With this improved form we can read off the values of the unknowns which satisfy all the equations directly.

The Gauss–Jordan elimination procedure is a procedure by which we can begin with one "configuration of coefficients" in a system of equations and transform that system into a new and equivalent system which has the desired form.

The Gauss–Jordan procedure states:

Given a system of equations, a new system of equations that is equivalent, in the sense that it has the same solution set, can be generated by *replacing* one of the equations in the original set by another equation that is the sum of (1) the equation we want to replace, plus (2) some nonzero multiple of any other equation in the original set.

Let us apply the G–J procedure to system of equations (14–3) and generate a new system of the desired form.

Beginning with

$$2X + 4X = 80$$
$$3X + 2Y = 60,$$

the desired form is:

$$X + 0Y = C_1$$
$$0X + Y = C_2.$$

Let us address ourselves first to the coefficients of X. They are now 2 and 3 in system of equations (14–3). We would like first to make the coefficient of X in the first equation be 1 rather than 2. To do this we divide the first equation by 2, yielding:

$$X + 2Y = 40 \qquad (14\text{–}5)$$
$$3X + 2Y = 60.$$

We would now like to make the coefficient of X in the *second* equation be 0 rather than 3. To do this we will use the G–J procedure, replacing the second equation in (14–5) by the sum of (1) itself as it now stands, plus (2) the first equation in (14–5) multiplied by −3. The sum we want to form is therefore:

$$
\begin{array}{r}
(-3X - 6Y = -120) \\
+ (\ \ 3X + 2Y = \ \ \ \ 60) \\
\hline
0X - 4Y = -\ 60
\end{array}
$$

We replace the second equation in system (14–5) with this sum, and we now have:

$$X + 2Y = \ \ \ 40 \qquad (14\text{–}6)$$
$$0X - 4Y = -60.$$

System of equations (14–6) is equivalent to system of equations (14–3). The coefficients of X in system (14–6) have the desired form, but the coefficients of Y do not. Let us now consider the coefficients of Y in system of equations (14–6).

First we would like to make the coefficient of Y in the second equation of system (14–6) be 1 rather than −4. We can do this by dividing the second equation of (14–6) by −4, yielding:

$$X + 2Y = 40$$
$$0X + \ \ Y = 15. \qquad (14\text{–}7)$$

To convert system of equations (14–7) into the desired form we now have only to convert the coefficient of Y in the first equation to 0 rather than 2. To do this we replace equation 1 in system (14–7) by adding to it equation 2 multiplied by −2. The sum we want to replace 1 with is, of course:

$$
\begin{array}{r}
X + 2Y = \ \ \ 40 \\
0X - 2Y = -30 \\
\hline
X + 0Y = \ \ \ 10
\end{array}
$$

and our new system (which *has* the desired form) is:

$$X + 0Y = 10$$
$$0X + Y = 15. \qquad (14\text{--}8)$$

System of equations (**14–8**) is the equivalent system we sought at the outset; from it we can read our solution directly:

$$X = 10$$
$$Y = 15.$$

Let us now turn to the composition of a computer program that would solve a system of equations and print out the values of the unknowns in the solution set, using the G–J procedure.

Solving **M** *Equations in* **N** *Unknowns,* **M = N.** Assume that we have *M* equations in *N* unknowns, such as:

$$49.96X_1 + 12.23X_2 + 36.78X_3 + 29.43X_4 = 40.43$$
$$22.46X_1 + 38.72X_2 + 40.15X_3 + 11.29X_4 = 15.50$$
$$36.45X_1 + 19.20X_2 + 37.28X_3 + 6.43X_4 = 42.40 \qquad (14\text{--}9)$$
$$17.84X_1 + 40.02X_2 + 27.86X_3 + 39.27X_4 = 25.57.$$

Assume further that the matrix of coefficients of the *N* unknowns is stored in the subscripted variable $D(M, N + 1)$ as follows:

X_1	X_2			X_n	X_{n+1}
D(1,1)	D(1,2)	.	. .	D(1,N)	D(1,N + 1)
D(2,1)	D(2,2)	.	. .	D(2,N)	D(2,N + 1)
.	.			.	.
.	.			.	.
.	.			.	.
D(M,1)	D(M,2)	.	. .	D(M,N)	D(M,N + 1)

with $(M, N + 1)$ holding the constants to the right of the equal sign.

We want to employ the Gauss–Jordan complete elimination procedure to convert $D(M,N)$ into a *unit matrix*. First let us initialize NOEQS with the number of equations in our system of equations:

$$\text{NOEQS} = \underline{\qquad}$$
$$\text{J} = \text{NOEQS} + 1$$

Now, let us designate MPIVRO (pivot row) as the *number* of the *row* whose element we want to be unity, and NPIVCO (pivot column) as the *number* of the *column* whose element we want to be unity. With the following statements we can generate, in row MPIVRO, a new and equivalent equation with coefficient 1, in column NPIVCO:

$$T = D(\text{MPIVRO},\text{NPIVCO})$$
$$\text{DO } 1 \ N = 1,J$$

```
1   D(MPIVRO,N) = D(MPIVRO,N)/T
```

Now to make other elements in column NPIVCO zero we might employ the following statements:

```
     M = 1
10   CONTINUE
     IF (MPIVRO.EQ.M) GO TO 8
     CM = -D(M,NPIVCO)
     DO 11 N = 1,J
     TM = D(MPIVRO,N) * CM
11   D(M,N) = D(M,N) + TM
 8   M = M + 1
     IF (M.LE.NOEQS) GO TO 10
```

In order to convert our entire matrix into a unit matrix we might place the above set of statements inside a DO loop:

```
DO 13 MPIVRO = 1,NOEQS
```

_____

_____

```
13   CONTINUE
```

Our complete simultaneous linear equation solver program would appear as shown in Figure 14–1.

To use the program of Figure 14–1 we would want first to properly dimension the matrix $D(M,N)$ by filling in the blanks in the DIMENSION statement; then we would want to prepare a data deck, the first card of which indicates the order of our matrix— that is, gives NOEQS the appropriate value; then we would want to complete our data deck with the matrix of coefficients and constants—that is, provide for reading into $D(M,N)$ the appropriate data. READ statements referring to FORMAT 100 and FORMAT 101 should then be prepared to correspond to the way we have prepared our data deck.

In using Figure 14–1 one should rearrange the rows of the input matrix so that there are no zeros in the diagonal.

For system of equations (**14–9**) our data deck might appear as follows:

49.96	12.23	36.78	29.43	40.43
22.46	38.72	40.15	11.29	15.50
36.45	19.20	37.28	6.43	42.40
17.84	40.02	27.86	39.27	25.57

FIGURE 14–1

Program for Solving Simultaneous Linear Equations Using the
Gauss–Jordan Eliminaton Procedure

```
      DIMENSION D(____,____)
100   FORMAT ( )
101   FORMAT ( )
      READ (5,100) NOEQS
      J = NOEQS + 1
      READ (5,101) ((D(M,N),N = 1,J), M = 1,NOEQS)
      DO 13 MPIVRO = 1,NOEQS
      NPIVCO = MPIVRO
      T = D(MPIVRO,NPIVCO)
      DO 1 N = 1,J
  1   D(MPIVRO,N) = D(MPIVRO,N)/T
      M = 1
 10   CONTINUE
      IF (MPIVRO.EQ.M) GO TO 8
      CM = −D(M,NPIVCO)
      DO 11 N = 1,J
      TM = D(MPIVRO,N) * CM
 11   D(M,N) = D(M,N) + TM
  8   M = M + 1
      IF (M.LE.NOEQS) GO TO 10
 13   CONTINUE
 14   DO 2 M = 1,NOEQS
  2   WRITE (6,102) M,D(M,J)
102   FORMAT ( )
      STOP
      END
```

On completion of the program, stored in $D(M,N)$ there should
be a unit matrix, and our output would display the solution:

UNKNOWN	VALUE
X_1	9.09
X_2	7.60
X_3	−11.08
X_4	−3.36

A MATRIX INVERTER

With a slight modification we can convert our G–J program for
solving simultaneous linear equations into a matrix inverter. To do

this we simply perform simultaneously on a unit matrix the operations we perform on the matrix of coefficients, reasoning as follows:

If

$$\begin{bmatrix} 2 & 4 \\ 3 & 2 \end{bmatrix} \begin{bmatrix} X \\ Y \end{bmatrix} = \begin{bmatrix} 80 \\ 60 \end{bmatrix}$$

that is,

$$A \begin{bmatrix} X \\ Y \end{bmatrix} = B$$

then:

$$\begin{bmatrix} 2 & 4 \\ 3 & 2 \end{bmatrix} \begin{bmatrix} X \\ Y \end{bmatrix} = \begin{bmatrix} 1 & 0 \\ 0 & 1 \end{bmatrix} \begin{bmatrix} 80 \\ 60 \end{bmatrix}$$

that is, $A \begin{bmatrix} X \\ Y \end{bmatrix} = UB$, where U is the unit or identity matrix.

We should be able to operate on matrix A without destroying the equality if we simultaneously perform the same operations on matrix U. This is equivalent to saying: "Given the scalar equation $aX + Y = C$, we do *not* destroy the equality if we multiply all *coefficients* in the equation by some value K, yielding $KaX + KY = KC$."

Let us therefore employ the G–J procedure beginning with the configuration:

$$\begin{bmatrix} 2 & 4 \\ 3 & 2 \end{bmatrix} \leftrightarrow \begin{bmatrix} 1 & 0 \\ 0 & 1 \end{bmatrix}.$$

Dividing the first row by 2, we obtain:

$$\begin{bmatrix} 1 & 2 \\ 3 & 2 \end{bmatrix} \leftrightarrow \begin{bmatrix} \frac{1}{2} & 0 \\ 0 & 1 \end{bmatrix}.$$

Replacing the second row by itself plus the first row multiplied by -3, we obtain:

$$\begin{bmatrix} 1 & 2 \\ 0 & -4 \end{bmatrix} \leftrightarrow \begin{bmatrix} \frac{1}{2} & 0 \\ -\frac{3}{2} & 1 \end{bmatrix}.$$

Dividing the second row by -4, then replacing the first row by itself plus the second row multiplied by -2, we obtain:

$$\begin{bmatrix} 1 & 0 \\ 0 & 1 \end{bmatrix} \leftrightarrow \begin{bmatrix} -\frac{1}{4} & \frac{1}{2} \\ \frac{3}{8} & -\frac{1}{4} \end{bmatrix}.$$

Restoring these coefficient matrices to our original equation, we have:

$$\begin{bmatrix} 1 & 0 \\ 0 & 1 \end{bmatrix}\begin{bmatrix} X \\ Y \end{bmatrix} = \begin{bmatrix} -\frac{1}{4} & \frac{1}{2} \\ \frac{3}{8} & -\frac{1}{4} \end{bmatrix}\begin{bmatrix} 80 \\ 60 \end{bmatrix} \qquad (14\text{--}10)$$

or:

$$U\begin{bmatrix} X \\ Y \end{bmatrix} = KB, \text{ where } K = \begin{bmatrix} -\frac{1}{4} & \frac{1}{2} \\ \frac{3}{8} & -\frac{1}{4} \end{bmatrix}.$$

Expanding (14–10), we obtain:

$$X = -20 + 30 = 10$$
$$Y = 30 - 15 = 15.$$

Matrix K is the inverse of our original coefficient matrix A; that is:

$$K = A^{-1}$$

where A^{-1} signifies the inverse of matrix A.

A slight modification of the program of Figure 14–1 yields matrix inverter 14–2. Note that the first 3 DO loops serve to load a unit matrix in $E(M,N)$. As before, the matrix to be inverted is loaded into $D(M,N)$, and the order of the matrix is stored at NOEQS by the first two READ statements. On completion of the program of Figure 14–2 the inverse of the original matrix is stored at $E(M,N)$. Provision for printing out the inverse is made via the final WRITE statement.

If we were to use our matrix inverter to find the inverse of the matrix of coefficients associated with system of equations (14–9) we would have generated the following inverse:

−.2028	−.3278	.4206	.1774
−.2140	−.2783	.3774	.1786
.2905	.4435	−.5463	−.2558
.1041	.1179	−.1881	−.0556

Solution of Linear Equations by Matrix Reduction

An alternative procedure for solving a system of linear equations is the reduction method in which the coefficient matrix is transformed into a triangular rather than a unit matrix. An example will illustrate the method.

Assume we have the following system of equations:

$$2X_1 + X_2 - X_3 = 3 \tag{14-11}$$
$$X_1 - X_2 + 2X_3 = 2 \tag{14-12}$$
$$3X_1 + 2X_2 - X_3 = 7. \tag{14-13}$$

Step 1. Divide (14-11) by 2 and solve for X_1 in terms of X_2 and X_3:

$$X_1 = \tfrac{3}{2} - \tfrac{1}{2}X_2 + \tfrac{1}{2}X_3.$$

FIGURE 14-2

A Program for Investing a Matrix

```
      DIMENSION D(___,___), E(___,___)
100   FORMAT ( )
101   FORMAT ( )
      READ (5,100) NOEQS
      READ (5,101) ((D(M,N),N = 1,NOEQS),M = 1,NOEQS)
      DO 2 I = 1,NOEQS
      DO 2 J = 1,NOEQS
   2  E(I,J) = 0.0
      DO 6 M = 1,NOEQS
   6  E(M,M) = 1.0
      DO 13 MPIVRO = 1,NOEQS
      NPIVCO = MPIVRO
      T = D(MPIVRO,NPIVCO)
      DO 1 N = 1,NOEQS
      E(MPIVRO,N) = E(MPIVRO,N)/T
   1  D(MPIVRO,N) = D(MPIVRO,N)/T
      M = 1
  10  CONTINUE
      IF (MPIVRO.EQ.M) GO TO 8
      CM = -D(M,NPIVCO)
      DO 11 N = 1,NOEQS
      TM = D(MPIVRO,N) * CM
      TA = E(MPIVRO,N) * CM
      E(M,N) = E(M,N) + TA
  11  D(M,N) = D(M,N) + TM
   8  M = M + 1
      IF (M.LE.NOEQS) GO TO 10
  13  CONTINUE
      WRITE(6,102) ((E(M,N),N = 1,NOEQS),M = 1,NOEQS)
 102  FORMAT ( )
      STOP
      END
```

Step 2. Substitute this value for X_1 in (**14–12**) and (**14–13**), yielding the set of equations:

$$X_1 + \tfrac{1}{2}X_2 - \tfrac{1}{2}X_3 = \tfrac{3}{2} \qquad (14\text{–}14)$$
$$-\tfrac{3}{2}X_2 + \tfrac{5}{2}X_3 = \tfrac{1}{2} \qquad (14\text{–}15)$$
$$\tfrac{1}{2}X_2 + \tfrac{1}{2}X_3 = \tfrac{5}{2}. \qquad (14\text{–}16)$$

Step 3. Divide (**14–15**) by $-\tfrac{3}{2}$ and solve for X_2 in terms of X_3:

$$X_2 = -\tfrac{1}{3} + \tfrac{5}{3}X_3.$$

Step 4. Substitute this value for X_2 in (**14–16**), yielding the system of equations:

$$X_1 + \tfrac{1}{2}X_2 - \tfrac{1}{2}X_3 = \tfrac{3}{2} \qquad (14\text{–}17)$$
$$X_2 - \tfrac{5}{3}X_3 = -\tfrac{1}{3} \qquad (14\text{–}18)$$
$$\tfrac{8}{6}X_3 = \tfrac{16}{6}. \qquad (14\text{–}19)$$

Step 5. Solve for X_3 in (**14–19**), yielding $X_3 = 2$.

Step 6. Substitute this value for X_3 in (**14–18**) and solve for X_2, yielding $X_2 = 3$.

Step 7. Substitute known values for X_2 and X_3 in (**14–17**), and solve for X_1, yielding $X_1 = 1$.

Notice that we began with the matrix equation:

$$\begin{bmatrix} 2 & 1 & -1 \\ 1 & -1 & 2 \\ 3 & 2 & -1 \end{bmatrix} \begin{bmatrix} X_1 \\ X_2 \\ X_3 \end{bmatrix} = \begin{bmatrix} 3 \\ 2 \\ 7 \end{bmatrix}$$

and terminated Step 5 with the triangular matrix:

$$\begin{bmatrix} 1 & \tfrac{1}{2} & -\tfrac{1}{2} \\ 0 & 1 & -\tfrac{5}{3} \\ 0 & 1 & 1 \end{bmatrix} \begin{bmatrix} X_1 \\ X_2 \\ X_3 \end{bmatrix} = \begin{bmatrix} \tfrac{3}{2} \\ -\tfrac{1}{3} \\ 2 \end{bmatrix}.$$

Computer Solution

Assume that the initial coefficient matrix is stored in $D(M,N)$, where M is the row number and N the column number. The constants in the vector on the right side of the equal sign are stored in $D(M,N+1)$. As before, we begin by storing in NOEQS the number of equations and hence the number of unknowns in our matrix. The following program segment will transform the initial coefficient matrix into the triangular matrix required, performing simultaneously the appropriate operations on the column vector of constants on the right of the equal sign.

FIGURE 14-3

```
NOEQS = _____
K = NOEQS + 1
DO 13 M = 1,NOEQS
T = D(M,M)
DO 1 N = 1,K
1   D(M,N) = D(M,N)/T
I1 = M + 1
IF (I1.GT.NOEQS) GO TO 7
DO 2 I2 = I1,NOEQS
T = -D(I2,M)
DO 3 I3 = M,K
3   D(I2,I3) = D(I2,I3) + D(M,I3) * T
2   CONTINUE
13  CONTINUE
```

The following program segment will now determine and store in $S(J)$ the values of the variables in the solution, thus $X_1 = S(1)$, $X_2 = S(2)$, and so on:

```
7   S(NOEQS) = D(NOEQS,K)
I4 = NOEQS - 1
DO 20 I = 1,I4
M = NOEQS - I
L = M + 1
T = 0.0
DO 21 J = L,NOEQS
21  T = T + D(M,J) * S(J)
20  S(M) = D(M,K) - T
```

The G–J procedure and the reduction methods are good, but with very large systems of equations rounding errors may yield quite unacceptable distortions. A more accurate scheme is the Gausse–Seidel method. Again we will illustrate the method with an example:

$$4X_1 - X_2 = 1. \qquad (14\text{--}20)$$
$$-X_1 + 4X_2 = 2. \qquad (14\text{--}21)$$

Assume that $X_2 = 0$, and solve for X_1 in $(14\text{--}20)$, yielding $X_1 = \frac{1}{4}$. Use this estimate of X_1 (i.e., $\frac{1}{4}$) in $(14\text{--}21)$, and solve for X_2, yielding $X_2 = 0.5625$.

Use this superior estimate of X_2 in $(14\text{--}20)$, and obtain a better approximation of X_1, yielding $X_1 = .3906$. As we continue this procedure we obtain the sequence:

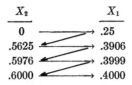

X_2	X_1
0	.25
.5625	.3906
.5976	.3999
.6000	.4000

the exact solution.

However, there are problems associated with the G–S procedure. Notice that if we had started with $X_2 = 0$ in (**14–21**) rather than in (**14–20**) we would have generated the sequence:

X_2	X_1
0	-2
-9	-38

and it gets worse.

It is not easy to predict whether a given method will converge quickly, or whether it will converge at all. The arrangements of the elements in the initial matrix, the size of the matrix, and others all contribute to determining whether the G–S procedure will work without major alterations in the matrix.

The Need for a Matrix Multiplier

We have already suggested that in the age of the computer, solving a system of linear equations by first determining the inverse of the coefficient matrix may not be the most appropriate strategy. Since in our example of the use of the reduction method for solving systems of linear equations we did *not* use an inverse, we had no occasion to multiply one matrix by another. However, in many kinds of systems analysis we have occasion to form the product of matrices. The parts requirement problem provides a persuasive example.

THE PARTS REQUIREMENTS PROBLEM

Assume that we are obliged to deliver varying quantities of four different finished products—A, B, C, and D—and that we have none of these products in inventory. Assume further that:

1. To produce one unit of product A requires two units of product B and three units of product C.

2.   To produce one unit of product D requires two units of product A, one unit of product C, and four units of product B.

The Assembly Diagram

These relationships are easier to perceive if we display them in an assembly diagram, as shown in Figure 14–4.

FIGURE 14–4

The Assembly Diagram

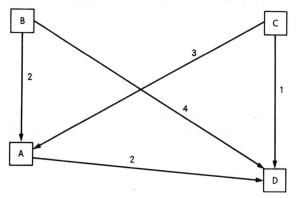

The assembly diagram of Figure 14–4 implies that product D is assembled from units of A, B, and C; A is assembled from units of B and C; and B and C may be finished products but are also raw materials for products A and D.

Assume that we are required to deliver the following quantities of these products:

Units of product A .... four each
Units of product B .... three each
Units of product C .... two each
Units of product D .... three each

How many units of each of our four parts will be required to meet the finished products requirement?

The Explosion Diagram

One systematic way to determine our parts requirement is to determine how many units of each are required to yield *one* finished product of each type. We can then multiply these quantities by the number of finished products required. In Figure 14–5 we explode one unit of each finished product at final assembly to reveal our requirement at Stage 1. Then we explode Stage 1 to reveal our requirement at Stage 2. We determine our total parts requirement to yield one unit of each of our finished products by summing requirements above Stage 2.

FIGURE 14–5

The Explosion Diagram

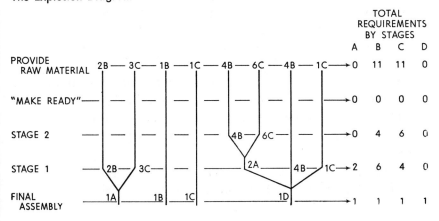

As Figure 14–5 suggests, output of one unit of each of our four finished products at final assembly requires different provisions at different stages. Thus output of one unit each of B and C at final assembly requires zero units of A, B, C, and D at Stages 1, 2, and makeready, but requires one unit each of B and C as input raw material. Output of one unit of product A at final assembly requires two units of B and three units of C at Stage 1, zero units of B and zero units of C at Stage 2, and provision of two units of B and three of C as raw material.

The Total Requirements column of Figure 14–5 should be interpreted as follows:

The final assembly of one unit of each product requires the assembly at Stage 1 of two units of A, six units of B, four of C, and zero of D. To meet this requirement *at Stage 1* requires the assembly at *Stage 2* of zero units of A, 4 of B, six of C, and zero of D. To meet this requirement *at Stage 2* requires no assemblies during makeready, and requires the provision of 11 units of B and 11 of C as raw materials.

Matrix Notation

Let us portray in matrix form the requirements as shown in Figure 14–4. (See Table 14–5.)

TABLE 14–5

The Assembly Matrix (input required per unit output)

		Output			
		A	*B*	*C*	*D*
Input required	A	0	0	0	2
	B	2	0	0	4
(Parts + assemblies)	C	3	0	0	1
	D	0	0	0	0

Table 14–5 might be called an assembly matrix. We will now see that our requirements at each stage are determined from the *powers* of the assembly matrix. (Notice that the sums of the elements in the rows of the assembly matrix are our assembly requirements for Stage 1.)

Using matrix notation, our final assembly requirement is one unit of each product—a unit matrix in matrix notation:

$$
\begin{array}{cccc}
A & B & C & D
\end{array}
$$
$$
\begin{bmatrix}
1 & 0 & 0 & 0 \\
0 & 1 & 0 & 0 \\
0 & 0 & 1 & 0 \\
0 & 0 & 0 & 1
\end{bmatrix}
$$

If we premultiply the unit matrix, which represents the desired output of final assembly, by our assembly matrix we get:

Total Requirements at Stage 1

$$
\begin{bmatrix}
0 & 0 & 0 & 2 \\
2 & 0 & 0 & 4 \\
3 & 0 & 0 & 1 \\
0 & 0 & 0 & 0
\end{bmatrix}
\times
\begin{bmatrix}
1 & 0 & 0 & 0 \\
0 & 1 & 0 & 0 \\
0 & 0 & 1 & 0 \\
0 & 0 & 0 & 1
\end{bmatrix}
=
\begin{bmatrix}
0 & 0 & 0 & 2 \\
2 & 0 & 0 & 4 \\
3 & 0 & 0 & 1 \\
0 & 0 & 0 & 0
\end{bmatrix}
\quad
\begin{matrix}
2 \\ 6 \\ 4 \\ 0
\end{matrix}
$$

The product is, of course, our assembly matrix itself. In a sense we used the assembly matrix as an operator—operating on the final assembly matrix to find our total requirement at Stage 1. Stage 1 requirement, then, is obtained by summing the elements in the rows of the first power of the assembly matrix, the final column above. Again in Figure 14–5 notice that to determine the number of units of product B to be assembled at Stage 2 in order to yield 1 unit of D at final assembly we form the product:

(No. of units of B at Stage 2 required for 1 A at Stage 1) × (No. of units of A at Stage 1 required for 1 D at final assembly) $= 2 \times 2 = 4$.

In more general terms, to determine the B *assemblies at Stage 1* to yield 1 unit of product D at final assembly we form the *sum* of the products:

(No. of B's at Stage 2 for 1 A at Stage 1) × (No. of A's at Stage 1 for 1 D at final assembly)

+ (No. of B's at Stage 2 for 1 B at Stage 1) × (No. of B's at Stage 1 for 1 D at final assembly)

+ (No. of B's at Stage 2 for 1 C at Stage 1) × (No. of C's at Stage 1 for 1 D at final assembly)

+ (No. of B's at Stage 2 for 1 D at Stage 1) × (No. of D's required at Stage 1 for 1 D at final assembly)

$$= 2 \times 2 + 0 \times 4 + 0 \times 1 + 4 \times 0 = 4.$$

This will be recognized as the product of the second row and fourth column of the assembly matrix.

$$\begin{bmatrix} 2 & 0 & 0 & 4 \end{bmatrix} \quad \times \quad \begin{bmatrix} 2 \\ 4 \\ 1 \\ 0 \end{bmatrix}$$

In fact, to determine a matrix that displays all our requirements at Stage 2 *to yield 1 unit of each product at final assembly* we simply form the square (second power) of the assembly matrix, or we premultiply the matrix from which our requirement at Stage 1 was obtained by the assembly matrix.

$$\begin{bmatrix} 0 & 0 & 0 & 2 \\ 2 & 0 & 0 & 4 \\ 3 & 0 & 0 & 1 \\ 0 & 0 & 0 & 0 \end{bmatrix} \times \begin{bmatrix} 0 & 0 & 0 & 2 \\ 2 & 0 & 0 & 4 \\ 3 & 0 & 0 & 1 \\ 0 & 0 & 0 & 0 \end{bmatrix} = \begin{bmatrix} 0 & 0 & 0 & 0 \\ 0 & 0 & 0 & 4 \\ 0 & 0 & 0 & 6 \\ 0 & 0 & 0 & 0 \end{bmatrix}$$

Total Requirements at Stage 2

0
4
6
0

As before, to determine our total requirement at Stage 2 we simply sum the elements of the rows of the resulting product matrix, as shown in the final column above.

To determine our requirement at makeready we cube the assembly matrix, or we premultiply the matrix from which we obtained our requirements for Stage 2 by the assembly matrix:

Total
Requirements
at Makeready

$$\begin{bmatrix} 0 & 0 & 0 & 2 \\ 2 & 0 & 0 & 4 \\ 3 & 0 & 0 & 1 \\ 0 & 0 & 0 & 0 \end{bmatrix} \times \begin{bmatrix} 0 & 0 & 0 & 0 \\ 0 & 0 & 0 & 4 \\ 0 & 0 & 0 & 6 \\ 0 & 0 & 0 & 0 \end{bmatrix} = \begin{bmatrix} 0 & 0 & 0 & 0 \\ 0 & 0 & 0 & 0 \\ 0 & 0 & 0 & 0 \\ 0 & 0 & 0 & 0 \end{bmatrix} \quad \begin{matrix} 0 \\ 0 \\ 0 \\ 0 \end{matrix}$$

Summing up what we have done, we can say: To determine the requirements at the various stages, in order to yield one unit of each product at final assembly, sum the elements of the rows of the *powers of the assembly matrix,* multiplying the assembly matrix by itself until a null (or zero) matrix is generated, at which point the makeready stage has been reached, and all assembly stages are accounted for.

Now, to determine total requirements at *all* stages we first form the *sum* of the requirements at the various stages, including final assembly:

$$\begin{bmatrix} 1 & 0 & 0 & 0 \\ 0 & 1 & 0 & 0 \\ 0 & 0 & 1 & 0 \\ 0 & 0 & 0 & 1 \end{bmatrix} + \begin{bmatrix} 0 & 0 & 0 & 2 \\ 2 & 0 & 0 & 4 \\ 3 & 0 & 0 & 1 \\ 0 & 0 & 0 & 0 \end{bmatrix} + \begin{bmatrix} 0 & 0 & 0 & 0 \\ 0 & 0 & 0 & 4 \\ 0 & 0 & 0 & 6 \\ 0 & 0 & 0 & 0 \end{bmatrix}$$

$$+ \begin{bmatrix} 0 & 0 & 0 & 0 \\ 0 & 0 & 0 & 0 \\ 0 & 0 & 0 & 0 \\ 0 & 0 & 0 & 0 \end{bmatrix} = \begin{bmatrix} 1 & 0 & 0 & 2 \\ 2 & 1 & 0 & 8 \\ 3 & 0 & 1 & 7 \\ 0 & 0 & 0 & 1 \end{bmatrix}$$

Summing the elements of the rows of the matrix which is the sum of these matrices, we obtain:

A	3
B	11
C	11
D	1

This means that at one time or another, in order to deliver at final assembly one unit of each product, we will be obliged to provide or assemble:

3 units of A
11 units of B
11 units of C
and   1 unit of D.

If we focus our attention only on products B and C, our raw materials, we see, as we expected, that 11 units each of these 2 are required as raw materials.

To determine the *total* units to be provided and assembled to meet our delivery commitment we premultiply the *vector* representing the number of units of each output product we want at final assembly by the matrix which is the sum of the matrices from which we obtained our requirements at the various stages, thus:

$$\begin{bmatrix} 1 & 0 & 0 & 2 \\ 2 & 1 & 0 & 8 \\ 3 & 0 & 1 & 7 \\ 0 & 0 & 0 & 1 \end{bmatrix} \times \begin{bmatrix} 4 \\ 3 \\ 2 \\ 3 \end{bmatrix} = \begin{bmatrix} 10 \\ 35 \\ 35 \\ 3 \end{bmatrix}$$

indicating that at one time or another we will be obliged to provide or assemble:

10 units of A
35 units of B
35 units of C
and   3 units of D.

Again, our total raw material requirements are the units of B and C required, namely, 35 units of B and 35 units of C.

Suppose, however, that for the benefit of our production department we had wanted to specify precisely how many units of each product should be assembled at each stage in order to meet our delivery schedule. Instead of dealing with the powers of the assembly matrix we would simply use the assembly matrix as an operator, premultiplying the matrix from which we obtain our requirements at each stage by the assembly matrix, in order to obtain the matrix from which we find our requirement for the preceding stage. Following this procedure we would begin with the diagonal matrix representing our delivery schedule (our requirement at final assembly):

$$\begin{bmatrix} 4 & 0 & 0 & 0 \\ 0 & 3 & 0 & 0 \\ 0 & 0 & 2 & 0 \\ 0 & 0 & 0 & 3 \end{bmatrix}$$

For our requirement at Stage 1 we would premultiply this matrix by our assembly matrix, and sum the elements of the rows of the product matrix:

$$
\begin{bmatrix} 0 & 0 & 0 & 2 \\ 2 & 0 & 0 & 4 \\ 3 & 0 & 0 & 1 \\ 0 & 0 & 0 & 0 \end{bmatrix} \times \begin{bmatrix} 4 & 0 & 0 & 0 \\ 0 & 3 & 0 & 0 \\ 0 & 0 & 2 & 0 \\ 0 & 0 & 0 & 3 \end{bmatrix} = \begin{bmatrix} 0 & 0 & 0 & 6 \\ 8 & 0 & 0 & 12 \\ 12 & 0 & 0 & 3 \\ 0 & 0 & 0 & 0 \end{bmatrix}
\qquad
\begin{array}{c} \textit{Total} \\ \textit{Requirement} \\ \textit{for Stage 1} \\[4pt] 6 \\ 20 \\ 15 \\ 0 \end{array}
$$

To find our requirement at Stage 2 we would premultiply the matrix from which we obtained our requirement for Stage 1 by our assembly matrix, and sum the elements of the rows as before:

$$
\begin{bmatrix} 0 & 0 & 0 & 2 \\ 2 & 0 & 0 & 4 \\ 3 & 0 & 0 & 1 \\ 0 & 0 & 0 & 0 \end{bmatrix} \times \begin{bmatrix} 0 & 0 & 0 & 6 \\ 8 & 0 & 0 & 12 \\ 12 & 0 & 0 & 3 \\ 0 & 0 & 0 & 0 \end{bmatrix} = \begin{bmatrix} 0 & 0 & 0 & 0 \\ 0 & 0 & 0 & 12 \\ 0 & 0 & 0 & 18 \\ 0 & 0 & 0 & 0 \end{bmatrix}
\qquad
\begin{array}{c} \textit{Total} \\ \textit{Requirement} \\ \textit{for Stage 2} \\[4pt] 0 \\ 12 \\ 18 \\ 0 \end{array}
$$

Finally for our requirement at makeready we would premultiply the matrix from which we obtained our requirement for Stage 2 by our assembly matrix, and sum the elements of the rows as before:

$$
\begin{bmatrix} 0 & 0 & 0 & 2 \\ 2 & 0 & 0 & 4 \\ 3 & 0 & 0 & 1 \\ 0 & 0 & 0 & 0 \end{bmatrix} \times \begin{bmatrix} 0 & 0 & 0 & 0 \\ 0 & 0 & 0 & 12 \\ 0 & 0 & 0 & 18 \\ 0 & 0 & 0 & 0 \end{bmatrix} = \begin{bmatrix} 0 & 0 & 0 & 0 \\ 0 & 0 & 0 & 0 \\ 0 & 0 & 0 & 0 \\ 0 & 0 & 0 & 0 \end{bmatrix}
\qquad
\begin{array}{c} \textit{Total} \\ \textit{Requirement} \\ \textit{for Makeready} \\[4pt] 0 \\ 0 \\ 0 \\ 0 \end{array}
$$

$$
\begin{bmatrix} 4 & 0 & 0 & 0 \\ 0 & 3 & 0 & 0 \\ 0 & 0 & 2 & 0 \\ 0 & 0 & 0 & 3 \end{bmatrix} + \begin{bmatrix} 0 & 0 & 0 & 6 \\ 8 & 0 & 0 & 12 \\ 12 & 0 & 0 & 3 \\ 0 & 0 & 0 & 0 \end{bmatrix} +
\qquad
\begin{array}{c} \textit{Total} \\ \textit{Requirement} \\ \textit{All Stages} \end{array}
$$

$$
\begin{bmatrix} 0 & 0 & 0 & 0 \\ 0 & 0 & 0 & 12 \\ 0 & 0 & 0 & 18 \\ 0 & 0 & 0 & 0 \end{bmatrix} = \begin{bmatrix} 4 & 0 & 0 & 6 \\ 8 & 3 & 0 & 24 \\ 12 & 0 & 2 & 21 \\ 0 & 0 & 0 & 3 \end{bmatrix}
\qquad
\begin{array}{c} 10 \\ 35 \\ 35 \\ 3 \end{array}
$$

which checks with our answer using the powers of the assembly matrix.

Cost Determination

Suppose we have the following final cost schedule for our four parts.

Cost of one unit of product A (including its components plus their assembly) ... $ 90
Cost of one unit of product B 12
Cost of one unit of product C 18
Cost of one unit of product D 250

To determine the cost of the total project we simply multiply the last row vector representing the costs of our various products by the column vector representing the total requirements:

$$\begin{bmatrix} 90 & 12 & 18 & 250 \end{bmatrix} \times \begin{bmatrix} 10 \\ 35 \\ 35 \\ 3 \end{bmatrix} = \qquad \$2,700$$

The Brand Switching Model

Imagine that there are three manufacturers, each with his own brand of a particular product, selling to customers in a rather self-contained market. We will represent the first manufacturer and his brand as A, the second as B, and the third as C. There is a certain degree of brand loyalty apparent in this market system, but there is also some brand switching by retail customers. It is observed at the end of period n that the market shares enjoyed by these manufacturers were as follows.

Brand	Market Share (Percent)
A	50
B	30
C	20

During the period $n + 1$ a sampling of customer purchases showed there was a good deal of brand switching. In fact, 10 percent of brand B sales in period $n + 1$ shifted to brand A purchases. Similarly 30 percent of brand C sales in period $n + 1$ shifted to brand A purchases. Finally, 30 percent of brand A sales in period n stayed with brand A in $n + 1$. We might therefore say that there was a 30 percent loyalty to brand A.

The complete brand switching experience during period $n + 1$ is portrayed in the matrix below.

Brand Switching Matrix

From			To
A	*B*	*C*	
30%	10%	30%	A
30%	40%	40%	B
40%	50%	30%	C

Knowing the shares of the market enjoyed by the three brands at the beginning of period $n + 1$, we can easily determine the distribution at the end of the period.

A's share would be 30 percent of the 50 percent A had at the beginning of the period, plus 10 percent of B's original 30 percent, plus 30 percent of C's original 20 percent, or:

$$A = .3(.5) + .1(.3) + .3(.2).$$

Similarly B's and C's shares would be:

$$B = .3(.5) + .4(.3) + .4(.2).$$
$$C = .4(.5) + .5(.3) + .3(.2).$$

Notice that we have, in fact, formed the product:

$$\begin{bmatrix} .3 & .1 & .3 \\ .3 & .4 & .4 \\ .4 & .5 & .3 \end{bmatrix} \begin{bmatrix} .5 \\ .3 \\ .2 \end{bmatrix}$$

In more general terms, viewing the column vector in the product above as:

$$\begin{bmatrix} A_n \\ B_n \\ C_n \end{bmatrix} = \begin{bmatrix} .5 \\ .3 \\ .2 \end{bmatrix}$$

we can write:

$$\begin{bmatrix} A_{n+1} \\ B_{n+1} \\ C_{n+1} \end{bmatrix} = \begin{bmatrix} .3 & .1 & .3 \\ .3 & .4 & .4 \\ .4 & .5 & .3 \end{bmatrix} \begin{bmatrix} A_n \\ B_n \\ C_n \end{bmatrix}.$$

Now, just as we found through recursive analysis in Chapter 4 that the solution of the *scalar* difference equation

$$S_{n+1} = (1 + r)S_n \quad \text{is} \quad S_n = (1 + r)^n S_0,$$

using the same process we find that the solution of the matrix equation

$$\psi_{n+1} = P\psi_n$$

where ψ is a vector of unknowns and P is a square, transition matrix . . . is:

$$\psi_n = P^n\psi_0.$$

The *solution* of our brand switching model, therefore, is:

$$\begin{bmatrix} A_n \\ B_n \\ C_n \end{bmatrix} = \begin{bmatrix} .3 & .1 & .3 \\ .3 & .4 & .4 \\ .4 & .5 & .3 \end{bmatrix}^n \begin{bmatrix} A_0 \\ B_0 \\ C_0 \end{bmatrix}.$$

That is to say, if we could assume that our customers' disposition to switch brands, as portrayed by the brand switching matrix, could be expected to persist in the intermediate future we could determine the market shares enjoyed by the three brands, say, three periods after time zero by either of two methods.

Method 1. In Method 1 we perform the calculations called for in the following sequence of equations through three iterations (the sequence of equations below is represented as a set of FORTRAN instructions to make fully apparent the fact that we want the values of our state variables to change with each iteration):

```
      A0 = .5
      B0 = .3
      C0 = .2
      DO 1 K = 1,3
      A = .3 * A0 + .1 * B0 + .3 * C0
      B = .3 * A0 + .4 * B0 + .4 * C0
      C = .4 * A0 + .5 * B0 + .3 * C0
      A0 = A
      B0 = B
    1 C0 = C
```

By completion of our DO loop, stored at A, B, and C are the market shares enjoyed by our three brands.

Method 2. In Method 2 we raise the transition matrix P to the third power, yielding:

$$\begin{bmatrix} .3 & .1 & .3 \\ .3 & .4 & .4 \\ .4 & .5 & .3 \end{bmatrix}^3 = \begin{bmatrix} .226 & .222 & .226 \\ .376 & .378 & .378 \\ .398 & .400 & .396 \end{bmatrix};$$

then form the product:

$$\begin{bmatrix} .226 & .222 & .226 \\ .376 & .378 & .378 \\ .398 & .400 & .396 \end{bmatrix} \begin{bmatrix} A_0 \\ B_0 \\ C_0 \end{bmatrix}, \begin{bmatrix} A_0 \\ B_0 \\ C_0 \end{bmatrix} = \begin{bmatrix} .5 \\ .3 \\ .2 \end{bmatrix}$$

yielding:

$$A_3 = .2248$$
$$B_3 = .3770$$
$$Q_3 = .3982.$$

Our brand switching matrix difference equation portrays a Markov process. Whether the particular process portrayed by our model has a steady state, and if so what that steady state is are questions of considerable interest. By *analysis* we can determine both whether the process has a steady state and how many time periods must elapse before the steady state has been approached with some specified proximity. Another way to get answers to these questions is to continue the simulation beyond the third time period, printing out the values of the state vector (i.e., the shares of the market enjoyed by each brand) after each iteration.

With the brand switching model we have another example of the need for a matrix multiplier.

A Square Matrix Multiplier

The following routine will cause the K by K matrix, stored in D(1,M,N) to be post multiplied by the K by K matrix in D(2,M,N,) and the K by K product matrix to be stored in D(3,M,N):

FIGURE 14–6

```
  DO 3 I = 1,K
  DO 2 J = 1,K
  D(3,I,J) = 0.0
  DO 1 N = 1,K
1 D(3,I,J) = D(3,I,J) + D(1,I,N) * D(2,N,J)
2 CONTINUE
3 CONTINUE
```

Thus:

$$D(1,M,N) \qquad\qquad D(2,M,N) \qquad\qquad D(3,M,N)$$

$$N = 1 \ N = 2 \ N = 3 \qquad N = 1 \ N = 2 \ N = 3 \qquad N = 1 \ N = 2 \ N = 3$$

$$
\begin{matrix} M = 1 \\ M = 2 \\ M = 3 \end{matrix}
\begin{bmatrix} 2 & 0 & 3 \\ 1 & 2 & 1 \\ 3 & 0 & 2 \end{bmatrix}
\times
\begin{bmatrix} 4 & 2 & 5 \\ 3 & 0 & 2 \\ 1 & 1 & 6 \end{bmatrix}
=
\begin{bmatrix} - & - & - \\ - & - & - \\ - & - & - \end{bmatrix}
$$

In simulating our brand switching process we were obliged to form the product of matrices of different dimensions. With a slight modification we should be able to alter our square matrix multiplier (Figure 14–6) so that it can be used to form the product of any two matrices for which a product exists. Recalling that the product A · B, in which the number of columns in matrix A is equal to the number of rows in matrix B, is a matrix with the same number of rows as A and the same number of columns as B, we might store in L the number of columns in B, in N the number of rows in A, and in M the number of columns in A; form the product A · B via the program in Figure 14–7; and store the product in matrix C.

FIGURE 14–7

A Nonsquare Matrix Multiplier

```
      DIMENSION A(  ,  ),B(  ,  ),C(  ,  )
      READ (5,50) L,M,N
 50   FORMAT (   )
      DO 1 I = 1,N
      DO 1 J = 1,L
  1   C(I,J) = 0.0
      READ(5,100) ((B(I,J),J = 1,L),I = 1,M)
100   FORMAT (   )
      READ (5,101) ((A(I,J),J = 1,M),I = 1,N)
101   FORMAT (   )
      DO 10 K = 1,L
      DO 10 I = 1,N
      DO 10 J = 1,M
      C(I,K) = C(I,K) + A(I,J) * B(J,K)
 10   CONTINUE
```

LINEAR PROGRAMMING

Linear programming problems are characterized by a linear function we would like to optimize (the objective function) and a set of linear constraints. The most general method for solving linear programming problems—the simplex algorithm—bears considerable similarity to our G–J procedure for solving simultaneous linear equations. An example will illustrate the class of problems and the method for solving them.

Each of two products, X and Y, is produced in a two-stage process involving two machines, A and B. The time each product requires on each machine is shown below.

Time Required per Unit of Output

Product	On Machine A (Hours)	On Machine B (Hours)
X	2	3
Y	4	2

In the planning period ahead there are available:

On Machine A .... 80 hours
On Machine B .... 60 hours

Profit per unit output is:

Product X \$60
Product Y \$50

If we let:

x = Number of units of product X we will produce
y = Number of units of product Y we will produce

we can express the constraints posed by the limited machine time available by the following inequalities:

$$2x + 4y \leq 80 \text{ hours} \qquad (14\text{--}22)$$
$$3x + 2y \leq 60 \text{ hours.}$$

Since we are more skillful at dealing with equalities than with inequalities we would like to convert (**14–22**) to two *equations*. We can do this easily by defining two new "slack" variables as follows:

I_A = Hours of idle time on Machine A in the period ahead.
I_B = Hours of idle time on Machine B in the period ahead.

(**14–22**) now becomes:

$$2x + 4y + I_A = 80$$
$$3x + 2y + I_B = 60$$

which may also be written:

$$2x + 4y + I_A + 0I_B = 80$$
$$3x + 2y + 0I_A + I_B = 60. \qquad (14\text{--}23)$$

In (14–23) we have four unknowns (x, y, I_A, I_B) and only two equations, and therefore we know that there is no one unique solution (i.e., no single set of values for the four variables which satisfies the two equations), but rather there is an infinite number of solutions.

Feasible Solution

Some of the solutions, among the infinite number of solutions, are not *feasible,* however. For example, the set of values:

$$x = -5$$
$$y = 10$$
$$I_A = 50$$
$$I_B = 55$$

satisfies the equations in (14–23), but since we cannot produce negative quanties of either product, $x = -5$ is not permissible.

The Optimal Solution

Of course, an infinite number of solutions for our two equations are *feasible*—that is, sets of nonnegative values for the unknowns for which the equalities in (14–23) hold. Among these, however, some are more *attractive* than others. Recall, for example, that profit, P, is:

$$P = \$60x + \$50y.$$

Below are two feasible solution sets for (14–23) and their associated profits.

Solution 1	Solution 2
$x = 0$	$x = 10$
$y = 0$	$y = 2$
$I_A = 80$	$I_A = 52$
$I_B = 60$	$I_B = 26$

Profit:
$P = \$60(0) + \$50(0) = 0$

Profit:
$P = \$60(10) + \$50(2) = \$700$

In solution 1, nothing is produced, machines A and B are idle throughout their full available time in the planning period ahead ($I_A = 80$, $I_B = 60$), and profit is zero.

In solution 2, 10 units of x are produced, 2 units of y, idle time on machine A is reduced to 52 hours, on machine B to 26 hours, and we expect a $700 profit.

The Linear Programming Problem

In this sample linear programming problem our objective is to find that unique solution (set of values for x, y, I_A, I_B) which satisfies (14–23), is feasible (i.e., the values of the unknowns violate no constraints), and will maximize our profit.

Mathematically our problem can be expressed thus:

$$\text{Maximize } (\$60x + \$50y)$$
$$x, y \qquad\qquad (14\text{–}24)$$

subject to the constraints:

1. $2x + 4y + I_A + 0I_B = 80$
    $3x + 2y + 0I_A + I_B = 60.$
2. $x, y, I_A, I_B \geq 0.$

Note: (14–24) should be read: "Maximize, by manipulating *control* variables x and y, the function: $\$60x + \$50y$."

The simplex algorithm is an efficient scheme for generating successive feasible solutions for (14–23), each one superior to its predecessor so that we can converge on the optimal solution (the solution that maximizes our profit function) most quickly.

The simplex algorithm is based on the *Gauss–Jordan elimination procedure,* which we employed earlier in this chapter to solve a system of M equations in N unknowns, $M = N$.

Using the G–J Procedure with Fewer Equations than Unknowns

Our original LP problem involves a search for the solution for system of equations (14–23):

$$2x + 4y + I_A + 0I_B = 80$$
$$3x + 2y + 0I_A + I_B = 60$$

that (1) is feasible, and (2) maximizes the profit function, $\$60x + \$50y.$

But in (14–23) we have fewer equations than unknowns. This fact does not eliminate the usefulness of the G–J procedure, however. Let us now define a *basic* solution.

Basic Solution for a System of M Equations in N Unknowns, M < N

Given a system of M equations in N unknowns, $M < N$, if we arbitrarily select any $N - M$ of the unknowns and give these unknowns the value zero, then what remains is a system of M equations in M unknowns, which we can solve via the G–J procedure to determine the values for the other M unknowns. These values, together with the zero values we gave the arbitrarily selected $N - M$ unknowns, constitute what we will call a *basic* solution.

For any system of M equations in N unknowns, $M < N$, there will be $\dfrac{N\,!}{M\,!\,(N-M)\,!}$ different *basic* solutions. Thus, for our system of equations (**14–23**) where

$$M = 2$$
$$N = 4$$
$$\frac{4\,!}{2\,!\,(4-2)\,!} = 6$$

and there are six basic solutions.

(1) $x = 0$	(2) $x = 0$	(3) $x = 0$
$y = 0$	$y = ?$	$y = ?$
$I_A = ?$	$I_A = 0$	$I_A = ?$
$I_B = ?$	$I_B = ?$	$I_B = 0$
(4) $x = ?$	(5) $x = ?$	(6) $x = ?$
$y = 0$	$y = 0$	$y = ?$
$I_A = 0$	$I_A = ?$	$I_A = 0$
$I_B = ?$	$I_B = 0$	$I_B = 0$

Notice that in each of these basic solutions we have, in effect, two equations in two unknowns.

In (1) we have:

$$2(0) + 4(0) + I_A + 0I_B = 80$$
$$3(0) + 2(0) + 0I_A + I_B = 60$$
or
$$I_A + 0I_B = 80$$
$$0I_A + I_B = 60.$$

In (2) we have:

$$2(0) + 4y + (0) + 0I_B = 80$$
$$3(0) + 2y + 0(0) + I_B = 60$$
or
$$4y + 0I_B = 80$$
$$2y + I_B = 60.$$

In (3) we have:

$$2(0) + 4y + I_A + 0(0) = 80$$
$$3(0) + 2y + 0I_A + (0) = 60$$
or
$$4y + I_A = 80$$
$$2y + 0I_A = 60.$$

In (4) we have:

$$2x + 4(0) + 0 \quad + 0I_B = 80 \quad \text{or} \quad 2x + 0I_B = 80$$
$$3x + 2(0) + 0(0) + \quad I_B = 60 \qquad 3x + \quad I_B = 60.$$

In (5) we have:

$$2x + 4(0) + \quad I_A + 0(0) = 80 \quad \text{or} \quad 2x + \quad I_A = 80$$
$$3x + 2(0) + 0I_A + \quad (0) = 60 \qquad 3x + 0I_A = 60.$$

In (6) we have:

$$2x + 4y + \quad (0) + 0(0) = 80 \quad \text{or} \quad 2x + 4y = 80$$
$$3x + 2y + 0(0) + \quad (0) = 60 \qquad 3x + 2y = 60.$$

In each of these six basic systems our requirement is to solve the two equations in two unknowns in order to determine the values of the unknowns which we did not, at the outset, equate to zero. Where the two equations in two unknowns are not already in the form from which we can directly read the solution we can use the G–J procedure to put them in that form.

The Optimum Solution as a Basic Solution

It can be shown that where there *is* an optimum solution (of the type we seek in our sample LP problem, for example) it will always be a *basic* solution!

Already our problem is simplified enormously. In any LP problem we need at most consider only: $\dfrac{N\,!}{M\,!\,(N-M)\,!}$ solutions, rather than an infinite number. However, we can restrict our search even further.

Notice that only four of the six basic solutions in our sample problem are feasible (solutions 1, 2, 5, and 6). The others involve negative values for one or more unknowns.

The Simplex Algorithm

The simplex algorithm is a procedure for searching among basic and feasible solutions (which we will hereinafter refer to as *basic feasible solutions,* BFS) for that solution which optimizes the objective function. The algorithm is best understood by an example. Let us take our sample LP problem and system of equations (14–23):

$$2x + 4y + \quad I_A + 0I_B = 80$$
$$3x + 2y + 0I_A + \quad I_B = 60$$

and add our profit equation (our objective function) to be maximized, *with all the unknowns in our profit equation on the left side of the equal sign.* We now have:

$$2x + \quad 4y + \quad I_A + 0I_B + 0P = 80$$
$$3x + \quad 2y + 0I_A + \quad I_B + 0P = 60$$
$$-60x - 50y + 0I_A + 0I_B + \quad P = \quad 0.$$

Now, it should not be necessary for us to continue rewriting our variable names each time we generate a new basic solution. Therefore let us detach the coefficients and work only with the matrix of coefficients:

x	y	I_A	I_B	P	Index
2	4	1	0	0	80
3	2	0	1	0	60
-60	-50	0	0	1	0

Since we are going to treat the final equation in a unique way, and further since the *constants* in the "index" column (to the right of the equal sign) are going to have a special meaning in the simplex algorithm, let us set these off as shown in (**14–25**).

x	y	I_A	I_B	P	Index	
2	4	1	0	0	80	
3	2	0	1	0	60	(**14–25**)
-60	-50	0	0	1	0	

It would appear that we are now dealing with three equations in five unknowns (with the addition of our profit equation). However, we need not consider the profit function as part of our system of equations in the same sense as the others, as will become apparent.

Given, then, our two equations in four unknowns, if we let x and y be zero we can ignore the first two columns of (**14–25**) and our matrix becomes (**14–26**) below:

I_A	I_B	P		
1	0	0	80	
0	1	0	60	(**14–26**)
0	0	1	0	

and we can read directly the values of our unknowns for *this* solution set:

$$x = 0$$
$$y = 0$$
$$I_A = 80$$
$$I_B = 60$$

and, of course, with this unattractive but feasible solution, profit, P, is zero.

Let us rewrite the matrix of (**14–26**), identifying the unknowns whose values, in this particular basic feasible solution, are shown in the index, as in (**14–27**).

I_A	I_B	P	Index	
1	0	0	80	I_A
0	1	0	60	I_B
0	0	1	0	P

(**14–27**)

We want now to call this portion of the matrix the *basis*. We will want to generate other more attractive basic feasible solutions with the same configuration as that shown in (**14–27**)—that is, with a basis *whose coefficients of the unknowns are ones and zeros*, so that we can, directly associate the unknowns and their values *in the index*. Let us now go back to the matrix format of (**14–25**).

		Basis				
x	y	I_A	I_B	P	Index	
2	4	1	0	0	80	I_A
3	2	0	1	0	60	I_B
-60	-50	0	0	1	0	P

Now we will want to generate another equivalent system of equations with x or y "entering" the basis, so that our objective function (and hence our profit) can become something larger than zero.

Recalling that the optimum solution will be a basic solution (and hence will involve a two-by-two basis), we begin by asking ourselves: "Which unknown, x or y, thrust into the basis, will make a larger contribution to profit?"

It should be apparent that a one-unit increase in x yields a larger contribution to profit than a one-unit increase in y, since we earn $60 profit on each unit of x and only $50 on each unit of y. Therefore we will thrust x rather than y into the basis of our first, *improved* basic solution.

The next question is: "In manipulating the coefficients of x into a one, zero configuration should we choose (a) or (b), below.

	(a)	(b)
	x	x
	1	0
	0	1

This decision involves the added question: "By how many units (above its present value of zero) should x be increased?"

Refer again to the two equations:

$$2x + 4y + I_A = 80$$
$$3x + 2y + I_B = 60.$$

Note that with $y = 0$, the maximum value we can give x in the first equation is $x = 40$; any larger value will cause I_A *to be negative*. Note further that with $y = 0$, the maximum value we can give x in the second equation is $x = 20$; any larger value will cause I_B to be negative.

We would like to make x as large as possible (to make our next basic feasible solution most attractive, profitwise). As we have seen, the second equation poses the constraint on the size of x. This means we must employ configuration (b) in moving x into the basis:

(b)
0
1

As we observed above, if we use the G–J procedure and generate a new and equivalent system of equations, equivalent to (**14–25**) with x in the basis and with the coefficient configuration of (b), then the value of x, as indicated by the constant in the second row of the index, will be the maximum permissible value, namely, $x = 20$.

Note: One rule in the simplex algorithm is: Choose as the *row* of the pivot column in which a coefficient of 1 is to be generated the row yielding the smallest quotient when the corresponding element in the index column is divided by the positive element in the pivot row (only positive, nonzero quotients need be considered). This would have done for us what we did by a more laborious thought process above.

To generate our new and equivalent basic feasible solution with x in the basis and with coefficient configuration (b), we use the G–J procedure. Our pivot column and pivot row are identified in $(14$–$128)$.

Pivot
column
↓

	x	y	I_A	I_B	P			
Pivot →	2	4	1	0	0	80	I_A	$(14$–$28)$
row	3	2	0	1	0	60	I_B	
	-60	-50	0	0	1	0	P	

To convert the coefficients of x to form (b), we divide the coefficients in the pivot row by 3, then replace the first row by the sum of (1) the first row and (2) the pivot row multiplied by -2, yielding:

x	y	I_A	I_B	P	
0	$8/3$	1	$-2/3$	0	40
1	$2/3$	0	$1/3$	0	20
-60	-50	0	0	1	0

Now, if we complete the iteration process and convert the coefficients of x in our objective function row to zero, using the G–J procedure, the value of our profit with this improved basic feasible solution can be read directly from the index:

x	y	I_A	I_B	P		
0	$8/3$	1	$-2/3$	0	40	I_A
1	$2/3$	0	$1/3$	0	20	x
0	-10	0	20	1	1200	P

The basic feasible solution displayed by the new tableau above is:

$$y = 0$$
$$I_B = 0$$
$$x = 20$$
$$I_A = 40$$

and profit:

$$P = 1200.$$

Now, it occurs to us that by increasing the value of y from zero (i.e., by moving y into the basis) we might make a further contribution to profit. Proceeding as before when we moved x into the basis, we identify the second column as our new pivot column and the first row the pivot row. Using the G–J procedure, we generate the *optimum* solution displayed in the matrix that follows:

x	y	I_A	I_B	P			
0	1	$\frac{3}{8}$	$-\frac{1}{4}$	0		15	y
1	0	$-\frac{1}{4}$	$\frac{1}{2}$	0		10	x
0	0	$\frac{3}{34}$	$17\frac{1}{4}$	1		1350	P

whose solution is:

$$I_A = 0$$
$$I_B = 0$$
$$y = 15 \text{ units}$$
$$x = 10 \text{ units}$$

and profit:

$$P = \$1350.$$

A General Rule for Choosing the Pivot Column

Notice that during our analysis above, the elements in the P column (the profit column) did *not* change as we went from tableau to tableau, improving on our initial BFS. In the future it should be possible to entirely leave out this column. This will make it unnecessary for us to express our objective function row with the initial coefficients of the *nonbasic* variables (x and y) *negative*—an awkward practice, made necessary if we were to have a +1 rather than a −1 coefficient for P in the objective function row.

Notice further that had we begun with the initial objective function row in the form:

$$60x + 50y + 0I_A + 0I_B = 0$$

we *might* have employed the rule: In each iteration, choose as the pivot column that column with the largest positive coefficient in the objective function row. When there are no more positive nonzero coefficients in the objective function row, the optimum solution has been obtained.

To develop a more general rule for identifying the pivot column let us acquaint ourselves with the simplex criterion.

The Simplex Criterion

Assume that we had the following LP problem:

$$a_{11}X_1 + a_{12}X_2 + a_{13}X_3 + X_4 + 0X_5 + 0X_6 = C_1$$
$$a_{21}X_1 + a_{22}X_2 + a_{23}X_3 + 0X_4 + X_5 + 0X_6 = C_2$$
$$a_{31}X_1 + a_{32}X_2 + a_{33}X_3 + 0X_4 + 0X_5 + X_6 = C_3$$

Maximize $Z = P_1X_1 + P_2X_2 + P_3X_3 + P_4X_4 + P_5X_5 + P_6X_6$.

Clearly we have an immediate BFS:

$$X_1 = X_2 = X_3 = 0; \quad X_4 = C_1$$
$$X_5 = C_2$$
$$X_6 = C_3$$

but with this solution $Z = 0$, assuming X_4, X_5, and X_6 are slack variables.

In our next iteration X_1 or X_2 or X_3 will replace one of the variables now in the basis. Let us introduce into the basis that variable which will make the *largest* contribution to improvement in our objective function *per unit* increase in the variable introduced. We can arrive at this as follows.

If we hold $X_2 = X_3 = 0$, but increase X_1 from 0 to 1, then from our first constraint equation X_4 is no longer C_1 but is:

$$C_1 - a_{11} \quad \text{or} \quad X_4 - a_{11}.$$

From our second constraint equation X_5 is no longer C_2 but is:

$$C_2 - a_{21} \quad \text{or} \quad X_5 - a_{21}$$

and from the third constraint equation X_6 becomes:

$$C_3 - a_{31} \quad \text{or} \quad X_6 - a_{31}.$$

Now, referring to the objective function equation, we observe that Z would be increased from:

$$P_1(0) + P_2(0) + P_3(0) + P_4X_4 + P_5X_5 + P_6X_6$$

to:

$$P_1 + P_2(0) + P_3(0) + P_4(X_4 - a_{11}) + P_5(X_5 - a_{21}) + P_6(X_6 - a_{31})$$

yielding a net increase in our objective function of:

$$(P_1 - a_{11}P_4 - a_{21}P_5 - a_{31}P_6).$$

The expression above is called the *simplex criterion* for the non-basic variable X_1. Note that it can be written:

$$P_1 - [P_4 \quad P_5 \quad P_6] \begin{bmatrix} a_{11} \\ a_{21} \\ a_{31} \end{bmatrix}$$

which is the coefficient of X_1 in the objective function row *less* the product of (a) the row vector of coefficients of the *basic* variables in the objective function row and (b) the column vector of coefficients of X_1.

Had we wanted to determine the simplex criterion for another of the nonbasic variables—X_2, for example—we would have reasoned as above and would have found for X_2's simplex criterion:

$$P_2 - [P_4 \quad P_5 \quad P_6] \begin{bmatrix} a_{12} \\ a_{22} \\ a_{32} \end{bmatrix}$$

. . . and for X_3's simplex criterion:

$$P_3 - [P_4 \quad P_5 \quad P_6] \begin{bmatrix} a_{13} \\ a_{23} \\ a_{33} \end{bmatrix}.$$

Note that the products summed in this row, column multiplication are, in each case, the product of (a) a coefficient in the *objective function* whose one coefficient in the *basis* is in the kth row and (b) the kth row coefficient of the nonbasic variable whose simplex criterion is being determined. The following diagram, in which the original basic feasible solution has been deliberately rearranged so that the unity coefficients in the basis are *not* on a diagonal, makes this more apparent:

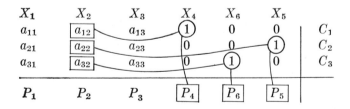

The simplex criterion for variable X_2 is:

$$P_2 - [P_4 \quad P_6 \quad P_5] \begin{bmatrix} a_{12} \\ a_{32} \\ a_{22} \end{bmatrix} = P_2 - [P_4 \quad P_5 \quad P_6] \begin{bmatrix} a_{12} \\ a_{22} \\ a_{32} \end{bmatrix}.$$

Now, in general we should always choose in each new iteration to introduce into the basis that nonbasic variable whose simplex criterion is largest—that is, choose as the pivot column that column whose variable has the largest simplex criterion. When there are no remaining variables with simplex criteria greater than zero, the optimum solution has been reached, and no further iterations are required.

Note that with this rule we will *not* alter the *objective function* row as we move from tableau to tableau, using the Gauss–Jordan elimination procedure, but instead will retain it in its original form. This should be apparent from our development of the simplex criterion concept.

We now have a general rule for choosing the pivot column. However, this rule seems awkward compared to the rule mentioned previously, namely, choose that column whose variable has the largest positive coefficient in the objective function row. Furthermore, our example so far has not demonstrated that the rule that uses the simplex criterion is superior. In fact, since the *row* vector we employed in our sample calculation of the simplex criterion (*i.e.*, $[P_4\,P_5\,P_6]$) consists entirely of zeros (initially $P_4 = P_5 = P_6 = 0$), the simplex criterion for each of our nonbasic variables proves to be that variable's coefficient in the objective function row!

However, the row vector we use in calculating the simplex criterion for our nonbasic variables will not always consist solely of zeros. We can demonstrate this best if we now address ourselves to minimizing rather than maximizing an objective function.

Minimizing an Objective Function

Suppose that we had the following LP problem.

Minimize $2X_1 + 4X_2 + X_3$, subject to the constraints:

a) $X_1 + 2X_2 - X_3 \leq 5$
$2X_1 - X_2 + 2X_3 = 2$
$-X_1 + 2X_2 + 2X_3 \geq 1.$
b)   All variables ≥ 0.

We are now sufficiently familiar with the simplex algorithm to recognize that we must begin our iterative process with a basic solution, and therefore we must add variables as required both to convert our inequalities to equalities and to initially display a unit matrix. We might add slack variable X_4 to the first constraint equation, yielding:

$$X_1 + 2X_2 - X_3 + X_4 = 5.$$

In the third constraint equation, if:

$$-X_1 + 2X_2 + 2X_3 \geq 1,$$

then if we subtract some variable X_6 we have the equality:

$$-X_1 + 2X_2 + 2X_3 - X_6 = 1.$$

Constraint equation 3 thus expressed will not provide us with a positive 1 coefficient for our initial unit matrix, however, since the coefficient of X_6 is -1. To remedy this we add "artificial" variable X_7, yielding:

$$-X_1 + 2X_2 + 2X_3 - X_6 + X_7 = 1.$$

(In effect, we have converted constraint 3 into an equality by subtracting the positive quantity $X_6 - X_7$.)

By a similar stratagem we provide for a variable with a coefficient of plus one in the second constraint equation by adding the artificial variable X_5, yielding:

$$2X_1 - X_2 + 2X_3 + X_5 = 2.$$

Our constraint equations now have the following appearance:

$$X_1 + 2X_2 - X_3 + X_4 = 5$$
$$2X_1 - X_2 + 2X_3 + X_5 = 2$$
$$-X_1 + 2X_2 + 2X_3 - X_6 + X_7 = 1.$$

Expanding so that each equation contains all the variables, and detaching the coefficients, we have our initial tableau:

X_1	X_2	X_3	X_4	X_5	X_6	X_7	
1	2	−1	1	0	0	0	5
2	−1	2	0	1	0	0	2
−1	2	2	0	0	−1	1	1

We must now take steps to guarantee that in our final, optimal solution our *artificial* variables X_5 and X_7 are zero. To assure that these two variables are driven out of the basis as we move from tableau to tableau let us give them large positive coefficients in our objective function. Letting M represent some very large positive number, our objective function now has the following appearance:

$$2X_1 + 4X_2 + X_3 + MX_5 + MX_7.$$

If our simplex procedure will cause this function to be a minimum it will surely seek first to eliminate MX_5 and MX_7—that is, to drive them out of the basis and make them zero.

The simplex procedure proceeds so as to maximize our objective function. It should be apparent that maximizing a function such as $2X$, in which X cannot be negative, is equivalent to minimizing the function $-2X$. Similarly, minimizing some function $2X$, in which X cannot be negative, is equivalent to maximizing the function $-2X$. Therefore, given the function:

$$2X_1 + 4X_2 + X_3 + MX_5 + MX_7$$

to be minimized, let us achieve the same result by maximizing the function:

$$-2X_1 - 4X_2 - X_3 - MX_5 - MX_7.$$

Our initial tableau now has the following appearance:

First Tableau.

X_1	X_2	X_3	X_4	X_5	X_6	X_7		
1	2	−1	1	0	0	0	5	X_4
2	−1	2	0	1	0	0	2	X_5
−1	2	②	0	0	−1	1	1	X_7
−2	−4	−1	0	−M	0	−M	0	

In this tableau we have an example of a simplex matrix in which the simplex criteria of the nonbasic variables are *not* the same as their coefficients in the objective function row. The greater generality of our simplex criterion rule for identifying the pivot column is now in evidence. Let us calculate the simplex criteria, SC, for the nonbasic variables, and identify the pivot column for our first iteration.

$$SC_{X1} = -2 = \begin{bmatrix} 0 & -M & -M \end{bmatrix} \begin{bmatrix} 1 \\ 2 \\ -1 \end{bmatrix} = M - 2$$

$$SC_{X2} = -4 - \begin{bmatrix} 0 & -M & -M \end{bmatrix} \begin{bmatrix} 2 \\ -1 \\ 2 \end{bmatrix} = M - 4$$

$$SC_{X3} = -1 - \begin{bmatrix} 0 & -M & -M \end{bmatrix} \begin{bmatrix} -1 \\ 2 \\ 2 \end{bmatrix} = 4M - 1$$

$$SC_{X6} = 0 - \begin{bmatrix} 0 & -M & -M \end{bmatrix} \begin{bmatrix} 0 \\ 0 \\ -1 \end{bmatrix} = -M$$

The largest simplex criterion is that associated with X_3, namely, $4M - 1$. Forming the ratios of the elements in the index column and those in the third column, we find that our pivot row should be the third row. The element circled in the first tableau is therefore our pivot for the first iteration. Employing the G–J procedure, we generate the second tableau, which follows. (Since the objective function row will not change, let us place it at the top of the tableau in future iterations.)

Second Tableau.

-2	-4	-1	0	$-M$	0	$-M$		
X_1	X_2	X_3	X_4	X_5	X_6	X_7		
$\frac{1}{2}$	3	0	1	0	$-\frac{1}{2}$	$\frac{1}{2}$	$1\frac{1}{2}$	X_4
③	-3	0	0	1	1	-1	1	X_5
$-\frac{1}{2}$	1	1	0	0	$-\frac{1}{2}$	$\frac{1}{2}$	$\frac{1}{2}$	X_3

Simplex criteria for *nonbasic* variables in our second tableau are:

$$SC_{X1} = -2 - [0 \quad -M \quad -1]\begin{bmatrix} \frac{1}{2} \\ 3 \\ -\frac{1}{2} \end{bmatrix} = 3M - \frac{5}{2}$$

$$SC_{X2} = -4 - [0 \quad -M \quad -1]\begin{bmatrix} 3 \\ -3 \\ 1 \end{bmatrix} = -3M - 3$$

$$SC_{X6} = 0 - [0 \quad -M \quad -1]\begin{bmatrix} -\frac{1}{2} \\ 1 \\ -\frac{1}{2} \end{bmatrix} = M - \frac{1}{2}$$

$$SC_{X7} = -M - [0 \quad -M \quad -1]\begin{bmatrix} \frac{1}{2} \\ -1 \\ \frac{1}{2} \end{bmatrix} = -2M + \frac{1}{2}$$

Since the largest simplex criterion is that associated with X_1, we want to introduce X_1 into the basis. Our pivot column is therefore the first column. Forming the ratios of the elements in the index column and those in the first column, we find that our pivot row should be the second row. The element circled in our second tableau is therefore our pivot for the third iteration. Employing the G–J procedure, we generate the third tableau, which follows.

Third Tableau.

-2	-4	-1	0	$-M$	0	$-M$		
X_1	X_2	X_3	X_4	X_5	X_6	X_7		
0	$\frac{7}{2}$	0	1	$-\frac{1}{6}$	$-\frac{2}{3}$	$\frac{2}{3}$	$1\frac{2}{3}$	X_4
1	-1	0	0	$\frac{1}{3}$	①/₃	$-\frac{1}{3}$	$\frac{1}{3}$	X_1
0	$\frac{1}{2}$	1	0	$\frac{1}{6}$	$-\frac{1}{3}$	$\frac{1}{3}$	$\frac{1}{3}$	X_3

Simplex criteria for nonbasic variables in our third tableau are:

$$SC_{X2} = -4 - \begin{bmatrix} 0 & -2 & -1 \end{bmatrix} \begin{bmatrix} 7/2 \\ -1 \\ 1/2 \end{bmatrix} = -11/2$$

$$SC_{X5} = -M - \begin{bmatrix} 0 & -2 & -1 \end{bmatrix} \begin{bmatrix} -1/6 \\ 1/3 \\ 1/6 \end{bmatrix} = -M + 5/6$$

$$SC_{X6} = 0 - \begin{bmatrix} 0 & -2 & -1 \end{bmatrix} \begin{bmatrix} -2/3 \\ 1/3 \\ -1/3 \end{bmatrix} = 1/3$$

$$SC_{X7} = -M - \begin{bmatrix} 0 & -2 & -1 \end{bmatrix} \begin{bmatrix} 2/3 \\ -1/3 \\ 1/3 \end{bmatrix} = -M - 1/3$$

Since the largest simplex criterion is that associated with X_6, we want to introduce X_6 into the basis. Our pivot column is therefore the sixth column. Forming the appropriate ratios, we find that our pivot row should be the second row. Our pivot for moving to the fourth iteration is circled in the third tableau, above.

Employing the G–J procedure again, we generate the fourth tableau.

Fourth Tableau.

-2	-4	-1	0	$-M$	0	$-M$		
X_1	X_2	X_3	X_4	X_5	X_6	X_7		
2	$3/2$	0	1	$1/2$	0	0	6	X_4
3	-3	0	0	1	1	-1	1	X_6
1	$-1/2$	1	0	$1/2$	0	0	1	X_3

Simplex criteria for nonbasic variables in our fourth tableau are:

$$SC_{X1} = -2 - \begin{bmatrix} 0 & 0 & -1 \end{bmatrix} \begin{bmatrix} 2 \\ 3 \\ 1 \end{bmatrix} = -1$$

$$SC_{X2} = -4 - \begin{bmatrix} 0 & 0 & -1 \end{bmatrix} \begin{bmatrix} 3/2 \\ -3 \\ -1/2 \end{bmatrix} = -41/2$$

$$SC_{X5} = -M - \begin{bmatrix} 0 & 0 & -1 \end{bmatrix} \begin{bmatrix} 1/2 \\ 1 \\ 1/2 \end{bmatrix} = -M + 1/2$$

$$SC_{X7} = -M - \begin{bmatrix} 0 & 0 & -1 \end{bmatrix} \begin{bmatrix} 0 \\ -1 \\ 0 \end{bmatrix} = -M$$

Since there are now no nonbasic variables with simplex criteria greater than zero, we need go no further, and our optimum solution is:

$$X_1 = 0, \ X_2 = 0, \ X_5 = 0, \ X_7 = 0$$

and

$$X_3 = 1, \ X_4 = 6, \ X_6 = 1.$$

Note that artificial variables X_5 and X_7 were driven out of our final solution ($X_5 = X_7 = 0$) as we had planned.

Recall that our objective function, to be minimized, was $2X_1 + 4X_2 + X_3$; the minimum value of our objective function is:

$$2(0) + 4(0) + 1 = 1.$$

Note further that our original constraints are not violated.

First constraint: $X_1 + 2X_2 - X_3 \leq 5$
and $0 + 2(0) - 1 \leq 5$
Second constraint: $2X_1 - X_2 + 2X_3 = 2$
and $2(0) - 0 + 2(1) = 2$
Third constraint: $-X_1 + 2X_2 + 2X_3 \geq 1$
and $-0 + 2(0) + 2(1) \geq 1$
and $X_1, \ X_2, \ X_3, \ X_4, \ X_5, \ X_6, \ X_7, \ \geq 0.$

Summing up

1. To minimize an objective function, maximize its negative.
2. If artificial variables are used in creating an initial basic solution, these variables should be given large negative coefficients in the objective function row.
3. Given an initial basic feasible solution, choose as the pivot column, in subsequent iterations, that column whose variable has the largest simplex criterion.
4. Choose as the pivot row, in subsequent iterations, that row in which the ratio of the constant in the index and the coefficient in the pivot column is the smallest positive, nonzero ratio.
5. When there are no positive, nonzero simplex criteria associated with any variable, no further iterations are required.

With these concepts in mind let us turn to the development of a computer routine for dealing with linear programming problems.

A Computer Model for Solving Linear Programming Problems

We have seen that the simplex method of solving a linear programming problem amounts to an algorithm for manipulating the elements in a tableau. To develop a computer program that would serve as a general model for solving linear programming problems we need only compose a FORTRAN program for converting our successive tableaux to the required configuration, keeping track of the identity (subscripts) of the variables in the basis whose values appear in the last column, so that we can properly interpret the final tableau, which gives us the optimum solution.

We might begin by storing at IW the number of rows in our initial matrix of constant equation coefficients, and at IZ the number of columns in that matrix (including the column of constants in the initial index).

We might facilitate preparation of our initial tableau for submission to the computer by making certain that all slack and artificial variables appear on the *right* side of our initial matrix and that all others are on the left of the matrix. In our initial tableau we will *not* require that the basis has the appearance of a unit matrix, but will cause our FORTRAN program to begin by searching on the right side of the initial matrix for the basic variables, and by associating with each its value in the constant column to identify the initial solution. For these purposes it will be useful to initialize the variable IY equal to the number of real variables +1.[1]

By now the essential dimensions of our problem have been specified. In some cases we might want the computer to print out each tableau as it goes from one iteration to the next. Let us employ the variable ITAB for that purpose. If we initialize ITAB with a value of one we will cause the computer to interpret this as meaning we want the successive tableaux printed out, while zero will mean we do *not* want the successive tableaux printed out.

We might use the subscripted variable $P(M)$ to store the objective function coefficients and read the matrix of constraint equation coefficients into the two dimension subscripted variable $D(M,N)$, $N = 1$, IZ; $M = 1$, IW.

In the subscripted variable $IBV(L)$ we might store the identity (subscript numbers) of the basic variables whose solution values appear in the index column. Thus for a particular tableau

---

[1] Real variables are those that are neither slack nor artificial variables.

IBV(6) = 12 would mean that the solution value for basic variable X_{12} is stored in the index column of row 6 of that tableau.

With the following instructions we might initialize our program, and cause the computer to determine and store at IBV(L) the initial solution:

```
      READ (5,  )IW,IZ,IY
      IX = IZ − 1
      READ (5,  )ITAB
      READ (5,  ) (P(M),M = 1,IX)
      READ (5,  ) ((D(M,N),N = 1,IZ),M = 1,IW)
      DO 20 N = IY,IX
      DO 30 L = 1,IW
      IF (D(L,N) .EQ. 1.0) GO TO 40
   30 CONTINUE
      GO TO 20
   40 IBV(L) = N
   20 CONTINUE
```

It will be useful to keep count of the number of pivots (iterations) employed through the final iteration, and we might use the variable NOPIVS for this purpose, loading it with zero at the beginning.

In preparation for the first and subsequent iterations we might calculate simplex criteria and identify the largest with the following instructions:

```
   13 SCMAX = 0.0
      DO 31 N = 1,IX
      DO 32 I = 1,IW
      IF (N .EQ.IBV(I)) GO TO 31
   32 CONTINUE
      SUM = 0.0
      DO 33 I = 1,IW
      J = IBV(I)
   33 SUM = SUM + P(J) * D(I,N)
      SC(N) = P(N) − SUM
      IF (SC(N) .LE.SCMAX) GO TO 31
      SCMAX = S C(N)
      IPIVCO = N
   31 CONTINUE
```

We should add an instruction to see if the maximum simplex criterion is positive:

$$\text{IF (SCMAX .LE.0.0) GO TO 14}$$

Next we need to determine the pivot row. We might use the variable IPIVRO to hold the number of the pivot row. The following set of statements should cause the computer to divide each of the positive elements in the pivot column into their corresponding elements in the index column, and to store in the variable IPIVRO the number of the row yielding the smallest quotient:

```
  SMLVAL = 9999999.
  DO 4 M = 1,IW
  IF (D(M,IPIVCO))4,4,5
5 QUONT = D(M,IZ)/D(M,IPIVCO)
  IF (QUONT - SMLVAL)6,4,4
6 IPIVRO = M
  SMLVAL = QUONT
4 CONTINUE
```

By now the position of the pivot has been determined. Its column number is stored in IPIVCO, and its row number is stored in IPIVRO.

On completion of this next iteration the value in the index column of row IPIVRO will be the solution value for the variable whose subscript is IPIVCO. We might use the following statement to make this change in the array IBV(L):

$$IBV(IPIVRO) = IPIVCO$$

We need now to divide all the elements in the pivot row by the elements in the pivot position in order to make that element equal to one:

```
  DIV = D(IPIVRO,IPIVCO)
  DO 7 N = 1,IZ
7 D(IPIVRO,N) = D(IPIVRO,N)/DIV
```

Now we should increase the number of pivots by one, and if successive tableaux are to be printed out produce a heading indicating after which pivot the forthcoming tableau was generated:

```
  NOPIVS = NOPIVS + 1
  IF (ITAB .NE. 1) GO TO 12
  WRITE (6,  )NOPIVS
```

Now we need to complete the iteration by making all the other elements in the pivot column zero, and by writing out the tableau (if it was desired). We can do this just as we would do it by hand, starting with the first row and proceeding through all the rows successively, taking care to avoid disturbing the elements in the pivot row but using these elements in the conversion process:

```
 12   DO 10 M = 1,IW
      IF (M − IPIVRO)9,8,9
  9   CM = −D(M,IPIVCO)
      DO 11 N = 1,IZ
      TM = D(IPIVRO,N) * CM
 11   D(M,N) = D(M,N) + TM
  8   IF (ITAB .NE. 1) GO TO 10
      WRITE (6   ) (D(M,N),N = 1,IZ)
 10   CONTINUE
```

Our complete program is shown in Figure 14–8.

FIGURE 14–8

A General Model for the Simplex Algorithm

```
      DIMENSION D( , ),P( ),IBV( ),SC( )
101   FORMAT (I1)
102   FORMAT (    )
103   FORMAT (    )
104   FORMAT (    )
105   FORMAT (1H1)
106   FORMAT (1H0,26HTABLEAU AFTER PIVOT NUMBER,I4)
107   FORMAT (    )
108   FORMAT (1H1,8HSOLUTION)
109   FORMAT (1H0,8HVARIABLE,4X,5HVALUE)
110   FORMAT (1H,I5,F12.2)
111   FORMAT (1H0,27HALL OTHER VARIABLES = ZERO.)
      READ (5,104)IW,IZ,IY
      IX = IZ − 1
      READ (5,101) ITAB
      READ (5,102) (P(M),M = 1,IX)
      READ (5,103) ( (D(M,N),N = 1,IZ),M = 1,IW)
      DO 20 N = IY,IX
      DO 30 L = 1,IW
      IF (D(L,N) .EQ. 1.0) GO TO 40
 30   CONTINUE
      GO TO 20
 40   IBV(L) = N
 20   CONTINUE
      NOPIVS = 0
      IF (ITAB .NE. 1) GO TO 13
      WRITE (6,105)
```

FIGURE 14–8 (*Continued*)

```
13   SCMAX = 0.0
     DO 31 N = 1,IX
     DO 32 I = 1,IW
     IF (N .EQ. IBV(I)) GO TO 31
32   CONTINUE
     SUM = 0.0
     DO 33 I = 1,IW
     J = IBV(I)
33   SUM = SUM + P(J) * D(I,N)
     SC(N) = P(N) - SUM
     IF (SC(N) .LE. SCMAX) GO TO 31
     SCMAX = SC(N)
     IPIVCO = N
31   CONTINUE
     IF (SCMAX .LE. 0.0) GO TO 14
     SMLVAL = 99999999.
     DO 4 M = 1,IW
     IF (D(M,IPIVCO))4,4,5
5    QUONT = D(M,IZ)/D(M,IPIVCO)
     IF (QUONT - SMLVAL)6,4,4
6    IPIVRO = M
     SMLVAL = QUONT
4    CONTINUE
     IBV(IPVRO) = IPIVCO
     DIV = D(IPIVRO,IPIVCO)
     DO 7 N = 1,IZ
7    D(IPIVRO,N) = D(IPIVRO,N)/DIV
     NOPIVS = NOPIVS + 1
     IF (ITAB .NE. 1) GO TO 12
     WRITE (6,106) NOPIVS
12   DO 10 M = 1,IW
     IF (M - IPIVRO)9,8,9
9    CM = - D(M,IPIVCO)
     DO 11 N = 1,IZ
     TM = D(IPIVRO,N) * CM
11   D(M,N) = D(M,N) + TM
8    IF (ITAB .NE. 1) GO TO 10
     WRITE (6,107) (D(M,N),N = 1,IZ)
10   CONTINUE
     GO TO 13
14   WRITE (6,108)
     WRITE (6,109)
     DO 21 M = 1,IW
```

FIGURE 14–8 (Concluded)

```
21  WRITE (6,110) IBV(M),D(M,IZ)
    WRITE (6,111)
    STOP
    END
```

We have endeavored to make the program of Figure 14–8 rather general so that any LP problem whose initial matrix does not exceed the available space in core memory can be solved. To use the program one should proceed as follows.

Step 1. Prepare the first data card and FORMAT statement number 104 for reading in values for IW, IZ, and IY:

IW = Number of rows of constraint equation coefficients.

IZ = Number of columns in our initial matrix, including the column of constants in the index.

IY = Number of real vaiables + 1.

Step 2. Prepare the second data card by punching 1 in the first column if it is desired that successive tableaux be printed out, and by punching 0 if successive tableaux are not desired.

Step 3. Prepare the next data card(s) and FORMAT statement number 102 for reading the coefficients in the objective function into P(M) = 1 to IZ − 1.

Step 4. Prepare the next data cards and FORMAT statement number 103 for reading into D(M,N) N = 1,IZ; M = 1,IW the initial tableau, making certain that the coefficients of all variables other than slack and artificial variables appear on the left side of the matrix, and all slack and artificial variables to the right, in a fashion symmetrical with the arrangement of the coefficients in the objective function row, now ready for storage in P(M).

Step 5. Prepare FORMAT statement number 107 for printing out a row of the successive tableaux stored in D(M,N), N = 1,IZ.

Step 6. Make provision in a DIMENSION statement for reserving adequate space, as follows:

D(M,N) where M = IW, N = IZ.
P(K)   where K = IZ − 1.
IBV(L) where L = IW.
SC(J)   where J = IZ − 1.

An Example of the Use of the LP Program of Figure 14–8. Let us employ the program of Figure 14–8 to solve our minimization problem and provide for each of the successive tableaux to be printed out. We make the following preparations.

Step 1. For our first data card we might use the following FORMAT statement:

104 FORMAT (3I2)

and punch on the first data card, left justified,

030804

indicating that our initial tableau has 3 rows, 8 columns and 3 real variables $(IY = 3 + 1)$.

Step 2. Since we want our successive tableaux printed out we will punch the integer 1 in the first column of our second data card.

Step 3. There are 7 variables in our LP problem, hence 7 coefficients in the objective function row. Let us employ the following FORMAT statement:

102 FORMAT (7F10.0)

for reading into $P(M)$ the coefficients of variables X_1 through X_7 from the third data card.

Step 4. There are 3 rows and 8 columns in our initial tableau, and we might employ the following FORMAT statement for reading the initial matrix into $D(M,N)$:

103 FORMAT (8F3.0).

Step 5. We will, of course, have 8 columns in each of our successive tableaux, and we may want greater accuracy than that provided by FORMAT statement number 103. For printing out our successive tableaux let us employ the following FORMAT statement:

107 FORMAT (1H,8F7.3).

Step 6. A suitable DIMENSION statement might be:

DIMENSION D(3,8),P(7),IBV(3),SC(7).

Our data deck for this example now has the following appearance:

```
030804
1
    -2.        -4.       -1.   0.  -99999.   0.  -99999.
  1.  2.-1.  1.  0.  0.  0.  5.
  2.-1.  2.  0.  1.  0.  0.  2.
 -1.  2.  2.  0.  0.-1.  1.  1.
```

and our printout appears as follows:

TABLEAU AFTER PIVOT NUMBER 1

.500	3.000	0.	1.000	0.	−.500	.500	5.500
3.000	−3.000	0.	0.	1.000	1.000	−1.000	1.000
−.500	1.000	1.000	0.	0.	−.500	.500	.500

TABLEAU AFTER PIVOT NUMBER 2

0.	3.500	0.	1.000	−.167	−.667	.667	5.333
1.000	−1.000	0.	0.	.333	.333	−.333	.333
0.	.500	1.000	0.	.167	−.333	.333	.667

TABLEAU AFTER PIVOT NUMBER 3

2.000	1.500	0.	1.000	.500	0.	0.	6.000
3.000	−3.000	0.	0.	1.000	1.000	−1.000	1.000
1.000	−.500	1.000	0.	.500	0.	0.	1.000

SOLUTION

VARIABLE	VALUE
4	6.00
6	1.00
3	1.00

ALL OTHER VARIABLES = ZERO.

The final portion of the printout tells us that our objective function is minimized without violating any of our constraints by the following optimal solution:

$$X_4 = 6 \qquad X_1 = 0$$
$$X_6 = 1 \qquad X_2 = 0$$
$$X_3 = 1 \qquad X_5 = 0$$
$$X_7 = 0.$$

LINEAR PROGRAMMING AND SYSTEM MODELING

The simplex procedure is a search procedure for finding the means for controlling optimally a system of interacting components. The constraints in an LP problem state the way the components in the system are related to each other. Thus the simplex tableau is a model of a system of interacting components.

Only in our discussion of LP and in our discussion of the inventory problem (Chapter 7) have we laid claim to modeling a system in such a way that we could, through analysis of the model, discern a means for causing the system to behave optimally.

In all systems studies our ultimate purpose is to discern means for controlling the systems we model—for causing them to behave as we wish them to behave.

Only in the simplex tableau do we have a model form which lends itself to an analytical procedure (the simplex algorithm) for identifying an optimal control strategy applicable to large-scale systems.

The inventory model developed in Chapter 7 yields an optimal inventory policy but the model has little value in other than inventory systems.

Figure 14–9 indicates the state of the arts in modeling for optimal control. Modeling structures and search procedures have been developed for dealing skillfully with problems with the following attributes:

1. A high degree of linearity.
2. Little uncertainty.
3. Few or many variables.

If we imagine a quadrant delineated by the three axes in Figure 14–9 as embracing the set of real world problems of interest to the systems analyst, the shaded region represents that subset which the

FIGURE 14–9

The State of the Arts in Modeling for Optimal Control

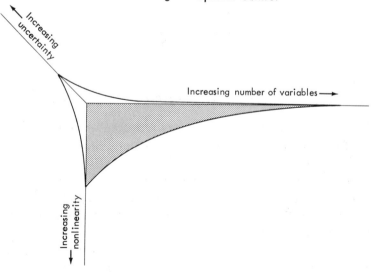

analyst is equipped to deal with in a highly sophisticated fashion. The rest of the quadrant—which is almost all of it—has to this point in time defied optimal control.

Mathematical programming has to do with procedures for finding optimal solutions to constrained resource allocation problems. The most general search procedure is the simplex algorithm of LP.

Modifications of the SP have been developed for dealing with nonlinear optimization problems—problems arising out of systems whose components are related to one another in a nonlinear fashion. Other search procedures—some including modification of the SP—have been developed for identifying optimal control strategy in systems where the element of uncertainty is modeled explicitly. Some of these procedures are applicable in those cases where only integer quantities of components are acceptable.

However, none of these search procedures assures optimal system control where functional relationships are highly nonlinear, components are large in number and certainty cannot be assumed.

Thus in spite of giant strides made in the past few decades optimal control in the behavioral sciences is still in a relatively primitive stage of development.

While our ultimate purpose, in systems studies, is optimal control, simply improving our understanding of their behavior can be of enormous value. For this reason we found it worthwhile to study, in Chapters 8 through 14, model forms which held little promise of leading to optimal control strategies.

The simplex procedure of LP is, to the behavioral scientist, the most fully developed and most operationally useful search procedure for systems control. Many large-scale computers spend much of their time conducting searches for optimal control strategies in real world system problems. The development of the SP is surely one of the great achievements in applied mathematics in this century.

The systems analyst would do well to acquaint himself with the many variants of the simplex procedure, the means by which it can be employed for sensitivity analysis in a wide range of applied system control problems and the modifications of the SP which equip him to deal with small-scale nonlinear and discrete system problems.

For further study in this important field the reader is referred to the bibliography at the end of this chapter.

SUPPLEMENT A

Determining Steady State and Transient Components via the Z-Transform

Consider the simple Markov process:

$$A(n) = .5A(n-1) + .4B(n-1) \quad (1)$$
$$B(n) = .5A(n-1) + .6B(n-1) \quad (2)$$

The flow graph counterpart of (1) is:

FIGURE A–1

... and of (2) is:

FIGURE A–2

Notice that in combining the two flow graph components we produce the following *closed system* flow graph model:

FIGURE A–3

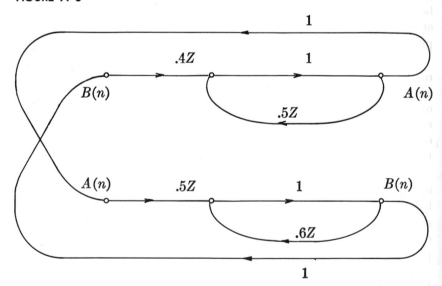

From Figure A–1 we can write the transform equations:

$$A^T = .5ZA^T + .4ZB^T$$

or

$$= [.5Z \quad .4Z]\begin{bmatrix} A^T \\ B^T \end{bmatrix}, \tag{3}$$

. . . and from Figure A–2:

$$B^T = .5ZA^T + .6ZB^T$$

$$= [.5Z \quad .6Z]\begin{bmatrix} A^T \\ B^T \end{bmatrix}. \tag{4}$$

Combining expressions (3) and (4) we produce the matrix transform equation:

$$\begin{bmatrix} A^T \\ B^T \end{bmatrix} = \begin{bmatrix} .5Z & .4Z \\ .5Z & .6Z \end{bmatrix}\begin{bmatrix} A^T \\ B^T \end{bmatrix}$$

. . . an equation we could have easily produced by inspection, from system equations (1) and (2).

We will now see, however, that by exploiting a very useful transform pair we can find the transient and steady state components of this system.

Clearly if

$$U(n) = PU(n - 1)$$

. . . then

$$U(n + 1) = PU(n). \tag{5}$$

Now if P is a constant (or a matrix of constants) and if $U(n)$ is a vector of time-related functions, then from our table of transform pairs (Table 8–2, Chapter 8), pair 2:

$$[PU(n)]^T = PU^T \tag{6}$$

. . . that is, the transform of $PU(n)$ is P times the transform of $U(n)$.

Now, consider transform pair 5 (Table 7–2). The symbol δ_k means "*delay* k periods." The symbol δ_{-k} means "*advance* k periods." Pair 5 therefore states:

"Given $f(n)$ and its transform f^T, the transform of $f(n + 1)$, $f(n)$ advanced 1 period, is:

$$Z^{-1}[f^T - f(0)]$$

. . . where $f(0)$ is f in period 0."

The usefulness of the transform of $f(n + 1)$ in terms of $f(0)$ will now become apparent.

Referring to expression (5), if $U(n + 1) = PU(n)$, then the transform of the left side of this equation will equal that on the right side:

$$[U(n + 1)]^T = [PU(n)]^T. \tag{7}$$

We saw above that

$$[U(n + 1)]^T = Z^{-1}[U^T - U(0)], \tag{8}$$

. . . therefore from expressions (6), (7), and (8) we have:

$$Z^{-1}[U^T - U(0)] = PU^T \tag{9}$$

. . . from which:

$$U^T - U(0) = ZPU^T$$
$$U^T - ZPU^T = U(0)$$

. . . and $U^T[I - ZP] = U(0)$, where I is the unit matrix,
. . . and finally:

$$U^T = \underbrace{[I - ZP]^{-1}}_{C}U(0). \tag{10}$$

In the Markov process we are considering:

$$U(n + 1) = PU(n)$$
$$= \begin{bmatrix} .5 & .4 \\ .5 & .6 \end{bmatrix} U(n)$$

. . . where

$$U(n) = \begin{bmatrix} A \\ B \end{bmatrix}_n.$$

Therefore matrix C, expression (10), is:

$$\left[\begin{bmatrix} 1 & 0 \\ 0 & 1 \end{bmatrix} - Z\begin{bmatrix} \frac{1}{2} & \frac{2}{5} \\ \frac{1}{2} & \frac{3}{5} \end{bmatrix}\right]^{-1} = \begin{bmatrix} 1 - Z/2 & -2Z/5 \\ -Z/2 & 1 - 3Z/5 \end{bmatrix}^{-1}. \tag{11}$$

The inverse of (11) proves to be:

$$\begin{bmatrix} \dfrac{1 - 3Z/5}{(1 - Z)(1 - Z/10)} & \dfrac{2Z/5}{(1 - Z)(1 - Z/10)} \\ \dfrac{Z/2}{(1 - Z)(1 - Z/10)} & \dfrac{1 - Z/2}{(1 - Z)(1 - Z/10)} \end{bmatrix}. \tag{12}$$

By partial fraction expansion expression (12) reduces to:

$$[I - zP]^{-1} = 1/(1 - Z)\begin{bmatrix} \frac{4}{9} & \frac{4}{9} \\ \frac{5}{9} & \frac{5}{9} \end{bmatrix}$$

$$+ \frac{1}{1 - Z/10}\begin{bmatrix} \frac{5}{9} & -\frac{4}{9} \\ -\frac{5}{9} & \frac{4}{9} \end{bmatrix}. \qquad (13)$$

Forming the inverse transform of expression (13), which we will label P', we have:

$$U(n) = P'U(0)$$

$$= \left[\underbrace{\begin{bmatrix} \frac{4}{9} & \frac{4}{9} \\ \frac{5}{9} & \frac{5}{9} \end{bmatrix}}_{D} + \underbrace{\begin{bmatrix} 5/(9 \cdot 10^n) & -4/(9 \cdot 10^n) \\ -5/(9 \cdot 10^n) & 4/(9 \cdot 10^n) \end{bmatrix}}_{E} \right] U(0). \qquad (14)$$

As n approaches ∞ matrix E approaches 0 and the steady state of the system is simply matrix D times the initial state vector, $U(0)$. Thus the ultimate state to which this system settles is indeed dependent upon its initial state, $U(0)$.

To determine the state of the system in any period n we simply evaluate matrix E for that value of n, add D and E and postmultiply their sum by $U(0)$. We could also use P', above, to determine how many periods must elapse before the system comes within some specified proximity of its steady state.

Since $U(n) = P^n U(0)$, from expression (14):

$$P^n = P'.$$

Thus by application of the Z transform we have decomposed the matrix of transition probabilities into its steady state component (matrix D) and its transient component (matrix E). While P^n and P' are equal, P' reveals behavioral attributes of this simple Markov system which P^n does not reveal.

SUPPLEMENT B

The Natchez Indians Problem

The Natchez Indians in the lower Mississippi valley had a social system which was remarkably advanced, early in the history of the United States. The society gradually deteriorated, however, and the cause of its deterioration has been sought by anthropologists for many years. One hypothesis is that their complex marriage and descent rules were incompatible with survival. This hypothesis is given some credence by an analysis of a model of the system due to R. R. Bush.[1]

The system consisted of four social classes: Suns, Nobles, Honoreds, and Stinkards. While the Stinkards were the lowest class, at least one partner in any marriage had to be a Stinkard. If the father was a Stinkard, the child took the social class of its mother. If the mother was a Stinkard, the child took the social class just below that of its father. If both parents were Stinkards, the child was a Stinkard.

These relationships are portrayed in tabular form in Table B–1.

TABLE B–1

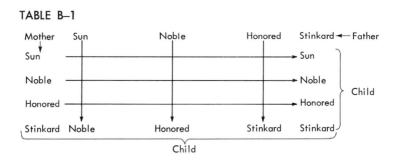

To build a model of the system which portrays the fashion in which one generation relates to the next, let us assume that:

1. Each social class has an equal number of men and women.
2. Each individual marries once and only once.
3. Each married couple has one son and one daughter only.

Clearly with these assumptions a model of the way in which the men in one generation relate to the men in the next will be the same as a model of the women from generation to generation.

We will let:

S_n = Number of male Suns in generation n
N_n = Number of male Nobles in generation n
H_n = Number of male Honoreds in generation n
ST_n = Number of male Stinkards in generation n

---

[1] R. R. Bush (now deceased) elaborated his model in an unpublished paper. For background information on the problem, see C. W. M. Hart, "A Reconsideration of the Natchez Social Structure," *American Anthropologist*, New Series 45 (1943), pp. 374–86.

Sun children are produced solely by Sun mothers. Since each mother produces one son we can write:

$$S_{n+1} = S_n. \tag{1}$$

Noble children are produced: by (a) Sun fathers and (b) Noble mothers, each of whom produces one son. Therefore:

$$N_{n+1} = S_n + N_n. \tag{2}$$

Honored children are produced by: (a) Noble fathers and (b) Honored mothers, each of whom produces one son. Therefore:

$$H_{n+1} = N_n + H_n. \tag{3}$$

To determine the number of Stinkards, let us assume that the total number of men and women in each generation is the same as that in the preceding generation—the system is stable. Therefore we can write:

$$S_{n+1} + N_{n+1} + H_{n+1} + ST_{n+1} = S_n + N_n + H_n + ST_n.$$

Expressing the variables on the left of the equal sign in terms of (1), (2), and (3), above, we have:

$$ST_{n+1} = -S_n - N_n + ST_n.$$

We now have the system of difference equations:

$$S_{n+1} = S_n$$
$$N_{n+1} = S_n + H_n$$
$$H_{n+1} = N_n + H_n$$
$$ST_{n+1} = -S_n - N_n + ST_n$$

. . . from which we can construct the state model:

$$\begin{bmatrix} S \\ N \\ H \\ ST \end{bmatrix}_{n+1} = \begin{bmatrix} 1 & 0 & 0 & 0 \\ 1 & 1 & 0 & 0 \\ 0 & 1 & 1 & 0 \\ -1 & -1 & 0 & 1 \end{bmatrix} \begin{bmatrix} S \\ N \\ H \\ ST \end{bmatrix}_n \tag{4}$$

. . . and also:

$$\begin{bmatrix} S \\ N \\ H \\ ST \end{bmatrix}_n = \underbrace{\begin{bmatrix} 1 & 0 & 0 & 0 \\ 1 & 1 & 0 & 0 \\ 0 & 1 & 1 & 0 \\ -1 & -1 & 0 & 1 \end{bmatrix}}_{A}^{n} \begin{bmatrix} S \\ N \\ H \\ ST \end{bmatrix}_0 . \tag{5}$$

The state of the system in any generation n is determined entirely by the original state of the system and matrix A. All the information required to predict the behavior of the system is provided in matrix A. Note that A can be written:

$$A = \underbrace{\begin{bmatrix} 1 & 0 & 0 & 0 \\ 0 & 1 & 0 & 0 \\ 0 & 0 & 1 & 0 \\ 0 & 0 & 0 & 1 \end{bmatrix}}_{U} + \underbrace{\begin{bmatrix} 0 & 0 & 0 & 0 \\ 1 & 0 & 0 & 0 \\ 0 & 0 & 1 & 0 \\ -1 & -1 & 0 & 0 \end{bmatrix}}_{B} \tag{6}$$

... and thus:

$$A^n = (U + B)^n \tag{7}$$

Recall that in scalar algebra:

$$(X + Y)^n = X^n + nX^{n-1}Y + \frac{n(n-1)}{2} X^{n-2}Y^2 + \dots Y^n. \tag{8}$$

Expression (8) holds also in matrix algebra if multiplication of X and Y is comutative. Any matrix is comutative with the unit matrix. Furthermore, $U^n = U$ and $UB = B$. Therefore (7) can be written:

$$A^n = U + nB + \frac{n(n-1)}{2} B^2 + \dots B^n. \tag{9}$$

Note, however, that:

$$B^2 = \begin{bmatrix} 0 & 0 & 0 & 0 \\ 0 & 0 & 0 & 0 \\ 1 & 0 & 0 & 0 \\ -1 & 0 & 0 & 0 \end{bmatrix}, \text{ and } B^3 = 0.$$

Therefore (9) becomes:

$$A^n = U + nB + \frac{n(n-1)}{2} B^2 = \begin{bmatrix} 1 & 0 & 0 & 0 \\ 0 & 1 & 0 & 0 \\ 0 & 0 & 1 & 0 \\ 0 & 0 & 0 & 1 \end{bmatrix}$$

$$+ n \begin{bmatrix} 0 & 0 & 0 & 0 \\ 1 & 0 & 0 & 0 \\ 0 & 1 & 0 & 0 \\ -1 & -1 & 0 & 0 \end{bmatrix} + \frac{n(n-1)}{2} \begin{bmatrix} 0 & 0 & 0 & 0 \\ 0 & 0 & 0 & 0 \\ 1 & 0 & 0 & 0 \\ -1 & 0 & 0 & 0 \end{bmatrix} \tag{10}$$

. . . and from (5) we have:

$$
\begin{bmatrix} S \\ N \\ H \\ ST \end{bmatrix}_n = \begin{bmatrix} S_0 \\ N_0 + nS_0 \\ H_0 + nN_0 + \dfrac{n(n-1)}{2} S_0 \\ ST_0 - nN_0 - \dfrac{n(n-1)}{2} S_0 \end{bmatrix} \tag{11}
$$

. . . where (11) portrays the number of men (or women) in the four social classes in generation n, given the status of the society in generation 0.

Now, the right side of (11) states that while the number of Suns seems stable, from generation to generation, the number of Nobles, Honoreds, and Stinkards changes. In fact, for stability to exist: $S_0 = N_0 = 0$, meaning that Suns and Nobles would have to be absent from the society at the outset. If the system began with some Suns and Nobles, then the number of Stinkards would decrease with n, from the final row of (11), until there were insufficient Stinkards to marry all the Suns, Nobles, and Honoreds required by the marriage rules, and the system could not persist.

It must occur to us that the assumptions which enabled us to construct so tractable a model may not be entirely fair. If some of these assumptions are relaxed, studying this system via formal analysis becomes more difficult and simulation becomes increasingly attractive. We will leave this for the exercises.

SUGGESTIONS FOR FURTHER STUDY

HADLEY, G. *Linear Programming*. Reading, Mass.: Addison-Wesley Publishing Co., Inc., 1962.

HARARY, FRANK, and LIPSTEIN, BENJAMIN. "The Dynamics of Brand Loyalty: A Markovian Approach," *Operations Research*, Vol. 10 (January 1962).

LLEWELLYN, ROBERT W. *Linear Programming*. New York: Holt, Rinehart & Winston, Inc., 1966.

ROSENTHAL, MYRON B. *Numerical Methods in Computer Programming*. Homewood, Ill.: Richard D. Irwin, Inc., 1966.

EXERCISES

1. Employ the program of Figure 14–3, which solves systems of linear equations by the matrix reduction method, to solve system of equations (14–2). In this simple input-output problem assume that:

$$C_a = 2.05$$
$$C_b = 16$$
$$C_c = 15$$

2. Employ the matrix inverter program of Figure 14–2 to invert the matrix of coefficients in system of equations (14–2).

3. Using the matrix multiplier of Figure 14–7, form the product of the matrix of coefficients in system of equations (14–9) and the inverse of that matrix, which appears just after Figure 14–2. The product should, of course, be the unit matrix.

4. **A Problem in Parametric Programming.** XYZ Company is a manufacturer of many products. The demand for all the products is such that all production can be sold. If none of some of the products are produced there is no effect on the company (such as loss of goodwill). Four of the products require processing by the same departments in order to make a finished product for sale. The products require time in each of the departments in varying amounts. Below is a schedule of the time required in each of the departments for each of these four products.

Product	Time Required in Department		
	1	*2*	*3*
X1	2	2	2
X2	3	1	2
X3	1	3	3
X4	2	2	1

Since other products also require time in these departments, scheduling must allocate time among the many products. As all these products require processing in only these departments, a lump-sum allocation is made to the four products, and the production manager must allocate time to each of the products from the lump sum. During the coming period there will be available for manufacture of these four products the following amounts of time in each of the departments:

Department	Time (in Hours)
1	1100
2	1250
3	500

The profit margin on each of the four products is as follows:

Product	Profit Margin (per Unit)
X1	$20
X2	8
X3	14
X4	12

a) Determine the optimum amounts of each of the four products to be produced in order to maximize profits during the coming period. What is the amount of profit?

b)   It is possible through the use of overtime to increase the amounts of time available in department 3 to 750 hours. This extra time will cost $6 per hour. Would it be profitable to the company to increase the amount of time in department 3 to 750 hours? If so, what is the optimum production allocation, and what is the added increment of profit?

c)   It is also possible *after* the increase in department 3 to increase the amount of time available in department 1 to 1,300 hours. The cost of the increase will be $6 per hour. Use this information to answer the questions that are posted in (*b*).

   If in (*b*) the question had been whether or not to increase the amount of time available in department 1 to 1,300 hours at a cost of $6 per hour, with department 3 remaining at 500 hours, what would be the answers to the questions?

5.   A Stochastic Linear Programming Problem.   Williams Company produces two products—product I and product J. Each unit of product I contributes $2.56 to profit, and each unit of product J contributes $5.10 to profit.

Production of units of product I and product J requires time on machines A and B as follows:

Product	Machine	
	A	B
	hrs.	hrs.
I	2.5	1.8
J	1.0	3.2
Available time on machs.	24,000	40,000

In addition to machine time on machines A and B, product J also requires time in the testing lab. Whereas machine times are constant, as shown in the table above, testing time is a random variable which, it has been found, can be approximated by the normal distribution with mean of one man-hour per unit of product J and standard deviation of 0.3 man-hours per unit of product J. (Testing is not required on product I.)

Eleven thousand man-hours of time are available in the testing department during the planning period ahead.

The data in the table above can be transformed into the following constraint equations:

$$2.5I + J \leq 24,000.$$
$$1.8I + 3.2J \leq 40,000.$$

But how shall we express the constraint attributable to limited man-hours available in the testing lab? If testing time should prove to be ≤ 1 man-hour per unit of product J, then our final constraint equation is:

$$J \leq 11,000.$$

If, on the other hand, the simplex algorithm applied to this linear programming problem yields a solution calling for 11,000 units of product J, and per unit testing time proved to average more than one man-hour per unit, the available testing time constraint would have been violated, and we might reason that we have an infeasible solution.

One way of dealing with an LP problem of this character (suggested by W. H. Evers in "A New Model for Stochastic Linear Programming," *IBM*, August 1966) is to assess as a *negative* contribution to profit the expected value of the nonfeasible solution, as described below.

Let us assume that if mean testing time per unit of product J exceeds 1 man-hour per unit of product J we will make up the shortage in units of product J by costs that amount to $25.61 per man-hour (costs associated with contracting for additional testing). The expected per unit testing *in excess* of 1 man-hour would be:*

$$\int_{1.0}^{\infty} xf(x)\, dx - 1.0. \tag{1}$$

In (1), above, $f(x)$ is the density function of the normally distributed random testing time variable (i.e., $\mu = 1.0$ and $\sigma = 0.3$).

Reference to an appropriate statistical table shows the integral in (1) above to be approximately $\mu + .675\sigma = 1.0 + .675(.3) = 1.203$. Expression (1), then, is $1.203 - 1.0 = 0.203$ man-hours expected testing time in excess of 1 man-hour per unit of product J. The expected infeasible solution cost is therefore:†

$$0.5 \times 0.203 \times J \times \$25.61 = \$2.60J$$

which is a negative contribution to profit. Our objective function to be maximized when testing time is assumed constant at 1 man-hour per unit of product J is:

$$\$2.56I + \$5.10J.$$

For the case where testing time is assumed to be a random variable with mean 1 and standard deviation .3 we subtract a penalty cost for the infeasible solution that results if average testing time exceeds 1 man-hour per unit, and obtain:

$$\$2.56I + \$5.10J - \$2.60J = \$2.56I + \$2.50J$$

both subject to the constraints:

$$2.5I + J \le 24{,}000.$$
$$1.8I + 3.2J \le 40{,}000.$$
$$J \le 11{,}000.$$
$$I, J \ge 0.$$

---

* See Paul G. Hoel, *Introduction to Mathematical Statistics* (New York: John Wiley & Sons, Inc., 1954), p. 196.

† Added costs will be required only if mean testing time proves to be greater than 1 man-hour per unit of J. The probability of this is 0.5. The expected penalty, then, is:
$$0.5 \times .203 \times J \times \$25.61 = \$2.60J$$

Compare optimum production plans when (1) testing time is assumed constant at 1 man-hour per unit of product J, and (2) testing time is assumed to be a random variable. Also compare the expected profit under each of the two conditions.

6. Refer to Supplement B at the end of this chapter. We assumed, among other things, that the population of the tribe would not change from generation to generation. Perhaps the marriage and descent rules ARE compatible with a *growing* population.

If we abandon the stability assumption we have no way of relating the number of Stinkards in one generation to the population in the various social classes in the previous generation. Stinkards are produced by those Stinkard mothers who marry Honored fathers and by those who marry Stinkard fathers. But Stinkards (unlike other social classes) may marry Suns, Nobles, Honoreds, and Stinkards, and we need to specify in our model what proportion marry in each class in order to determine the number of Stinkards produced by the current generation.

Let us examine the following "alliances" for the Stinkards, in each generation:

	Suns	*Nobles*	*Honoreds*	*Stinkards*
Case 1	.1	.2	.3	.4
Case 2	.4	.3	.2	.1
Case 3	.25	.25	.25	.25

For Case 1, the number of Sun men in generation $n + 1$ will be the number of Sun women in generation n OR one tenth of the number of Stinkards in generation n, whichever is smaller. The number of Noble men in $n + 1$ will be the sum of (a) the number of Noble men in n or 20 percent of the number of Stinkards in n, whichever is smaller, plus (b) the number of Sun women in generation n or 10 percent of the number of Stinkards in n, whichever is smaller. The number of Honoreds in $n + 1$ will be the sum of (a) the number of Honored men in n or 30 percent of the number of Stinkards in n, whichever is smaller, plus (b) the number of Noble women in n or 20 percent of the number of Stinkards in n, whichever is smaller. Finally the number of Stinkard men in generation $n + 1$ will be the sum of (a) the number of Honored women in generation n or 30 percent of the number of Stinkards in n, plus (b) 40 percent of the number of Stinkards in n.

It is not possible to portray this system by a state model of linear, first-order difference equations, whose transition matrix can be analyzed as before. Lacking an analytical solution we might simulate, however.

Construct a simulation model to predict the outcome of Cases 1, 2, and 3, above. Assume a starting population of 25 Suns, 25 Nobles, 25 Honoreds, and 10 Stinkards (a "favorable" initial condition).

Carry the simulation through 30 generations and observe the results. Can you think of other models which might still better test the hypothesis, "The Natchez Indians' demise was the consequence of their marriage and descent rules."? (The taking of captives, among the early Indian tribes, was a common way of increasing the supply of workers and wives. How many would have to be taken, in successive generations, to maintain an adequate supply?)

7. Part *b*, exercise 9, Chapter 4, asks you to formulate a state model for the Keynes Co. which, while experiencing rapid sales and profitability growth, is running out of cash. Form the sixth power of the transition matrix of that state model (the firm runs out of cash in the sixth month after time 0), premultiply the state vector at time 0 by the sixth power of the transition matrix, and compare the state of the firm with that found in exercise 9, Chapter 4, part *a*, through simulation. (Note that in Supplement A, Chapter 7, this same system is formulated via flow graph and its behavior determined via transform algebra.)

chapter 15

Simulating Human Behavior

ONE MIGHT ARGUE that anything a human does constitutes *human behavior*. As the term is used here, it means goal-oriented behavior of individuals or groups. Learning, perception, choice, and influence are particular kinds of behavior studied by behavioral scientists.

In this chapter three models are presented. The first depicts individual behavior. It concerns the decision process of an inventory clerk. His environment is that of Chapter 7 in which the management of a stock of inventory of the Brown Electronics Company was discussed.

Our second model illustrates a situation in which two persons interact. The activity modeled is the choice made by one of two players in a game called "the prisoner's dilemma."

The third model represents the information-decision system of a firm. Despite the fact that others have extended some aspects of the original model, it remains on important work and affords insights about model design and construction.

INDIVIDUAL BEHAVIOR

In Chapter 7 we developed a decision rule, which if applied to one of Brown Electronics Company's inventory items would result in minimum *total annual cost*, as that variable was defined. The rule directed that whenever the inventory quantity was equal or less than 4 units, a replenishment order for 13 units should be written.

Recall that expected daily demand was 1 unit, and that 13 units would be ordered from the supplier about every 28 days (365/13).

On a return visit to the company the authors stopped by to ask the firm's inventory control clerk how the rule was working. The following dialogue (protocol) is a shortened version of the conversation between authors (A) and clerk (CL). Bracketed remarks were later added to clarify the meanings of some terms used by the clerk.[1]

A: It's good to see you again. How is our rule working out?
CL: Well, pretty good—I use it most of the time.
A: Most of the time?
CL: Yeh—if the amount [inventory on hand] gets too low, I order 13 [units].
A: What do you mean, too low?
CL: Well, when it [inventory on hand] falls below the safe level [4 units, the reorder level].
A: But isn't that what the rule calls for?
CL: Not exactly, you see if I follow the book [reorder rule] every time it says to reorder, the stuff piles up sometimes and sometimes I run out.
A: Let's go back to the notion of what's too low.
CL: Okay, suppose it's time to reorder and I have an order due in but the stock is moving fast—you know it's *hot*—then I'll write an order for maybe 10.
A: You're saying that when we figured out the rule we didn't consider the total as including both inventory on hand and on the truck [inventory on order]?
CL: That's part of it—if it's time to order 13 and I don't have an order coming, I'll order the 13.
A: That seems reasonable.
CL: I should mention that I wouldn't order the 13 *if* I had too much on hand.
A: How much is *too much?*
CL: Well, I figure the stock is too high if I have enough to carry me two days.
A: How do you put a number on that?
CL: I just double the amount I issued today.
A: A minute ago you used the word *hot*, what does that mean?
CL: Well, that's when I've got to issue more than average.
A: Can you give us an example?

[1] The model which follows is based on a discussion by John M. Dutton and Warren G. Briggs, "Simulation Model Construction," in John M. Dutton and William H. Starbuck, *Computer Simulation of Human Behavior* (New York: John Wiley & Sons, Inc., 1971), pp. 103–12.

CL: Suppose I'm running two units [daily average] and then get a call for four. When I see that I check if I got an order coming—if not, I write an order for 13 even though it's not really time to reorder.

At this point the authors broke off the questioning when they noticed a work sheet on the clerk's desk. He acknowledged that it contained information he used to arrive at reorder decisions on the stock item. Ten entries from the work sheet were selected *randomly* and are reproduced in Table 15–1.

TABLE 15–1

Inventory Clerk's Data and Decision Record

Decision Number	DCUR Current Usage	IOH Amount On Hand	IORD Amount On Order	DAVE Average Usage	R Reorder Level	Q Economic Order Q	Clerk's Decision
1	3	4	0	2	4	13	Order 13
2	2	4	13	2	4	13	Order 0
3	3	4	10	1	4	13	Order 10
4	2	6	0	2	4	13	Order 0
5	1	3	0	2	4	13	Order 0
6	1	2	0	1	4	13	Order 0
7	4	5	0	2	4	13	Order 13
8	1	7	0	2	4	13	Order 0
9	1	2	13	2	4	13	Order 0
10	4	5	13	2	4	13	Order 10

We now have considerable information about the clerk's decisions. He described a number of variables and states (inventory levels, presence or absence of outstanding order, hot or not hot demand). His goal seems to be to prevent inventory from piling up while avoiding stock-outs. Given the information contained in the protocol and the sample of the clerk's written record, can we construct a model descriptive of the clerk's behavior? The test of the model will be its ability to output the same decisions as the clerk.

Constructing the Model

Our model building begins with the organization of information revealed in the protocol. Six variables were reasonably well-defined by the clerk.

1. Inventory on hand.
2. Inventory on order.

3. Average demand—this variable was recorded in the work sheet and mentioned in the protocol but the manner of computation was not stated.
4. Current demand—the quantity demanded or issued today.
5. Reorder level or point—4 units.
6. Economic order quantity—13 units.

Four relationships, phrased as tests, were spoken of by the clerk. The tests were employed to discern that a particular state or condition existed.

Test 1. Is it time to reorder? This is based on the original reorder rule; if inventory on hand is equal to or less than 4 units, order 13 units.
Test 2. Is the item hot? Is current demand 1.5 times (greater) than average demand? Selection of the parameter 1.5 is based on the numerical example in the protocol.
Test 3. Is an order enroute or due in?
Test 4. Is the inventory on hand too high? Is the stock sufficient for two days' usage? This amount, computed by the clerk, is twice the *current* demand.

Three outcomes of the process were mentioned by the clerk.

1. Order 0 units—place no order.
2. Order 10 units—order less than Q units.
3. Order 13 units—order Q units.

Our initial model in flow diagrom form is shown in Figure 15–1. The model accounts for four decisions outcomes mentioned by the clerk and correspondingly numbered in Figure 15–1.

1. Reorder time, item is hot, order is due in—order 10 units.
2. Reorder time, no outstanding order, inventory not high—order 13 units.
3. Reorder time, no outstanding order, inventory high—order 0 units.
4. Not reorder time, item is hot, no outstanding order—order 13 units.

Examination of Figure 15–1 reveals that three of the tests have only *one* exit branch. We speculated that the clerk did have branches leading from those test nodes to decision outcomes. Further interview of the clerk was carried out and part of the protocol about the missing links is reproduced.

FIGURE 15–1

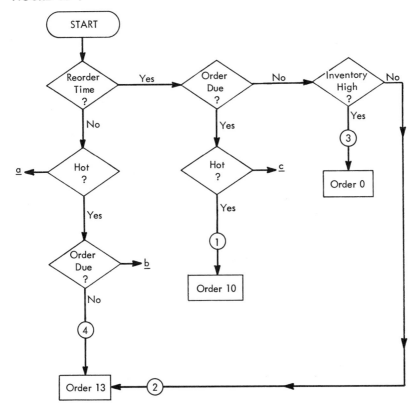

A: Tell us about the case when it's not time to reorder [inventory on hand is above the safe level] and the item is not hot. [Corresponds to *a* in Figure 15–1]

CL: Well, I just pass [order 0 units]. [Decision 5, Figure 15–2]

A: Okay, what happens when inventory on hand is above the safe level [not order time], the item is hot, but you have an order due in? [Corresponds to *b* in Figure 15–1]

CL: In that case I'll order 10. [Decision 6, Figure 15–2]

A: Just one more question. If it's time to write an order, and you have an order due in, but the item is not hot, what do you do? [Missing branch *c* in Figure 15–1]

CL: "Well, sometimes it doesn't work out too good, but I don't order." [Decision 7, Figure 15–2]

The revised model contains seven rules. Each consists of a sequence of two or three tests. Employing the tests, the clerk establishes the state of the system. His decision depends upon the state

FIGURE 15–2

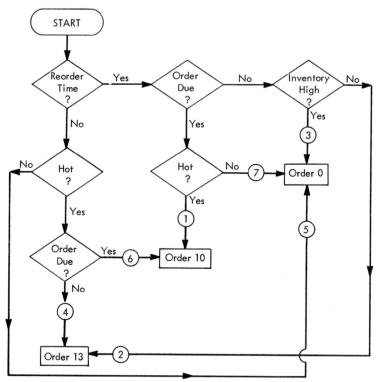

he observes—at least that is our explanation. The clerk is modeled as an information processor who constantly checks the state of the system and compares inventory levels with desired levels. When inventory is too low, he orders new stock.

Our model may be depicted as a network of tests. In Figure 15–3, the decision rules are numbered as in previous figures.

A flow diagram of the model substituting FORTRAN expressions for the test questions used above is given in Figure 15–4.

The model as a computer program written in FORTRAN appears in Figure 15–5.2. Program output follows the listing.

How well does the program simulate the clerk's behavior (decisions)? It produced outcomes identical to those of the clerk. On this basis the model is said to be a sufficient explanation. Nothing more can be claimed for the model. It has not been shown to be a general model—either of this subject's behavior or of the decision behavior of other inventory clerks. We believe that the clerk does process

FIGURE 15–3

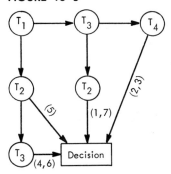

T_1—Time to reorder?
T_2—Item hot?
T_3—Order due?
T_4—Inventory high?

FIGURE 15–4

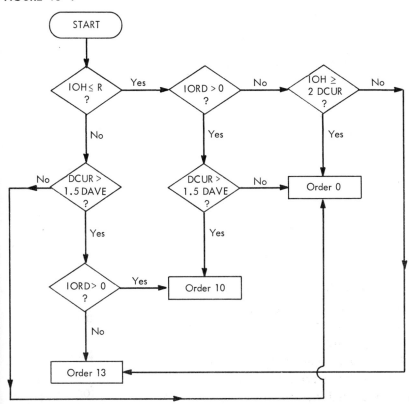

FIGURE 15–5

PROGRAM   INVENT

```
PROGRAM INVENT(INPUT,OUTPUT)
DIMENSION DCUR(10),IOH(10),IORD(10),DAVE(10),ORDER(10),IACT(10)
INTEGER DCUR,DAVE,ORDER,R,Q
DO 100 N=1,10
READ 2,DCUR(N),IOH(N),IORD(N),DAVE(N),ORDER(N)
2 FORMAT (5I4)
100 CONTINUE
PRINT 31
PRINT 32
31 FORMAT(1H1,9X,6HNUMBER,5X,7HCURRENT,4X,9HINVENTORY,3X,9HINVENTORY,
*4X,7HAVERAGE,4X,8HCOMPUTED,5X,6HACTUAL)
32 FORMAT(1H ,21X,6HDEMAND,5X,7HON HAND,5X,8HON ORDER,5X,6HDEMAND,5X,
*6HACTION,6X,5HORDER,/)
R=4
Q=13
INTER=10
DO 20 N=1,10
IF(IOH(N)-R)4,4,7
4 IF(IORD(N)-0)5,5,12
5 IF(IOH(N)-2*DCUR(N))6,15,15
6 IACT(N)=Q
GO TO 1
7 IF(DCUR(N)-1.5*DAVE(N))8,8,9
8 IACT(N)=0
GO TO 1
9 IF(IORD(N)-0)10,10,11
10 IACT(N)=Q
GO TO 1
11 IACT(N)=INTER
GO TO 1
12 IF(DCUR(N)-1.5*DAVE(N))13,14,14
13 IACT(N)=0
GO TO 1
14 IACT(N)=INTER
GO TO 1
15 IACT(N)=0
1 PRINT 16,N,DCUR(N),IOH(N),IORD(N),DAVE(N),IACT(N),ORDER(N)
16 FORMAT (7I12)
20 CONTINUE
STOP
END
```

NUMBER	CURRENT DEMAND	INVENTORY ON HAND	INVENTORY ON ORDER	AVERAGE DEMAND	COMPUTED ACTION	ACTUAL ORDER
1	3	4	0	2	13	13
2	2	4	13	2	0	0
3	3	4	10	1	10	10
4	2	6	0	2	0	0
5	1	3	0	2	0	0
6	1	2	0	1	0	0
7	4	5	0	2	13	13
8	1	7	0	2	0	0
9	1	5	13	2	0	0
10	4	5	13	2	10	10

information the way our model does. Some structure of the behavior has been specified and so the model is more than a black box.
Needless to say, there is more to decision behavior than information processing.

If the model were supplied fresh data, and if it performed as well
as before, then a stronger case can be made that the clerk's behavior
has been well described. Yet the question, "How good is the

model?" goes unanswered. How good is the model compared with what? An objective judgment of the model depends upon the availability of alternative explanations of the clerk's behavior. If a second model outputs equally well the set of decisions, but in a more economical or parsimonious fashion, then the second model is better.

While unable to make a stronger statement about the quality of the model, we are satisfied that its construction helps us to better understand what takes place. Within the limits of our experience the explanation represented by the model accounts for the clerk's decisions. This is a descriptive model, a normative model, without reference to external criteria. We did not set out to construct a model to predict behavior, or to model behavior such that an objective criterion is satisfied.

INTERPERSONAL BEHAVIOR

Two suspects, A and B, are arrested and charged with the commission of a crime. Evidence is insufficient to ensure conviction without a confession. A and B are separated and told that each must decide whether to confess or not. The consequences are outlined by the prosecutor.

1. If *both refuse* to confess, the prosecutor will charge them with a lesser offense that he can make stick. The sentence is three years apiece.
2. If *both confess* prosecution will ask for a lenient sentence from the court. Assume that this means one year each.
3. Should *one* confess, but the other refuse, the confessor will receive the maximum sentence (five years) while the other goes free.

The situation described above is one formulation of a game called "the prisoner's dilemma." It will be used to illustrate interaction between persons. Interaction means that one's behavior is somehow affected by that of another.

The choice and outcomes for A and B are shown as a payoff matrix. (See page 478). The first of the paired numbers is the sentence for "player" A, the second for B. Choice number 1 means *confess;* choice 2 means *refuse.*

It turns out that each player is better off selecting 2, no matter what his opponent does. For example, if B chooses 1 (confess), A

B

	1	2
A 1	1,1	5,0
A 2	0,5	3,3

obtains the lesser of the alternatives one or zero years by choosing 2. Should B select 2 (refuse), A is still better off with 2; he receives a three-year sentence rather than one for five years.

The dilemma is that *jointly* they are better off when both confess—choose 1. But that is a high-risk choice. Failure to cooperate (with each other) results in very uneven payoffs. For this reasons, choice 1 is called the cooperative strategy. Choice 2 is the noncooperative or defection strategy.

This game has long intrigued behaviorists because it is an analogue of conflict situations that have serious dimensions. For instance, arms reduction undertaken by two superpowers. Various theories are offered to explain the expected behavior of players cast in real or experimental roles.

For our purpose, the premise of the game is changed slightly. Two players are enlisted and told that their joint decisions will produce payoffs described by the matrix below.

B

	1	2
A 1	3¢, 3¢	1¢, 5¢
A 2	5¢, 1¢	1¢, 1¢

Players are not told how to play nor instructed about the purpose of their participation. On each of 20 trials they separately make their choices. Afterward they are informed about the opponent's choice and receive their payments. Table 15–2 records their choices and payments.

As before, choice 1 is the cooperative strategy. For cooperating, each receives 3 cents (trial 9). Noncooperation pays 1 cent (trials 2, 4, and so on). Mixed strategies return 1 or 5 cents (trials 1, 3, and so on). Players seeking to optimize their economic positions are expected to settle on strategy 2.

Interaction exists in the game but the model described below purports to explain only the choices made by A. B's decisions are input to the model of A's behavior. Nevertheless, A's perception of B is implicit in the model. To this extent it is a more complex model of behavior than the inventory clerk model.

TABLE 15–2

Prisoner's Dilemma—Results

Trial	Choice A	B	Payment (Cents) A	B	Trial	Choice A	B	Payment (Cents) A	B
1	1	2	1	5	11	1	2	1	5
2	2	2	1	1	12	2	2	1	1
3	2	1	5	1	13	2	2	1	1
4	2	2	1	1	14	2	1	5	1
5	1	2	1	5	15	1	2	1	5
6	2	2	1	1	16	2	2	1	1
7	2	2	1	1	17	2	2	1	1
8	1	2	1	5	18	2	2	1	1
9	1	1	3	3	19	2	2	1	1
10	1	2	1	5	20	2	2	1	1

Examination of A's decision sequence (Table 15–2) shows switching between 1 and 2 during the early trials before seeming to settle on 2. Seven of 20 choices are options for cooperation. Several naïve explanations of A are thus ruled out, e.g., $P (A_n = 1) = 7/20$, or $A_n = A_{n-1}$. The reason is not that these models are simple, but because they discount B's choices as determinants of A's behavior.

We hypothesize that A tends toward cooperation and tests B's cooperation. This appears to be the case when A switches from 2 to 1 in trials 5 and 15, as well as his persistence in choosing 1 from trials 8 through 11.

On trials 2, 6, 12, and 16, A switched from cooperation (1) to noncooperation (2) following an unfavorable outcome in the preceding trial. Let's propose a rule to this effect as part of the model. This rule does not however explain A's choice of 1 on trials 9 and 11.

Efforts to model the run of 1's from trials 8 through 11 are based on the conjecture that A tried to influence B to elect a cooperative strategy. The run of 1's will be referred to as a *test*. A experienced three unfavorable outcomes during the test. He earned 6 cents and B 18 cents for trials 8 through 11. At the conclusion of the test the score over the 11 trials was 17 for A, 33 for B. We think the post-test difference caused A to forego further runs of 1's. Either he believed he was too far behind, or had satisfied himself that B could not be influenced.

The subject is modeled to perceive B's noncooperative strategy early in the game. He elects to test his opponent but ends the test and decides on the less adventuresome strategy. Perception of B's strategy is modeled after the fact that he chose 2 on four consecutive trials (4 through 7). Thus A begins his test with trial number 8. It's proposed that the test continues ($A_n = 1$) so long as A does not lose twice in succession. A payoff of 1 cent to A and 5 cents to B is regarded as a loss.

Trial 12, a switch to 2 from 1, can be explained by two rules already proposed. Selection of 1 in trial 11 is considered part of the

FIGURE 15–6

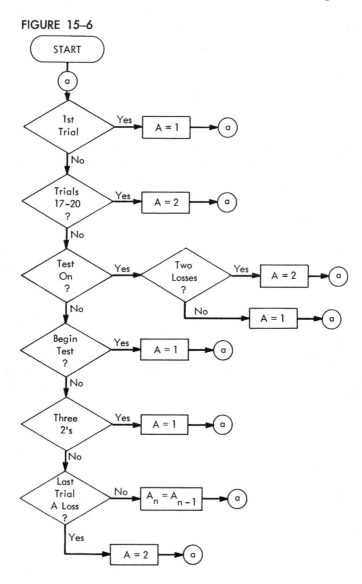

test, and the test termination rule will operate in the model to explain A's trial 12 choice. Continuation of the test takes precedence over the outcome of the *single* previous trial.

A secondary test is suggested by noting that except for the final run of 2's, A does not select 2 more than three times in a row. This "rule of three" accounts for trial 5 and 15.

Finally, a rule to get A started in trial 1 is necessary, and a rule to account for choices in trials 17 through 20. A is modeled to select 1 on the initial trial. This reflects his assumed inclination to cooperate. After the 16th trial a final rule causes him to choose 2.

Schematically the model consisting of the proposed rules is shown in Figure 15–6.

The model in detailed flow diagram (Figure15-7) and FORTRAN listing (Figure 15–8) with output are shown below.

Evaluation of the model was briefly considered. Output of the model $P(A = 1) = 7/20$ was generated. This naïve model duplicated A's choice 50 percent of the time. There can be no doubt that this qualifies as a parsimonious model but the tradeoff is not acceptable. No further efforts were made to validate the original model. An exercise at the end of this chapter contains another sample of A's choices in a 20-trial game with a different opponent.

THE BONINI MODEL

The Bonini model builds on a theory of the firm postulated by March and Cyert.[2] The behavioral theory of the firm represents both a departure from and an attempt to draw from the many partial theories of organizational behavior. March and Cyert challenge several basic assumptions which are part of the classical economics theory of the firm.

They fault the cognitive and motivational assumptions of classical theory. On the one hand, they argue, perfect information is not available to the decision maker; rather, he must go out and search for it, and even then information is subject to bias. This means that the decision maker does not know all alternatives; neither does he know with certainty the price tags that go with the set of alternatives. Furthermore, the search for information is both time-consum-

---

[2] See Richard M. Cyert and James G. March, *A Behavioral Theory of the Firm* (Englewood Cliffs, N.J.: Prentice-Hall, Inc., 1963).

FIGURE 15-7

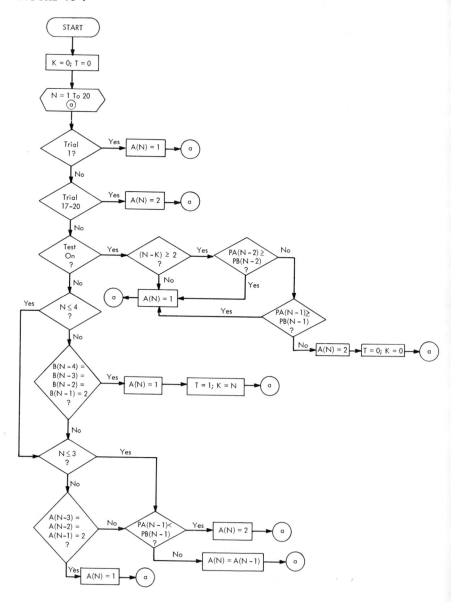

Variable Dictionary

A—Player A's choice
B—Player B's choice
PA—A's payoff
PB—B's payoff
  a   implies computation of payoffs and return to beginning of the loop.

FIGURE 15–8

```
PROGRAM PRISON(INPUT,OUTPUT)
DIMENSION A(20),B(20),PB(20),PA(20)
INTEGER A,B,PA,PB,T
K=0
T=0
READ 1,(B(N),N=1,20)
1 FORMAT (20I1)
PRINT 2
2 FORMAT(1H1,3X,6HCHOICE,9X,6HPAYOFF,//,4X,1HA,4X,1HB,9X,1HA,4X,1HB)
DO 20 N=1,20
IF(N.NE.1)GO TO 5
A(N)=1
GO TO 18
5 IF(N.LT.16)GO TO 6
A(N)=2
GO TO 18
6 IF(T.EQ.1)GO TO 10
IF(N.LE.4)GO TO 4
DO 3 J=1,4
IF(B(N-J).EQ.2)GO TO 3
GO TO 4
3 CONTINUE
T=1
K=N
A(N)=1
GO TO 18
4 IF(N.LE.3)GO TO 8
DO 7 J=1,3
IF(A(N-J).EQ.2)GO TO 7
GO TO 8
7 CONTINUE
A(N)=1
GO TO 18
8 IF(PA(N-1).LT.PB(N-1))GO TO 9
A(N)=A(N-1)
GO TO 18
9 A(N)=2
GO TO 18
10 IF((N-K).GE.2)GO TO 11
A(N)=1
GO TO 18
11 IF(PA(N-2).GE.PB(N-2))GO TO 12
IF(PA(N-1).GE.PB(N-1))GO TO 12
A(N)=2
T=0
K=0
GO TO 18
12 A(N)=1
18 IF(A(N).EQ.1)GO TO 19
IF(B(N).EQ.1)GO TO 15
PA(N)=1
PB(N)=1
GO TO 20
15 PA(N)=5
PB(N)=1
GO TO 20
19 IF(B(N).EQ.1)GO TO 16
PA(N)=1
PB(N)=5
GO TO 20
16 PA(N)=3
PB(N)=3
20 CONTINUE
PRINT 21,(A(N),B(N),PA(N),PB(N),N=1,20)
21 FORMAT (2I5,5X,2I5)
STOP
END
```

```
221222221222212222222
```

OUTPUT

CHOICE		PAYOFF	
A	B	A	B
1	2	1	5
2	2	1	1
2	1	5	1
2	2	1	1
1	2	1	5
2	2	1	1
2	2	1	1
1	2	1	5
1	1	3	3
1	2	1	5
1	2	1	5
2	2	1	1
2	2	1	1
1	1	3	3
1	2	1	5
2	2	1	1
2	2	1	1
2	2	1	1
2	2	1	1

ing and costly. The second challenge is concerned with the motivation of the business decision maker. There is much evidence that profit is not the only objective; and profit maximization, while described as rational, does not describe what business firms really do about profits. Decision makers, as individuals and as members of large-scale organizations, have objectives that change through time and can be ordered in a variety of ways.

There is more dissatisfaction with the economists' classical theory of the firm as an explanation of organizational decision making. Bonini argues that the economist has tended to look at the business firm in terms of its relationships with its environment, particularly at those variables which enter the marketplace, such as output, price, costs, and wages. "From the standpoint of such a market-oriented analysis, the firm is considered as a 'black box' wherein changes in outside variables produced changes in the economic outputs of the box."[3] The economist may be criticized for viewing the firm from a great distance, for failing to differentiate among firms, and for ignoring the contents of the black box.

According to Bonini, behaviorists look at the business firm as a social institution. The firm is simply the setting for human interactions. Explanations of organizational behavior take the form of inquiries about how groups are formed, how attitudes develop or change, how aspiration levels are affected, and how social change takes place. No one denies that a better understanding of these processes is desirable, but the fact remains that these aspects of organizational behavior do not constitute its totality.

Prefacing his work, Bonini voices a complaint frequently heard not only in the academic world but also in the business world. The complaint has to do with the very human practice of constructing theory in terms of one's own area of specialization, or of structuring problems in such a way that a particular set of tools can be brought to bear. In each of the disciplines mentioned, as well as in areas of specialization within business administration, the tendency has been to focus on only certain aspects of the total business firm. Those who would regard themselves as generalists have, according to Bonini, foregone analytical characterizations for descriptions that are not particularly powerful for understanding or controlling complex business systems.

---

[3] Charles P. Bonini, "Simulation of Information and Decision Systems in the Firm" (Stanford University Graduate School of Business, Stanford, Calif., May, 1962).

Current theory lacks comprehensiveness and builds on certain assumptions whose reasonableness may be severely questioned. In addition, Bonini points out that many large "pieces of the firm are not replicated in any of the existing models." For example, there is no aspiring middle-management group, budget, day-to-day allocation of resources, or explicit modeling of information variables. Analysis in classical economics is static. Equilibrium analysis falls short of explaining the behavior of a management group in the very short run to make the necessary adjustments which are implied by equilibrium.

Given these very summary observations we come back to the realization that in order to construct models that are more comprehensive, realistic, and dynamic, and that replicate the behavioral aspects of goal formation, information processing, and decision making, we need modeling techniques that are much more powerful than those used in the past.

Structure of the Firm

There are three major areas in the firm for planning and control —manufacturing, sales, and an executive committee. Figure 15–9 represents the formal organization of the model firm. In manufacturing there is a plant supervisor superior to five foremen (one for each of four manufacturing departments and a service department). A staff relationship exists between industrial engineering and production. Industrial engineering reviews and modifies production standards. The general sales manager heads up the sales organization, which includes seven district sales managers. They in turn direct the activities of field salesmen, whose number per district is indicated in the organizational chart.

Figure 15–10 indicates the decisions made at various levels in the firm. Decisions are made at eight points or, as they are defined, *decision centers*. These are the executive committee, manufacturing vice president, general sales manager, plant supervisor, industrial engineering department, district sales managers, foremen, and field salesmen. A decision center is a place in the organization where a decision or part of a decision is made. Such a definition implies that the decision maker may be an individual, a group, or a nonhuman element.

An *information center* is a place where information is collected, transmitted, stored, analyzed, or compiled. The information relates

FIGURE 15–9

Formal Organization of the Simulated Firm*

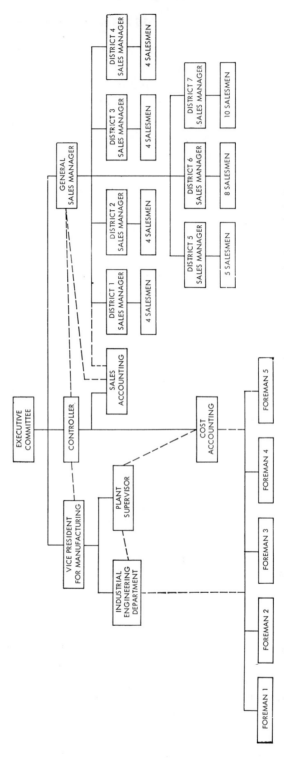

* Source: Charles P. Bonini, "Simulation of Information and Decision Systems in the Firm" (Stanford, Calif.: Stanford University Graduate School of Business, May 1962), p. 41.

FIGURE 15–10

Decisions Made at Various Levels in the Firm*

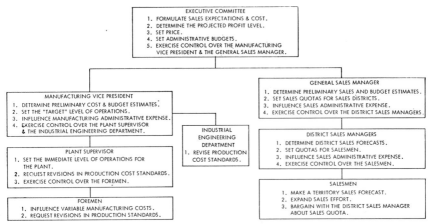

* Source: Charles P. Bonini, "Simulation of Information and Decision Systems in the Firm," p. 42.

to the internal operation of the firm as well as to the environment. Quite obviously, decision centers and information centers in the firm are inextricably bound together. Decision centers generally transmit decisions to others in the organization, and in a sense act as information centers.

When the decision premises are specified, the decision center acts according to a program called a *decision rule*. This is a specific procedure. Consider, for example, a decision rule associated with pricing. One such rule would be: Set price to obtain a 10 percent rate of return on investment. Such a rule assumes, as premises, estimates of costs, sales, investment, and so on, and there are, of course, many other possible decision rules.

It is also important at this time to distinguish between general decision rules and what we shall term *decision parameters*. A decision parameter is a specific numerical constant associated with a decision rule. In the example above, 10 percent is the decision parameter. This rule could be changed without affecting the essence of the decision.[4]

Information and decision centers are tied together by information links. Information links determine flows of information among the centers. Such linkage is quite complex in the typical firm, and

---

[4] Ibid., p. 21.

we note that the same decision center may send out different versions of information to different decision centers.

The *information system* of the firm is finally defined as the complete set of linkings of information within the organization. The information system is thus the total information network. "A given information system means complete and explicit specifications so that we will know who receives what information in the firm, where the information is collected, how and when the information is transmitted. . . ."

A *decision system*, as defined, totals all the decision rules in the organization. "Thus, a specific decision system means a specific set of decision rules (including specified decision parameters)." Since decision rules are dependent on information, specification of the information system is implicit.

In order to build his model, Bonini specified the major areas in the firm in which decisions are made. A set of specific decisions to be rendered was identified for each of these areas or decision centers. One of the prior conditions for decision making is the availability of information. Thus there is a flow of information to each decision center in the model about internal as well as external activity or conditions. This information can be accounting data, informational variables that are estimates of the state of the environment, or the reporting of decisions made elsewhere in the organization.

In order to generate activity in the model, decision rules must be prescribed. For example (as we shall see in the case of sales forecasting), given the information necessary, the decision maker applies a specified set of decision rules to render a forecast. For the most part, the decision rules to be described are those that have been observed and which pragmatic managers recognize. There is nothing to suggest that any particular rule is the best possible one. Bonini states generally that if we abstract from the practices of managers, the rules included in the model are reasonable.

In other cases, where empirical evidence does not exist or where the decision-making process is so complex as to defy modeling, or where the importance of a decision is relatively minor, Bonini has chosen to produce the results of a decision process rather than to explicitly model the process.

In the industrial engineering department, which reviews requests for looser production standards, observation of the decision process led to the conclusion that approximately 50 percent of the requests in a given period were approved and 50 percent were disallowed. In this case the decision was judged to be relatively unimportant, and the decision process could be modeled as if allowance or disallowance was decided by the flip of a coin. The outcomes of the process were treated as if they were probabilistic and produced by Monte Carlo methods. "In this case, we are not trying to duplicate the *procedures* in the real world, but to duplicate the *results* of real world procedures."

Behavioral Concepts

Perhaps the distinguishing element of the model is that decisions are not simply the result of applying a decision rule to a given set of information inputs. If decision making is a behavioral and organizational phenomenon, then the model should reflect those elements of the decision-making process. To achieve this, Bonini makes use of certain behavioral concepts. The first and most important, since it provides the driving force in the model, relates to the existence of pressure within the organization and its opposite effect, organizational slack.

When an organization is failing to perform up to expectations, there is a tendency for pressure to build up within an organization, and this pressure generally results in attempts to achieve better performance. On the other hand, when the organization has been successful in achieving its expectations for a period of time, pressure is relaxed and organizational slack in the form of inefficiency creeps in. Consider, as an example, decisions about budgets. If times have been good and the organization has been doing well, then a relaxation of cost conscientiousness may occur and a simultaneous upward trend in departmental budgets may also occur. If the profit picture grows worse, however, pressure may build up in the firm, budgets slashed, and other cost-cutting devices employed. The amount of pressure affects other decisions, of course, besides budget decisions. Control decisions, decisions on new plant equipment replacement, decisions on maintenance, decisions about dividends are some of the other kinds of decisions that may be affected as pressure builds up and slack is reduced within the firm.[5]

Identifying things like organizational slack and pressure is one thing; explicit modeling of them is another matter. Each decision maker in the model is given an "index of felt pressure." The index represents pressure or slack as a function of *performance relative*

[5] Ibid., p. 24.

to expectations. This definition holds whether we are considering the entire organization or one of its decision makers. The index summarizes and weights those factors, both formal and informal, that are thought to exert pressure on the decision maker. For example, the factors and corresponding weights that make up the index of felt pressure for a salesman are:

Factor	Weight
Index of pressure of his superior	25
His quota as a percentage of his sales the past month	40
Sales of the "average" salesman in his district as a percentage of his sales	10
.75 + (percentage of his products less than 75% of quota)	10
His total quota for the past quarter as a percentage of his total sales for the last quarter	15

Different factors and different weights are used for the other decision makers in the model. Pressure is partly the result of information which reaches a decision maker through the accounting information system. Individuals react to information by feeling pressure. Pressure causes them to act, although individuals do not act uniformly given the same information or the same amount of pressure.

The second source of pressure is that exerted downward through the organization. Superiors pass on a part of their felt pressure to subordinates. Contagion of pressure is transmitted from one level to the next. The index of pressure, then, performs a most important function in the model.

In summary, the "index of pressure" is a major mechanism through which the concepts of slack and pressure become operative in the model. The index provides the bridge for tying together information and behavior, and provides for the contagion of pressure within the organization.[6]

Management Planning

Top-level planning is done by the executive committee, which renders decisions about budgets and prices. Earlier we noted dissatisfaction with the motivational assumption that managers always make decisions to maximize profits. The *Behavioral Theory of the Firm* substitutes the notion of "satisficing profits": decisions are made so as to achieve *satisfactory profits*. Each period the

---

[6] Ibid., p. 26.

executive committee follows a procedure that results in the specification of a budget as well as a final price. The procedure, outlined
below and diagrammed in Figure 15–11, is iterative.

FIGURE 15–11

Planning Procedure in the Model

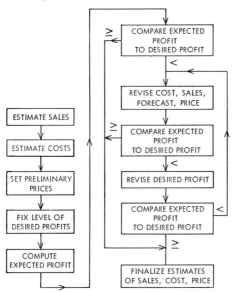

1. Make preliminary estimates of sales and costs.
2. Use current prices as preliminary prices.
3. Determine profit goal (level of aspiration) as a function of
    past profits.
4. Estimate expected profit using the preliminary estimates ob-
    tained from (1), above.
5. If expected profit is greater than aspired profit, finalize esti-
    mated profits.
6. If the expected profit is below aspired profit, revise the esti-
    mates of costs, sales, and price in turn and in that order until
    expected costs reach aspired costs, at which point estimates
    become finalized.
7. If expected profit, after revisions of costs and sales budget
    price, still does not measure up to aspired profits, then the goal
    or aspiration level is modified downward (aspired profits be-
    come a more modest figure).

8. The process is repeated in the above fashion until expected profit measures up to aspired profit, and the last estimate of sales and costs become finalized in the budgets; and, correspondingly, the last estimated price is accepted as the final one.[7]

If, on the basis of preliminary estimates of costs and price, aspiration levels can be reached, then no problems exist, and the preliminary estimates of price and output become the basis for fixing a budget. If the aspiration level cannot be attained using preliminary estimates of cost and price, then problems exist and a search is begun which is motivated and characterized as "simple minded." This implies that the decision maker looks first to those factors that are immediate or local, or that he can control and modify in order to attain the desired goals. As alternatives are identified they are evaluated, and so long as the problem is not resolved, the search expands and the decision maker negotiates with factors outside his control.

We shall see in more detail how these concepts have been modeled. The planning process is such that if goals are unattainable after modifying or negotiating constraints, then the goals are modified downward. That is, aspiration levels are lowered and the procedure is repeated. If as a result of initial lowering of the profit goal or aspiration level there still exists an inequality between aspiration level and estimated level of profits, the aspiration level is lowered a second time. Eventually the problem will be resolved and the price and outlook decision will be finalized.

Management is motivated because of the frustration of achieving aspiration levels. The firm is regarded as an adaptive system; organizational learning takes place in the sense that solutions to prior problems can be recalled, and decision rules are modified in the course of resolving conflict situations.

Forecasting

Each quarter the executive committee makes use of preliminary sales estimates and estimated price, as well as preliminary estimates of costs, to develop an estimate of profit for the period. The initial planning begins with the preparation of a sales forecast. The sales estimates are developed through three levels—the field sales-

[7] Ibid., pp. 27–28.

men, district sales managers, and the general sales manager. The
flowchart of the sales forecasting process is shown in Figure 15–12.
Inputs of past sales data are first reviewed and field forecasts are
developed according to a set of simple rules. Estimates of field
salesmen are then aggregated at the level of the district sales man-

FIGURE 15–12

Flowchart: Sales Forecasting Procedure*

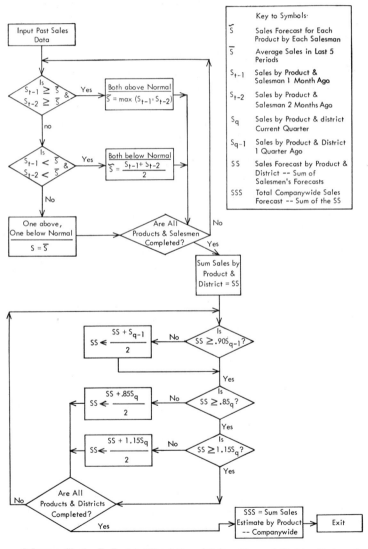

* Source: Charles P. Bonini, "Simulation of Information and Decision Systems in the Firm," p. 48.

ager and are reviewed. Aggregation of estimates from the districts is then made, and this figure represents the sales estimate for the company for the coming quarter.

The field salesman begins by comparing his average sales during the past five periods (months) with his sales one month ago and two months ago. If the two most recent monthly sales figures are both above the average, then his sales forecast for the next month is equal to the larger. If, on the other hand, sales for the preceding two months were each below the five-month normal, then the salesman's estimate for next month is the average of the sales for the two preceding months. Finally if sales in one of the two preceding months were above normal (five-month average), while sales for the other preceding month were below normal, then his estimate for next month is equal to the five-month average.

This procedure is followed until estimates by each salesman have been completed and reported to the district sales level; the estimate of sales in each district is then compared with district sales during the current quarter and one quarter ago. If the estimate for next quarter is equal to or less than 90 percent of the sales for the district one quarter ago, then the estimate for the coming quarter is computed as the average of the estimate for the next quarter and the actual sales one quarter ago. If the sales estimate is equal to or less than 85 percent of sales last quarter in the district, then the estimate is computed as the average of the estimate for next quarter and 85 percent of the sales during last quarter. If the estimate is equal to or less than 115 percent of sales last quarter, then the estimate is computed as the average of the estimate for the next quarter plus 115 percent of sales last quarter. This procedure is followed for the various districts included in the sales organization.

Finally, aggregation of the revised estimates for the districts is made. This becomes, as noted above, the preliminary estimate of sales for the coming quarter. One might question the simplicity of the decision rules involved in the estimation process; nevertheless, Bonini contends that in actual practice rules similar to these are very much in evidence and, in fact, that the estimating biases evident in the procedure do exist. For example, the field salesman reflects optimism if his two most recent months' experience was above the five-month moving average. On the other hand, if both previous months' experience were below the average, he protects himself (in a manner of speaking) by averaging the most recent experience. If the most recent experience is not indicative of a trend, then presumably he does not alter the estimate since he has no hard evidence to serve as a guide. Modifications of a similar nature are made by the district sales manager. We see in this procedure further evidence of the way in which slack has been built into the model.

Budgets

We are still considering the sales organization of the firm, and another kind of planning takes place in the determination of a sales administrative expense budget. The previous budget figure is input and becomes the basis for the sales administrative expense budget for the coming period, given the value of the index of pressure for the general sales manager. If the index for the general sales manager for the most current three periods was greater than 110, then the preceding budget is reduced by multiplying by the factor .98. If, on the other hand, the index value for each of the preceding three periods was less than 95, the expense budget from the preceding period is increased by multiplying by the factor 1.03. If the index values do not fit either of the described conditions, then the expense budget for the coming period is unchanged from the preceding period.

A similar budget is set by the vice president of manufacturing.

Extended low pressure implies a rise in administrative expenses. Extended high pressure implies a cut in administrative expenses. In particular, if the "index of felt pressure" for the vice president of manufacturing is less than 75 for all three periods in the preceding quarter, then the budget is increased by 3 percent. If the index is greater than 110 for all periods in the past quarter, then the budget is decreased by 2 percent. Otherwise, the previous budget remains intact.[8]

The preliminary estimate of unit production cost is made in the manufacturing department. Estimated cost per unit is determined by the following procedure:

Compute the *actual average cost* per unit in the last quarter for each product; determine the *standard cost at "normal" volume* of operations; then the expected or estimated cost per unit equals the average of the actual and standard costs computed.

---

[8] Ibid., p. 53.

Once again, the procedure involved may be overly simple. Bonini contends that this is a reasonable procedure, and that costs are not expected to be exactly what they were in previous periods, nor is the measure of standard cost taken to be definitive. If costs in the past were high relative to standard costs, then they should be expected to fall in the future, and vice versa.

The Overall Plan

Returning to the planning procedure for estimating budgets and price, and given the definition of the aspiration level, we may now combine these to trace through the quarterly planning activity of the executive committee. The preliminary estimates of costs per unit, sales by product, and budgeted administrative expenses have been developed by the sales and manufacturing decision makers. The preliminary estimate of price per product is taken to be the price that existed in the previous period. To operationally define the level of *aspiration,* or *satisfactory profits,* profits for the past 10 quarters are averaged.

The expected profit may now be calculated from the standard accounting equation that profits are equal to net sales minus direct costs, minus administrative expenses. If this expected profit is equal to or greater than the profit goal, all the estimates mentioned up to this point are finalized in the company's quarterly plan. If the expected profit is less than the goal, then some of the estimates must be reexamined.

Costs are the first constraints to which management turns in this model. Standard costs are decreased by 5 percent in the departments that had the best relative performance in the preceding quarter. Given the reduction of these costs, the expected profit is again computed.

If the profit goal is still not met, the sales forecast is modified by increasing by 5 percent the forecast for those products in which sales last quarter were below those of the previous quarter. Once again expected profit is computed, and if it is equal to or greater than the profit goal, then the revised estimates of price and budgetary items are finalized.

If neither a cut in costs nor an increase in sales forecast results in a projected satisfactory profit, a further price cut is in order. Prices are cut by 5 percent on the two products that have the highest expected percent of gross margin. An assumption about the elasticity of demand is implicit: The sales manager estimates that total revenue will increase 12 percent for each 5 percent decrease in price. Price cuts below a certain point would decrease expected profits, and if such is the case, the price reduction is not made.

If the combination of modifications discussed so far does not result in a satisfactory level of profits, the profit goal itself is decreased by 5 percent. If expected profits still do not measure up, a second set of modifications is ordered.

A second round of cost reexamination results in reductions of costs on the three departments not previously changed. The reduction is 5 percent. Budgets for administrative expenses for manufacturing and sales are cut 2 percent. With the revised cost estimates, expected profits are recalculated, and if still unsatisfactory, a second change of the sales forecast is made. The sales estimate is increased by another 5 percent. If it is still unsatisfactory, a 5 percent price cut is made on the two remaining products (those not previously reduced).

If the profit goal still cannot be achieved, the goal is reduced another 5 percent. The procedure now reverts to the step in which the initial reexamination of costs took place. All subsequent steps may be implemented; the process is iterative, and the gap between estimated and desired profit is finally closed. A flowchart of this process is shown in Figure 15–13.

There is one last planning procedure. A target level of production for each product for the coming quarter is set by the manufacturing vice president, who uses sales of the preceding quarter as an estimate of sales by product. The target level of production is fixed so as to meet the expected sales and to maintain an inventory of three months' sales at the end of the quarter.

We are not primarily concerned with the rationale underlying the above. Persuasive evidence shows that the procedures and decision rules outlined can be observed in the real world. Our main interest here is to see the way in which a complex planning and decision process has been explicitly modeled.

Management Control

Control in the model is accomplished by establishing performance standards which are used to evaluate performance. On the basis of this evaluation, decisions are made that will affect future performance. We may note that the implicit definition of managerial control is orthodox, and that the managerial activities of planning and control are, of course, linked.

FIGURE 15–13

Flowchart: Determination of the Overall Company Plan*

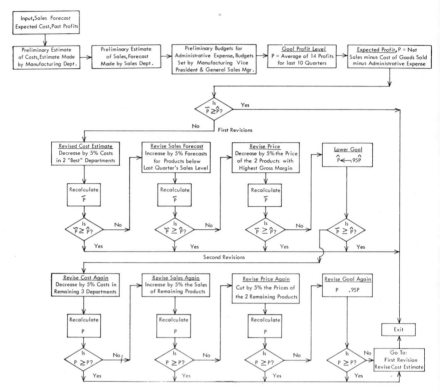

* Source: Charles P. Bonini, "Simulation of Information and Decision Systems in the Firms," p. 60.

Two kinds of performance standards are determined periodically. The first of these is the *sales quota.* Briefly, the overall company sales quota for a product is arbitrarily set at 10 percent above the sales forecast for that product. Quotas are then determined for sales districts, taking into consideration the number of salesmen in the district as well as the comparative past sales performance in that district.

The district managers use a similar procedure to allocate quotas to field salesmen. The district quota is divided among the number of salesmen, with consideration given to the comparative sales performance of the man. Some change of a salesman's quotas is allowed, with upward or downward adjustment based upon a comparison of his quota with his forecast of sales in his territory.

The standard of performance in the manufacturing organization is *standard cost*. Given five manufacturing departments, each with nine accounts, 45 standard costs must be maintained. Standard costs can be increased by 2 percent—or decreased by 2 percent—depending on a review by the industrial engineering department or on a request for change initiated by the foreman.

The details of the standard cost adjustment need not concern us, although we should note that in the model actual costs are determined probabilistically, given a distribution and variance for each cost. When actual costs consistently exceed standard costs, requests for loosening the standard may be initiated by the foreman. When standards are consistently loose (defined as a situation where actual costs are consistently less than the standard), the industrial engineering department seeks to tighten them. "Hence, standard costs are constantly changed over time with the foreman striving to loosen standards, and the industrial engineering department striving to tighten them."[9] We note earlier that the matter of adjusting standard costs—the allowance or disallowance of a request for change by the foreman—was modeled stochastically. Requests initiated by the foreman are screened by the plant supervisor, who passes along a certain portion to industrial engineering, which grants about 50 percent of them.

We have seen, then, that the model provides for the generation of standards of performance for each decision maker or decision-making group in the firm, such as (1) standard costs for manufacturing, (2) sales quotas, (3) sales expense budgets, (4) manufacturing expense budgets, (5) target levels of production, (6) estimated sales, and (7) estimated profits.

Deviations between standard and actual performance cause an increase in pressure. The mechanism for translating comparative past performance into actions or decisions is the index of felt pressure, "the major control mechanism in the firm." Pressure from information inputs is built into the index by including those factors that measure actual performance in terms of the standards listed above—quotas, standard costs, and so on. Changes in the information system to influence decision making can be made experimentally by changing the weights given the informational factors. To model the effect of an absence of information, the informational factor need only be assigned a zero weight. In this way, changes in the kinds, amounts, and methods of presentation of information can be made to show how the decision system will be modified.

---

[9] Ibid., p. 69.

As an example, the effect that inventory level information would have on the general sales manager was studied. If he had information about inventory turnover, a weight of 10 or 15 was assigned, depending on the value of turnover. If a change in information transmission were made in which information was *not* available, then the factor would be given a zero weight.

Since these indexes are of central importance, we present them below for the general sales manager, district sales manager, and the vice president of manufacturing (the salesman's index was described earlier).

Index of Pressure for Vice President of Manufacturing

Factor	Weight
Company index of pressure	20
Manufacturing cost relative to standard cost	35
Manufacturing administrative expense relative to budget	10
.75 plus .25 times the number of products in which cost was greater than 10% above standard cost	10
.75 plus the number of departments in which cost was greater than 5% above standard cost	15
The increase of the index of volume of operations	10

The index of pressure for foremen is made up in a way different from those just listed. The index of pressure of the superior (vice president of manufacturing) is weighted 10. The balance, or 90, is the product of the percent of unfavorable cost variances in a department and the percent of the supervisor's time spent in direct supervision of his department. This time allocation is determined by the number of costs that exceed standards by 10 percent. The net result is to model the concern that a supervisor would feel in the event of poor performance in his department and the need to devote time in the personal supervision of the activity.

Index of Pressure for General Sales Manager

Factor	Weight
Company index of pressure	20
Company sales quota relative to actual sales last month	25
Expected company profit relative to actual profit last month	10
Sales administrative expense relative to budgeted expense last month	15
.25 plus .25 times the number of districts and products that achieved less than 85 percent of quota	05
Total company quota relative to company sales last quarter	25

Index of Pressure for the District Sales Manager

Factor	Weight
Index of pressure of general sales manager	25
District quota relative to actual sales last month	35
Average sales per salesman in district relative to companywide average sales per salesman	05
District administrative expense relative to budget	10
.75 plus the fraction of the products in his district that were below 80 percent of quota	05
Total district quota relative to total district sales last quarter	20

The companywide index represents the pressure felt by the executive committee. This index reflects the difficulty of formulating a satisfactory company plan. As shown in the flow chart of overall company planning (Figure 15–13), if the first preliminary estimate is satisfactory, the index is set at 90. Each revision from the first preliminary plan increases the index by five.

If the company inventory at the end of the month exceeds 3½ months' sales, the index is increased by 10; if inventory exceeds 4 months' sales, the index is increased by 15.

Activity in the Model

The actual level of production is established by functions that relate target and actual production volume. We noted earlier that target inventory was computed from estimated sales plus an allowance for inventory. Estimates in the case of the manufacturing organization reflect sales a quarter ago. If target volume is within 5 percent of current actual volume, it is determined that the target volume can be produced next month. If target volume is between 5 to 25 percent of current actual volume, production next month is taken to be two thirds of the way between target and current actual volume. Finally, if target volume is not within 25 percent of current actual volume, production the next month is one half the way between the target and the current level.

Manufacturing costs vary stochastically to model the unforeseen factors which are not controllable. A distribution is specified for each cost, and actual costs are generated. Given the foreman's index of pressure and actual costs incurred, the model provides for a degree of control over costs from period to period. The initial mean and the standard deviation for each cost are specified in the model.

The foreman can affect the mean and standard deviation according to the following.

Foreman's Index of Pressure	Change in the Mean of the Cost Distribution	Change in the Standard Deviation of the Cost Distribution
Less than 25	+ 5%	+10%
Between 25 and 75	none	+10%
Between 75 and 125	none	none
Between 125 and 175	none	− 9%
Above 175	−4.5%	− 9%

Thus when pressure is great, the foreman is motivated to reduce costs. When pressure is normal, he does nothing. When pressure is low, organization slack—in the form of increased costs—sets in.

Changes of the standard deviation represent the foreman's efforts to reduce the variability of costs. He tries to reduce the likelihood of extremely high or low costs, since one leads to greater pressure and the other to a tighter standard.

Only when pressure is very high does the foreman resort to a more drastic measure to reduce the mean or average cost—to laying off people, trying new technology, and so on. Even so, there are limits to the cost reductions the foreman can effect.

The definition of high, normal, or low pressure was quantified in the above schedule. These values for the index would be different for different foremen. They represent *sensitivity* to pressure. In a sense, they describe action points or limits that trigger activity; in this case, cost-reducing measures. If successful, the index value falls —and we see how the index provides the motivation for managerial control activity.

Sales and sales performance are modeled in a similar fashion. Actual sales are stochastically generated, given a sales probability distribution. Salesmen can modify the mean and standard deviation in response to their pressure index values. Four types of salesmen, who react differently to pressure, "exist" in the model. For example, 20 of the 40 salesmen are constituted to react to pressure by increasing sales effort in all areas, sure customers as well as new prospects. Therefore they realize changes in the mean of the distribution as well as in the standard deviation. A different type of salesman calls only on sure customers, which is translated into a decrease in the standard deviation. Yet other men are presumed to react adversely to pressure by borrowing sales from the future—that is, convincing customers to buy for inventory.

Experimentation

The elaborate model we have been discussing was built for the purpose of experimentation. Changes in eight factors were carefully planned to modify the environment, information system, and decision system of the firm. The changes were introduced to test the reasonableness of the model, evaluate critical decision rules or parameters, and generally to test existing hypotheses about behavior of the firm. Each of the eight factors had two values—a normal and an alternative value. These factors were:

Inventory valuation
Contagion of pressure
Sensitivity to pressure
Sales force knowledge of inventory

Environment variability
Market growth trend
Industrial engineering department
Past versus present information in control

There were 2^8 (or 256) possible experiments, but the number was reduced to 64. Each experiment simulated activity in the firm for 108 months.

Observations of the values of a set of system variables were recorded, summarized, and evaluated statistically to measure the effects of the changes. The system variables tracked were price, cost, pressure, inventory, sales, and profit.

The two values for each of the factors were as follows.

Factor	Standard	Alternative
1. Environment	Stable	Variable
2. Market growth	2% per year with moderate cycle	10% per year (irregular)
3. Industrial engineering	Loose	Tight
4. Contagious pressure	Slight	Much
5. Sensitivity to pressure	High	Low (insensitive)
6. Inventory valuation	LIFO	Average cost
7. Sales force knowledge of inventory	Knowledge	No knowledge
8. Past versus present information in control	Present information	Past information

The first two factors change the firm's environment. Modifying the probability distribution for the variable demand is all that is involved when modeling the alternate to relatively stable environment. The next three factors modify decision parameters. Factor 6 changes a decision rule, while the last two factors model different amounts of available information and its content—i.e., whether historical data is reported or merely current data.

Bonini's experimental results will not be discussed here.[10] Most of the experiments were satisfactory, and the model was reasonably well behaved over the range of changes introduced.

SUGGESTIONS FOR FURTHER STUDY

BONINI, C. P. *Simulation of Information and Decision Systems in the Firm.* Englewood Cliffs, N.J.: Prentice-Hall, Inc., 1963.

DUTTON, JOHN M., and STARBUCK, WILLIAM H. *Computer Simulation of Human Behavior.* New York: John Wiley & Sons, Inc., 1971.

FEIGENBAUM, E. A., and FELDMAN, J. *Computers and Thought.* New York: McGraw-Hill Book Co., 1963.

GUETZKOW, HAROLD; KOTLER, PHILIP; and SCHULTZ, RANDALL L. *Simulation in Social and Administrative Science.* Englewood Cliffs, N.J.: Prentice-Hall, Inc., 1972.

EXERCISES

1. Mark 20 of 50 cards with the numeral 1. The other 30 are marked with 0. Unknown to the subject, order the deck in any desired manner. Let a subject predict the 50 outcomes sequentially.

On each of 50 trials announce the number of the trial and ask the subject for his prediction. Then tell him what the outcome is and whether he is correct or incorrect. Repeat for all 50 trials. Record the trial number, prediction, and outcome, and ask the subject to explain his prediction. If the written protocol is visible to the subject, he should only be permitted to see the most recent prediction.

2. From the protocol produced in Exercise 1, construct a model to explain your subject's behavior. Test the model using the same "deck" as the subject. This requires a FORTRAN version of your model and input of the deck. How many of the 50 events were correctly predicted by your model?

3. Reorder the deck from Exercise 2 and test both your subject and FORTRAN model. Compare program output with that of the subject.

4. Player A engaged a different opponent in a prisoner's dilemma game. Choices of A and player C over 20 trials are as follows:

---

[10] See Chapter 18.

Trial	1	2	3	4	5	6	7	8	9	10
A	1	2	1	2	1	1	2	2	2	1
C	1	1	2	1	2	2	1	2	1	2

Trial	11	12	13	14	15	16	17	18	19	20
A	2	2	2	2	2	2	1	2	2	2
C	2	2	1	2	1	2	2	2	2	2

Test the model, Figure 15–8, using these new data.

5. Propose and test naïve models of A and C's behavior.

6. Construct models that do a better job of imitating the choices of A and C.

7. From the two samples of A's behavior, does it appear that his style of play has changed? In what ways?

chapter 16

Industrial Dynamics

AN IMPORTANT APPROACH to the modeling of economic and urban systems is proposed by Forrester who has named his form of analysis and simulation Industrial Dynamics. We begin by turning to some concepts about organization, decision making, and the relationship between information and managing. Management is the process of converting information into action. The conversion process is what we generally recognize and define as decision making. Management success depends on the availability of information and the manner in which conversion takes place. Typically only a fraction of the available information is used, and then in an incomplete and erratic fashion.

The manager sets the stage for his accomplishments by his choice of which information sources to take seriously and which to ignore. After choice has been made of certain classes of information and certain information sources to carry the highest priority, managerial success depends on what use is made of this information. How quickly or slowly is it converted to action? What is the relative weight given to different information sources in the light of desired objectives? How are these desired objectives created from the information available?[1]

The manager is viewed, almost literally, as an information converter or processor. From an organization and from its environ-

---

[1] J. W. Forrester, "Managerial Decision Making," in Martin Greenberger (ed.), *Management and the Computer of the Future* (Cambridge, Mass., and New York: The M.I.T. Press and John Wiley & Sons, Inc., 1962), p. 38.

ment, information flows to the manager, who in turn outputs a flow of decisions that control activities within the organization. As Forrester notes, the modern manager does not himself convert information into physical action, but rather outputs a stream of instructions or decisions which directs the efforts of the human or nonhuman elements in the organization.

Proceeding from these concepts of decision making and information flows, we can agree that the most critical system of the firm is the information system. "An industrial organization is a complex, interlocking network of information channels."[2]

At various points throughout this network the information is acted on by management, in its decision-making role, to control such physical processes as hiring employees, building factories, and producing goods. Those points throughout the network where control is exerted are action points. Thus we see the important sequence of information, decision making, and control activity (action) illustrated in Figure 16–1.

FIGURE 16–1

Decisions and Information Feedback*

* Source: Forrester, "Managerial Decision Making," p. 41.

Figure 16–1 also illustrates an important characteristic of the information network or system in the firm. The decision that leads to control over a physical process is based on information about the prior state of that process. Information about the state of the system is said to be fed back through the information network to the decision point. In actual practice the decision point relies on information sources that may be located throughout the organization and the system environment itself. We noted the definition of the information feedback system in Chapter 1: "An information-feedback system exists whenever the environment leads to a decision that results in action which affects the environment."[3]

Managerial decision making is purposive; that is, managers interpret information for the purpose of rendering decisions in a way

---

[2] Ibid.
[3] Ibid., p. 39.

that will influence future system states and in a manner that is satisfactory, given the objectives or the purpose for which the system was designed. However, information feedback systems have properties that result in system behavior that is not always predictable and not always satisfactory. These properties are *structure, delays,* and *amplification.*

As we might anticipate, *structure* simply implies the manner in which system parts are interrelated. *Delays* exist because information must be generated and transmitted, and further delays are experienced in the information conversion or decision-making process itself. *Amplification* is defined in the following way: "Amplification is manifested by actions being more forceful than might at first seem to be implied by the information inputs to the governing decisions."[4]

Amplification is perhaps best illustrated by specific example. Consumer demand for electrical power is a function of population and of changes in technology. In the United States, at least, demand for electrical energy is increasing, but at a regular and predictable rate. Eventually the demand for electrical energy is translated through information feedback and management decision making at various levels into a demand placed against the manufacturers who produce the electrical generating equipment. This demand for generating equipment has fluctuated as much as 10 to 1 from year to year, with a five- to six-year cycle. The manufacturers, on the other hand, have varied their output as much as four to one from year to year.

Evidence such as this led Forrester to conclude that information-decision making systems are poorly designed in industry; that they react slowly to input variation; and that the response or behavior of these systems (measured by such system variables as orders, employment, inventory, cash, and investment) is erratic and inefficient because of the structure through which information is fed back and acted on, as well as the delays in the transmission of information. They can be designed for more effective managerial control.

From the somewhat general nature of the information-decision making process and from the nature of the information feedback, we move to the detailed concept of the decision-making process as it is modeled in Industrial Dynamics. Decisions based on information reporting the state of the system result in action meant to control physical processes. To explcitly model the system structure within which the decision process exists, Forrester specifies the existence of six interconnected networks which constitute the structure of the

---

4 Ibid., p. 40.

basic model. In four of the networks—the *materials, money, personnel,* and *capital equipment* networks—resources flow. The fifth network is labeled the *orders* network. The sixth network is the *information* network, to which we have already referred.

The networks are distinguished one from the other by the kind of material or resource contained. The information network serves to link the other networks and is an integrating network. Briefly, the several networks are described in the following fashion.

The materials network includes flows and stocks of physical goods in all stages of processing.

The orders network includes orders for goods, requisitions for new employees, and contracts for new plant space. "Orders are the result of decisions that have not been executed into flows in one of the other networks."[5]

Money is defined in the cash sense; money flows imply the exchange of payments between points in the network. On the other hand, accounts receivable are not defined as money and are therefore included in the information network.

"In the personnel network we deal with people as countable individuals. . . . In most situations we shall need to distinguish men in the personnel network from the variables that are in the information network, such as length of work-week and the productivity per man-hour."[6]

"The capital equipment network includes factory space, tools, and equipment necessary to the production of goods. It describes the way that factories and machines come into existence, the stock of existing capital equipment, what part . . . of our capital equipment stock is in use at any instant, and the discard rate of capital equipment."[7]

To better understand the nature of these networks, we can focus momentarily on the material network most conventionally defined in the model and most familiar to us. Throughout the materials network are various points that at a given instant in time hold quantities of materials in a variety of forms. Points of interest to us in a materials network might include the raw materials warehouse, various production stages in the plant, the finished goods warehouse in the factory, the shipper's warehouse, the wholesaler's warehouse, and perhaps the retailer's stock room. Quantities located at such

---

[5] J. W. Forrester, *Industrial Dynamics* (Cambridge, Mass., and New York: The M.I.T. Press and John Wiley & Sons, Inc., 1961), p. 70.

[6] Ibid., p. 71.

[7] Ibid., p. 71.

points throughout the network are called *levels*. Part of the information that flows through the information network is concerned with these levels. In general: "A level may be an inventory, the number of employees, the average sales for last month, the accomplishment we believe has been made to date in a research project, the degree of optimism about the economic future, the size of bank balance, etc."[8]

Still considering the material network, we know that changes in the various levels throughout the network take place as the result of the exchange of material from one point in the network to another. Having identified a network of interest to us, and having specified important points along the network, we are thus able to describe the state of the network at a point in time by noting the levels throughout the network. Perhaps more importantly, given information about the *rate* at which material flows between network levels, we are able to anticipate succeeding levels throughout the network. Figure 16–2 illustrates the concepts of levels, flow rates,

FIGURE 16–2

Decision Making in the System Structure*

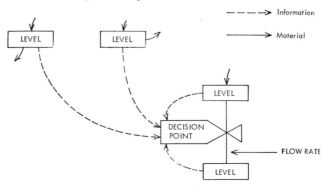

* Source: Greenberger (ed.), *Management and the Computer of the Computer of the Future*, p. 43.

and decision making. To generalize, and somewhat simplify these concepts, the state of the network or subsystem is literally defined by the quantity of resources held at various points throughout the system. Decision making is seen as the managerial activity of deciding future system states by specifying the rates at which resources flow, and hence of determining the changes of system levels.

A still closer view of the decision process is represented in Figure

---

[8] Greenberger (ed.), *Management and the Computer of the Future*, p. 43.

FIGURE 16–3

The Decision Process*

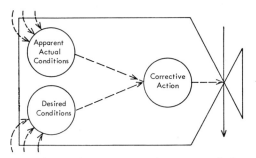

* Source: Greenberger (ed), *Management and the Computer of the Future.* p. 44.

16–3. The figure represents a somewhat conventional view of decision making and its control aspects. Information reporting the apparent state of the system as well as the desired state of the system are inputs to the decision point. Depending on the discrepancy between the apparent state of actual conditions and the desired state, action will be prescribed. The greater the discrepancy, presumably the greater the action, and vice versa.

Decision making is being presented here as a continuous process. It is a conversion mechanism for changing continuously varying flows of information into control signals that determine rates of flows in the system. The decision point is continually yielding to the pressures of environment. It is taking advantage of new developments as they occur. It is always adjusting to the state of affairs. It is treading a narrow path between too much action and too little. It is always attempting to adjust toward the desired goals. The amount of action is some function of the discrepancy between goals and observed system states.

We note that we are viewing the decision process from a very particular distance. We are not close enough to be concerned with the mechanisms of human thought. We are not even close enough to see each separate decision as we ordinarily think of decisions. We may not be close enough to care whether one person or a group action creates the decision. On the other hand, we are not so far away as to be unaware of the decision point and its place in the system. This proper distance and perspective is important to our purposes. We are not the psychologist delving into the nature and sources of personality and motivation, nor are we the biophysicist interested in the physical and logical structure of the brain. On the other hand we are not the stockholder who is so far from the corporation as to be unaware of the internal structure, social pressures, and decision points.[9]

---

[9] J. W. Forrester, *Industrial Dynamics*, p. 96.

To preview the nature of an Industrial Dynamics model, its output, and its experimental use, we turn to a frequently used illustration. Figure 16–4 represents a simple production–distribution system. Two networks are modeled—the information and the materials networks. A demand function has been specified in order to generate orders from the ultimate customer. At each level (factory, distributor, retailer) an inventory of the stock item is held and periodically replenished. Delays in processing orders are assumed, as well as delays in the transmission of orders between levels. Material flows are delayed between levels to represent time required for shipment.

In this system inventories are adjusted to replace goods that are sold, to adjust inventories upward or downward as the level of business activity changes, and to keep the supply pipelines filled with in-process orders as well as shipments.

FIGURE 16–4*

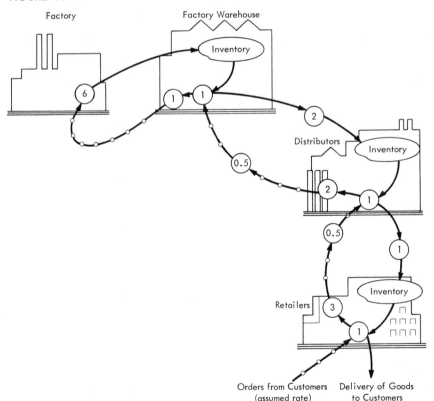

Factory

Factory Warehouse

Inventory

Distributors

Inventory

Retailers

Inventory

Orders from Customers   Delivery of Goods
(assumed rate)   to Customers

* Source: Forrester, *Industrial Dynamics*, p. 22.

Thus we have a relatively simple model in which decision rules have been specified to generate actions that lead to the development of orders for product, the processing of orders, and the shipment of the product. Delays in information transmission have been specified. Certain assumptions about the nature of demand have been made. Initially it will be constant through time. The structure of the system has been designed to include the factory, factory warehouse, distributor level, retailer level, and the final customer. Behavior of the system can be noted by changes through time in the levels of the various inventories as well as in the levels of orders.

For example, inventory levels for the retailer, distributor, and factory warehouse can be noted. So also can the levels of factory orders from distributors, manufacturing orders to factory, and distributor orders from retailers be noted. In addition, the levels for factory production, factory warehouse unfilled orders, and factory warehouse average order filling delays can be generated.

Using this model, Forrester introduced the following kinds of changes in order to learn the nature of the system response. The first change was a simple step increase of 10 percent in the demand level, i.e., a sudden change from one constant level to another. Amplification took place with respect to the system levels or variables noted earlier. The striking thing, however, is the magnitude of amplification. Changes in distributor orders from retailers lagged changes in demand by about a month, and eventually peaked at 18 percent above the prechange level after 11 weeks. Then 27 weeks later the distributor orders from retailers leveled off at 10 percent of the prechange value. This amplification was explained in terms of the response by retailers to increase inventories as well as to raise the level of orders and goods in transit in the supply pipeline. The inventory and pipeline increments in this case are defined as "transient" or nonrepeating additions to the order rate. Once the orders have been placed and the demand satisfied, the retail order level drops back to reflect the increase in customer demand.

The retail inventory level declined 4 percent 7 weeks after the step increase, and leveled off about 34 weeks later at 20 percent above the prechange level.

Manufacturing orders to the factory peaked 51 percent above the prechange level about 15 weeks after the step increase, and even 70 weeks after the change had not stabilized, while factory production rose 45 percent above the prechange level, peaking about 21 weeks after the introduction of the change.

FIGURE 16-5*

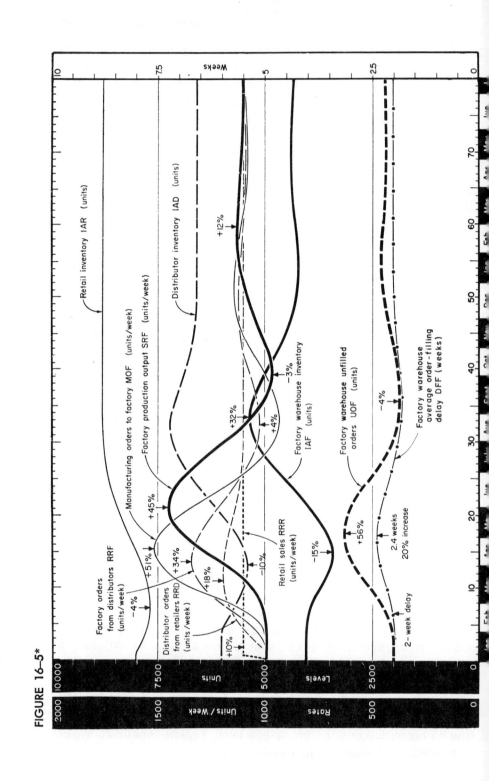

The response of other system variables is shown in Figure 16–5. One should recall that the pronounced amplification was the result of a modest change in an informational input, a change that was not irregular or complex. While managers may intuitively know that such response frequently occurs, they tend to underestimate the severity of the amplification and heretofore have been at a loss to explain exactly why or when it occurs.

A second change introduced by Forrester involved a 10 percent unexpected rise and fall in retail sales over a one-year period. This was a smoothly fluctuating disturbance, or sinusoid pattern, as opposed to the step increase. As might be expected, amplification was more marked. Without regard to the timing at which maximum and minimum inventory levels occurred, the following was observed: Factory inventories ranged from 62 percent above the pre change level to −45 percent. Distributor inventories ranged from +32 percent to −33 percent of the prechange level. Manufacturing orders to the factory peaked at +80 percent about 65 weeks after the change, while factory output fluctuated from a high of +72 percent to a low of −61 percent of the prechange level. Even after a simulation run of 120 weeks, dampening or mitigation of the amplification had not yet taken place to a significant degree.

More complex input changes were produced by Forrester. In a third experiment an irregular fluctuating retail sales pattern was studied. Additional experiments modeled the effect of reducing certain delays, particularly those involved in the clerical work and data processing of orders.

CONSTRUCTING AN INDUSTRIAL DYNAMICS MODEL

We now turn from the general to the specifics of building a model of a system to gain a working understanding of the concepts discussed above.

The structure of a retailer's distribution system is portrayed by the diagram in Figure 16–6. Requisitions (orders) arrive from customers and go into an unfilled order file. Shipments from the distributor arrive and enter inventory. From this inventory deliveries are made to fill customers' requisitions.

Decisions concerning shipments to customers and quantities to order to replenish the inventory are made at a decision center on the basis of knowledge of (or information from) unfilled orders, actual inventory, and desired inventory.

FIGURE 16–6

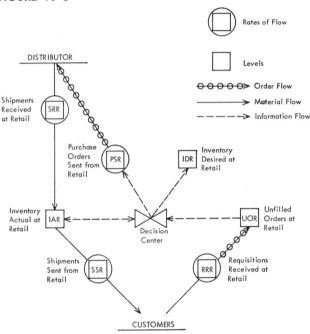

Three kinds of flow can be traced in the system: material flow, information flow, and order flow.

Let us assume the following.

1. The retailer likes to maintain an inventory level equal to six and two thirds the average requisitions received over each of the past three weeks.

2. At the end of each week the retailer orders an amount of new stock equal to: (*a*) the quantity requisitioned during the week and (*b*) one half the difference between his desired inventory and his actual inventory at the end of the week.

3. The retailer's customers experience a two-week delay in getting their requisitions filled, and the retailer experiences a three-week delay in getting his purchase orders filled from the distributor.

4. At time 0, actual inventory on hand is 2,000 units; for each of the past two weeks, 300 units have been requisitioned by customers; and the retailer has ordered 300 units for each of the past three weeks to replenish his inventory.

If we assume that the system is in this "steady state," then at time 0 desired inventory would be 2,000 units and the retailer would have 600 units in unfilled back orders.

We might hand simulate the retailer's system by use of a tabular format (Table 16–1). In our notation system we use the letter R at the end of each three-letter element name to indicate that we refer to the *retail* level. Later we will see how Industrial Dynamics ties the retail level into the distributor and factory levels in order to study total system behavior.

TABLE 16–1

	Week	RRR	SSR	PSR	SRR	UOR	IAR	IDR
	−3			300				
	−2	300		300				
Time	−1	300		300		600	2000	2000
Zero								
	1							
	2							
	3							

We can determine the state of the system at the end of each week after time zero, using the following relationships, all of which follow from the preceding description of the retailer's system.

1. Requisitions received at retail (RRR) = the amount requisitioned in a week (the essential system input).
2. Shipments sent from retail (SSR) = the value of RRR two weeks ago.
3. Shipments received at retail (SRR) = the value of PSR three weeks ago.
4. Unfilled orders at retail (UOR) = UOR$_{old}$ + RRR − SSR.
5. Inventory actual at retail (IAR) = IAR$_{old}$ + SRR − SSR.
6. Inventory desired at retail (IDR) = 6⅔ (average RRR during *past* three weeks).
7. Purchase orders sent from retail (PSR) = RRR + ½(IDR − IAR).

These relationships can be expressed by the following system of difference equations:

$$RRR_n = f(n)$$
$$SSR_n = RRR_{n-2}$$
$$SRR_n = PSR_{n-3}$$
$$UOR_n = UOR_{n-1} + RRR_n - SSR_n$$
$$IAR_n = IAR_{n-1} + SRR_n - SSR_n$$
$$IDR_n = 20/9\,[RRR_n + RRR_{n-1} + RRR_{n-2}]$$
$$PSR_n = RRR_n + ½\,[IDR_n - IAR_n]$$

. . . in which RRR_n, the "driver" or "exciter" of the system, is a function of time, n. The "state vector" is:

$$\begin{bmatrix} RRR_n \\ SSR_n \\ SRR_n \\ UOR_n \\ IAR_n \\ IDR_n \\ PSR_n \end{bmatrix}$$

that is, the state of the system at any period in time, n, is simply the values of the variables in this vector in period n.

We might initialize our system with three weeks of past history, and continue in this "steady state" with RRR = 300 through the first three weeks of our simulation.

Now let us assume that in the fourth week customer requisitions jump to 330 per week and continue at that rate; that is, the system experiences a 10 percent *step* increase. The effect of this change is apparent if we calculate values for the system variables (see Table

TABLE 16–2

	Week	*RRR*	*SSR*	*PSR*	*SRR*	*UOR*	*IAR*	*IDR*
	−3			300				
	−2			300				
Time	−1	300		300				
Zero	1	300	300	300	300	600	2000	2000
	2	300	300	300	300	600	2000	2000
	3	300	300	300	300	600	2000	2000
	4	330	300	364	300	630	2000	2067
	5	330	300	397	300	660	2000	2133
	6	330	330	445	300	660	1970	2200
	7	330	330	428	364	660	2004	2200
	8	330	330	395	398	660	2071	2200
	9	330	330	337	445	660	2186	2200
	10	330	330	288	428	660	2284	2200
	11	330	330	255	395	660	2349	2200
	12	330	330	252	337	660	2356	2200
	13	330	330	273	288	660	2314	2200
	14	330	330	310	255	660	2239	2200
	15	330	330	350	252	660	2161	2200
	16	330	330	378	273	660	2104	2200
	17	330	330	388	310	660	2084	2200
	18	330	330	378	350	660	2104	2200
	19	330	330	354	378	660	2152	2200
	20	330	330	325	388	660	2210	2200
	21	330	330	301	378	660	2258	2200
	22	330	330	289	354	660	2282	2200
	23	330	330	292	325	660	2277	2200
	24	330	330	306	301	660	2248	2200

FIGURE 16–7

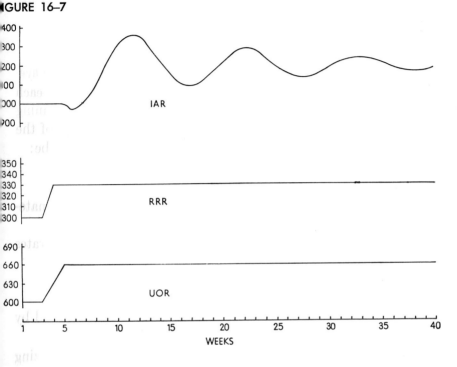

16–2), and if we then plot, against time, values for RRR, UOR, and IAR (Figure 16–7).

Preparatory to understanding the nature of DYNAMO, we would do well to observe more closely the character of the elements in our retailer's system. We have two different kinds of elements—levels and rates.

IAR and UOR are *levels*, measured at any moment in time in *number of units*.

RRR, SSR, PSR, and SRR are *rates* of flow. RRR and PSR are measured in *units ordered per week;* SSR and SRR are measured in *units* of material *sent or received per week.*

If we think of the beginning of a week as moment in time J, the end of the week as moment in time K, and the period of time in between as JK, then the relationship between IAR, SSR, and SRR might be expressed as follows:

$$IAR_K = IAR_J + 1(SRR_{JK} - SSR_{JK}).$$

As the equation above implies, we determine the inventory level at the end of the week by adding to the inventory level at the beginning of the week a quantity equal to the *net rate of inflow* of material during the week, in units per week *times* the amount of time this net rate of inflow has been under way (that is, one week). We see by the following dimensional analysis that our units of measure in the equation are consistent:

$$\text{Units} = \text{Units} + \text{Weeks(Units/Week)}.$$

Now, we could more readily detect changes in our retailer's system if instead of determining the state of the system *once* each week we did so *twice* each week. If we think of J as the beginning of the week, as before, but we now think of K as the *middle* of the week, our equation for IAR as of the middle of the week would be:

$$IAR_K = IAR_J + \tfrac{1}{2}(SRR_{JK} - SSR_{JK}).$$

As before, $SRR_{JK} - SSR_{JK}$ means the *net rate of inflow* of material into inventory, during the period JK, in units per week.

To generalize our model that relates the inventory level to rates of flow in and out of inventory we might write:

$$IAR_K = IAR_J + DT(SRR_{JK} - SSR_{JK}).$$

where DT (Delta T) means the fraction of a week represented by the interval of time JK.

The usefulness of this more dynamic means of conceptualizing the relationship between the elements of our retailer's system will become apparent if we express the relationship between all the elements of the system in this same fashion.

Our file of unfilled orders would be related to the inflow of new requisitions and delivery on those orders in much the same fashion as the inventory level is related to the inflow and outflow of materials:

$$UOR_K = UOR_J + DT(RRR_{JK} - SSR_{JK}).$$

Preparatory to expressing the relationship between desired inventory and the average weekly requisition rate, let us switch from a simple moving average of the past three weeks to an exponentially smoothed mean of RRR. If we determine our mean by exponential smoothing, we can avoid the necessity of carrying a record of the past three weeks' requisition rates as we move from period to period. In this procedural scheme our new mean requisition rate each period is the mean rate used the previous period plus a fraction (the smoothing constant) of the difference between the actual rate of requisitions received in the current period and the previous exponentially smoothed mean. The fraction employed as a smoothing constant can be selected so as to provide the equivalent of two weeks, three weeks, four weeks—or a sequence of any other length—as a basis for our average. A smoothing constant of 0.5, for example, would be the approximate equivalent of a moving average of requisition rates for the past 3 periods.

If we let RSR represent requisition rate smoothed at retail, and let DRR represent the *reciprocal* of our smoothing constant, the current week's RSR would be related to the current requisition rate and last week's RSR in the following way:[10]

$$RSR = RSR_{old} + \frac{1}{DRR}(RRR - RSR_{old})$$

Now if we return to our use of J and K to represent the beginning and end of the week, respectively, we would have:

$$RSR_K = RSR_J + \frac{1}{DRR}(RRR_{JK} - RSR_J)$$

and the general model for a fractional part of one week, DT, would be:

$$RSR_K = RSR_J + \frac{DT}{DRR}(RRR_{JK} - RSR_J)$$

Now we can determine the desired inventory level at moment in time K. For the general relationship we will let AIR (constant for inventory at retail [in weeks]) represent the constant that relates our desired inventory to the smoothed mean of recent requisition rates (this was $6\frac{2}{3}$ in our earlier hand simulation). Then we would have:

$$IDR_K = AIR(RSR_K)$$

To express the relationship between purchase orders sent from retail, the current rate of requisitions received from retail, and the desired and actual inventory levels, let us let DIR represent the *reciprocal* of the fraction of the difference between our desired and the actual inventory, which we will add to the current requisition rate. (As in the case of DRR, DIR can be thought of as a delay in adjusting inventory at retail [in weeks].)

---

[10] The reciprocal of DRR can be thought of as a delay, measured in number of weeks. Thus DRR means Delay in smoothing requisitions at retail, in weeks.

We need also to think of rate of purchase orders sent as applying to a *succeeding* period. That is, if RRR_{JK} represents the rate of requisitions received in the current period, the value for PSR calculated from RRR_{JK} would be the rate at which purchase orders will be sent in the immediately *succeeding* period. For the general model, then, let us let KL represent the interval of time, DT in duration, which begins at moment in time K. Our model for PSR_{KL} then would be:

$$PSR_{KL} = RRR_{JK} + (1/DIR)(IDR_K - IAR_K).$$

It should be apparent that if DT is one week, our equations for IAR, UOR, and PSR precisely represent the relationship we used in conducting our hand simulation of the retailer's system.

Before expressing shipments sent from retail we want to enrich our model a bit and make it more realistic.

In real systems of the type we are modeling we know that the rate of shipment to customers tends to be proportional to the magnitude of back orders. If we let DFR (delay in filling orders retail [in weeks]) represent the reciprocal of the constant that relates shipments sent from retail to our unfilled order file, we would have:

$$SSR_{KL} = UOR_K/DFR.$$

We need to make another provision in determining the rate of shipments sent from retail. If our actual inventory at moment in time K is less than (UOR/DFR)DT, then the rate of shipments sent from retail in interval of time KL will not be UOR_K/DFR, but rather IAR_K/DT.

Our rate equation for SSR, during interval of time KL, would then be the minimum of these two quantities and, as a general model, we might express it thus:

$$SSR_{KL} = MIN(UOR_K/DFR, IAR_K/DT).$$

It will be recalled that (in our hand simulation) shipments received at retail in a given week were equal to purchase orders sent from retail three weeks previously. If we let DTR (delay in transit at retail [in weeks]) represent the number of weeks of delay between the sending of a purchase order and the receipt of materials, and if we think of PSR_{JK} as representing the rate of submission of purchase orders DTR weeks ago, then we might use the following notation to represent the rate of receipt of shipments at retail in interval of time KL:

$$SRR_{KL} = DELAY(PSR_{JK}, DTR).$$

Let us hand simulate the retailer's system again, this time using the equations we have just developed which portray the relationships between the elements of the system as the system moves from state to state in intervals of time (DT). We will begin with the following initial conditions (with J representing the beginning of the *last* period, DT, before time zero, and K representing time zero):

IAR_J = 2,000 units $\qquad$ RSR_J = 300 units
IDR_J = 2,000 units $\qquad$ RRR_{JK} = 300 units per week
UOR_J = 600 units $\qquad$ SSR_{JK} = 300 units per week

And let us give our constants the following values:

DRR = 0.67 weeks $\qquad$ DFR = 2 weeks
AIR = 6⅔ weeks $\qquad$ DTR = 3 weeks
DIR = 2 weeks

Given these initial values, we can calculate values for RRR_K, then IAR_K, and then UOR_K and IDR_K. Then, having these values, we can proceed to determine: SSR_{KL}, PSR_{KL}, RSR_{KL}, and SRR_{KL} for the coming period.

It is evident that there is a required order in calculating the values of the elements from moment in time to succeeding moment in time, just as in our previous hand simulation of the retailer's model. But this time it is different: Given, as initial values, *levels* at the *beginning* of a period, DT, and *rates* of flow *during* the period, we calculate *levels* at the *beginning* of the next period, then *rates during* the period.

A hand simulation of the retailer's system, beginning with the initial conditions set forth above, would yield the sequence of states shown in Table 16–3, assuming that DT = 0.2 weeks and assuming that the rate of requisitions received at retail increases by 10 percent at the beginning of the second week after time 0—that is, after the lapse of 5 intervals of time.

Were we to continue these calculations over 300 time periods (60 weeks of simulation) and plot curves for our variables, we would get step response curves similar to those of Figure 16–7. Curves for IAR, PSR, and SSR are shown in Figure 16–8.

The Impulse Response

It should be apparent that the fashion in which our retailer's system *responds* to an input *stimulus* (such as the 10 percent increase in rate of requisitions received) is determined by the structure of the

TABLE 16–3

Elements (in Order of Determination) for Each Period

	RRR	*RSR*	*IDR*	*IAR*	*UOR*	*PSR*	*SSR*	*SRR*
−15*						300		
−14						300		
−13						300		
. . . .
−1	300	300	2000	2000	600	300	300	300
Time								
Zero								
1	300	300	2000	2000	600	300	300	300
2	300	300	2000	2000	600	300	300	300
3	300	300	2000	2000	600	300	300	300
4	300	300	2000	2000	600	300	300	300
5	300	300	2000	2000	600	300	300	300
6	330	309	2000	2000	606	330	303	300
7	330	315	2060	1999	611	330	306	300
8	330	320	2102	1998	616	361	308	300
9	330	323	2131	1997	621	383	310	300
10	330	325	2152	1995	625	398	312	300
11	330	326	2166	1992	628	410	314	300
12	330	328	2176	1989	631	419	316	300
13	330	328	2184	1986	634	425	317	300
14	330	329	2188	1983	637	430	318	300
15	330	329	2192	1979	639	435	320	300

* The system has been in a steady state for the past three weeks (15 DT's). We need to retain data relating to purchase orders sent three weeks ago to determine SRR in the current period.

system; that is, the way in which its various elements are interrelated. The fashion in which the elements are interrelated determines the way in which an input stimulus will influence the state of the system in the next period.

The impulse response of the file of unfilled orders to a unit increase in the rate of receipt of requisitions could be developed from the following two relationships:

$$\text{UOR}_K = \text{UOR}_J + \text{DT}(\text{RRR}_{JK} - \text{SSR}_{JK})$$
$$\text{SSR}_{JK} = \text{UOR}_J/\text{DFR}.$$

Substituting the second in the first, we get:

$$\text{UOR}_K = \text{UOR}_J + \text{DT}(\text{RRR}_{JK} - \text{UOR}_J/\text{DFR})$$
$$= \text{UOR}_J(1 - \text{DT}/\text{DFR}) + \text{DT}(\text{RRR}_{JK}).$$

Now, if we begin (at time zero) with:

$$\text{UOR}_J = 2.0$$
$$\text{RRR}_{JK} = 1.0,$$

FIGURE 16-8

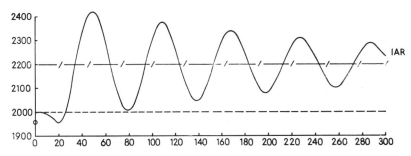

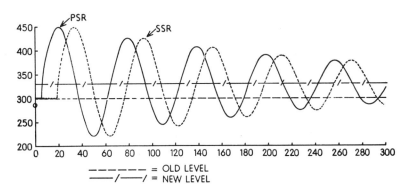

-------- = OLD LEVEL
——/——/ = NEW LEVEL

and if we assume that:

$$DT = 0.2$$
$$DFR = 2.0,$$

then:

$$UOR_K = 1.0.$$

If we hand simulate the "unfilled order file-requisitions received" subsystem, and if we input an increase of unity in the rate of receipt of requisitions at the beginning of the third time interval, we get an impulse response for this subsystem (Table 16-4 and Figure 16-9).

The expression $UOR_J(1 - DT/DFR + DT(RRR_{JK})$ is analogous to the transfer function in engineering and biological systems. It specifies how conditions at the input will be transferred to the output.

We could develop a similar expression to specify how any other subsystem of our retailer's system responds to an impulse.

The concept of an impulse response is very important in systems

TABLE 16–4

Period	RRR	UOR	Period	RRR	UOR
1	1.00000	2.00000	13	1.00000	2.06974
2	1.00000	2.00000	14	1.00000	2.06276
3	2.00000	2.20000	15	1.00000	2.05649
4	1.00000	2.18000	16	1.00000	2.05084
5	1.00000	2.16200	17	1.00000	2.04575
6	1.00000	2.14580	18	1.00000	2.04118
7	1.00000	2.13122	19	1.00000	2.03706
8	1.00000	2.11810	20	1.00000	2.03335
9	1.00000	2.10629	21	1.00000	2.03002
10	1.00000	2.09566	22	1.00000	2.02702
11	1.00000	2.08609	23	1.00000	2.02432
12	1.00000	2.07748	24	1.00000	2.02188

FIGURE 16–9

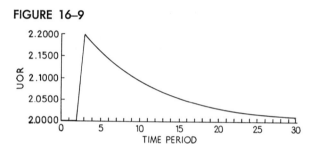

analyis. It develops that any discrete, linear, time invariant system can be completely described by its impulse response.

In complex systems it becomes difficult to develop an analytical expression for the impulse response of the total system. However, we can examine the impulse response by simply subjecting the system to a unit impulse and observing the response of any of the elements of the system to the impulse.

DYNAMO

To facilitate simulation of systems of the character we have dealt with in this chapter, DYNAMO was developed. DYNAMO is a computer language in the same sense that FORTRAN is a computer language. As with FORTRAN, programs written in DYNAMO language must conform to the peculiar conventions of the language. A few of the DYNAMO conventions will be described.

In DYNAMO, subscripts are expressed by use of a decimal point. Thus IAR_K can be written in DYNAMO as IAR.K, and SSR_{KL} can be written SSR.KL.

In DYNAMO the relationship between our retailer's actual inventory at one moment in time and (1) the actual inventory at a previous moment in time and (2) the net rate of inflow can be expressed:

$$\text{IAR.K} = \text{IAR.J} + (\text{DT})(\text{SRR.JK} - \text{SSR.JK}).$$

The equation above is one of a *class* of DYNAMO equations, which has the form:

$$\text{V.K.} = \text{V.J.} + (\text{DT})(\pm\text{P}, \pm\text{Q}).$$

There are approximately 60 admissible DYNAMO equation forms. To translate an ordinary algebraic statement into DYNAMO, one sometimes must do a bit of maneuvering. For example, there is no DYNAMO form into which the following expression can be translated directly:

$$\text{SSR.KL} = \text{MIN}(\text{UOR.K/DFR},\text{IAR.K/DT}).$$

But there *is* one which reads:

$$\text{V} = \text{MIN}(\pm\text{P}, \pm\text{Q})$$

in which P and Q are two *variables,* but not *ratios.*

Furthermore, we have another DYNAMO equation of the form $\text{V} = \text{P/Q}$. Therefore, if we let NIR (negative inventory at retail) correspond to P, we can write:

$$\text{NIR.K} = \text{IAR.K/DT}.$$

And if we let STR (shipments tried at retail) correspond to Q, we can write:

$$\text{STR.K} = \text{UOR.K/DFR}.$$

Then finally we can express the relationship between SSR, UOR, and IAR by the three following legitimate DYNAMO equations:

$$\text{NIR.K} = \text{IAR.K/DT}$$
$$\text{STR.K} = \text{UOR.K/DFR}$$
$$\text{SSR.KL} = \text{MIN}(\text{STR.K},\text{NIR.K}).$$

Another legitimate DYNAMO equation is:

$$\text{V.KL} = \text{DELAY } 3(\pm\text{P,C}),$$

which can be employed to express the relationship between SRR and PSR:[11]

---

[11] For a full discussion of DYNAMO and how the DYNAMO compiler works, see Alexander L. Pugh, III, *DYNAMO User's Manual* (2d ed.; Cambridge, Mass.: The M.I.T. Press, 1963).

FIGURE 16–10*

IAR=I, UOR=U, RRR=R, SSR=S, PSR=P, SRR=Q

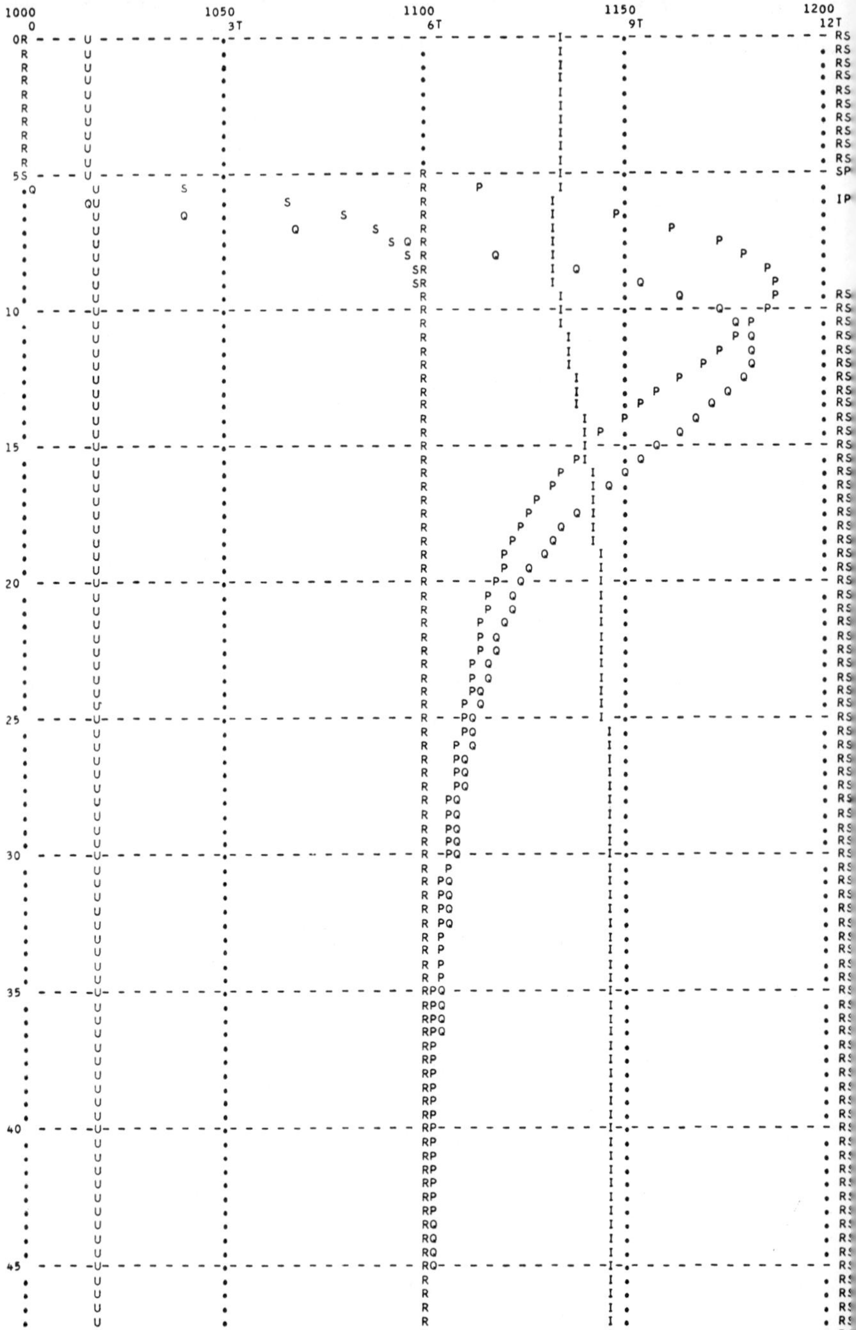

1000	1050	1100	1150	1200
0	3T	6T	9T	12T

(Character plot: vertical scale marked 0, 5, 10, 15, 20, 25, 30, 35, 40, 45, 50; horizontal time axis from 1000 to 1200. The plotted symbols I, U, R, S, P, Q trace the DYNAMO simulation output across the grid.)

* Source: Pugh, *DYNAMO User's Manual*, p. 13.

SRR.KL = DELAY3(PSR.JK,DTR).

The DYNAMO compiler is so constructed that some functions which one would have to structure were he to do this kind of systems simulation in FORTRAN are accommodated automatically, or in a shortcut fashion, by systems functions in the compiler.

Another virtue of DYNAMO for this kind of simulation is the use it makes of the printer as a plotter. By use of what amounts to a variable FORMAT specification, DYNAMO can cause to be printed out, as a system moves from state to state, a number of curves, each corresponding to a system element. In this arrangement, letters, rather than short lines, form the curve, as shown in Figure 16–10, on the facing page.

DISTRIBUTOR AND FACTORY LEVELS

In our retailer's system we concerned ourselves only with the retail level. We know, of course, that just as elements at the retail level are interrelated, and just as these elements are related to customer requisitions as an input, so also are elements within the distributor level interrelated, and related to the retail level as an input. Similarly, the factory level is made up of interrelated elements, and is related to the distributor level and to its own sources of supply.

Forrester's system of notation:

RRR   for Requisitions Received at Retail
DPC   for Delay in Purchasing at Consumer sector
MAF   for Manufacturing Average rate at Factory

quickly becomes intelligible, so that the structure of a "total" system can be translated rather readily into DYNAMO equations, and thus into a DYNAMO program.

EXERCISE

Write a FORTRAN program that will simulate the retailer's system, as portrayed by the equations on page 517 of this chapter.

SUGGESTIONS FOR FURTHER STUDY

FORRESTER, JAY W. *Urban Dynamics.* Cambridge, Mass.: The M.I.T. Press, 1964.

———. *World Dynamics.* Cambridge, Mass.: Wright-Allen Press, 1971. ·

chapter 17

A Study in "Total" Systems Simulation

IN DEVELOPING SIMULATION MODELS one is continually tempted to abandon specific cases and to pursue the elusive but intriguing *universal* model, the general systems simulator, or, as an ultimate, the general problem solver.

From a theoretical point of view, the universal model is potentially a powerful analytical construct by means of which we can immensely improve our understanding of the decision-making process. But in dealing with applied problems in business and industry we must concern ourselves with the specific. Thus we find ourselves building models that portray specific systems with specified parameters.

To improve our feel for total systems simulation, we will build a model for a specific system with specified parameters. We will then employ that model, in the exercises at the end of this chapter, to study the behavior of the total system it represents.

The total system with which we will deal is a business firm we will call the Simco Sales Company.

SIMCO SALES COMPANY

Simco Sales Company sells one product, an electronic air purifier, for domestic use. Simco has these units custom-made by a variety of suppliers, and it resells them under the brand name Filtron.

Lead time for delivery of new stock from their suppliers, Simco

530

has found, varies in a random fashion, with the following distribution:

Lead Time (Weeks)	Probability
4	.10
5	.15
6	.50
7	.15
8	.10

While Simco management is uncertain about demand from week to week (and uses a sales forecasting strategy that will be described shortly), demand is, in fact, normally distributed about a mean of 50 Filtrons per week, with a standard deviation of 15.

When customers request Filtrons and Simco is unable to deliver immediately due to stock-outs, customer orders are back ordered, and customer back orders are first satisfied out of new stock received. New stock is received over the weekend.

At the end of each week Simco management appraises its operating experience during the week, updates records, and makes two decisions: (1) whether to declare a price markdown if demand has been less than that deemed satisfactory, and (2) how much new stock to order, if any. The order itself, however, is not placed until early Monday morning.

If demand during the week was less than 70 percent of the forecasted demand that week, the sales price for the coming week is marked down from the normal retail price of $100 per Filtron to $85. The price markdown, however, is made only if the inventory of Filtrons on hand at the end of the week, plus new stock scheduled to arrive over the weekend, is more than 150 percent of forecast demand for the coming week. At the end of each week Simco management currently forecasts demand for the coming week simply by averaging the demand during the past three weeks.

Experience has shown that during a week in which the special reduced price of $85 per Filtron prevails, demand is stimulated to a 5 percent increase.

Simco currently determines at the end of the week how much to order. The amount to order is determined by adding the quantity of Filtrons sold during the week to one half the sum of:

1. The difference between the desired and actual inventory,
2. The difference between the desired and actual supply back order (pipeline).

The desired inventory is three times the demand forecast for the coming week. The desired pipeline is the expected demand during lead time, based on the demand forecast for the coming week.

Simco has observed that about 20 percent of the back ordered demand not filled the following week is lost.

Simco pays $50 per Filtron received from its suppliers, and payment is due during the week following receipt of a new shipment of stock.

Fixed costs amount to $2,000 per week, and variable costs are as follows:

1. 20 percent of the investment in inventory at the beginning of the week, at a yearly rate, and
2. 8 percent of the investment in accounts receivable at the beginning of the week, at a yearly rate.

The above costs are all cash costs and constitute a cash drain at the end of the week.

At the beginning of the period of operations with which we are concerned, the state of the Simco system is as follows.

Demand during the past 10 weeks has been 50 units each week.

Simco is destined to receive, on each of the coming six weekends, 50 units of new stock.

The actual inventory on hand is 150 units.

There are no customer back orders outstanding.

Demand forecast for the current week is 50 units.

No price markdown is planned for the current week.

$2,500 is scheduled to be received from accounts receivable collections over each of the coming four weeks (thus total accounts receivable are $10,000).

Cash on hand stands at $4,000.

Half of Simco's weekly sales are cash sales. Charge sales do not bear interest and are payable four weeks later.

The problem is to construct a program by which Simco's operating experience can be simulated so that certain policy decisions (notably the demand and forecasting strategy and the inventory management policy) can be tested to determine their influence on profits, and so on.

It would be preferable to design subroutines for (1) generating demand and determining lead times, and (2) making policy decisions.

A "TOTAL" SYSTEM MODEL FOR SIMULATING THE OPERATIONS OF SIMCO SALES COMPANY

Let us construct a FORTRAN program by means of which we can cause the computer to simulate the operating experience of Simco Sales Company, and let it determine and print out summary data that will enable us to test various demand forecasting strategies and various inventory management policies.

We will begin by constructing a supply subroutine whose purpose will be to determine how much new stock was received over the weekend and to update our back order pipeline. We will assume that it is early Monday morning, before the hour Simco opens for business.

The Supply Subroutine

Since we review weekly our inventory on hand and our stock on order, and since we may place an order at the beginning of each week, we may have outstanding at any one time orders "destined to be delivered" in 1, 2, 3, 4, 5, 6, 7, or 8 weeks. (A reexamination of Simco's expected lead time distribution will make it apparent that we will never have outstanding an order that will take longer than eight weeks to arrive.)

In order to simulate weekly receipts of new shipments from our suppliers we will have to keep a record of when our various past orders (our pipeline) are "destined to be delivered." It will be convenient for us to use a one-dimension subscripted variable here. Let us designate the variable PIPLIN(K) for this purpose. We will let:

PIPLIN(1)   hold the amount of previously back ordered stock destined to be delivered to Simco in one week;

PIPLIN(2)   hold the amount of previously back ordered stock destined to be delivered to Simco in two weeks;

and so on.

Since that stock which we were destined to receive last week in two weeks is now destined to be received in one week, and that which we were destined to receive last week in three weeks is now destined to be received in two weeks, and so on, it is necessary each Monday to update Simco's supply pipeline.

```
        DO 2 K = 1,7
    2   PIPLIN(K) = PIPLIN(K + 1)
        PIPLIN(8) = 0.0
```

In composing the supply subroutine, let us assume that the initial state of Simco's back order pipeline will be loaded into the program at the beginning of our *main* program. In this circumstance it will be necessary to make provision for the variable PIPLIN(K) in our CALL and SUBROUTINE statements.

Let us also assume that the decision about how much to order, always made at the end of the week, has been made, and that by the time we are ready in the main program to call our Supply Subroutine, the variable UO (units ordered) will have been given the value of the order quantity decided on.

Basically, then, the function of our supply subroutine, which we will call the first thing Monday morning, will be:

1. To inquire how much stock was delivered over the weekend;
2. To determine when the order quantity UO, decided on at the end of last week, will be delivered (thus we "negotiate" delivery terms with our suppliers and place an order for UO Filtrons Monday morning);

and with this information we update our supply pipeline. (This means that while the lead time Simco can expect is random, when Simco places a Monday morning order Simco gets a delivery date commitment from its suppliers. We assume that the commitment date is always honored, so that Simco *knows* the delivery dates of all stock in its back order pipeline at all times.)

The following program segment, constructed so as to simulate the lead time distribution Simco expects to experience, should do this:

```
        M = RANDOM(X) * 100.0
        IF (M − 9)3,3,4
    3   LT = 4
        GO TO 11
    4   IF (M − 24)5,5,6
    5   LT = 5
        GO TO 11
    6   IF (M − 74(7,7,8
    7   LT = 6
        GO TO 11
    8   IF (M − 89)9,9,10
    9   LT = 7
        GO TO 11
   10   LT = 8
   11   CONTINUE
```

Now, if a currently simulated lead time should tell us that our ordered quantity of Filtrons is destined to be delivered, for example, in five weeks, we would want to add this quantity to our updated pipeline, increasing any outstanding back order already destined to be delivered in five weeks by an amount equal to the current value of UO.

Let SR hold the stock just received over the weekend, and our supply subroutine might appear as follows:

```
     SUBROUTINE SUPPLY (PIPLIN,SR,UO)
     DIMENSION PIPLIN(9)
     SR = PIPLIN(1)
     DO 2 K = 1,7
   2 PIPLIN(K) = PIPLIN(K + 1)
     PIPLIN(8) = 0.0
     M = RANDOM(X) * 100.0
     IF (M - 9)3,3,4
   3 LT = 4
     GO TO 11
   4 IF (M - 24)5,5,6
   5 LT = 5
     GO TO 11
   6 IF (M - 74)7,7,8
   7 LT = 6
     GO TO 11
   8 IF (M - 89)9,9,10
   9 LT = 7
     GO TO 11
  10 LT = 8
  11 CONTINUE
     PIPLIN(LT) = PIPLIN(LT) + UO
     RETURN
     END
```

The Main Program

We will want to provide in our main program for initializing the state of Simco at the beginning of our simulation of Simco's operating experience. We might do this with the following statements:

```
     DO 5 M = 1,6        Variables not already identified are:
   5 PIPLIN(M) = 50.0
     PIPLIN(7) = 0.0
     PIPLIN(8) = 0.0
     TMU = 50.0
```

$$SD = 15.0$$
$$UO = 50.0$$

$ULS = 0.0$	ULS, units of lost sales
$AIEW = 150.0$	AIEW, actual inventory at end of week
$CBQ = 0.0$	CBQ, customer back order queue [more will be said about this shortly]

$$DO\ 6\ J = 1,10$$
$$6 \quad DDP(J) = 50.0 \qquad DDP(J), \text{ past demand, by weeks, for 10 weeks}$$

$FD = 50.0$	FD, demand forecast for current week
$PMD = 0.0$	PMD, price markdown
$SSF = 0.0$	SSF, sales stimulation factor

$$DO\ 7\ K = 1,4$$

$7 \quad AR(K) = 2500.0$	AR(K), accounts receivable, by weeks
$TAR = 10000.0$	TAR, total accounts receivable
$COH = 4000.0$	COH, cash on hand

Let us assume that it is Monday morning of our first week of simulated operations. By calling SUBROUTINE SUPPLY we can:

1. Determine stock received over the weekend (the current value of SR).
2. Update our backorder pipeline.

This requires the statement: CALL SUPPLY (PIPLIN,SR,UO).

Now, in our main program we would do well to record the arrival of new stock over the weekend and to apply any new stock received over the weekend to customer back orders, if any. In a program segment designed to deal with this we will let the variable BS represent back ordered sales—those sales resulting from reduction of the customer back order queue by delivery of Filtrons at the beginning of the week (from stock received over the weekend) to customers whose orders we were unable to fill during the previous week.

The variable CBQ, customer back order queue, holds the quantity of back ordered Filtrons; the variable AIEW will hold the actual inventory at the end of the previous week (and before the receipt of any new stock over the weekend); and AIBW will hold the actual inventory at the beginning of the week (i.e., AIEW plus SR).

The following program segment should do these things for us:

```
        AIBW = AIEW + SR
        IF (CBQ - AIBW)8,8,9
    8   BS = CBQ
        AAIBW = AIBW - CBQ
```

```
      CBQ = 0.0
      ULS = 0.0
      GO TO 10
   9  BS = AIBW
      AAIBW = 0.0
      ULS = (CBQ − AIBW) * 0.20
      CBQ = (CBQ − AIBW) * 0.80
  10  N = CBQ
      CBQ = N
      N = ULS
      ULS = N
```

In the above program segment we use AAIBW, adjusted actual inventory at the beginning of the week, to hold the value of inventory *after* customer back orders at the beginning of the week, if any, have been dealt with, but before the current week's demand has been considered.

We provide for reducing the customer back order queue and units of lost sales to zero if the actual inventory at the beginning of the week (AIBW) is greater than CBQ, and we provide for reducing AAIBW to zero if CBQ is greater than AIBW.

Recalling that 20 percent of customer back orders *not* satisfied at the beginning of the week are lost, we also provide for reducing unsatisfied CBQ by 20 percent; then we record in the variable ULS (units of lost sales) the number of Filtrons we failed to sell due to stock-out.

Finally in the last four statements we truncate any fractional part of the customer back order queue and units of lost sales.

We are now ready to accommodate the current week's customers. We need a demand subroutine to determine what demand we are "destined to experience" this week.

The Demand Generator Subroutine

We would like to construct a demand subroutine in such a way that each time we call the subroutine, the demand Simco is "destined to experience" during the coming week will be determined for us. Since Simco's demand pattern will be normally distributed, we can use the normal generator described in Chapter 10 to simulate weekly demand.

However, we must make special provision for modifying the demand thus generated under two conditions:

1. When a negative demand is generated. With a mean demand of 50 units and a standard deviation of 15 it is extremely unlikely that a negative demand will be generated, but it is a distinct possibility; and under this condition we should simply give demand a value of zero.

2. When because of the past week's unsatisfactory demand Simco's markdown policy calls for reducing the sale price by 15 percent, yielding an expected 5 percent stimulus in the succeeding week's demand.

In composing our demand subroutine we will assume that by the time this subroutine is called (from the main program), demand the *previous* week has been compared to demand *forecast* for the previous week, and that the variable PMD (price markdown) has been given a value of 0.0 or 0.15, as the past week's demand has been judged satisfactory or unsatisfactory.

We employ the variable SSF as a sales stimulation factor. If last week's demand was judged unsatisfactory, and it was decided to reduce the price of Filtrons by 15 percent, SSF will be given a value of 0.05 and used to increase this week's demand, just generated, by 5 percent. Otherwise, SSF will be given a value of 0.0.

In the CALL and SUBROUTINE statements we will want to make provision for transferring values for PMD and also ADDW (actual demand during the current week) in and out of the subroutine.

To permit us to test a variety of policies under a variety of conditions let us treat the mean and the standard deviations of the demand pattern as variables. We can read in values for these variables at the beginning of our main program. These variables—TMU for the mean and SD for the standard deviation—must also be provided for in our CALL and SUBROUTINE statements.

A subroutine suitable for generating weekly demand might appear as follows:

```
  SUBROUTINE DEMAND (ADDW,PMD,TMU,SD,SSF)
  V = (−2.0 * LOGF(RANDOM(X))) ** 0.5 * COSF(6.283 *
    RANDOM(X))
  D = TMU + SD * V
  IF (D)1,2,2
1 D = 0.0
2 IF (PMD − 0.15)3,4,4
3 SSF = 0.0
  GO TO 5
```

```
4   SSF = 0.05
5   ADDW = D * (1.0 + SSF)
    N = ADDW
    ADDW = N
    RETURN
    END
```

In the first IF statement, in SUBROUTINE DEMAND, we provide for making demand zero if our generator has generated a negative demand.

In the second IF statement (statement 2) we determine whether a decision to reduce the price was made in the main program—in which event PMD will have been given a value of 0.15—and therefore whether we should stimulate demand by 5 percent.

In the two statements just preceding the RETURN statement we truncate the decimal part of the demand just generated to avoid sales with a fractional part of a unit.

Now we are ready to conduct normal sales operations during the current week, and we call our demand subroutine to determine the demand we are "destined to experience" during the week. We simply: CALL DEMAND (ADDW,PMD,TMU,SD,SSF), and the variable ADDW gets a new value corresponding to the quantity of Filtrons customers will demand during the current week.

Let us now assume that the week's operations have been conducted, the end of the week has arrived, and we are ready to record and interpret the week's experience, to update our accounts, to forecast next week's demand, and to make a reorder decision.

First we should provide for dealing with the current week's demand. Let us add a program segment that will translate our knowledge of the current week's demand (ADDW), inventory on hand after customer back orders were dealt with (AAIBW), and back order sales at the beginning of the week (BS) into:

1. Total sales during the week.
2. Actual inventory at the end of the week.
3. Gross profit and gross income from the week's sales.

We will let the variable TUS (total units sold) hold the value of the week's total sales in number of Filtrons; the variable WGP hold the week's gross profit; and the variable GIS hold gross income from sales during the week. The following statements should determine what is required.

```
        IF (ADDW − AAIBW)11,11,12
11   TUS = BS + ADDW
        GO TO 13
12   TUS = BS + AAIBW
        CBQ = CBQ + (ADDW − AAIBW)
13   GIS = 100.0 * (1.0 − PMD) * TUS
        WGP = GIS − 50.0 * TUS
        AIEW = AAIBW − ADDW
        IF (AIEW)14,15,15
14   AIEW = 0.0
15   CONTINUE
```

In the program segment above, when actual demand during the week (ADDW) exceeded our adjusted actual inventory at the beginning of the week (AAIBW):

1. We calculated total units sold (TUS) on the basis of units available (AAIBW) rather than units demanded (ADDW).
2. We "lengthened" our customer back order queue (CBQ) by an amount equal to the unsatisfied demand.
3. We reduced actual inventory at the end of the week (AIEW) to zero (see the statement preceding statement 14).

When actual demand was equal to or less than adjusted inventory at the beginning of the week, total units sold was based on actual demand, and therefore the customer back order queue, already zero, was not altered.

In the statement after statement 13 in the above program segment, the week's gross profit is determined. The sale price, it will be recalled, is $100 per Filtron except when a price markdown has been declared. And the cost per Filtron to Simco is $50.

Let us now update our cash on hand (COH). Cash on hand will be increased by:

1. Accounts receivable collected during the week.
2. Income from cash sales during the week.

And cash on hand will be decreased by:

1. Payment for new stock received over the past weekend (recall that payment to our suppliers must be made during the week following delivery of new stock).
2. Fixed charges (FC) of $2,000 per week.
3. Variable charges, including:[1]

---

[1] Some of these would not normally be considered cash costs, but rather would be deferred charges. To simplify our model let us assume that all these are costs that constitute an immediate cash drain.

a)   Inventory holding charges, at a rate of 20 percent per year, calculated on the basis of the dollar cost of the actual inventory at the beginning of the week (AIBW).

b)   Accounts receivable investment charge, calculated at a rate of 8 percent per year on the total accounts receivable at the beginning of the week (TAR).

With the following statements we can update our cash on hand account:

$$FC = 2000.0$$
$$COH = COH + AR(1) + 0.5 * GIS - SR * 50.0 - FC$$
$$- (0.20/52.) * 50.0 * AIBW - (0.08/52.0) * TAR$$

We might now update our accounts receivable. Recall that half the week's sales are cash sales, and that charge sales are collected four weeks later. We have designated AR(J) as a one-dimension subscripted variable for keeping track of our accounts receivable (see the initializing statements at the beginning of our main program).

As with our supply pipeline, we will want to update our accounts receivable record. This might be done thus:

$$DO \ 18 \ J = 1,3$$
$$18 \quad AR(J) = AR(J + 1)$$
$$AR(4) = 0.5 * GIS$$
$$TAR = AR(1) + AR(2) + AR(3) + AR(4)$$

One half of the current week's gross income from sales will be an addition to accounts receivable and will be collected four weeks from now. In the next to last statement in the program segment above we make provision for this as part of the process of updating the accounts receivable record.

In the final statement above we sum our total accounts receivable (TAR) to prepare for printing out our statement of accounts later.

We can determine the week's net profit (WNP) using our knowledge of the week's gross profit (WGP), already calculated, and the operating costs employed above to update our cash on hand account:

$$WNP = WGP - (0.20/52.0) * 50.0 * AIBW - (0.08/52.0) * TAR - FC$$

We are now ready to make decisions concerning:

1.   Whether to declare a price markdown next week.
2.   How much new stock to order.

Recall that Simco declares a price markdown if these two conditions prevail:

1. The current week's demand was less than 70 percent of forecast demand.
2. The actual inventory on hand at the end of the week (AIEW), plus the stock destined to be received over the coming weekend (PIPLIN(1)), is more than 150 percent of the demand forecast for the coming week.

The variable FD holds our last weekend's forecast of the current week's demand (see the initializing program at the beginning of the main program).

With the following statement we can determine whether condition (1), above, warrants a price markdown:

$$\text{IF (ADDW} - 0.7 * \text{FD)19,21,21}$$

But to determine whether condition (2) warrants a price markdown, we must forecast sales for the coming week.

As suggested earlier, it will be convenient to design subroutines for demand forecasting and for reorder decisions. These are the two management practices we are interested in testing, and it will be convenient if we can manipulate the program segments concerned with these practices without disturbing the remainder of the program. Subroutines nicely serve this purpose.

The Demand Forecasting Subroutine

We have designed DDP(L) as the one-dimension subscripted variable in which we want to store demand during the past, with:

>DDP(1)   holding the demand 1 week past
>DDP(2)   holding the demand 2 weeks past,

and so on.

As before, we will want to update this record each week. This might be done as follows:

$$\text{DO 1 IB} = 1,9$$
$$\text{L} = 11 - \text{IB}$$
$$1 \quad \text{DDP(L)} = \text{DDP(L} - 1)$$
$$\text{DDP(1)} = \text{ADDW}$$

Let us design this subroutine initially to test Simco's *current* demand forecasting strategy. Later we will alter it to test alternative strategies.

At present Simco forecasts demand during the coming week simply by averaging the demand during the past three weeks. We will let the variable FD hold the current value of forecast demand, determined thus:

$$FD = (DDP(1) + DDP(2) + DDP(3))/3.0.$$

Our demand forecasting subroutine, then, is simply:

```
SUBROUTINE FORECAS (DDP,FD,ADDW)
DIMENSION DDP(11)
DO 1 IB = 1,9
L = 11 - IB
1   DDP(L) = DDP(L - 1)
DDP(1) = ADDW
FD = (DDP(1) + DDP(2) + DDP(3))/3.0
RETURN
END
```

Now, with the statement, CALL FORECAS (DDP,FD, ADDW), we can cause FD to be given the value of our demand forecast for the coming week, and we are equipped to decide whether actual inventory on hand (AIEW), plus new stock to be received over the weekend (PIPLIN(1)), is sufficient, compared with the demand forecast for the coming week, to warrant a price markdown. This requires only an IF statement:

$$IF (AIEW + PIPLIN(1) - 1.5 * FD)22,22,20$$

From the above it should be apparent that our pricing decision can be made by the following program segment:

```
    IF (ADDW - 0.7 * FD)19,21,21
19  CALL FORECAS (DDP,FD,ADDW)
    IF (AIEW + PIPLIN(1) - 1.5 * FD)22,22,20
20  PMD = 0.15
    SSF = 0.05
    GO TO 23
21  CALL FORECAS (DDP,FD,ADDW)
22  PMD = 0.0
    SSF = 0.0
23  CONTINUE
```

In the above program segment, when the conditions dictating a price markdown prevail we set PMD, the variable holding the value of the price markdown, equal to 0.15; and we provide a sales stimulation factor of 5 percent by setting SSF = 0.05; otherwise we set PMD = 0.0 and SSF = 0.0.

By the addition of statement 21 in the program segment above, we make certain that SUBROUTINE FORECAS has been called, regardless of whether a price markdown was declared, and thereby prepare for determining how much stock should be ordered.

The Reorder Subroutine

Recall that under Simco's *present* policy an order is placed at the end of the week for a quantity of Filtrons equal to total units sold during the week plus half the sum of (1) the difference between the desired and the actual inventory and (2) the difference between the desired and the actual supply back order pipeline, where desired inventory = 3 times the demand forecast for the coming week, and desired supply back order = expected demand during lead time, based on the demand forecast for the coming week.

Actual inventory on hand is AIEW. With the following statements we can determine desired inventory (DI), actual supply back order (ASB), and desired supply back order (DSB):

$$DI = 3.0 * FD$$
$$ASB = 0.0$$
$$DO \; 1 \; N = 1,8$$
$$1 \quad ASB = ASB + PIPLIN(N)$$
$$DSB = 6.0 * FD$$

If our ordering policy should yield a decision to order a negative quantity of Filtrons we will, of course, want to order zero. An order subroutine suitable for Simco's *present* ordering policy might therefore be:

```
        SUBROUTINE ORDER (PIPLIN,UO,TUS,AIEW,FD,
            ASB,DI,DSB)
        DIMENSION PIPLIN(9)
        DI = 3.0 * FD
        ASB = 0.0
        DO 1 N = 1,8
    1   ASB = ASB + PIPLIN(N)
        DSB = 6.0 * FD
        UO = TUS + 0.5 * (DI − AIEW + DSB − ASB)
        N = UO
        UO = N
        IF (UO)2,3,3
    2   UO = 0.0
    3   CONTINUE
        RETURN
        END
```

To determine the number of Filtrons to be ordered at the end of the week we simply:

CALL ORDER (PIPLIN,UO,TUS,AIEW,FD,ASB,DI,DSB).

Report Generating

We would like to study the behavior of Simco. Let us simulate Simco's operating experience over a sample of 100 weeks, and store, after each week's simulation, data required for determining the mean and the variance associated with each account we are interested in. To do this, we might store in the one-dimension subscripted variable $R(K)$ the cumulative sums of the accounts we are interested in and the cumulative sums of their squares, as these are generated weekly. Thus:

R(1)   holds cumulative sum of values generated weekly for ADDW
R(3)   "   "   "   "   "   "   "   " CBQ
R(5)   "   "   "   "   "   "   "   " AIEW
R(7)   "   "   "   "   "   "   "   " ASB
R(9)   "   "   "   "   "   "   "   " TAR
R(11)   "   "   "   "   "   "   "   " COH
R(13)   "   "   "   "   "   "   "   " TUS
R(15)   "   "   "   "   "   "   "   " GIS
R(17)   "   "   "   "   "   "   "   " WGP
R(19)   "   "   "   "   "   "   "   " WNP
R(21)   "   "   "   "   "   "   "   " ULS

and:

R(2)   holds cumulative sum of squares of values generated for ADDW
R(4)   "   "   "   "   "   "   "   "   " CBQ
R(6)   "   "   "   "   "   "   "   "   " AIEW
R(8)   "   "   "   "   "   "   "   "   " ASB
R(10)   "   "   "   "   "   "   "   "   " TAR
R(12)   "   "   "   "   "   "   "   "   " COH
R(14)   "   "   "   "   "   "   "   "   " TUS
R(16)   "   "   "   "   "   "   "   "   " GIS
R(18)   "   "   "   "   "   "   "   "   " WGP
R(20)   "   "   "   "   "   "   "   "   " WNP
R(22)   "   "   "   "   "   "   "   "   " ULS

We would want to initialize these variables at zero, at the beginning of our main program:

```
      DO 4 K = 1,22
   4  R(K) = 0.0
```

Toward the end of our main program we might employ the following set of statements to store the required data as it is generated:

$$
\begin{aligned}
R(1) &= R(1) + ADDW \\
R(2) &= R(2) + ADDW ** 2 \\
R(3) &= R(3) + CBQ \\
R(4) &= R(4) + CBQ ** 2 \\
R(5) &= R(5) + AIEW \\
R(6) &= R(6) + AIEW ** 2 \\
R(7) &= R(7) + ASB \\
R(8) &= R(8) + ASB ** 2 \\
R(9) &= R(9) + TAR \\
R(10) &= R(10) + TAR ** 2 \\
R(11) &= R(11) + COH \\
R(12) &= R(12) + COH ** 2 \\
R(13) &= R(13) + TUS \\
R(14) &= R(14) + TUS ** 2 \\
R(15) &= R(15) + GIS \\
R(16) &= R(16) + GIS ** 2 \\
R(17) &= R(17) + WGP \\
R(18) &= R(18) + WGP ** 2 \\
R(19) &= R(19) + WNP \\
R(20) &= R(20) + WNP ** 2 \\
R(21) &= R(21) + ULS \\
R(22) &= R(22) + ULS ** 2
\end{aligned}
$$

After simulation of 100 weeks of operating experience we can summarize and translate these data into means and standard deviations (A(I) for the means, and STDEV(I) for the standard deviations) by the following statements:

```
    DO 26 I = 1,21,2
    A(I) = R(I)/100.0
26  STDEV(I) = SQRTF( (R(I + 1) − R(I) ** 2/100.0)/99.0)
```

Now, by the addition of the required DIMENSION statement at the beginning of the main program we are ready to simulate one week's experience:

```
DIMENSION AR(5),PIPLIN(9),DDP(11),R(22),
    A(22),STDEV(22)
```

By adding a suitably placed DO statement, we can oblige the computer to conduct the simulation over the desired 100 weeks of operations. Finally, we would want to add suitably composed

PRINT and FORMAT statements to print out for us the desired data.

Our complete program for simulating the experience of Simco Sales Company over 100 weeks' operations is portrayed in the Flow Diagram of Figure 17–1. And in Figure 17–2 we have a complete computer program, with comment statements liberally interspersed to facilitate interpretation.

The printout of the program in Figure 17–2 is shown in Figure 17–3.[2] During this sample of 100 weeks of simulated experience, actual inventory at the end of the week (AIEW) dropped to zero twice, and customer back order queues formed both times. The price of Filtrons was marked down during 17 of the 100 weeks. Simco lost money during 40 of the 100 weeks, but experienced an average weekly net profit of $368.51, with a standard deviation of $802.01. Cash on hand (COH) built up rather steadily during the 100 weeks. Simco is a profitable company, and no dividends are currently being paid out.

Whether alternative policies relative to forecasting, price markdown, and inventory management would be superior remains to be seen. By adjusting the model of Figure 17–2 we could test a variety of policies under a variety of market conditions, and thus improve our understanding of the system and equip ourselves to make better management decisions (see Figure 17–3).

Note: Exercises begin on page 554.

---

[2] This output is the result of a particular random number generator. Since the sample is small, other generators can be expected to yield somewhat different results.

FIGURE 17–1

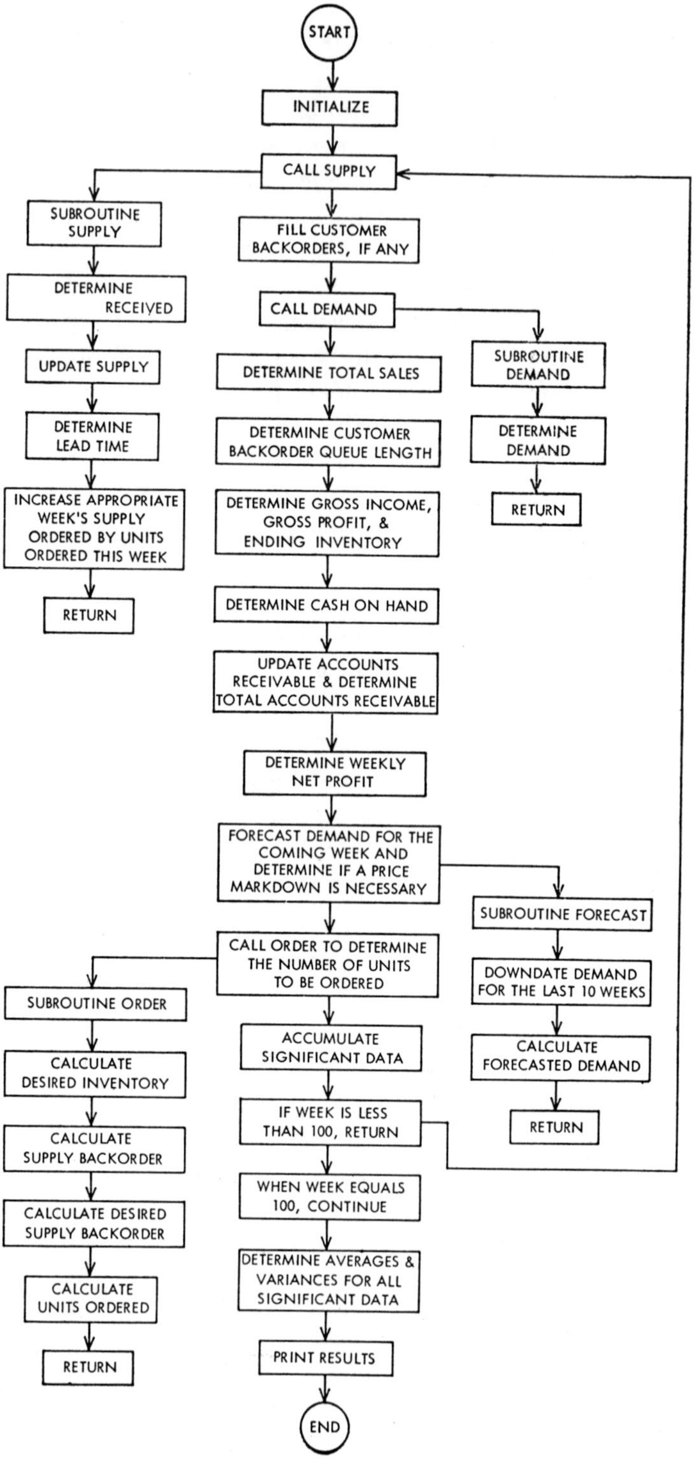

START

INITIALIZE

CALL SUPPLY

SUBROUTINE SUPPLY

DETERMINE RECEIVED

UPDATE SUPPLY

DETERMINE LEAD TIME

INCREASE APPROPRIATE WEEK'S SUPPLY ORDERED BY UNITS ORDERED THIS WEEK

RETURN

FILL CUSTOMER BACKORDERS, IF ANY

CALL DEMAND

DETERMINE TOTAL SALES

DETERMINE CUSTOMER BACKORDER QUEUE LENGTH

DETERMINE GROSS INCOME, GROSS PROFIT, & ENDING INVENTORY

DETERMINE CASH ON HAND

UPDATE ACCOUNTS RECEIVABLE & DETERMINE TOTAL ACCOUNTS RECEIVABLE

DETERMINE WEEKLY NET PROFIT

FORECAST DEMAND FOR THE COMING WEEK AND DETERMINE IF A PRICE MARKDOWN IS NECESSARY

CALL ORDER TO DETERMINE THE NUMBER OF UNITS TO BE ORDERED

ACCUMULATE SIGNIFICANT DATA

IF WEEK IS LESS THAN 100, RETURN

WHEN WEEK EQUALS 100, CONTINUE

DETERMINE AVERAGES & VARIANCES FOR ALL SIGNIFICANT DATA

PRINT RESULTS

END

SUBROUTINE DEMAND

DETERMINE DEMAND

RETURN

SUBROUTINE FORECAST

DOWNDATE DEMAND FOR THE LAST 10 WEEKS

CALCULATE FORECASTED DEMAND

RETURN

SUBROUTINE ORDER

CALCULATE DESIRED INVENTORY

CALCULATE SUPPLY BACKORDER

CALCULATE DESIRED SUPPLY BACKORDER

CALCULATE UNITS ORDERED

RETURN

FIGURE 17-2

```
      PROGRAM SIMCO
      DIMENSION AR(5), PIPLIN(9), DDP(11),R(22), A(22),STDEV(22)
    1 FORMAT(14H WEEKLY DEMAND,F27.4,F25.4/23H BACKORDER QUEUE LENGTH,F1
     18.4,F25.4/25H INVENTORY AT END OF WEEK,F16.4,F25.4/17H SUPPLY BACK
     2ORDER,F24.4,F25.4/20H ACCOUNTS RECEIVABLE,F21.4,F25.4/13H CASH ON
     3HAND,F28.4,F25.4/6H SALES,F35.4,F25.4/24H GROSS INCOME FROM SALES,
     4F17.4,F25.4/20H WEEKLY GROSS PROFIT,F21.4,F25.4/18H WEEKLY NET PRO
     5FIT,F23.4,F25.4/20H UNITS OF LOST SALES,F21.4,F25.4)
    2 FORMAT(//33X,8H AVERAGE,10X,19H STANDARD DEVIATION)
    3 FORMAT(///3X,4HWEEK,5H ADDW,5X,3HCBQ,5X,4HAIEW,5X,3HABS,7X,3HTAR,
     19X,3HCOH,5X,3HTUS,6X,3HGIS,7X,3HWGP,7X,3HWNP,4X,3HULS,5X,2HFD,3X,3
     2HPMD/)
      PRINT 3
C     INITIALIZE VALUES.
C     INITIALIZE DATA ACCUMULATION VALUES AT ZERO,
      DO 4 K = 1,22
    4 R(K) = 0.0
C     INITIALIZE PIPELINE FOR THE NEXT 8 WEEKS,
      DO 5 M = 1,6
    5 PIPLIN(M) = 50.0
      PIPLIN(7) = 0.0
      PIPLIN(8) = 0.0
      TMU=50.0
      SD=15.0
      UO=50.
      ULS = 0.0
      AIEW = 150.0
      CBQ = 0.0
      DO 6 J = 1,10
    6 DDP(J) = 50.0
      FD = 50.0
      PMD = 0.0
      SSF = 0.0
C     INITIALIZE ACCOUNTS RECEIVABLE FOR THE NEXT 4 WEEKS,
      DO 7 K = 1,4
    7 AR(K) = 2500.0
      TAR = 10000.0
      COH = 4000.0
C     RUN FOR 100 WEEKS.
      DO 25 JWKS = 1,100
C     CALL SUPPLY TO DETERMINE LEAD TIME FOR UNITS ORDERED,
      CALL SUPPLY (PIPLIN,SR,UO)
C     FILL CUSTOMER BACKORDERS, IF ANY.
      AIBW = AIEW + SR
      IF (CBQ - AIBW) 8,8,9
    8 BS = CBQ
      AAIBW = AIBW - CBQ
      CBQ = 0.0
      ULS=0.0
      GO TO 10
    9 BS = AIBW
      AAIBW = 0.0
      ULS = (CBQ - AIBW) * 0.20
      CBQ = (CBQ - AIBW) * 0.80
   10 N = CRQ
      CRQ = N
      N = ULS
      ULS = N
C     CALL DEMAND TO DETERMINE DEMAND FOR THIS WEEK,
      CALL DEMAND (ADDW, PMD, TMU, SD, SSF)
C     DETERMINE TOTAL SALES DURING THE WEEK.
      IF (ADDW - AAIBW) 11,11,12
   11 TUS = BS + ADDW
      GO TO 13
   12 TUS = BS + AAIBW
C     DETERMINE CUSTOMER BACKORDER QUEUE LENGTH.
      CRQ = CBQ + (ADDW - AAIBW)
C     DETERMINE GROSS INCOME, GROSS PROFIT, AND ENDING INVENTORY.
   13 GIS = 100.0 * (1.0 - PMD) * TUS
```

FIGURE 17-2 (Continued)

```
      WGP = GIS - 50.0 * TUS
      AIEW = AAIBW - ADDW
      IF (AIEW) 14,15,15
   14 AIEW = 0.0
   15 CONTINUE
   16 FC = 2000.0
C     DETERMINE CASH ON HAND.
   17 COH=COH+AR(1)+.5*GIS-SR*50.-FC-(.2/52.)*50.*AIBW-(.08/52.)*TAR
C     UPDATE ACCOUNTS RECEIVABLE AND DETERMINE TOTAL A.R.
      DO 18   J = 1,3
   18 AR(J) = AR(J + 1)
      AR(4) = 0.5 * GIS
      TAR = AR(1) +AR(2) + AR(3) + AR(4)
C     DETERMINE WEEKLY NET PROFIT.
      WNP = WGP -(0.2 / 52.) *50. * AIBW - (0.08 / 52.)*TAR- FC
      IF (ADDW - 0.70 *FD) 19,21,21
C     FORECAST DEMAND FOR THE COMING WEEK AND DETERMINE IF A PRICE MARKDOW
C     IS NECESSARY.
   19 CALL FORECAS (DDP,FD,ADDW)
      IF(AIEW + PIPLIN(1) - 1.5 * FD) 22,22,20
   20 PMD = 0.15
      SSF = 0.05
      GO TO 23
   21 CALL FORECAS (DDP,FD,ADDW)
   22 PMD = 0.0
      SSF = 0.0
   23 CONTINUE
C     CALL ORDER TO DETERMINE THE NUMBER OF UNITS TO BE ORDERED.
      CALL ORDER (PIPLIN,UO,TUS,AIEW,FD,ASB,DI,DSB)
      PRINT 24, JWKS,ADDW,CBQ,AIEW,ASB,TAR,COH,TUS,GIS,WGP,WNP,ULS,FD,PM
     1D
   24 FORMAT(I7,F6.0,F8.2,2F9.2,F11.2,F12.2,F6.0,3F10.2,F6.1,F6.0,F5.2)
C     ACCUMULATE SIGNIFICANT DATA.
      R(1) = R(1) + ADDW
      R(2) = R(2) + ADDW**2
      R(3) = R(3) + CBQ
      R(4) = R(4) + CBQ**2
      R(5) = R(5) + AIEW
      R(6) = R(6) + AIEW**2
      R(7) = R(7) + ASB
      R(8) = R(8) + ASB**2
      R(9) = R(9) +TAR
      R(10) = R(10) +TAR**2
      R(11) = R(11) + COH
      R(12) = R(12) + COH**2
      R(13) = R(13) + TUS
      R(14) = R(14) + TUS**2
      R(15) = R(15) + GIS
      R(16) = R(16) + GIS**2
      R(17) = R(17) + WGP
      R(18) = R(18) + WGP**2
      R(19) = R(19) + WNP
      R(20) = R(20) + WNP**2
      R(21) = R(21) + ULS
   25 R(22) = R(22) + ULS**2
C     IF WEEK IS LESS THAN 100, RETURN TO THE TOP OF THE DO LOOP.
C     WHEN WEEK EQUALS 100, CONTINUE.
C     DETERMINE AVERAGES AND VARIANCES FOR ALL SIGNIFICANT DATA.
      DO 26 I = 1,21,2
      A(I) =R(I) / 100.
   26 STDEV(I)=SQRTF((R(I+1)-R(I)**2/100.0)/99.0)
C     PRINT COLUMN HEADINGS.
      PRINT 2
C     PRINT RESULTS.
      PRINT 1, (A(I),STDEV(I),I=1,21,2)
      STOP
      END
C     DETERMINE DEMAND.
      SUBROUTINE DEMAND (ADDW, PMD, TMU, SD, SSF)
```

FIGURE 17–2 (Concluded)

```
      V = (-2.0 *LOGF(RANDOM(X)))**0.5 * COSF(6.283 * RANDOM(X))
      D = TMU + SD *V
      IF (D) 1,2,2
    1 D = 0.0
    2 IF (PMD - 0.15) 3,4,4
    3 SSF = 0.0
      GO TO 5
    4 SSF = 0.05
    5 ADDW = D * (1.0 + SSF)
      N = ADDW
      ADDW = N
      RETURN
      END
      SUBROUTINE SUPPLY (PIPLIN,SR,UO)
      DIMENSION PIPLIN(9)
C     DETERMINE SHIPMENTS RECEIVED.
      SR = PIPLIN(1)
C     UPDATE SUPPLY.
      DO 2 K=1,7
    2 PIPLIN(K) = PIPLIN(K + 1)
      PIPLIN(8) = 0.0
C     DETERMINE LEAD TIME.
      M = RANDOM(X) * 100.
      IF (M - 9) 3,3,4
    3 LT = 4
      GO TO 11
    4 IF (M - 24) 5,5,6
    5 LT = 5
      GO TO 11
    6 IF (M - 74) 7,7,8
    7 LT = 6
      GO TO 11
    8 IF (M - 89) 9,9,10
    9 LT = 7
      GO TO 11
   10 LT = 8
C     INCREASE APPROPRIATE WEEKS SUPPLY ORDERED BY UNITS ORDERED THIS WEEK.
   11 PIPLIN(LT) = PIPLIN(LT) + UO
      RETURN
      END
      SUBROUTINE FORECAS (DDP,FD,ADDW)
      DIMENSION DDP(11)
C     DOWNDATE DEMAND FOR THE LAST TEN WEEKS.
      DO 1 IB = 1,9
      L = 11 - IB
    1 DDP(L) = DDP(L-1)
      DDP (1) = ADDW
C     CALCULATE FORECASTED DEMAND.
      FD = (DDP(1) + DDP(2) + DDP(3)) / 3.0
      RETURN
      END
      SUBROUTINE ORDER (PIPLIN,UO,TUS,AIEW,FD,ASB,DI,DSB)
      DIMENSION PIPLIN(9)
C     CALCULATE DESIRED INVENTORY.
      DI = 3.0 * FD
C     CALCULATE SUPPLY BACKORDER.
      ASB = 0.0
      DO 1 N=1,8
    1 ASB = ASB + PIPLIN(N)
C     CALCULATE DESIRED SUPPLY BACKORDER.
      DSB = 6.0 * FD
C     CALCULATE UNITS ORDERED.
      UO = TUS + 0.5 * (DI - AIEW + DSB - ASB)
      IF(UO) 2,3,3
    2 UO = 0.0
    3 CONTINUE
      RETURN
      END
      END
```

FIGURE 17-3

WEEK	ADDW	CBO	AIEW	ABS	TAR	COH	TUS	GIS	WGP	WNP	ULS	FD	PMD
1	37.	.00	163.00	300.00	9350.00	3796.15	37.	3700.00	1850.00	-202.85	.0	46.	.00
2	40.	.00	173.00	261.00	8850.00	3740.81	40.	4000.00	2000.00	-54.58	.0	42.	.00
3	56.	.00	167.00	224.50	9150.00	4484.31	56.	5600.00	2800.00	743.04	.0	44.	.00
4	54.	.00	163.00	234.25	9350.00	5128.50	54.	5600.00	2700.00	643.88	.0	50.	.00
5	55.	.00	158.00	264.63	10250.00	5173.15	55.	5500.00	2750.00	693.27	.0	55.	.00
6	55.	.00	153.00	305.81	11000.00	5367.38	55.	5500.00	2750.00	693.08	.0	55.	.00
7	45.	.00	158.00	327.41	10450.00	5861.42	45.	4500.00	2250.00	194.88	.0	52.	.00
8	54.	.00	115.00	351.20	10450.00	8662.85	54.	5400.00	2250.00	651.42	.0	51.	.00
9	36.	.00	92.50	389.06	9450.00	10497.06	36.	3600.00	1800.00	-239.33	.0	45.	.00
10	54.	.00	38.50	389.60	9450.00	13914.65	54.	5400.00	2700.00	667.67	.0	48.	.00
11	54.	.00	44.25	385.60	9900.00	13843.72	54.	5400.00	2700.00	665.88	.0	48.	.00
12	55.	.00	60.84	369.18	9950.00	13676.53	55.	5500.00	2750.00	712.41	.0	54.	.00
13	46.	.00	186.41	282.11	10450.00	7138.40	46.	4600.00	2300.00	239.23	.0	52.	.00
14	53.	.00	133.41	326.35	10400.00	10436.47	53.	5300.00	2650.00	598.15	.0	51.	.00
15	54.	.00	166.10	293.78	10400.00	9443.38	54.	5400.00	2700.00	641.67	.0	51.	.00
16	45.	.00	121.10	347.34	9900.00	12395.44	45.	5500.00	2250.00	202.83	.0	51.	.00
17	55.	.00	122.05	330.17	10350.00	12598.70	45.	5500.00	2750.00	700.03	.0	51.	.00
18	55.	.00	132.03	335.08	9950.00	12700.00	45.	5500.00	2750.00	200.65	.0	48.	.00
19	55.	.00	161.51	279.54	10000.00	11868.69	54.	5400.00	2750.00	692.98	.0	52.	.00
20	54.	.00	151.76	302.27	10450.00	12551.56	54.	5400.00	2700.00	644.35	.0	51.	.00
21	52.	.00	192.66	267.36	10650.00	11193.32	52.	5200.00	2600.00	537.10	.0	54.	.00
22	52.	.00	194.22	277.29	10650.00	11302.07	52.	5200.00	2600.00	536.27	.0	53.	.00
23	54.	.00	140.22	330.53	10650.00	14698.34	54.	5400.00	2750.00	646.34	.0	53.	.00
24	55.	.00	85.22	386.13	10650.00	18105.07	55.	5500.00	2750.00	706.65	.0	54.	.00
25	61.	.00	113.05	358.13	11100.00	17263.44	61.	6100.00	3050.00	999.45	.0	57.	.00
26	37.	.00	143.03	371.57	10650.00	16513.12	37.	3700.00	1850.00	-200.54	.0	51.	.15
27	47.	.00	154.01	322.78	9647.50	16056.72	47.	3995.00	1645.00	-408.50	.0	48.	.00
28	33.	.00	121.01	348.88	8847.50	18412.26	33.	3300.00	1655.00	-392.77	.0	39.	.15
29	57.	.00	124.83	288.07	7920.00	18796.07	57.	4845.00	1995.00	-52.15	.0	46.	.00
30	95.	.00	148.94	225.01	10800.00	17381.15	95.	9550.00	4750.00	2686.15	.0	62.	.00
31	44.	.00	158.19	357.29	11022.50	16860.79	44.	4400.00	2950.00	144.16	.0	65.	.00
32	79.	.00	159.59	357.14	13322.50	16377.66	79.	7900.00	3950.00	1883.62	.0	73.	.00
33	73.	.00	121.90	469.47	14450.00	18626.96	73.	7300.00	3650.00	1590.13	.0	65.	.00
34	71.	.00	106.95	484.74	13350.00	22067.82	71.	7300.00	3650.00	1495.24	.0	74.	.00
35	93.	.00	13.95	594.39	15800.00	26876.72	93.	9300.00	4650.00	2605.13	.0	78.	.15
36	92.	36.05	99.84	738.72	12547.46	29497.19	14.	1394.93	697.46	-1324.52	.0	71.	.15
37	50.	.00	231.37	510.83	14339.62	25131.51	128.	10484.31	4481.78	245.89	.0	78.	.15
38	54.	.00	135.37	500.52	13489.62	20028.31	54.	5400.00	2700.00	624.37	.0	65.	.00
39	96.	.00	171.68	570.26	13972.16	23515.12	35.	3500.00	1750.00	-311.24	.0	81.	.15
40	35.	.00	194.34	460.60	12227.50	25096.28	87.	7395.00	3045.00	972.08	.0	62.	.15
41	87.	.00	299.67	402.80	10202.50	20445.84	39.	3900.00	1950.00	-132.79	.0	73.	.00
42	39.	.00	233.67	402.80	11252.50	25255.61	66.	5410.00	2310.00	236.67	.0	54.	.00
43	66.	.00	177.67	438.56	11252.50	25744.97	56.	5600.00	2800.00	737.75	.0	54.	.00
44	56.	.00	320.89	263.35	9155.00	22196.54	32.	3200.00	1600.00	-481.95	.0	51.	.15
45	32.	.00	421.94	122.29	8905.00	16690.78	40.	3400.00	1400.00	-702.54	.0	43.	.15
46	40.	.00	382.94	122.29	8050.00	19350.93	39.	3900.00	1950.00	-143.53	.0	37.	.00
47	39.	.00	435.47	35.76	6900.00	17371.85	33.	3300.00	1650.00	-450.90	.0	36.	.00
48	33.	.00	435.24	.00	7150.00	16332.20	37.	3700.00	1850.00	-251.81	.0	36.	.00

FIGURE 17-3 (Continued)

n											
50	90.	.00	345.24	.00	.00	9950.00	21037.51	90.	9000.00	4500.00	2400.99
51	31.	.00	314.24	.00	157.38	9557.00	22255.81	31.	3100.00	1550.00	-531.08
52	63.	.00	251.24	.00	189.57	10577.50	24708.18	63.	5355.00	2205.00	128.30
53	31.	.00	220.24	.00	308.17	10277.50	26043.65	31.	3100.00	1550.00	-514.13
54	62.	.00	158.24	.00	308.17	8412.50	31120.43	62.	5270.00	2170.00	114.70
55	55.	.00	103.24	.00	370.87	9412.50	33337.06	55.	5500.00	2750.00	704.78
56	32.	.00	71.24	.00	410.87	8535.00	35619.92	32.	3200.00	1600.00	-432.98
57	38.	.00	190.62	.00	267.93	8600.00	28858.72	38.	3230.00	1330.00	-727.20
58	54.	.00	168.81	.00	235.74	8665.00	30528.09	54.	5400.00	2700.00	643.82
59	54.	.00	233.40	.00	154.87	8615.00	30528.09	54.	5400.00	2700.00	631.48
60	36.	.00	197.40	.00	233.73	8815.00	29321.57	36.	3600.00	1800.00	-258.45
61	31.	.00	161.40	.00	270.16	9000.00	30685.04	31.	3600.00	1550.00	-251.81
62	59.	.00	170.30	.00	239.48	7850.00	31340.75	59.	3100.00	2050.00	-500.79
63	33.	.00	174.10	.00	176.68	8100.00	28786.52	33.	5900.00	1650.00	892.71
64	51.	.00	219.96	.00	170.43	7950.00	30056.74	51.	3300.00	2750.00	-410.88
65	55.	.00	183.41	.00	178.28	8700.00	30714.59	55.	5100.00	1650.00	491.54
66	33.	.00	166.14	.00	225.21	9900.00	31438.85	33.	5500.00	1550.00	692.24
67	31.	.00	169.57	.00	256.61	8600.00	32130.46	31.	3300.00	1260.00	-402.19
68	36.	.00	275.80	.00	275.80	8500.00	33049.48	36.	3100.00	2700.00	-497.46
69	32.	.00	253.50	.00	253.57	7480.00	35362.18	32.	3060.00	1650.00	-784.22
70	54.	.00	134.09	.00	115.77	6330.00	30633.12	54.	3200.00	2750.00	-435.52
71	33.	.00	102.09	.00	115.97	7380.00	27557.63	33.	5400.00	3750.00	642.01
72	31.	.00	188.52	.00	149.40	7480.00	28554.94	31.	3300.00	3050.00	-414.04
73	55.	.00	240.17	.00	178.11	7600.00	30858.17	55.	3100.00	1650.00	-507.73
74	75.	.00	209.17	.00	217.06	8650.00	33839.10	75.	5500.00	1785.00	696.47
75	36.	.00	154.17	.00	371.23	9700.00	35253.49	36.	7500.00	2378.67	1699.96
76	61.	.00	107.59	.00	434.82	9850.00	37824.57	61.	3600.00	3671.33	-235.84
77	33.	.00	71.59	.00	412.84	11350.00	34268.33	33.	6100.00	1995.00	1018.77
78	51.	.00	10.59	.00	410.13	10250.00	38015.78	51.	3330.00	3800.00	-390.55
79	85.	.00	95.87	.00	449.78	8667.50	40171.97	85.	4335.00	3115.00	-247.29
80	36.	37.43	47.57	.00	366.30	9246.17	36865.41	36.	4757.34	2600.00	-355.30
81	57.	.00	.00	.00	317.28	8467.50	31167.58	57.	7342.66	2700.00	1625.45
82	38.	.00	86.23	.00	390.94	10640.50	33183.44	38.	4845.00	1190.00	-67.60
83	89.	.00	183.41	.00	532.26	10372.50	37300.69	89.	3800.00	2400.00	-151.23
84	52.	.00	145.41	.00	448.48	11176.33	41543.06	52.	7565.00	3200.00	-1068.92
85	54.	.00	56.41	.00	451.38	10705.00	37825.00	54.	5200.00	245.00	572.68
86	36.	.00	4.41	.00	346.62	10082.50	35667.66	36.	5400.00	2400.00	656.11
87	34.	.00	86.35	.00	272.57	10082.50	33575.94	34.	2890.00	2450.00	-244.00
88	48.	.00	126.54	.00	375.61	8545.00	37286.36	48.	4800.00	1645.00	-867.70
89	76.	.00	197.69	.00	492.13	8345.00	40243.49	76.	7400.00	2030.00	349.14
90	49.	.00	147.69	.00	288.82	9445.00	42105.78	49.	6400.00	2750.00	1742.52
91	48.	.00	83.35	.00	304.47	10845.00	31199.98	48.	4900.00	4350.00	1154.98
92	49.	.00	34.35	.00	315.27	11850.00	35381.95	49.	4900.00	1700.00	415.74
93	33.	.00	258.92	.00	95.71	11850.00	38175.43	33.	3300.00	1925.00	322.75
94	58.	.00	209.92	.00	146.61	11500.00	30022.36	58.	4930.00		-384.05
95	55.	.00	176.92	.00	205.57	8950.00	33093.47	55.	5500.00		-404.14
96	87.	.00	338.48	.00	306.65	8965.00	34858.75	87.	8700.00		-60.04
97	34.	.00	283.48	.00	327.64	9315.00	37596.35	34.	3400.00		670.58
98	55.	.00	196.65	.00		11265.00		55.	4675.00		2278.23
99		.00	247.37	.00		11137.50					-371.44
100		.00	192.37	.00							-139.71

FIGURE 17–3 (Concluded)

	AVERAGE	STANDARD DEVIATION
WEEKLY DEMAND	51.7000	16.7468
BACKORDER QUEUE LENGTH	.7348	5.1703
INVENTORY AT END OF WEEK	163.9244	88.1368
SUPPLY BACKORDER	313.2099	125.4132
ACCOUNTS RECEIVABLE	10023.1598	1712.9372
CASH ON HAND	24437.6888	10533.0383
SALES	51.7000	18.1259
GROSS INCOME FROM SALES	5010.3924	1668.3601
WEEKLY GROSS PROFIT	2425.3924	802.7297
WEEKLY NET PROFIT	368.5059	802.0908
UNITS OF LOST SALES	.0000	.0000

SIMCO SATISFACTORILY COMPLETED.

EXERCISES

1. Write a complete FORTRAN program that will print out the mean weekly demand for a given product for one year. The mean is 35 units the first 5 weeks; then it increases at a rate of 11 percent per week until the 25th week; is constant for 5 more weeks; then decreases at a rate of 5.5 percent for the rest of the year. Below is a graphic representation of mean demand as a function of time.

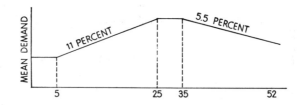

2. Rerun the program of Figure 17–2, with the following variables initialized at zero: COH,AR,TAR,AIEW; and with CBQ = 500.0. Comment on the results.

3. Eliminate in the program of Figure 17–2 the PRINT and FOR-MAT statements which cause *weekly statements* to be printed out, and arrange to have Simco's operations simulated for 500 weeks rather than 100 weeks.

a) Run a 500-week operations simulation.

b) Arrange to have the mean of weekly demand begin at 50.0, as in the model of Figure 17–2, but cause the mean to increase by one-half unit each week. Let the standard deviation be one third of the weekly demand, and run the simulation called for in (*a*) under these conditions.

c) Arrange to have the mean of weekly demand begin at 50.0, but cause the mean to increase by 0.5 percent each week. Let the standard deviation continue to be one-third of the mean weekly demand. Run the simulation under these conditions. Interpret the results of these experiments.

4–1. Alter Simco's program in Exercise 3 to cause the demand forecast (FD) to be determined by single exponential smoothing with a smoothing constant of 0.3. Rerun parts (*a*), (*b*), and (*c*) of Exercise 3 under these conditions.

4–2. Repeat what is called for in 4–1, but use double exponential smoothing with a smoothing constant of 0.3. Interpret the results of these experiments.

5–1. Employ the model called for in Exercise 3 with mean weekly demand constant at 50.0. Alter this program to cause weekly demand to be gamma distributed, with a mean of 50.0 and a standard deviation equal to $\frac{1}{3}$ of the mean. Run the simulation under this condition.

5–2. Repeat what is called for in 5–1, but with a standard deviation of twice the mean. Run the program under this condition and interpret the results of these experiments.

ADDITIONAL SYSTEMS EXERCISES

6. A local retailer of combination heating–air conditioning units is concerned with maximizing his profits over the coming year. He has discovered over the past few years that his demand takes on the following characteristics:

a) During the first 10 weeks of the year demand is normally distributed, with a mean of 65 and a standard deviation of 10.

b) During the next 15 weeks the mean demand increases at a rate of 5 percent per week.

c) During the next 20 years the mean demand is constant.

d) During the last seven weeks the mean decreases at a rate of 7 percent per week.

When a purchase order is placed with the manufacturer of these units, the lead time distribution is as follows:

Lead Time (Weeks)	Probability
2	.29
3	.38
4	.10
5	.03
6	.07
7	.13

Our retailer buys his units at a cost of $150 per unit and sells them at $250 per unit—a profit per unit of $100.

His inventory holding costs are $20 per unit per week.

Each time he places an order with the manufacturer of the units he experiences a $600 ordering and shipping cost, regardless of the number of units ordered.

His beginning inventory is 400 units.

This retailer finds it most necessary to maintain a good public image. Thus when demand exceeds inventory he has the required number of units flown in from the manufacturer at an additional cost of $250 per unit.

Our retailer's inventory ordering policy is that when inventory drops below 210 units he orders an amount that is equal to 3 times that week's demand.

His weekly profit, then, equals: Demand × (selling price − purchase price) − cost per order (if an order has been placed that week) − inventory holding cost × inventory at the end of the week − stock-out cost × (demand − inventory) (if a stock-out occurs).

A necessary order of calculations each week is as follows.

1. Determine if a shipment from the manufacturer is due this week. If so, add it to inventory.
2. Determine demand for this week, and satisfy it.
3. Recalculate inventory. If demand exceeded inventory, calculate stock-out cost.
4. If it is necessary to place an order, do so; determine lead time and thus the week in which the order is due.
5. Determine inventory costs on the remaining inventory.
6. Calculate profit for the week.

In order to determine an average profit under these conditions we find it necessary to simulate this retailer's experience for 100 *noncumulative* years. In effect, we are simulating the same year 100 times; that is, we are beginning each year with an inventory of 400 units, a mean demand of 65, and so on. Thus we want to simulate this retailer's experience in the marketplace 100 times. At the end of each year of calculation we want to print out:

TOTAL STOCKOUT COST
TOTAL ORDERING COST
TOTAL HOLDING COST
TOTAL PROFIT

At the end of the 100 years these figures should then be averaged and the average stock-cost, average ordering cost, and so on should be printed out.

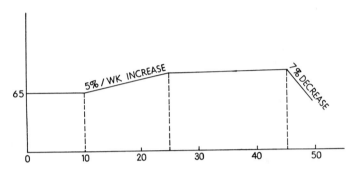

7. The Z Company operates a power plant to provide electricity and steam for heating the company's various buildings. The electrical power is provided by means of three turbogenerators. Steam is fed into the turbines, producing electricity. Also, steam is extracted from two of the turbines for heating the buildings. Each turbine's efficiency varies according to the electrical load and the (extracted) heating steam load placed on the turbine.

The steam is produced by a system of boilers. A relationship of linearity exists among the amount of steam produced, the amount of coal required, and the cost of the coal. Thus a minimization of the steam required to produce a specific electrical load and heating load will also represent a minimization of total cost of satisfying these requirements. The problem, then, is to determine the minimum amount of steam required and the allocation of the steam to each of the three turbines, given certain electrical and heating loads.

For each combination of requirements there are several thousand combinations of possible allocations of steam to each of the turbines; the problem is to find the minimum combination in each case. From information furnished from the turbine manufacturers, it is seen that although turbine 2 is the most efficient in generating electricity, it is not capable of furnishing heating steam. Turbine 3 is more efficient than turbine 1 in generating electricity, but turbine 1 is the more efficient heating steam producer. Obviously, then, only turbines 1 and 3 are capable of furnishing heating steam; if the heating requirements exceed the amount of steam extracted from these two turbines, the remaining required steam must be taken directly from the boilers.

Rules and Assumptions

1. All three turbines must be kept operating under normal conditions. Starting and stopping of the turbines is unduly hard on them, thus they must be kept running at points equal to, or above, their minimum operating points at all times.

2. The turbines are naturally most efficient at maximum heating steam extraction.

3. From the graphs supplied by the manufacturers, equations have been developed to describe the limits of the operating range for each turbine. Since each line appearing on the performance curves is a straight line, an equation of the form $Y = a + bX$ can be developed to describe these lines. For example, in turbine 1:

$$Y = \text{Throttle flow (steam required)}$$
$$X = \text{KW (kilowatt load)}$$
$$a = 0.65 \text{ (heating extract)} + 10{,}000$$
$$b = 15.4.$$

The following parameters exist for the three turbines:

Turbine 1
Throttle flow = 15.4 × (kw.) + 0.55 × heat + 10,000
Maximum extraction = 12,310 + 9.23 × kw.
Minimum kw. = 2,500   Maximum kw. = 6,500

Turbine 2
Throttle flow = 5,000 + 6.3 × kw.
Maximum throttle flow = 8,000 + 21.5 × kw.
Minimum kw. = 800   Maximum kw. = 3,200

Turbine 3
Throttle flow = 8,000 + 8.25 × kw. + 0.9 × heat
Maximum throttle flow = 8,500 + 20.5 × kw. + 0.8 × heat
Maximum extraction = 25,000
Minimum kw. = 800   Maximum kw. = 3,200

We want the computer to do the work of determining the most efficient combination. The method is to specify a load on the system, and then to calculate the most efficient method of providing the load.

The printout should include the system load in terms of electricity and heat, the amount of steam required, the amount of steam directed into each turbine, the amount of heating steam extracted from each turbine, and the amount of heating steam drawn directly from the boilers (if necessary). This should be done for electrical loads of 4,500 kw. up to 12,500 kw., increasing by increments of 500 kw.; and heating loads of 40,000 pounds to 140,000 pounds, increasing by increments of 20,000 pounds.

Method of Calculation

The steps of the calculation might be as follows.

1. Specify an electrical load.
2. Specify a heating load.
3. Set load on turbine 1 = 2,000 kw.
4. Increase the load on turbine 1 by 500 kw.
5. Set load on turbine 2 at 600 kw.
6. Increase load on turbine 2 by 200 kw.
7. Set the load on turbine 3 to meet the demand.
8. If turbine 3 is overloaded, go to step 7.
9. Set heat extraction on turbine 1 at its maximum.
10. Increase heat extraction on turbine 1 by 10,000.
11. Set heat extraction on turbine 3 to meet the demand.
12. If turbine 3 is overloaded, determine the amount of direct steam required.
13. Determine the steam required to provide this loading.
14. If this is cheaper than the previous method, save and return to step 12. If not cheaper do not save, but return to step 12.
15. Return to step 2 until all heating loads have been satisfied.
16. Return to step 1 until all electrical loads have been satisfied.

For a clearer picture of the system see the the figure below.

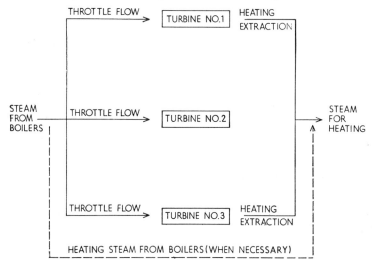

8. Esto Oil Company is considering bidding on a contract to supply fuel oil to a port in the United Kingdom. Esto's plan is to tap its production facilities in Africa and transport the oil to the United Kingdom in its own tankers.

The fuel is to be delivered to the customer's tank facilities in port in the United Kingdom. The capacity of these facilities is 1,250 units of oil, and the customer's invitation to bid specifies that the supplier must not permit the supply to drop below the level of 250 units more than 5 percent of the time.

Demand on the tank facilities in the United Kingdom is found to be normally distributed with a mean of 100 units per day and a standard deviation of 25 units.

Esto management wants to know whether it will be able to maintain this service level by using on a full-time basis 3 of its standard 625 unit tankers.

Other constraints are:

1. The limited storage capacity in the United Kingdom (i.e., 1,250 units maximum capacity).
2. Berth facilities both in the United Kingdom (one berth) and Africa (two berths). One day is required to load a ship berthed in Africa, and one day is required to unload a ship berthed in the United Kingdom.
3. Travel time. Eight days are required for a ship to make the trip from Africa to Britain, and another eight days for the return trip.
4. Weather. While weather does not influence the speed of travel at sea, a ship cannot enter or leave a berth during a storm. Storms are seasonal with the following pattern:

	Probability of a Storm Each Day	
	April 1 to Sept. 30	*Rest of Year*
In Africa harbor	0.2	0.1
In United Kingdom harbor	0.1	0.2

Esto's production facilities in Africa do not pose a constraint.

Esto's plan is that ships that cannot unload in the United Kingdom because the customer's tank facilities are loaded will anchor in the harbor and wait, constituting a floating inventory.

Construct a computer model for simulating Esto's proposed transportation system, and determine if the required service level can be met with three of its ships.

Suggestions

It is useful to think of the eight days travel time as involving intervals between seven successive positions in the ocean, plus the harbor (see diagram below). Each day after a ship leaves harbor it advances one inter-

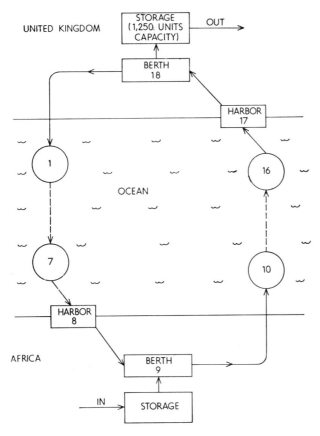

val. Positions 1 through 7 represent the trip from the United Kingdom to Africa, and positions 10 through 16 represent the return trip. For each day of simulated operations the location of each of the three ships should be updated.

A subscripted variable, SHIP(M), might be employed to keep track of the position of each ship:

SHIP(1) = 12.0 means ship 1 is in position 12, etc.

The system might be initialized with all three ships at sea, perhaps as follows:

SHIP$(1) = 1.0$, SHIP$(2) = 5.0$, and SHIP$(3) = 12.0$

BERTH$(1) = 0.0$ might mean that berth 1 is empty.
BERTH$(2) = 1.0$ might mean that berth 2 is occupied.

Assume that the simulation begins on January 1, with 750 units of oil in storage in the United Kingdom, and run the simulation for 6 years.

chapter 18

Experimentation and Validation

IN ALL THE PRECEDING we have directed attention to constructing specific models and implementing them, i.e., translating them into computer programs. Purposely, nothing has been said about proposing experiments that employ the models, or executing the experiments. These topics have not been treated, even though it would seem reasonable to bring them up preliminary to the first experimental use of a systems model. That this was not done reflects our primary objective, which was to acquaint the student with particular model forms and to demonstrate how the computer program may be written and used as a simulator.

As we considered models of increasing complexity we chose to omit general discussion of experiment planning and execution. Some intuitive (and we hope reasonable) experiments were proposed and carried out for each of the models discussed. The various experiments could have been replicated in order to generate systems behavior in addition to that produced or traced. Where a model was used to evaluate several forms of a decision rule we could have replicated the experiment on many sets of data or for other forms of the decision rule. But given the introductory level of the material presented, focus has been on conceptualization of the system, construction of the model, and use of the model in limited experiments which were arbitrarily selected because they yielded information that could not be easily obtained, if at all, with other methods, and which would be generally valuable or interesting to the decision maker.

The second and more compelling reason for deferring discussion of the design and execution of experiments is that simulation, as we have described it, is a new analytical procedure. There are many unanswered methodological questions which simply have not been tackled. The major effort so far has been devoted to formulating and implementing models, i.e., not only overcoming the problems of constructing models that parallel real systems, but also doing so within the limits imposed by the computer.

Without question, impressive strides have been made in this phase of simulation. Practitioners of the art have been quick to make use of increasing computer size and sophistication. Special problem-oriented simulation languages have been devised which facilitate the tasks of modeling systems, stepping the models through time and generating reports of system behavior. If we define simulation to include not only model construction but also design, execution, and evaluation of the results of experiments, then we conclude that there remain few obstacles to building sizable and complex models of particular or theoretical systems. This comment is not meant to deprecate the difficulties that have been surmounted, but it does imply that initial simulation efforts have concentrated on obtaining operational models whose reasonableness has been judged in terms of how well they reproduce data which has been obtained by observing the real system.

A Critical Comment. The foregoing helps us understand criticisms of simulation methods. It is contended that while all sorts of data can be generated from the models, procedures have not been developed for:

1.   Determining the implications that changes of inputs (parameters, exogenous variables) will have generally.
2.   Planning and executing experiments efficiently.

The purpose of this chapter is to offer some suggestions to guide the student so as to preclude grossly inefficient experimental work. However, before proceeding we should like to comment on the more serious criticisms.

Those with extensive experience with simulation point out that they are able to produce results that have reasonable posterior explanations. Yet they admit that they have no way of deriving general implications of changes in their models. When one speaks of solving a simulation model, he means that from a set of starting conditions the model will track a set of system variables. One then seeks to explain the way in which forces in the systems interact, or the output is displayed graphically.

Reviewing several large simulation models, Sprowls[1], concluded that these shortcomings in methodology were persistent, fundamental, and disturbing. He noted that two analysts (Bonini and Roberts) conducted experiments with decision-information models of the firm in which both specified similar starting conditions but obtained contradictory results. Bonini defined a highly variable environment in terms of customer orders and market growth trend, and his model produced lower costs and higher sales and profits. Roberts, using Forrester's techniques, observed that a similar environment led to great fluctuations of inventory, back orders, employment, and, we presume, profits.

In each case a reasonable-sounding explanation of the results was offered. We would agree that repeated instances such as this would cast doubts about the methodology, but we cannot fully agree with Sprowls, who contends that given such evidence:

> I can only conclude at this time that there is no question but that a computer simulation model can generate time paths of many variables from many kinds of initial conditions. There is still a very large question whether anyone understands the model, although reasonable sounding explanations can be given for almost any input-output phenomenon observed. . . . I am prepared only to look at each of them as an interesting isolated case which can be described to me but from which I shall draw no conclusions.[2]

For the models compared above, the inputs were not identical, and there were important differences in assumptions as well as in the procedures for simulating decision making. Obviously if a model operating on identical inputs produced different results, the model would be suspect. But it would seem that some of the current criticism is a bit premature. The method is relatively new, and our knowledge of the nature of decision making is quite incomplete.

Evaluating or generalizing the output of a model being used to explore a behavioral theory of decision making is more difficult than evaluating a model that simulates a physical system in which one wants only to compare *relative* behavior of the system under varia-

---

[1] Clay Sprowls, "Simulation and Management Control," in C. P. Bonini, R. K. Jaedicke, and H. M. Wagner (eds.), *Management Controls: New Directions in Basic Research* (New York: McGraw-Hill Book Co., 1964), pp. 146–48.

[2] Ibid., p. 147.

tions of a particular decision rule. In the second case, the output can be used to indicate which rule to select without raising serious doubts about the generality of the model or its output under greatly modified assumptions.

The important thing is that simulation can be helpful to the on-line decision maker. Conway notes:

> Fortunately, a large number of investigations appropriate for simulation compare a sequence of alternatives. With proper operating procedures a simulation model can produce *relative results* much more efficiently than *absolute results*.[3]

Such comparative information provides an adequate basis for making a choice among the alternatives.

Ideally, the contrast of alternatives should be performed by using the same "experimental media," as Conway calls it, or, as we commonly say, the experiments should be performed under identical conditions. In simulation, identical conditions are maintained by specifying initial values for each variable, system parameters, and the data representing sequences of exogenous events—customer orders, shipments received, machine failures, and others.[4] The unique advantage of simulation is that not just closely identical but *absolutely identical* conditions can be maintained through repeated experiments or runs. For example, to evaluate alternative inventory reorder rules the same sequence of orders and material receipt delays can be reused. Perfect homogeneity of the experimental media is thus possible.

From this aside, we turn now to some specific suggestions about designing and executing experiments.

PLANNING EXPERIMENTS

Given an operational model of a system there is almost no end to the variety of changes that might be introduced, and hence some limitations must be imposed. We want to ignore, on the one hand, trivial changes and, on the other hand, combinations of changes whose effects cannot be readily measured by statistical methods. At the same time we need to remember that the execution of experi-

---

[3] R. W. Conway, "Some Tactical Problems in Simulation Method" (Memorandum RM–3244–PR [Santa Monica, Calif.: The Rand Corporation, October 1962]), p. 13.

[4] Alternatively, as we have seen, a procedure for generating values of the exogenous random variables may be used in place of a list of events.

ments is not without cost.[5] It is simply not feasible to perform a complete replicate of even modest designs involving small sets of changes. Recall Bonini's design in which eight changes were introduced, each having two values or "cases." This means that 2^8, or 256, experimental runs would have been necessary to obtain a complete replicate of the experiment, i.e., one run for each of the possible combinations of changes. Subject to the length of the runs (number of simulated time periods), we are now talking about time requirements of large-scale computers on the order of hours—not to mention computation time to obtain estimates of parameters for numerous distributions as well as to evaluate the significance of observed differences.

Therefore use is made of fractional factorial design in which high-order interaction effects are not computed.[6] The use of analysis of variance techniques is subject to question as regards evaluation of the so-called observed differences. Some experimenters hypothesize that changes or combinations of changes will not modify system behavior (the *null hypothesis*). Others insist that such a hypothesis is not appropriate for the rather typical experiment in which changes really represent such alternatives as a set of alternative decision rules. These rules, it is contended, are different, and differences of system behavior, however slight, will follow. Failure to reject the null hypothesis indicates only that the test is not sensitive to the differences for the given sample size or length of run. In addition, the analyst wants to identify the best alternative, or he wants to rank the alternatives; he does not want to conclude that they are merely different.[7]

The question remains, "What experiments should we undertake?" Generally, two kinds of experiments should be considered:

1. Those that serve to test the reasonableness of the model.
2. Those that evaluate or obtain estimates of important properties of the model.

Reasonableness of the Model

Such criteria (above) are more easily spelled out than applied, and it goes without saying that from this point on judgment and

---

[5] See Daniel Teichroew and John F. Lubin, "Computer Simulation: Discussion of the Technique and Comparison of Languages" (Working Paper No. 20 [Stanford, Calif.: Graduate School of Business, Stanford University, 1964]).

[6] See C. P. Bonini, *Simulation of Information and Decision Systems in the Firm* (Englewood Cliffs, N.J.: Prentice-Hall, Inc., 1963), pp. 85–96.

[7] R. W. Conway, "Some Tactical Problems in Simulation Method," op. cit., p. 16.

a priori feelings about the nature of the system modeled play an important part. With respect to experiments of the first kind:

Some tests should be made upon the reasonableness and stability of the model. This can be done by studying the effects upon the firms of different external factors. In other words, we should test to see whether under different conditions in the external environment the firm of our model behaves reasonably (in line with the way we would expect a real world firm to behave). For example, we should not expect the model to "blow up" and go off to infinity as a result of only relatively minor changes in its external environments.[8]

To achieve such a test we might simply redefine the probability distribution (for an exogenous variable) as having a variance greater than in the initial or standard version of the environment. If one wants to introduce a fast and irregular growth rate for a variable, random fluctuations can be superimposed on the trend of the variable. Precisely what constitutes fast or slow rates and irregular or smooth cyclical patterns is left to the discretion of the analyst.

EVALUATING PROPERTIES OF THE MODEL

Parametric Changes

Parameters (particularly of decision rules) may be modified to obtain a parametric value that optimizes a measure of effectiveness of system behavior. The very first models taken up in this textbook involved simulation of inventory systems, the search for parameter values for the reorder point, and the reorder quantity so that total inventory cost could be minimized. Recall in these examples that not all parameter values were considered, and that we compared sequential costs and stopped searching when total cost began to increase.

Evaluation of parameters (sensitivity analysis) has been demonstrated in numerous examples throughout the book, so that further discussion is not necessary. This is an obvious but highly useful form of change and experimentation. The values proposed are usually indicated by *a priori* knowledge of what values are reasonable or possible in the real world. Evaluation of parameter values that are not available to the decision maker results in data that cannot be acted on. Finally, even within a specified interval it is not nec-

---

[8] C. P. Bonini, *Simulation of Information and Decision Systems*, p. 75.

essary to consider very small incremental changes of a parameter. Many functions of measures of effectiveness are insensitive to slight absolute differences, as we can recall, for example, from the shape of the inventory total cost curve.

Changes of Relationships

A second type of change is the modification, or rather substitution, of relationships among system variables. Virtually each example in this book demonstrated or proposed such substitutions. Inventory reorder rules, queue disciplines, forecasting rules, and pricing rules, among others, have been altered or substituted in our examples. In addition, the information flows, delays, and links, which we regard as decisions about organizational structure, can be modified to test the effects on decision making.

Simulation is usually undertaken because we have raised questions or posed hypotheses about the system behavior under various component configurations. We thus begin with the purpose of sampling behavior or response subject to alterations that are feasible. The output of the model furnishes comparative system performances, which are then used to decide the system's design. The model can be made to operate successively on a real or synthetically produced sequence of exogenous events, and here we may note that the use of the same sequence for all runs of an experiment minimizes residual variation and obtains comparable data with smaller sample size than is possible if different sequences are used for each run.

The use of a common sequence of events to test alternatives (relationships in this case) is an important procedural question in simulation.[9] The procedure is preferred because it permits smaller sample sizes and sharpens differences among alternatives. If the analyst has a sequence obtained by observation of the real system he would be led to use this procedure simply because of the cost of obtaining the data.

Starting Conditions

We have continually assumed that (given a model) not only is a sequence of exogenous variables generated, or read in, but that the initial state of the system is specified; that is, values are provided

---

[9] R. W. Conway, "Some Tactical Problems in Simulation Methods," p. 14.

for system variables at simulated time zero. Here the problem is that the output of the model will be biased by the set of initial values until the model has warmed up or, more precisely, has obtained the steady state where that term is taken to mean an arbitrarily close approximation to the system's equilibrium state.

Several suggestions are usually proposed, but they are difficult to apply and require considerable exercise of judgment.

1. Discard data generated during an initial interval of the simulation run.
2. Select starting conditions that reduce the duration of the warm-up or transient period.
3. Select such starting conditions that bias is not introduced.

As for the third suggestion, if the analyst had such knowledge that he could start the model in its steady state, he would not have to resort to simulation.

Assume for the moment that the state of a system is defined on a single variable. The steady state is assumed to exist and is described by the probability distribution of the variable. The distribution is said to be a property of the system and is constant. Thus it is incorrect to suggest that the variance of the steady state distribution decreases through time. The variance that decreases (as the simulation is extended) is the one obtained by simulation, which we treat as an estimate of the system parameter. These estimates or approximations approach the inherent or limiting distribution at a rate influenced by the starting conditions.

Differences between the system parameter and the obtained estimate decrease with time, but Conway cautions that for complex systems the rate of approach is slow and the error (difference) remains large (even after long runs)! This can be verified from our own experience with the Simco model. Although we would not call 100 periods (two years) a long time, nevertheless the variances obtained were disappointingly large.

The suggestions to eliminate the bias induced by a particular set of starting conditions by discarding some portion of the output really poses the problem of when to begin measurement. The following guides are proposed.[10]

1. Delete an early portion of the output of a run. A rule of thumb is to truncate a series of measurements when the first of the se-

---

[10] Ibid., p. 5.

ries is neither the maximum nor the minimum of the remaining set.

2. Deletion should be done with due consideration, given the complexity of the system, i.e., the number of elements in the system as well as the number of events that take place. The more complex the system, the longer the bias persists.

3. All runs of a given experiment should be treated similarly when deletion is done.

The suggestion to select starting conditions to minimize or, rather, shorten the warm-up period is really an alternative to starting the system in the empty or idle condition. Such a choice (empty or idle) has the disadvantage of being artificial (except for simple queuing systems), and the consequent time to achieve the steady state is long. The selection of nonempty conditions requires *a priori* knowledge of the system, but, as Conway notes, it is rare that the analyst has no such information.

Length of the Run

Determination of the length of the simulation run is implied in the preceding discussion. It is tempting to exploit the computer to generate extremely long runs, but economy usually rules against such a practice. When our purpose is to trace systems response, the simulation is continued until the variables have settled down. Recall the demonstrations of impulse response for the Simco model. For many purposes, however, we are interested in short-run effects, and we settle on simulation periods of relatively short duration. Bonini decided on an interval of nine years in his experiments, with the model moved through 108 monthly periods. In much of Forrester's work, intervals of two to three years are common, although activity was generated in fractional parts of a day.

There seem to be no objective rules for fixing the proper length of the run. Variances are reduced through time, but at a cost that should be appraised in terms of the precision gained. We are also warned that such gains in complex systems require extremely lengthy runs. In many cases the proper length cannot be decided beforehand simply because we want to process the model until specific conditions result. Thus we are, in fact, interpreting time as one of the information outputs rather than as the mere magnitude of sample size.

On this point it seems evident that the analyst should use all the data generated and that he need not resort to sampling from the output. If additional data are required, the simulation should be *continued*, rather than started again from a second set of initial conditions. The expanded output is then treated as a single sample.

Characterizing the Output

It is not our purpose to discuss statistical methods used to summarize the output of the simulation. In addition to graphically depicting output, descriptive statistical measures such as the mean, the standard deviation, the variance, and the trend are used to characterize system variables.[11] The use of classical analysis of variance seems widespread in simulation, despite the awareness that the null hypothesis may be improper, and that independence of samples is often assumed when, in fact, as we noted, because of common starting conditions or because of use of a common sequence of exogenous events, dependence is the case.

In summary, Conway concludes:

> . . . a single experimental run should be made for each alternative tested. Variability should be reduced and replication provided by extending the length of the run rather than executing completely separate and independent runs. Performance measures will be based on the entire run (except for the "warmup" and possibly a "cooling-off" period at the end of the run) but the run must be subdivided and a sequence of interval measures obtained in order to estimate the precision of the results. The positive correlation that almost surely exists between neighboring measurements guarantees that the estimate of variance computed under the usual assumption of independence will understate the true variance. . . . It clearly requires some investigations of the degree of autocorrelation.[12]

The manner of treating these tactical problems should be described when reporting simulations, along with the description of the model and its output. Criticism of methodology will continue, and for the present each simulation will be judged in terms of its credibility and utility.

----

[11] For example, SIMSCRIPT provides a COMPUTE statement, which can be used to obtain any one of seven statistics, including the mean, standard deviation, and variance.

[12] Ibid., p. 34.

VALIDATION

In this concluding section we borrow at length from Gilmour's proposed general procedure for validating computer simulation models.[13] From his comments it will be apparent that little agreement exists about validation or how it may be established. Validation is not a problem unique to simulation methods, but it is the major unresolved question in connection with the use of these models. For good reasons the model builder is warned that he must proceed with caution. We know that the implications of a model's output may be obscured because of the complexity of the model. Or perhaps a model becomes unique when written in a particular language, or processed on a given piece of hardware. In order to meet the demand for specificity, and so ensure that some output will result, the model builder may make grossly incorrect assumptions about a system. These are the concerns that have led some to argue that computer simulation is, or should be, a method of last resort.

Gilmour's scheme is an alternative to simple caution. He undertook the validation of a complex model eclectically and with regard for the costs involved. An introductory and summary statement of his procedure follows.

Introduction

The aim of computer simulation can basically be described as system design or system analysis. *System design* is an attempt to find the combination of exogenous variables and parameter values that will optimize a specified endogenous variable. *System analysis* is an explanation of the relationship between the endogenous variable and the controllable exogenous variables and parameters.

Simulation allows the analyst, in his drive for greater realism, to develop a much more detailed and complex model than he could using an analytical technique. But a simulation model is a symbolic or numerical abstraction of the real process, and the danger exists that the limitations and assumptions of the model will become hidden (or not adequately considered) by its complexity.

Validation of the operation of a simulation model is as desirable

---

[13] Peter Gilmour, "Development of a Dynamic Simulation Model for Planning Physical Distribution Systems: Validation," Unpublished Ph.D. dissertation, Michigan State University, 1971.

See also, D. J. Bowersox, et al., *Dynamic Simulation of Physical Distribution Systems* (East Lansing, Mich.: Division of Research, Michigan State University, 1971).

as the validation of the operation of any other scientific experiment. While the basic problem of validation is no different for a simulation experiment, the complexity of the model is such that the processes by which its validity is established are quite different. With most scientific experiments it is rather easy and inexpensive to carry out several independent replications. Due to the complextiy of most simulation models, the expense of performing more than one experiment is often prohibitive, while longitudinal observations during this one experiment are autocorrelated.

The time and effort needed to develop and make operational a computer simulation model are at present so great that the problem of its validation has generally been neglected. A common attitude seems to be that crude judgmental and graphic methods are preferable to completely ignoring validation.

The Meaning of Validation

To validate a model in a strict sense means to prove that the model is true. That truth is a rather elusive concept can be seen in the difficulty one has in developing a set of criteria for differentiating between a model which is "true" and one which is "not true." Fortunately most simulations are seldom concerned with proving the "truth" of the model. Popper,[14] therefore, suggests that efforts should be concentrated on determining the degree of confirmation rather than verification. Models should be subjected to tests, the results of which could be negative with respect to the aims of the model. Each such test passed will add confidence to our assumption that the model behavior confirms the behavior of the real system. "Thus instead of verification, we may speak of gradually increasing confirmation of the law."[15]

Van Horn describes validation as the "process of building an acceptable level of confidence that an inference about a simulated process is a correct or valid inference for the actual process."[16] The focus for validation should be to understand the input-output relationships in the model and to be able to translate "learning" from

---

[14] K. R. Popper, *The Logic of Scientific Discovery* (New York: Basic Books, Inc., 1959).

[15] R. Carnap, "Testability and Meaning," *Philosophy of Science*, Vol. 3, No. 4 (October 1936).

[16] R. Van Horn, "Validation," *The Design of Computer Simulation Experiments*, ed. by T. H. Naylor (Durham, N.C.: Duke University Press, 1969), pp. 232–51.

the simulation to "learning" about the actual process. Naylor and Finger[17] basically agree and provide some insight as to how this focus can be operationalized. The computer simulation model and its output are based on inductive inferences about behavior of the real system in the form of behavioral assumptions or operating characteristics. The real situation under study is usually so complex that the construction of an exact model is not possible. Another factor besides complexity which makes computer simulation the desirable method of analysis is the random nature of one or more of the exogenous variables. Therefore:

The validity of the model is made probable, not certain, by the assumptions underlying the model. . . . The rules for validating computer simulation models and the data generated by these models are sampling rules resting entirely on the theory of probability.[18]

Three major methodological positions on validation are summarized by Naylor and Finger: rationalism, empiricism, and positive economics.

Rationalism. Models or theory are a system of logical deductions from a series of synthetic premises of unquestionable truth. Validation is the search for the basic assumptions underlying the behavior of the system.

Empiricism. The opposite view to rationalism is that empirical science is the ideal form of knowledge. The model should be constructed with facts, not assumptions. So any postulates or assumptions which cannot be independently verified should not be considered.

Positive Economics. This view championed by Friedman is that the validity of a model depends upon its ability to predict the behavior of the dependent variables and *not* on the validity of the assumptions on which the model rests.

These three positions are combined by Naylor and Finger into a multistage verification procedure, each stage of which is necessary but not sufficient. Stage 1 is the formulation of a set of postulates or hypotheses describing the behavior of the system. This involves specification of components, selection of variables, and formulation of functional relationships using observation, general knowledge, relevant theory, and intuition. Stage 2 is the attempt to verify the

---

[17] T. H. Naylor and J. M. Finger, "Verification of Computer Simulation Models," *Management Science*, Vol. 14 (October 1967), pp. 92–101.

[18] Ibid., p. 93.

assumptions of the model by statistical analysis, and the final stage is to test the degree to which data generated by the model conforms to observed data. The multistage verification procedure attempts to include all major ways in which to build confidence in a model.

A final view on validation is that of Fishman and Kiviat[19] which is a narrower concept because they divide simulation testing into three parts.

(1) Verification insures that a simulation model behaves as an experimenter intends. (2) Validation tests the agreement between the behavior of the simulation model and a real system. (3) Problem analysis embraces statistical problems relating to (the analysis) of data generated by computer simulation.[20]

Experimental Design and Validation

It is difficult to distinguish where experimental design ends and validation begins. The process of computer simulation experimentation is iterative: model construction, model operation, validation, and experimental design. If the validation criteria are not satisfied, the process is repeated making adjustments until validity is indicated.

The aim of a simulation experiment may be stated as the desire to explore and describe the response surface over some region in the factor space (system analysis) or to optimize the response over some feasible region in the factor space (system design). In order to achieve this aim in the most economical manner, careful attention must be paid to experimental design.[21] The types of experiments for which the model is used will depend upon the particular requirements that the model was designed to meet.[22] But the types of problems that can be associated with experimental design are universal.

A single run of a computer simulation provides an estimate of population parameters. Because the model contains exogenous random variables, this estimation, or sample of one, will not exactly

---

[19] G. S. Fishman and P. J. Kiviat, *Digital Computer Simulation: Statistical Considerations* (Santa Monica, Calif.: The Rand Corporation, 1962), RM–3281–PR.

[20] Ibid.

[21] T. H. Naylor, D. S. Burdick, and W. E. Sasser, Jr., "The Design of Computer Simulation Experiments," *The Design of Computer Simulation Experiments*, ed. by T. H. Naylor (Durham, N.C.: Duke University Press, 1969), pp. 3–35.

[22] R. T. Rogers, "Development of a Dynamic Simulation Model for Planning Physical Distribution Systems: Experimental Design and Analysis of Results," unpublished Ph.D. dissertation, Michigan State University, forthcoming.

equal the population parameter. However, the larger the sample or the more runs that are made, the greater is the probability that the sample averages will be very close to the population averages. The convergence of sample averages to population averages with increasing sample size is called stochastic convergence. Because stochastic convergence is slow, methods other than increasing the sample size may be required.

Another problem is that of size. The number of cells required for a full factorial experiment becomes very large even with few levels of a moderate number of factors. If a complete investigation of all factors is not essential, fractional factorial designs can ameliorate the problem.

Yet another common problem associated with experimental design arises from the desire to observe many different response variables in a given experiment.

It is often possible to bypass the multiple response problem by treating an experiment with many responses as many experiments each with a single response. Or several responses could be combined (e.g., by addition) and treated as a single response. However, it is not always possible to bypass the multiple response problem; often multiple responses are inherent to the situation under study. Unfortunately, experimental design techniques for multiple response experiments are virtually nonexistent.[23]

Validation—Procedure

From the rather diverse views on validation examined earlier, a position must be taken. The validity of a computer simulation model can be shown by the model's ability to satisfy three distinct validation procedures.

The output of a simulation model is in the form of a time path for each of the endogenous variables. *The first validation procedure is to determine if these time series are statistically under control.* Being under control broadly means that over the long run the time path will show convergence properties or else the rate of change of the endogenous variable under study will be proportional to or acceptable to the rate of change in all other endogenous variables.

Simulation models can be broadly classified as positive or normative. Positive models must by definition show reasonable correspondence to the real system, while normative models indicate a

---

[23] Naylor, Burdick, and Sasser, "The Design of Computer Simulation Experiments," p. 30.

desirable level of operation for the real system which may or may not be currently achieved. But is it reasonable for a model to show the desired state and not to indicate how to reach this state from the current real state? If the normative model was built by changing starting conditions and parameter values of the positive model, [one] would be provided with the means to move from the current actual position to the more desirable normative position. The normative model should then be built from the basis of the positive model. For the positive simulation model, then, *the second validation procedure is to compare the model output over a past time period to the actual historical data from the same time period.*

The assumptions upon which a model is based often cannot be examined beyond the level of *face validity. . . . the sensitivity of these assumptions can be examined, and this is the third validation procedure.* If the values of the key endogenous variables are sensitive to the nature of the assumption, then [one's] knowledge and intuition must be applied to confirm the assumption, or else the model must be restructured to eliminate or replace the assumption.

GENERALIZING THE PROCEDURE

It is admitted that some degree of design validity testing (face validity testing) is required during the construction of any computer simulation model. To this extent a generalized validation procedure cannot be developed. But once the model passes this coarse testing, output validity can be established by a general procedure. . . .

The procedure is general, but two inputs to the procedure are specific: the assumptions of the particular model under consideration to evaluate, and the assumptions of the statistical validation techniques which are violated in this particular situation. These two considerations are of similar significance to this generalized procedure, as is the need for specific endogenous data streams in any particular analysis.

Interpretation of the results of this procedure involves a reasonable judgmental factor event with the consideration of the violated assumptions. So it is of interest to consider the construction of a validity index for a given simulation model. Each statistical technique generates results, a percentage of which are favorable to the proposition that the model is valid. This percentage is weighted by the inverse of the number of assumptions this technique has violated plus one. The result is summed for all techniques used in the validation procedure, and then this total is divided by the sum of the weights used. The result is an index of validity with a range from 0 to 1.

$$\text{Index of validity} = \frac{\sum_{i=1}^{n}\left\{\left(\begin{array}{c}\text{Percentage of}\\\text{favorable results}\end{array}\right)\left(\dfrac{1}{\begin{array}{c}\text{Number of assump-}\\\text{tions violated}+1\end{array}}\right)\right\}}{\sum_{i=1}^{n}\left\{\dfrac{1}{\begin{array}{c}\text{Number of assumptions}\\\text{violated}+1\end{array}}\right\}}$$

where n = number of statistical techniques used.

Actually an index is determined for the long-term stability of the model I^s, another index calculated for the model's predictive ability I^{pa}, and a third index for the sensitivity of the model to its major assumptions I^a. The overall index of validity . . . is the mean of the three component indexes. Table 18–1 shows these indexes for the model [examined by the author].

TABLE 18–1

Indexes of Validity

	Number of Assumptions Violated	Weight	Percentage of Favorable Results		
			Stability	*Prediction*	*Sensitivity*
Graphical analysis	4	0.20	100.0	50.0	100.0
Analysis of variance	3	0.25		100.0	50.0
Multiple comparison	3	0.25		0.0	88.0
The F test	3	0.25		50.0	75.0
Correlation analysis	2	0.33	100.0	0.0	50.0
Regression analysis	2	0.33		50.0	100.0
The Chi-square test	2	0.33		88.0	100.0
Theil's inequality coefficient	1	0.50	50.0	50.0	75.0
Spectral analysis	0	1.00	100.0	50.0	100.0
Factor analysis	3	0.25	13.0	100.0	
			$I^s = 0.877$	$I^{pa} = 0.466$	$I^a = 0.867$
				$I = 0.737$	

An analyst may not want to carry out all the tests of Table 18–1. He should select techniques for each of the three validation procedures starting with those that violate the least assumptions. If time and money permit, he can then move to techniques which violate more assumptions and provide information of poorer quality. With this selection procedure the value of the validity index may tend to vary inversely with the number of techniques used.[24]

The [above] procedures . . . provide a generalized validation procedure, and the validity index provides a basis for intramodel analysis and intermodel comparison.

SUGGESTIONS FOR FURTHER STUDY

CONWAY, R. W.; JOHNSON, B. M.; and MAXWELL, W. L. "Some Problems of Digital Systems Simulation," *Management Science,* Vol. 6, October 1959.

FISHMAN, G. S., and KIVIAT, P. J. *Digital Computer Simulation: Statistical Considerations.* Santa Monica, Calif.: The Rand Corporation, RM–3281, 1962.

NAYLOR, T. H.; BURDOCK, D. S.; and SASSER, W. E., JR. *The Design of Computer Simulation Experiments.* Durham, N.C.: Duke University Press, 1969.

---

[24] The truth of this statement can be established or rejected by sensitivity analysis. If the index does vary in this manner the appropriate corrective weighting system can also be determined.

appendixes

Appendix A

TABLE A-1

Areas of the Standard Normal Distribution

This table gives value of the area under the curve between $z = 0$ and positive value of the variate.

	.00	.01	.02	.03	.04	.05	.06	.07	.08	.09
0.0	.0000	.0040	.0080	.0120	.0160	.0199	.0239	.0279	.0319	.0359
0.1	.0398	.0438	.0478	.0517	.0557	.0596	.0636	.0675	.0714	.0753
0.2	.0793	.0832	.0871	.0910	.0948	.0987	.1026	.1064	.1103	.1141
0.3	.1179	.1217	.1255	.1293	.1331	.1368	.1406	.1443	.1480	.1517
0.4	.1554	.1591	.1628	.1664	.1700	.1736	.1772	.1808	.1844	.1879
0.5	.1915	.1950	.1985	.2019	.2054	.2088	.2123	.2157	.2190	.2224
0.6	.2257	.2291	.2324	.2357	.2389	.2422	.2454	.2486	.2518	.2549
0.7	.2580	.2612	.2642	.2673	.2704	.2734	.2764	.2794	.2823	.2852
0.8	.2881	.2910	.2939	.2967	.2995	.3023	.3051	.3078	.3106	.3133
0.9	.3159	.3186	.3212	.3238	.3264	.3289	.3315	.3340	.3365	.3389
1.0	.3413	.3438	.3461	.3485	.3508	.3531	.3554	.3577	.3599	.3621
1.1	.3643	.3665	.3686	.3708	.3729	.3749	.3770	.3790	.3810	.3830
1.2	.3849	.3869	.3888	.3907	.3925	.3944	.3962	.3980	.3997	.4015
1.3	.4032	.4049	.4066	.4082	.4099	.4115	.4131	.4147	.4162	.4177
1.4	.4192	.4207	.4222	.4236	.4251	.4265	.4279	.4292	.4306	.4319
1.5	.4332	.4345	.4357	.4370	.4382	.4394	.4406	.4418	.4429	.4441
1.6	.4452	.4463	.4474	.4484	.4495	.4505	.4515	.4525	.4535	.4545
1.7	.4554	.4564	.4573	.4582	.4591	.4599	.4608	.4616	.4625	.4633
1.8	.4641	.4649	.4656	.4664	.4671	.4678	.4686	.4693	.4699	.4706
1.9	.4713	.4719	.4726	.4732	.4738	.4744	.4750	.4756	.4761	.4767
2.0	.4772	.4778	.4783	.4788	.4793	.4798	.4803	.4808	.4812	.4817
2.1	.4821	.4826	.4830	.4834	.4838	.4842	.4846	.4850	.4854	.4857
2.2	.4861	.4864	.4868	.4871	.4875	.4878	.4881	.4884	.4887	.4890
2.3	.4893	.4896	.4898	.4901	.4904	.4906	.4909	.4911	.4913	.4916
2.4	.4918	.4920	.4922	.4925	.4927	.4929	.4931	.4932	.4934	.4936
2.5	.4938	.4940	.4941	.4943	.4945	.4946	.4948	.4949	.4951	.4952
2.6	.4953	.4955	.4956	.4957	.4959	.4960	.4961	.4962	.4963	.4964
2.7	.4965	.4966	.4967	.4968	.4969	.4970	.4971	.4972	.4973	.4974
2.8	.4974	.4975	.4976	.4977	.4977	.4978	.4979	.4979	.4980	.4981
2.9	.4981	.4982	.4982	.4983	.4984	.4984	.4985	.4985	.4986	.4986
3.0	.49865	.4987	.4987	.4988	.4988	.4989	.4989	.4989	.4990	.4990
3.1	.49903	.4991	.4991	.4991	.4992	.4992	.4992	.4992	.4993	.4993
3.2	.4993129	.4993	.4994	.4994	.4994	.4994	.4994	.4995	.4995	.4995
3.3	.4995166	.4995	.4995	.4996	.4996	.4996	.4996	.4996	.4996	.4997
3.4	.4996631	.4997	.4997	.4997	.4997	.4997	.4997	.4997	.4998	.4998
3.5	.4997674	.4998	.4998	.4998	.4998	.4998	.4998	.4998	.4998	.4998
3.6	.4998409	.4998	.4999	.4999	.4999	.4999	.4999	.4999	.4999	.4999
3.7	.4998922	.4999	.4999	.4999	.4999	.4999	.4999	.4999	.4999	.4999
3.8	.4999277	.4999	.4999	.4999	.4999	.4999	.4999	.4999	.5000	.5000
3.9	.4999519	.5000	.5000	.5000	.5000	.5000	.5000	.5000	.5000	.5000
4.0	.4999683									
4.5	.4999966									
5.0	.4999997133									

Appendix B

MATRIX OPERATIONS

Mathematical operations involving the manipulation of arrays of data can be greatly simplified by manipulating "packages" of data in accordance with the rules of matrix algebra. In matrix algebra certain operations such as addition, subtraction, and multiplication are so defined that the results of these package operations correspond precisely to the results that would be obtained if the same problem were attacked via scalar algebra.

We will begin with a few definitions, then we will describe the rules governing these operations.

Matrix. A matrix is a rectangular array of elements, such as those portrayed in Figure B–1.

FIGURE B–1

$$(a) \quad \begin{bmatrix} a_{11} & a_{12} & a_{13} & \cdots & a_{1n} \\ a_{21} & a_{22} & a_{23} & \cdots & a_{2n} \\ \cdot & & & & \\ \cdot & & & & \\ \cdot & & & & \\ a_{m1} & a_{m2} & a_{m3} & \cdots & a_{mn} \end{bmatrix} \qquad (b) \quad \begin{bmatrix} 2 & 3 \\ 1 & 4 \end{bmatrix}$$

$$(c) \quad \begin{bmatrix} f_1(x) & f_2(x) & f_3(x) \\ f_4(x) & f_5(x) & f_6(x) \end{bmatrix} \qquad (d) \quad \begin{bmatrix} c_3 & c_7 \\ c_1 & c_2 \\ c_8 & c_6 \end{bmatrix}$$

(e) $\begin{bmatrix} 4 & 7 & 6 \end{bmatrix}$ 　　(f) $\begin{bmatrix} 9 \\ 3 \\ 1 \end{bmatrix}$ 　　(g) $\begin{bmatrix} 1 & 0 & 0 & 0 \\ 0 & 1 & 0 & 0 \\ 0 & 0 & 1 & 0 \\ 0 & 0 & 0 & 1 \end{bmatrix}$

Order. The order of a matrix specifies its dimensions, with the number of rows generally specified first. In (a) (Figure B–1) we have an m by n matrix, in (b) a 2×2 matrix, in (c) a 2×3 matrix, and so on.

Vectors. In Figure B–1 (e) is a row *vector* or a 1 by 3 matrix; (f) is a column *vector* or a 3 by 1 matrix.

Transpose. The transpose of a matrix results from the interchange of rows and columns, so that the first *row* becomes the first column; the second row becomes the second column; and so on. Thus the transpose of (b) in Figure B–1 is:

$$\begin{bmatrix} 2 & 1 \\ 3 & 4 \end{bmatrix}$$

The transpose of (e) is:

$$\begin{bmatrix} 4 \\ 7 \\ 6 \end{bmatrix},$$

and the transpose of (f) is:

$$\begin{bmatrix} 9 & 3 & 1 \end{bmatrix}.$$

Equality. Two matrices are equal if and only if their corresponding elements are equal; that is, the a_{ij} element in one is the same as the b_{ij} element in the other:

$$\begin{array}{c} j=1 \ \ j=2 \ \ j=3 \\ \begin{matrix} i=1 \\ i=2 \end{matrix} \begin{bmatrix} a_{11} & a_{12} & a_{13} \\ a_{21} & a_{22} & a_{23} \end{bmatrix} = \begin{bmatrix} b_{11} & b_{12} & b_{13} \\ b_{21} & b_{22} & b_{23} \end{bmatrix}. \end{array}$$

Clearly, then, to be equal two matrices must have the same order.

Addition. When two matrices are added, the sum is a new matrix whose elements are the sums of corresponding elements in the original matrices (Figure B–2).

FIGURE B–2

$$\begin{bmatrix} 2 & 3 & 6 \\ 1 & 2 & 0 \end{bmatrix} + \begin{bmatrix} -1 & 2 & 7 \\ 0 & 3 & -1 \end{bmatrix} = \begin{bmatrix} 1 & 5 & 13 \\ 1 & 5 & -1 \end{bmatrix}$$

(a)   (b)   (c)

To be added, two matrices must have the same order. Note that matrix addition is associative and commutative. Thus in Figure B–2, matrix (a) plus matrix (b) = matrix (b) plus matrix (a). Similarly, if X, Y, and Z are three matrices of the same order, then:

$$X+Y+Z = Y+X+Z = Z+Y+X = (X+Y)+Z = X+(Y+Z).$$

Multiplication

Vector Multiplication.   The product of a column vector post-multiplied by a row vector is not defined. However, the product of a row vector postmultiplied by a column vector is defined. The operation is best demonstrated by an example:

$$\begin{bmatrix} 4 & 7 & 6 \end{bmatrix} \cdot \begin{bmatrix} 9 \\ 3 \\ 1 \end{bmatrix} = 4 \times 9 + 7 \times 3 + 6 \times 1 = 63.$$

Thus the product of a row vector and a column vector is a single element which is the sum of: (1) the product of the first element in the row and the first element in the column, (2) the product of the second element in the row and the second element in the column, and so on.

For a row vector postmultiplied by a column vector to have a product, the number of elements in the row must equal the number of elements in the column.

Matrix Multiplication.   The *first* element in the *first* row of a matrix (c) which is the product of matrix (a) postmultiplied by matrix (b) is the vector product of the first row of (a) and the first column of (b). The second element in the first row of (c) is the product of the first row of (a) and the second column of (b), and so on.

The *first* element in the *second* row of (c) is the product of the second row of (a) and the first column of (b). The *second* element in the *second* row of (c) is the product of the second row of (a) and the second column of (b), and so on. The example in Figure B–3 illustrates the multiplication of matrices:

FIGURE B–3

(a) $\begin{bmatrix} 2 & 3 \\ 1 & 4 \end{bmatrix} \cdot \begin{bmatrix} 1 & 0 \\ 3 & -2 \end{bmatrix} =$

$$\begin{bmatrix} 11 & -6 \\ 13 & -8 \end{bmatrix} \rightarrow \begin{cases} [2 \ 3] \cdot \begin{bmatrix} 1 \\ 3 \end{bmatrix} = 11 \, ; [2 \ 3] \cdot \begin{bmatrix} 0 \\ -2 \end{bmatrix} = -6 \\ [1 \ 4] \cdot \begin{bmatrix} 1 \\ 3 \end{bmatrix} = 13 \, ; [1 \ 4] \cdot \begin{bmatrix} 0 \\ -2 \end{bmatrix} = -8 \end{cases}$$

(b) $\begin{bmatrix} 2 & 3 \\ 4 & -1 \\ 0 & 2 \end{bmatrix} \cdot \begin{bmatrix} 3 & 0 & 6 & 4 \\ 1 & 2 & 5 & -3 \end{bmatrix} = \begin{bmatrix} 9 & 6 & 27 & -1 \\ 11 & -2 & 19 & 19 \\ 2 & 4 & 10 & -6 \end{bmatrix}$

Clearly for two matrices, (a) and (b), to have a product, the number of columns in (a) must equal the number of rows in (b), and the resulting matrix has the same number of rows as (a) and the same number of columns as (b), as illustrated in (b) of Figure B–3.

This should lead us to suspect that matrix multiplication is not commutative. This is the case, even if the matrices whose products are desired are both square matrices, as is illustrated in Figure B–4.

FIGURE B–4

$$\begin{bmatrix} 2 & 3 \\ 1 & 4 \end{bmatrix} \cdot \begin{bmatrix} 1 & 0 \\ 3 & -2 \end{bmatrix} = \begin{bmatrix} 11 & -6 \\ 13 & -8 \end{bmatrix}; \textit{but } \begin{bmatrix} 1 & 0 \\ 3 & -2 \end{bmatrix} \cdot \begin{bmatrix} 2 & 3 \\ 1 & 4 \end{bmatrix} = \begin{bmatrix} 2 & 3 \\ 4 & 1 \end{bmatrix}$$

The Unit or Identity Matrix

Matrix (g) of Figure B–1 is a *unit* or *identity* matrix. The unit matrix, which is always a square matrix, corresponds to 1 in scalar algebra. Note that if U is a unit matrix and A is a matrix such that the product $U \times A$ can be formed, then

$$U \times A = A.$$

Similarly if the product $A \times U$ can be formed, then

$$A \times U = A.$$

The Inverse of a Matrix.   In matrix algebra we do not divide a matrix by another matrix, but rather we form the product of one and the inverse of the other. Suppose we had the following system of linear equations:

$$2X + 3Y + Z = A + 2B + 0C$$
$$0X + Y + 2Z = 3A + 0B + C$$
$$3X + 2Y + Z = 0A + 2B + C.$$

Note that these equations could be expressed as follows (Figure B–5):

FIGURE B–5

$$\begin{bmatrix} 2 & 3 & 1 \\ 0 & 1 & 2 \\ 3 & 2 & 1 \end{bmatrix} \begin{bmatrix} X \\ Y \\ Z \end{bmatrix} = \begin{bmatrix} 1 & 2 & 0 \\ 3 & 0 & 1 \\ 0 & 2 & 1 \end{bmatrix} \begin{bmatrix} A \\ B \\ C \end{bmatrix}$$
$$\qquad (J) \qquad\qquad\qquad (K)$$

If J is the coefficient matrix of the column vector

$$\begin{bmatrix} X \\ Y \\ Z \end{bmatrix},$$

and K is the coefficient matrix of column vector

$$\begin{bmatrix} A \\ B \\ C \end{bmatrix},$$

then our system of equations could be written:

$$J \begin{bmatrix} X \\ Y \\ Z \end{bmatrix} = K \begin{bmatrix} A \\ B \\ C \end{bmatrix}$$

If we solve our initial system of equations simultaneously to obtain X, Y, and Z in terms of A, B, and C, we obtain:

$$X = (-\tfrac{2}{3})A + (\tfrac{4}{9})B + (\tfrac{4}{9})C$$
$$Y = (\ \tfrac{1}{3})A + (\tfrac{4}{9})B - (\tfrac{5}{9})C$$
$$Z = (\ \tfrac{4}{3})A - (\tfrac{2}{9})B + (\tfrac{7}{9})C$$

which can be written:

$$\begin{bmatrix} 1 & 0 & 0 \\ 0 & 1 & 0 \\ 0 & 0 & 1 \end{bmatrix} \begin{bmatrix} X \\ Y \\ Z \end{bmatrix} = \begin{bmatrix} -\tfrac{2}{3} & \tfrac{4}{9} & \tfrac{4}{9} \\ \tfrac{1}{3} & \tfrac{4}{9} & -\tfrac{5}{9} \\ \tfrac{4}{3} & -\tfrac{2}{9} & \tfrac{7}{9} \end{bmatrix} \begin{bmatrix} A \\ B \\ C \end{bmatrix}.$$
$$\qquad (U) \qquad\qquad\qquad (L)$$

Note that we have made the following observations about our initial system of equations:

$$J \begin{bmatrix} X \\ Y \\ Z \end{bmatrix} = K \begin{bmatrix} A \\ B \\ C \end{bmatrix}$$

and

$$U \begin{bmatrix} X \\ Y \\ Z \end{bmatrix} = L \begin{bmatrix} A \\ B \\ C \end{bmatrix}.$$

where J, K, and L are coefficient matrices and U is the unit matrix.

In scalar algebra, when we consider an equation such as:

$$jX = kA,$$

where j and k are coefficients of variables X and A respectively, we commonly say there must be some quantity q that if coefficients j and k are multiplied by this quantity we will generate a new and equivalent equation,

$$1X = (kq)A,$$

which directly expresses the value of X in terms of A that satisfies our original equation (that is, the *solution* of the equation). The quantity q that will do this is, of course:

$$q = 1/j$$

or "q is the *inverse* of j."

In a similar way concerning the matrix equation of Figure B–5 we would like to be able to say there must be some matrix Q that if coefficient matrices J and K are premultiplied by that matrix we will generate a new and equivalent matrix equation of the form:

$$U \begin{bmatrix} X \\ Y \\ Z \end{bmatrix} = L \begin{bmatrix} A \\ B \\ C \end{bmatrix}$$

which directly expresses the values of X, Y, and Z in terms of A,B, and C. Matrix Q will be the *inverse* of matrix J, so that

$$Q \times J = U$$

and therefore $Q = J^{-1}$, where J^{-1} is the inverse of matrix J.

A computationally attractive scheme for finding the inverse of a matrix is described in Chapter 14. The inverse of matrix J proves to be:

$$Q = J^{-1} = \begin{bmatrix} -\tfrac{1}{3} & -\tfrac{1}{9} & \tfrac{5}{9} \\ \tfrac{2}{3} & -\tfrac{1}{9} & -\tfrac{4}{9} \\ -\tfrac{1}{3} & \tfrac{5}{9} & \tfrac{2}{9} \end{bmatrix}$$

and, as we should expect,

$$\begin{bmatrix} -\tfrac{1}{3} & -\tfrac{1}{9} & \tfrac{5}{9} \\ \tfrac{2}{3} & -\tfrac{1}{9} & -\tfrac{4}{9} \\ -\tfrac{1}{3} & \tfrac{5}{9} & \tfrac{2}{9} \end{bmatrix} \begin{bmatrix} 2 & 3 & 1 \\ 0 & 1 & 2 \\ 3 & 2 & 1 \end{bmatrix} = \begin{bmatrix} 1 & 0 & 0 \\ 0 & 1 & 0 \\ 0 & 0 & 1 \end{bmatrix}$$

that is,

$$Q \text{ or } J^{-1} \quad \times \quad J \quad = \quad U.$$

Similarly:

$$\begin{bmatrix} -\tfrac{1}{3} & -\tfrac{1}{9} & \tfrac{5}{9} \\ \tfrac{2}{3} & -\tfrac{1}{9} & -\tfrac{4}{9} \\ -\tfrac{1}{3} & \tfrac{5}{9} & \tfrac{2}{9} \end{bmatrix} \begin{bmatrix} 1 & 2 & 0 \\ 3 & 0 & 1 \\ 0 & 2 & 1 \end{bmatrix} = \begin{bmatrix} -\tfrac{2}{3} & \tfrac{4}{9} & \tfrac{4}{9} \\ \tfrac{1}{3} & \tfrac{4}{9} & -\tfrac{5}{9} \\ \tfrac{4}{3} & -\tfrac{2}{9} & \tfrac{7}{9} \end{bmatrix}$$

from which we can write:

$$\begin{bmatrix} 1 & 0 & 0 \\ 0 & 1 & 0 \\ 0 & 0 & 1 \end{bmatrix} \begin{bmatrix} X \\ Y \\ Z \end{bmatrix} = \begin{bmatrix} -\tfrac{2}{3} & \tfrac{4}{9} & \tfrac{4}{9} \\ \tfrac{1}{3} & \tfrac{4}{9} & -\tfrac{5}{9} \\ \tfrac{4}{3} & -\tfrac{2}{9} & \tfrac{7}{9} \end{bmatrix} \begin{bmatrix} A \\ B \\ C \end{bmatrix}$$

which, in scalar algebra becomes:

$$\begin{aligned} X &= (-\tfrac{2}{3})A + (\tfrac{4}{9})B + (\tfrac{4}{9})C \\ Y &= (\ \ \tfrac{1}{3})A + (\tfrac{4}{9})B - (\tfrac{5}{9})C \\ Z &= (\ \ \tfrac{4}{3})A - (\tfrac{2}{9})B + (\tfrac{7}{9})C. \end{aligned}$$

Comments

1. Whereas in scalar algebra every number has an inverse (reciprocal), all matrices do not have inverses. A matrix that does not have an inverse is called a singular matrix. Those with inverses are nonsingular.

2. In scalar algebra the product of two nonzero real numbers cannot be zero. In matrix algebra two nonzero matrices (a zero or null matrix has nothing but zeros for elements) may have a zero product.

SUGGESTIONS FOR FURTHER STUDY

HORST, PAUL. *Matrix Algebra for Social Scientists.* New York: Holt, Rinehart & Winston, Inc., 1963.

KEMENY, SCHLAIFER, SNELL, and THOMPSON. *Finite Mathematics,* chap 5. Englewood Cliffs, N.J.: Prentice-Hall, Inc., 1962.

TEICHROEW, DANIEL. *An Introduction to Management Science, Deterministic Models,* chaps. 12, 13, and 14. New York: John Wiley & Sons, Inc., 1964.

Appendix C

BASIC Language Counterpart Programs for the Major FORTRAN Programs Presented, Through Chapter 15.

FIGURE 3-1

```
0010 LET P=1000
0020 LET R=.04
0030 LET N=1
0040 LET S=P*(1+R)↑N
0050 PRINT S
0060 LET P=S
0070 GOTO 0040
```

FIGURE 3-2

```
0010 LET P=1000
0020 LET R=.04
0030 LET N=1
0040 FOR J=1 TO 10
0045    LET Y=Y+1
0050    LET S=P*(1+R)↑N
0060    LET P=S
0070    PRINT J,S
0080 NEXT J
```

FIGURE 5-4

```
0010 LET Q=2
0020 LET T1=7300/Q+50*Q
0030 LET Q=Q+1
0040 LET T2=7300/Q+50*Q
0050 IF T2<T1 GOTO  0020
0060 LET Q=Q-1
0070 PRINT "OPTIMUM Q =";Q," MINIMUM T =";T1
```

FIGURE 5-5

```
0005 REM   INITIALIZE Q AT SOME SMALL VALUE
0010 LET Q=2
0015 REM   CALCULATE T1
0020 LET T1=7300/Q+50*Q
0025 REM   INCREASE Q BY 1
0030 LET Q=Q+1
0035 REM   CALCULATE T2
0040 LET T2=7300/Q+50*Q
0045 REM   COMPARE T1 WITH T2 AND DECIDE WHETHER TO CONTINUE ITERATION
0050 IF T2<T1 GOTO  0020
0060 LET Q=Q-1
0070 PRINT " OPTIMUM Q = ";Q," MINIMUM T =";T1
```

FIGURE 5–7

```
0010 LET B=999999
0020 FOR I=2 TO 10000
0030    LET Q=I
0040    LET T=7300/Q+50*Q
0050    IF T>=B GOTO 0080
0060    LET B=T
0070 NEXT I
0080 LET I=I-1
0090 PRINT " OPTIMUM Q =";I," MINIMUM T";T
```

FIGURE 5–8

```
0020 REM   C = THE COST PRICE / UNIT
0030 REM   C1 = THE ORDERING COST / ORDER PROCESSED
0040 REM   D = THE DEMAND / YEAR IN UNITS
0050 INPUT U,C,C1,D
0060 LET B=999999
0070 FOR I=2 TO 10000
0080    LET Q=I
0090    LET T=U*C*(Q/2)+C1*(D/Q)
0100    IF T>=B GOTO 0130
0110    LET B=T
0120 NEXT I
0130 LET I=I-1
0140 PRINT " OPTIMUM Q =";I;" MINIMUM T =";T
```

FIGURE 7–3

```
0010 REM   I = A TWO DIGIT RANDOM NUMBER
0020 INPUT I
0030 IF I>24 GOTO 0060
0040 LET L=1
0050 GOTO 0100
0060 IF I>74 GOTO 0090
0070 LET L=2
0080 GOTO 0100
0090 LET L=3
0100 LET I1=0
0110 FOR J=1 TO L
0120    INPUT I
0130    IF I>39 GOTO 0160
0140    LET I2=0
0150    GOTO 0230
0160    IF I>69 GOTO 0190
0170    LET I2=1
0180    GOTO 0230
0190    IF I>89 GOTO 0220
0200    LET I2=2
0210    GOTO 0230
0220    LET I2=3
0230    LET I1=I1+I2
0240 NEXT J
0250 PRINT I1
```

FIGURE 7-7

```
0010 REM   E(I) = EXPECTED STOCK-OUT / LEAD TIME PERIOD
0020 DIM E[9]
0030 FOR I=1 TO 9
0040    READ E[I]
0050 NEXT I
0060 LET A=99999
0070 FOR I=1 TO 9
0080    LET R=I
0090    LET B=99999
0100    FOR J=1 TO 10000
0110       LET Q=J
0120       LET T=.2*500*(Q/2+R-2)+20*365/Q+40*E[I]*365/Q
0130       IF T>=B GOTO 0160
0140       LET B=T
0150    NEXT J
0160    LET S=B
0170    IF S>=A GOTO 0210
0180    LET N=J-1
0190    LET A=S
0200 NEXT I
0210 LET I=I-1
0220 PRINT N,I,A
0230 DATA  1.1864, .6234, .2764, .1091, .0353, .0092, .0021, .0003, 0
```

FIGURE 7-9

```
0010 REM   GENERAL INVENTORY MODEL UNDER UNCERTAINTY
0020 REM   PARAMETERS
0030 REM   N = NUMBER OF POSITIONS IN THE ARRAY REPRESENTING
0040 REM       THE EXPECTED VALUES OF STOCKOUT "SCHEDULE"
0050 REM   U = ANNUAL UNIT HOLDING COST AS A % OF THE COST / UNIT
0060 REM   C = COST / UNIT
0070 REM   E2 = EXPECTED DEMAND DURING LEAD TIME
0080 REM   C1 = ORDERING COST / ORDER PROCESSED
0090 REM   D = DEMAND / YEAR
0100 REM   S = STOCKOUT COST / UNIT STOCKOUT
0110 REM   E(I) = HOLDS THE EXPECTED STOCKOUT "SCHEDULE"
0120 DIM E[9]
0130 LET N=9
0140 LET U=.2
0150 LET C=500
0160 LET E2=2
0170 LET C1=20
0180 LET D=365
0190 LET S=40
0200 FOR I=1 TO N
0210    READ E[I]
0220 NEXT I
0230 LET A=999999
0240 FOR I=1 TO N
0250    LET R=I
0260    LET B=999999
0270    FOR J=1 TO 10000
0280       LET Q=J
0290       LET T=U*C*(Q/2+R-E2)+C1*(D/Q)+S*E[I]*D/Q
0300       IF T>=B GOTO 0330
0310       LET B=T
0320    NEXT J
0330    LET S1=B
0340    IF S1>=A GOTO   0380
0350    LET N1=J-1
0360    LET A=S1
0370 NEXT I
0380 LET I=I-1
0390 PRINT N1,I,A
0400 DATA  1.1864, .6234, .2764, .1091, .0353, .0092, .0021, .0003, 0
```

MODEL 7-1

```
0005 REM   I = A TWO DIGIT RANDOM NUMBER
0010 DIM S[10]
0020 FOR K=1 TO 10
0030   LET S[K]=0
0040 NEXT K
0050 FOR K=1 TO 1000
0060   READ I
0070   IF I>24 GOTO 0100
0080   LET L=1
0090   GOTO 0140
0100   IF I>74 GOTO 0130
0110   LET L=2
0120   GOTO 0140
0130   LET L=3
0140   LET I1=0
0150   FOR J=1 TO L
0160     READ I
0170     IF I>39 GOTO 0200
0180     LET I2=0
0190     GOTO 0270
0200     IF I>69 GOTO 0230
0210     LET I2=1
0220     GOTO 0270
0230     IF I>89 GOTO 0260
0240     LET I2=2
0250     GOTO 0270
0260     LET I2=3
0270     LET I1=I1+I2
0280   NEXT J
0290   LET S[I1+1]=S[I1+1]+1
0300 NEXT K
0310 FOR J=1 TO 10
0320   LET P=S[J]/1000
0330   LET K=J-1
0340   PRINT " PROB OF A DEMAND FOR ";K;" DURING LEAD TIME IS ";P
0350 NEXT J
```

FIGURE 9-2

```
0010 LET K1=0
0020 LET N=8
0030 LET P=.01
0040 LET T=0
0050 FOR K=1 TO K1
0060   LET I=K
0070   LET T1=0
0080   FOR J=1 TO N
0090     LET D=J
0100     LET T1=T1+LOG(D)
0110   NEXT J
0120   LET T2=0
0130   FOR J=1 TO I
0140     LET D=J
0150     LET T2=T2+LOG(D)
0160   NEXT J
0170   LET L=N-I
0180   LET T3=0
0190   FOR J=1 TO L
0200     LET D=J
0210     LET T3=T3+LOG(D)
0220   NEXT J
0230   LET S1=I
0240   LET S2=N
0250   LET C1=S1*LOG(P)+(S2-S1)*LOG(1-P)
0260   LET C3=C1+T1-(T2+T3)
0270   LET P1=EXP(C3)
0280   LET T=T+P1
0290 NEXT K
0300 LET T=T+(1-P)↑N
0310 PRINT N,K1,P,T
```

FIGURE 11-5

```
0010 LET X=12.63
0015 INPUT T1,S
0020 LET I1=(T1/S)↑2
0030 LET T2=T1/S↑2
0040 LET T=1
0050 FOR J=1 TO I1
0060   LET T=T*RND(X)
0070 NEXT J
0080 LET G=-LOG(T)/T2
0090 PRINT ,G
```

FIGURE 12–2

```
0010 REM    A=AVTIS
0020 REM    C=CUMQUE
0030 REM    C1=CUMUTL
0040 REM    C2=CUMSERV
0050 REM    H=H
0060 REM    H1=HRST
0070 REM    L=L
0080 REM    M=M
0090 REM    P=PLUTIL
0100 REM    Q=QUE
0110 REM    R=R
0120 REM    S=STATUS
0130 REM    T=T
0140 REM    T1=TIME
0150 REM    T2=TNARV
0160 REM    T3=TNDPR
0170 DIM C[20]
0180 REM    INITIALIZE SYSTEM AT TIME ZERO
0190 LET T1=0
0200 LET T3=99999
0210 FOR M=1 TO 20
0220    LET C[M]=0
0230 NEXT M
0240 LET S=0
0250 LET Q=0
0260 LET C1=0
0270 LET C2=0
0279 LET X=12.56
0280 LET R=RND(X)
0290 LET T2=-1/2*LOG(R)
0300 REM    DECIDE WHETHER YOU HAVE AN ARRIVIAL OR DEPARTURE
0310 IF T2>=T3 GOTO 0520
0320 REM    ARRIVE SUBPROGRAM
0330 REM    UPDATE CUMQUE,RESET TIME
0340 LET M=Q
0350 LET C[M+1]=C[M+1]+T2-T1
0360 LET T1=T2
0370 REM    CHECK QUEUE LENGTH AND STATE OF SERVICE FACILITY
0380 IF Q>=1 GOTO 0480
0390 IF S>=1 GOTO 0480
0400 LET S=1
0410 REM    ESTABLISH TIME IN SERVICE FACILITY AND TIME OF NEXT DEPARTUR
0420 LET T=-1/3*LOG(RND(X))
0430 LET T3=T1+T
0440 REM    UPDATE CUMUTL
0450 LET C1=C1+T
0460 GOTO 0500
0470 REM    INCREASE QUEUE LENGTH
0480 LET Q=Q+1
0490 REM    ESTABLISH TIME OF NEXT ARRIVAL
0500 LET T2=-1/2*LOG(RND(X))+T1
0510 GOTO 0310
0520 REM    DEPART SUBPROGRAM
0530 REM    UPDATE CUMQUE,RESET TIME
0540 LET M=Q
0550 LET C[M+1]=C[M+1]+T3-T1
0560 LET T1=T3
0570 REM    CHECK QUEUE LENGTH
```

FIGURE 12-2 (Continued)

```
0580 IF Q>=1 GOTO 0630
0590 LET S=0
0600 LET T3=99999
0610 GOTO 0690
0620 REM   DECREASE QUEUE LENGTH
0630 LET Q=Q-1
0640 REM   ESTABLISH TIME IN SERVICE FACILITY AND TIME OF NEXT DEPARTUR
0650 LET T=-1/3*LOG(RND(X))
0660 LET T3=T1+T
0670 REM   UPDATE CUMUTL AND CUSERV
0680 LET C1=C1+T
0690 LET C2=C2+1
0700 REM   TERMINATE SIMULATION IF 1,000 ARRIVALS HAVE BEEN SERVICED
0710 IF C2<1000 GOTO  0310
0720 REM   DETERMINE PERCENTAGE UTILIZATION OF SERVICE FACILITY
0730 LET P=C1/T1*100
0740 REM   DETERMINE FROM CUMQUE CUSTOMER HOURS SPENT IN QUEUE
0750 LET H1=0
0760 FOR M=1 TO 19
0770    LET H=M
0780    LET H1=H1+H*C[M]
0790 NEXT M
0800 REM   ADD CUSTOMER-HOURS IN FACILITY AND DETERMINE AVERAGE
0810 REM   TIME IN SYSTEM
0820 LET A=(H1+C1)/1000
0830 REM   CONVERT CONTENTS OF CUMQUE TO PROBABILITIES
0840 FOR M=1 TO 20
0850    LET C[M]=C[M]/T1
0860 NEXT M
0870 REM   WRITE PCUTIL AND AVTIS
0880 PRINT " PERCENTAGE UTILIZATION OF SERVICE FACILITY = ";P
0890 PRINT " AVERAGE TIME IN SYSTEM PER CUSTOMER = ";A
0900 REM   PRINT PROBABILITIES OF QUEUES OF VARYING LENGTHS
0910 FOR M=1 TO 19
0920    LET L=M-1
0930    PRINT " PROBABILITY OF ";L;" CUSTOMERS IN QUEUE = ";C[M]
0940 NEXT M
```

FIGURE 13-9

```
00100 DIM V(100,20),P(100),E(100),J(100)
00110 FOR K=1 TO 100
00120    LET P(K)=0
00130 NEXT K
00140 LET N1=0
00150 READ N2
00160 FOR N=1 TO 8
00170    READ V(N2,N)
00180 NEXT N
00190 LET N1=N1+1
00200 IF N2<99 THEN 00150
00210 LET N1=N1-1
00220 LET K=1
00230 LET P(K)=1
00240 LET K=K+1
00250 LET P(K)=V(1,1)
00260 LET N=V(1,1)
00270 IF V(N,7)>0 THEN 00320
00280 LET K=K+1
00290 LET P(K)=V(N,1)
00300 LET N=V(N,1)
00310 GOTO 00270
00320 LET T1=V(N,7)
00330 LET V1=V(N,8)
00340 LET K=K-1
00350 LET N=P(K)
00360 LET T3=T1+V(N,2)
00370 LET V3=V1+V(N,3)
00380 IF V(N,4)>0 THEN 00420
00390 LET V(N,7)=T1+V(N,2)
00400 LET V(N,8)=V1+V(N,3)
00410 GOTO 00580
00420 LET K=K+1
00430 LET P(K)=V(N,4)
00440 LET N=V(N,4)
00450 IF V(N,7)<=0 THEN 00280
00460 LET T2=V(N,7)
00470 LET V2=V(N,8)
00480 LET K=K-1
00490 LET N=P(K)
00500 LET T4=T2+V(N,5)
00510 LET V4=V2+V(N,6)
00520 IF T3>T4 THEN 00560
00530 LET V(N,7)=T2+V(N,5)
00540 LET V(N,8)=V2+V(N,6)
00550 GOTO 00580
00560 LET V(N,7)=T1+V(N,2)
00570 LET V(N,8)=V1+V(N,3)
00580 IF K<=1 THEN 620
00590 LET K=K-1
00600 LET N=P(K)
00610 GOTO 00270
00620 FOR N=1 TO N1
00630    LET V(N,9)=0
00640    LET V(N,10)=0
00650    LET V(N,11)=0
```

FIGURE 13-9 (Continued)

```
00660    LET V(N,12)=0
00670    LET V(N,13)=0
00680    LET V(N,14)=0
00690 NEXT N
00700 FOR N=1 TO N1
00710    LET L=V(N,1)
00720    LET J1=V(N,4)
00730    IF L<=0 THEN 870
00740    IF V(L,9)>0 THEN 780
00750    LET V(L,9)=N
00760    LET V(L,10)=V(N,2)
00770    GOTO 00800
00780    LET V(L,11)=N
00790    LET V(L,12)=V(N,2)
00800    IF J1<=0 THEN 870
00810    IF V(J1,9)>0 THEN 850
00820    LET V(J1,9)=N
00830    LET V(J1,10)=V(N,5)
00840    GOTO 00870
00850    LET V(J1,11)=N
00860    LET V(J1,12)=V(N,5)
00870 NEXT N
00880 LET K=N1
00890 LET V(1,13)=V(1,7)
00900 LET N=V(1,1)
00910 IF V(N,13)>0 THEN 1020
00920 IF V(N,11)>0 THEN 1070
00930 LET M=V(N,9)
00940 IF V(M,13)>0 THEN 990
00950 LET K=K+1
00960 LET P(K)=N
00970 LET N=M
00980 GOTO 00920
00990 LET V(N,13)=V(M,13)-V(N,10)
01000 LET N=P(K)
01010 IF N>0 THEN 910
01020 FOR N9=1 TO N1
01030    LET N=N9
01040    IF V(N,13)<=0 THEN 920
01050 NEXT N9
01060 GOTO 01260
01070 LET M1=V(N,9)
01080 IF V(M1,13)>0 THEN 1130
01090 LET K=K+1
01100 LET P(K)=N
01110 LET N=M1
01120 GOTO 00920
01130 LET M2=V(N,11)
01140 IF V(M2,13)>0 THEN 1190
01150 LET K=K+1
01160 LET P(K)=N
01170 LET N=M2
01180 GOTO 00920
01190 LET T5=V(M1,13)-V(N,10)
01200 LET T6=V(M2,13)-V(N,12)
01210 IF T5>T6 THEN 1240
```

FIGURE 13–9 (Concluded)

```
01220    LET V(N,13)=T5
01230    GOTO 01000
01240    LET V(N,13)=T6
01250    GOTO 01000
01260    FOR N=1 TO N1
01270      LET V(N,14)=V(N,13)-V(N,7)
01280    NEXT N
01290    FOR M=1 TO N1
01300      LET E(M)=V(M,7)
01310    NEXT M
01320    FOR L=1 TO N1
01330      LET A=E(1)
01340      LET K=1
01350      FOR M=2 TO N1
01360        IF E(M)>=A THEN 1390
01370        LET A=E(M)
01380        LET K=M
01390      NEXT M
01400      LET J(L)=K
01410      LET E(K)=99999
01420    NEXT L
01430    PRINT ≡ EVENT NO.          TE          SLACK          VARIANCE≡
01440    FOR L=1 TO N1
01450      LET N=J(L)
01460      PRINT N,V(N,7),V(N,14),V(N,8)
01470    NEXT L
01480    DATA  3, 8, 32, 21, 5, 36, 12, 0, 0
01490    DATA  7, 4, 9, 6, 9, 12, 9, 0, 0
01500    DATA  4, 2, 21, 18, 9, 4, 2, 0, 0
01510    DATA  2, 6, 8, 6, 3, 20, 12, 0, 0
01520    DATA  5, 0, 0, 0, 0, 0, 0, 18, 11
01530    DATA  8, 0, 0, 0, 0, 0, 0, 10, 9
01540    DATA 6, 5, 12, 8, 0, 0, 0, 0, 0
01550    DATA 1, 4, 7, 5, 7, 13, 8, 0, 0
01560    DATA 9, 2, 6, 5, 8, 41, 28, 0, 0
01570    DATA 99, 0, 0, 0, 0, 0, 0, 0, 0
```

EVENT NO.	TE	SLACK	VARIANCE
8	10	12	9
5	18	0	11
6	30	36	19
3	54	0	23
2	74	0	35
9	80	11	40
4	95	0	53
7	104	0	59
1	117	0	67

FIGURE 14–1

```
0010 REM   N1= NUMBER OF EQUATIONS
0020 REM      D(I,N)= COEFFICIENTS OF LINEAR EQUATIONS
0030 DIM D[4,5]
0040 INPUT N1
0050 LET J=N1+1
0060 FOR I=1 TO N1
0070    FOR N=1 TO J
0080       READ D[I,N]
0090    NEXT N
0100 NEXT I
0110 FOR M1=1 TO N1
0120    LET N2=M1
0130    LET T=D[M1,N2]
0140    FOR N=1 TO J
0150       LET D[M1,N]=D[M1,N]/T
0160    NEXT N
0170    LET M=1
0180    IF M1=M GOTO 0240
0190    LET C=-D[M,N2]
0200    FOR N=1 TO J
0210       LET T=D[M1,N]*C
0220       LET D[M,N]=D[M,N]+T
0230    NEXT N
0240    LET M=M+1
0250    IF M<=N1 GOTO  0180
0260 NEXT M1
0270 PRINT
0280 FOR M=1 TO N1
0290    PRINT ,M,D[M,J]
0300 NEXT M
0310 DATA  40.96,  12.34,  36.78,  29.43,  40.43
0320 DATA  22.46,  38.72,  40.15,  11.29,  15.5
0330 DATA  36.45,  19.2,  37.28,  6.43,  42.4
0340 DATA  17.84,  40.02,  27.86,  39.27,  25.57
```

FIGURE 14–2

```
0010 REM  N1= NUMBER OF EQUATIONS
0020 REM   D(I,N)=COEFFICIENTS OF MATRIX
0030 DIM D[4,4],E[4,4]
0040 INPUT N1
0050 FOR I=1 TO N1
0060   FOR N=1 TO N1
0070     READ D[I,N]
0080   NEXT N
0090 NEXT I
0100 FOR I=1 TO N1
0110   FOR J=1 TO N1
0120     LET E[I,J]=0
0130   NEXT J
0140 NEXT I
0150 FOR M=1 TO N1
0160   LET E[M,M]=1
0170 NEXT M
0180 FOR M1=1 TO N1
0190   LET N2=M1
0200   LET T=D[M1,N2]
0210   FOR N=1 TO N1
0220     LET E[M1,N]=E[M1,N]/T
0230     LET D[M1,N]=D[M1,N]/T
0240   NEXT N
0250   LET M=1
0260   IF M1=M GOTO 0340
0270   LET C=-D[M,N2]
0280   FOR N=1 TO N1
0290     LET T1=D[M1,N]*C
0300     LET T2=E[M1,N]*C
0310     LET E[M,N]=E[M,N]+T2
0320     LET D[M,N]=D[M,N]+T1
0330   NEXT N
0340   LET M=M+1
0350   IF M<=N1 GOTO  0260
0360 NEXT M1
0370 PRINT
0380 FOR I=1 TO N1
0390   FOR N=1 TO N1
0400     PRINT E[I,N],
0410   NEXT N
0420   PRINT
0430 NEXT I
0440 DATA  40.96, 12.34, 36.78, 29.43
0450 DATA  22.46, 38.72, 40.15, 11.29
0460 DATA  36.45, 19.2, 37.28, 6.43
0470 DATA  17.84, 40.02, 27.86, 39.27
```

FIGURE 14–3

```
0010 REM  N1= NUMBER OF EQUATIONS
0020 DIM D[4,5],S[4]
0030 INPUT N1
0040 LET K=N1+1
0050 FOR I=1 TO N1
0060   FOR J=1 TO K
0070     READ D[I,J]
0080   NEXT J
0090 NEXT I
0100 FOR M1=1 TO N1
0110   LET N2=M1
0120   LET T=D[M1,N2]
0130   FOR N=1 TO K
0140     LET D[M1,N]=D[M1,N]/T
0150   NEXT N
0160   LET I1=M1+1
0170   IF I1>N1 GOTO  0250
0180   FOR I2=I1 TO N1
0190     LET T=-D[I2,N2]
0200     FOR I3=M1 TO K
0210       LET D[I2,I3]=D[I2,I3]+D[M1,I3]*T
0220     NEXT I3
0230   NEXT I2
0240 NEXT M1
0250 LET S[N1]=D[N1,K]
0260 LET I4=N1-1
0270 PRINT
0280 FOR I=1 TO I4
0290   LET M=N1-I
0300   LET L=M+1
0310   LET T=0
0320   FOR J=L TO N1
0330     LET T=T+D[M,J]*S[J]
0340   NEXT J
0350   LET S[M]=D[M,K]-T
0360   PRINT M,S[M]
0370 NEXT I
0380 DATA  40.96, 12.34, 36.78, 29.43, 40.43
0390 DATA  22.46, 38.72, 40.15, 11.29, 15.5
0400 DATA  36.45, 19.2, 37.28, 6.43, 42.4
0410 DATA  17.84, 40.02, 27.86, 39.27, 25.57
```

FIGURE 14-6

```
0010 REM   K= NUMBER OF ROWS OR COLUMNS IN THE SQUARE MATRIX
0020 REM   A(K,K)*B(K,K)=D(K,K)
0030 DIM A[3,3],B[3,3],D[3,3]
0040 INPUT K
0050 PRINT
0060 FOR I=1 TO K
0070    FOR J=1 TO K
0080       READ A[I,J]
0090    NEXT J
0100 NEXT I
0110 FOR I=1 TO K
0120    FOR J=1 TO K
0130       READ B[I,J]
0140    NEXT J
0150 NEXT I
0160 FOR I=1 TO K
0170    FOR J=1 TO K
0180       LET D[I,J]=0
0190       FOR N=1 TO K
0200          LET D[I,J]=D[I,J]+A[I,N]*B[N,J]
0210       NEXT N
0220    NEXT J
0230 NEXT I
0240 FOR I=1 TO K
0250    FOR J=1 TO K
0260       PRINT D[I,J],
0270    NEXT J
0280    PRINT
0290 NEXT I
0300 DATA   2, 0, 3
0310 DATA   1, 2, 1
0320 DATA   3, 0, 2
0330 DATA   4, 2, 5
0340 DATA   3, 0, 2
0350 DATA   1, 1, 6
```

FIGURE 14-8

```
00100 REM  IBV=B
00110 REM  CM=C
00120 REM  DIV=D1
00130 REM  IPIVC0=I1
00140 REM  IPIVR0=I2
00150 REM  ITAB=I3
00160 REM  IW=I4
00170 REM  IX=I5
00180 REM  IY=I6
00190 REM  IZ=I7
00200 REM  N0PIVS=N1
00210 REM  QU0NT=Q
00220 REM  SC=S
00230 REM  SCMAX=S1
00240 REM  SMLVAL=S2
00250 REM  SUM=S3
00260 REM  TM=T
00270 DIM  D(10,10),P(10),B(10),S(10)
00280 READ I4,I7,I6
00290 LET I5=I7-1
00300 READ I3
00310 FOR M=1 TO I5
00320 READ P(M)
00330 NEXT M
00340 FOR M=1 TO I4
00350 FOR N=1 TO I7
00360 READ D(M,N)
00370 NEXT N
00380 NEXT M
00390 FOR N= I6 TO I5
00400 FOR L=1 TO I4
00410 IF D(L,N)=1. THEN 00440
00420 NEXT L
00430 GO TO 00450
00440 LET B(L)=N
00450 NEXT N
00460 LET N1=0.
00470 IF I3<>1. THEN 00490
00480 PRINT
00490 LET S1=0.
00500 FOR N=1 TO I5
00510 FOR I=1 TO I4
00520 IF N=B(I) THEN 00630.
00530 NEXT I
00540 LET S3=0.
00550 FOR I=1 TO I4
00560 LET J=B(I)
00570 LET S3=S3+P(J)*D(I,N)
00580 NEXT I
00590 LET S(N)=P(N)-S3
00600 IF S(N)<=S1 THEN 00630
00610 LET S1=S(N)
00620 LET I1=N
00630 NEXT N
00640 IF S1<=0 THEN 00950
00650 LET S2=999999.
```

FIGURE 14-8 (Continued)

```
00660 FØR M=1 TØ I4
00670 IF D(M,I7)<=O THEN 00720
00680 LET Q=D(M,I7)/D(M,I1)
00690 IF Q>=S2 THEN 00720
00700 LET I2=M
00710 LET S2=Q
00720 NEXT M
00730 LET B(I2)=I1
00740 LET D1=D(I2,I1)
00750 FØR N=1 TØ I7
00760 LET D(I2,N)=D(I2,N)/D1
00770 NEXT N
00780 LET N1=N1+1
00790 IF I3<>1 THEN 00810
00800 PRINT" TABLEAU AFTER PIVØT NUMBER";N1
00810 FØR M=1 TØ I4
00820 IF M=I2 THEN 00880
00830 LET C=-D(M,I1)
00840 FØR N=1 TØ I7
00850 LET T=D(I2,N)*C
00860 LET D(M,N)=D(M,N)+T
00870 NEXT N
00880 IF I3<>1 THEN 00930
00890 FØR N=1 TØ I7
00900 PRINT D(M,N);
00910 NEXT N
00920 PRINT
00930 NEXT M
00940 GØ TØ 00490
00950 PRINT " SØLUTIØN"
00960 PRINT" VARIABLE     VALUE"
00970 FØR M=1 TØ I4
00980 PRINT B(M),D(M,I7)
00990 NEXT M
01000 PRINT" ALL ØTHER VARIABLES = ZERØ"
01010 DATA 3,8,4,1
01020 DATA -2.,-4.,-1.,0.,-999999.,0.,-999999.
01030 DATA 1,2,-1,1,0,0,0,5
01040 DATA 2,-1,2,0,1,0,0,2
01050 DATA -1,2,2,0,0,-1,1,1
```

FIGURE 15–5

```
100 DIM I1(10),I2(10),I3(10),J1(10),J2(10),J3(10)
110 FØR N=1 TØ 10
120 READ I1(N),I2(N),I3(N),J1(N),J2(N)
130 NEXT N
140 PRINT
150 PRINT " N   DCUR   IØH    IØRD    DAVE   ØRDER AØRDER"
160 PRINT
170 LET K1=4
180 LET K2=13
190 LET K3=10
200 FØR N=1 TØ 10
210 IF I2(N)>K1 THEN 310
270 IF I3(N)>0 THEN 400
280 IF I2(N)>=2*I1(N) THEN 450
290 LET J3(N)=K2
300 GØ TØ 500
310 IF I1(N)>1.5*J1(N) THEN 340
320 LET J3(N)=0
330 GØ TØ 500
340 IF I3(N)>0 THEN 370
350 LET J3(N)=K2
360 GØ TØ 500
370 LET J3(N)=K3
380 GØ TØ 500
400 IF I1(N)>=1.5*J1(N) THEN 430
410 LET J3(N)=0
420 GØ TØ 500
430 LET J3(N)=K3
440 GØ TØ 500
450 LET J3(N)=0
500 PRINT N;I1(N);I2(N);I3(N);J1(N);J2(N);J3(N)
510 NEXT N
520 DATA 3,4,0,2,13,2,4,13,2,0,3,4,10,1,10,2,6,0,2,0,1,3,0,2,0,
530 DATA 1,2,0,1,0,4,5,0,2,13,1,7,0,2,0,1,2,13,2,0,4,5,13,2,10
```

N	DCUR	IØH	IØRD	DAVE	ØRDER	AØRDER
1	3	4	0	2	13	13
2	2	4	13	2	0	0
3	3	4	10	1	10	10
4	2	6	0	2	0	0
5	1	3	0	2	0	0
6	1	2	0	1	0	0
7	4	5	0	2	13	13
8	1	7	0	2	0	0
9	1	2	13	2	0	0
10	4	5	13	2	10	10

FIGURE 15–8

```
100 DIM I1(20),I2(20),K1(20),K2(20)
110 LET K=0
120 LET K3=0
130 FØR N=1 TØ 20
140 READ I2(N)
150 NEXT N
160 PRINT
170 PRINT " CHØICE PAYØFF"
180 PRINT
190 PRINT " A B A B"
200 FØR N=1 TØ 20
210 IF N<>1 THEN 240
220 LET I1(N)=1
230 GØ TØ 600
240 IF N<16 THEN 270
250 LET I1(N)=2
260 GØ TØ 600
270 IF K3=1 THEN 490
280 IF N<=4 THEN 370
290 FØR J=1 TØ 4
300 IF I2(N-J)=2 THEN 320
310 GØ TØ 370
320 NEXT J
330 LET K3=1
340 LET K=N
350 LET I1(N)=1
360 GØ TØ 600
370 IF N<=3 THEN 440
380 FØR J=1 TØ 3
390 IF I1(N-J)=2 THEN 410
400 GØ TØ 440
410 NEXT J
420 LET I1(N)=1
430 GØ TØ 600
440 IF K1(N-1)<K2(N-1) THEN 470
450 LET I1(N)=I1(N-1)
460 GØ TØ 600
470 LET I1(N)=2
480 GØ TØ 600
490 IF (N-K)>=2 THEN 520
500 LET I1(N)=1
510 GØ TØ 600
520 IF K1(N-2)>=K2(N-2) THEN 580
530 IF K1(N-1)>=K2(N-1) THEN 580
540 LET I1(N)=2
550 LET K3=0
560 LET K=0
570 GØ TØ 600
580 LET I1(N)=1
600 IF I1(N) =1 THEN 680
610 IF I2(N)=1 THEN 650
620 LET K1(N)=1
630 LET K2(N)=1
640 GØ TØ 750
65C LET K1(N)=5
660 LET K2(N)=1
670 GØ TØ 750
680 IF I2(N)=1 THEN 730
690 LET K1(N)=1
700 LET K2(N)=5
710 GØ TØ 750
730 LET K1(N)=3
740 LET K2(N)=3
750 NEXT N
760 FØR N=1 TØ 20
770 PRINT I1(N);I2(N);K1(N);K2(N)
780 NEXT N
790 DATA 2,2,1,2,2,2,2,2,1,2,2,2,2,1,2,2,2,2,2,2
800 STØP
810 END
```

Index

*This book has been set in 11 and 10 point
Modern #21, leaded 2 points. Chapter
numbers and titles are in 24 point 20th
Century Medium. The size of the type
page is 27 × 46 picas.*